Environmental

Education

Pre K–8
Activity

Guide

TABLE OF CONTENTS

DIVERSITY

INTERRELATIONSHIPS

SYSTEMS

STRUCTURE AND SCALE

PATTERNS OF CHANGE

INTRODUCTION

PROJECT LEARNING TREE
THE NEXT GENERATION

SINCE ITS INTRODUCTION in the early 1970s, Project Learning Tree has been recognized as one of the premier environmental education programs in the world. Through hands-on, interdisciplinary activities, PLT provides students with opportunities to investigate environmental issues and encourages them to make informed, responsible decisions.

PLT is now used in all 50 of the United States, U.S. Territories, Canada, Japan, Mexico, Sweden, Finland, and Brazil. Each year in the United States alone, nearly 60,000 educators attend PLT workshops to learn how to use the program with young people.

Beginning in 1990, a multi-year revision project was initiated to ensure that PLT would remain at the leading edge of environmental education. At the beginning, more than 50,000 teachers, environmental educators and curriculum specialists from across North America were surveyed to determine how the program could be improved. Recommendations from these groups revealed that the revision process would require an effort of tremendous magnitude and scope. An entirely new curriculum would have to be created–from conceptual framework to the format and design. New topics and more background information for elementary school teachers would be needed, and an entirely new approach for middle and senior high schools would have to be developed.

By necessity, the revision of the PLT curriculum was a slow and deliberate process. The development of new models, outlines, and raw materials took place at regional writing workshops and revisions sessions around the country. The actual writing included numerous professionals, working closely with PLT's editorial staff and review committee.

Participation in the entire process was extraordinary. Besides those responding to the survey instruments, more than 300 professionals took part in writing workshops and editing sessions. Another 300 educators participated in the pilot-test, field-test, and formal evaluation of the materials—conducted by the Research Commission of the North American Association for Environmental Education. Materials were reviewed by a team of scientists, natural resource managers, educators, and technical specialists.

The formal evaluation of the "new" PLT involved more than 3,000 students across North America. The formal evaluation included both traditional pre-test/intervention/post-test procedures as well as alternative assessment techniques. The results of this evaluation—the most extensive and intensive of its type ever conducted—confirmed that the new PLT is an effective program for helping students become more environmentally literate young citizens. While the evaluation was very costly in both time and money, this component of the revision process was considered critical by the PLT staff and educational advisory board to help ensure that the new PLT would continue to serve as an outstanding environmental education program for students across the nation, and, indeed, the world.

DR. LOU IOZZI, *Professor of Science and Environmental Education,* Rutgers University
Co-Chair, PLT Operating Committee

PROJECT LEARNING TREE
A PROUD TRADITION–A BRIGHT AND PROMISING FUTURE

THOUSANDS OF PEOPLE, throughout the United States and several other countries as well, are justly proud of the new PLT activity guide you hold in your hands. It represents lots of hard work—reviewing the old guides, re-writing activities, writing new ones, field testing, and editing. We did our best, and we know that we have a state of the art product. And most important, it WORKS in the classroom.

But the new guide is by no means all of which we may be proud. Our most important asset is our network of PLT people—state coordinators, workshop leaders, classroom teachers, resource management professionals, state and federal governmental agencies, professional associations, business and industry, PLT staff—literally hundreds of people who work together to help students learn about resource utilization and environmental quality. Through their efforts over the past twenty years approximately 20 million students have been reached through the program.

We also have a past and traditions of which we may be proud. PLT began way back in 1973 when the American Forest Institute entered into a partnership with the Western Regional Environmental Education Council (WREEC), an association of educators and resource professionals from 13 western states, to produce an educational program for use in the elementary and secondary schools of these states. It was agreed that the materials would be produced by teachers and management professionals working together, and that they would be factually accurate and nonbiased. Early on we agreed that our goal was helping students learn HOW to think, not WHAT to think. The program was so successful that other states and countries asked to join the network, with the result that PLT became, within a few years, both national and international.

What about the future? As I see it, this activity guide is but one milestone in a long and perhaps never ending journey. All of us involved in PLT share a great tradition. We do important things for students, the land and for the future, and we're justly proud of our accomplishments.

RUDOLPH J.H. SCHAFER, *Retired,* California Department of Education, Environmental Education Program Manager, *Founder and Past President,* WREEC

"PARTNERSHIP" IS A MUCH–USED WORD IN THESE times. However, I can't think of a better way to describe the foundation on which Project Learning Tree was built. From its conception in 1973, PLT has always been the product of educators, scientists, resource managers, and industry professionals working together.

Now, two decades later, this partnership is more than intact; it's thriving. That may surprise some who suspect our goals are incompatible. The fact is, they aren't. PLT works because we have always had only one agenda: to help kids learn *how* to think about local and global environmental issues. PLT isn't apocalyptic; it isn't pro- or anti-business. Simply put, it is pro-learning.

The activities contained in this volume were designed to provide students with the awareness, understanding and skills they need to become intelligent environmental decision makers. They are intended to help students develop attitudes and inform their actions through analysis—and through critical evaluation of all the information that is available to them.

We believe this is the kind of environmental education that young people deserve. And we are committed, as always, to making certain this is the kind of environmental education PLT delivers.

JOHN A. LUKE, JR., *Chairman and CEO,* Westvaco Corporation Chairman, American Forest Foundation

PROJECT LEARNING TREE
MISSION, GOALS, METHODS

MISSION

PLT USES THE FOREST AS A "WINDOW ON THE

world" to increase students' understanding of our complex environment; to stimulate critical and creative thinking; to develop the ability to make informed decisions on environmental issues; and to instill the confidence and commitment to take responsible action on behalf of the environment.

GOALS

PLT'S GOALS ARE TO:

1. Provide students with the awareness, appreciation, understanding, skills, and commitment to address environmental issues.
2. Enable students to apply scientific processes and higher order thinking skills to resolve environmental problems.
3. Help students acquire an appreciation and tolerance of diverse viewpoints on environmental issues, and develop attitudes and actions based on analysis and evaluation of the available information.
4. Encourage creativity, originality, and flexibility to resolve environmental problems and issues.
5. Inspire and empower students to become responsible, productive, and participatory members of society.

METHODS

PLT FOCUSES ON DEVELOPING CRITICAL THINKING

skills. PLT doesn't try to teach children what to think about the environment. It gives teachers the tools they need to help children learn how to think about the environment.

PLT is a comprehensive environmental education curriculum. PLT is not just about trees. It's about the total environment: land, air and water. It is local, national and global in scope.

PLT can be applied in many different contexts. PLT can be used in formal education settings, with youth organizations, or by parents with their children. It can be used in museums, nature centers, and by scout troops. It appeals to the broadest range of young people—children of all ages, learning styles, ethnic and racial background.

PLT is designed to be included in busy classroom schedules. The new PLT was designed by educators to be used by educators. It is "classroom friendly"—and requires minimal preparation to be included in lesson plans or to be aligned with state curriculum objectives or guidelines. PLT has been approved for classroom use in all 50 states and, in many states, correlated with state science, social studies and environmental education curriculum objectives.

PLT is activity based. PLT piggybacks important environmental "lessons" on to other elements of the elementary and secondary curriculum. PLT can be infused in science, language arts, social studies, reading, arithmetic, art, music, special education, and civics lessons—among others.

PLT is self contained. Activities are easy to implement without pre-planning or assembling hard-to-find materials. They take advantage of indoor and outdoor settings and materials accessible to virtually any classroom—city, suburb or rural. Extensions, student pages and assessment opportunities are included.

PLT is interdisciplinary. It isn't just for environmental educators—but for all educators who want to introduce environmental objectives into their general curriculum.

PLT is real. In simulations, students can play roles that echo the kinds of real decisions that are being made in their communities. It helps them discover what it takes to be an advocate for a new or unfamiliar idea—or to sort through rhetoric to make decisions intelligently. PLT permits students to discuss values and to recognize that there are differing values which can be held. It helps them understand how conflicts arise, and how they can be resolved.

ORGANIZATION OF THE ACTIVITY GUIDE

PROJECT LEARNING TREE'S PreK-8th Grade Activity Guide is arranged under five major themes: Diversity, Interrelationships, Systems, Structure and Scale, and Patterns of Change. Each theme covers the areas of Environment, Resource Management & Technology, and Society & Culture. (See Conceptual Framework on page 375.) The PLT activities integrate the themes within science, language arts, social studies, art, music, and physical education.

PLT is not designed to be an all-inclusive or comprehensive curriculum. Instead, teachers are invited to fill in the gaps designed into the program with content that relates to their community, expertise, interests, or the needs of their students.

The activities can be used individually to teach specific concepts or they can be used with other activities as part of a conceptual storyline. (See Storylines on page ix)

The activities reflect several methods of teaching environmental literacy and values. Each activity attempts to guide the learner through the process of awareness, understanding, challenge, motivation, and action using active involvement and hands-on experiences. The activities are based largely on constructivist learning theory and whole language teaching strategies.

CONSTRUCTIVISM The constructivist theory of learning recognizes that students construct new understandings by combining previous understandings with new discoveries. Learning specialists have found that students' preconceptions about the way the world works have a profound effect on their ability to integrate new scientific explanations of natural phenomena. With this in mind, the new PLT provides opportunities for teachers to guide their students toward new discovery and scientific understanding and, simultaneously, help to develop critical thinking and creative problem solving skills.

WHOLE LANGUAGE In teaching using the whole language approach, the students are taught holistically rather than in "bits" and "pieces." In the new PLT, this is done by focusing on connecting themes, conceptual understandings, and critical thinking skills rather than on the simple transfer of bits of information. Students frequently engage in writing and oral language activities related to experiential learning.

The PLT program employs several highly effective and well tested teaching strategies. These include cooperative learning and problem solving:

COOPERATIVE LEARNING–This approach is more than a simple "grouping" technique. Rather, students are organized into small teams that work together to accomplish academic and non-academic tasks while, at the same time, developing important social skills.

PROBLEM SOLVING– Emphasizing a problem solving approach to learning promotes the development of such skills as identifying problems, determining desired outcomes, selecting possible solutions, choosing strategies, testing solutions, evaluating outcomes, revising and repeating steps, and predicting new problems.

Environmental action is one of the most important components in the new PLT curriculum. When students work together on an action project, they develop a sense of belonging and self-esteem, and strengthen the feeling that they can make a difference and, in fact, contribute towards positive change. Class projects such as adopting a tree, improving a school site, providing habitat for wildlife, and many other opportunities are outlined in the activities.

ACTIVITY COMPONENTS

ACH PLT ACTIVITY contains several parts. Some parts may prove more or less effective with your students; however, we recommend trying as many of these as possible. Each activity is designed to uncover students' preconceptions, and guide them from awareness to conceptual understanding and responsible action.

The **TITLE** is the "attention grabber" that relates to the activity's content.

The **OVERVIEW** appears directly under the title and provides two or three sentences describing the activity.

The **SIDE-BAR** on the first page of each activity contains the following important information for incorporating an activity into your program or curriculum. Much of this information is based on field testing comments from teachers.

LEVELS–Indicates the grade levels for which various parts of the activity are recommended. Activities can usually be geared up or down with slight modifications.

SUBJECTS–Indicates the subjects such as mathematics, science, social studies, or language arts, that the activity incorporates.

CONCEPTS–Lists the concepts (from the Conceptual Framework on page 375) that the activity addresses.

SKILLS–Lists the thinking processes and skills that the activity develops.

OBJECTIVES–States the content objectives targeted in the activity.

MATERIALS–Lists materials needed to do the activity.

TIME CONSIDERATIONS–Recommended time allotments for each part of the core activity, including preparation. These are based on the recommendations of the teachers who have pilot-tested the activity. Times are based on 50-minute class periods.

The **BACKGROUND** is selected information for teachers. It may be too advanced for students' understanding. It provides the teacher with an understanding and perspective for doing the activity. Bold italicized words appear in the Glossary on page 371.

GETTING READY describes how to prepare for doing the activity.

DOING THE ACTIVITY is a step-by-step procedure for leading the activity. It includes:

AWARENESS–The initial phase attempts to uncover students' preconceptions and allows the teacher to assess what students presently know or understand about a concept.

KNOWLEDGE–In this phase, students build conceptual understanding through experiential learning and investigation.

CHALLENGE–In this phase, students explore viewpoints, challenge ideas and values, and seek consensus.

ACTION–In the final phase, students attempt personal or group action projects based on the knowledge they have gained.

VARIATIONS provide alternative procedures for doing the activity. These have similar objectives to the core activity, but appeal to different age levels, learning styles, audiences, situations, or concerns.

The **ENRICHMENT** contains recommendations for exercises that enrich or extend the learning experience in the activity.

Each activity has **END-NOTES,** which include:

REFERENCES–Sources of information used in the activity and additional resources which might be acquired.

RELATED ACTIVITIES–Lists other PLT activities which address closely related topics.

ASSESSMENT OPPORTUNITIES– Guides the educator toward assessing students' understanding of the concepts covered in the activity. They also provide opportunities for students to apply the knowledge they have gained.

STORYLINES

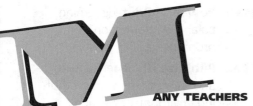

M **ANY TEACHERS** find the storyline technique useful for teaching PLT activities to students. A storyline groups several PLT activities around a central core of knowledge and skills relevant to the students. Storylines provide connectedness and continuity to activities, and can serve as "instructional glue" that holds many areas of knowledge and skills together.

Following are some suggestions as to how PLT activities might be linked using the storyline technique. These can serve as a springboard toward developing your own storylines using PLT and other materials to meet the specific needs and interests of your students.

DIVERSITY

Throughout the world, there is great diversity of habitats, organisms, societies, technologies, and cultures.

STORYLINE Humans can explore the environment using a variety of senses.

1. **The Shape Of Things**–sight
2. **Get In Touch With Trees**–touch
3. **Peppermint Beetle**–smell, taste
4. **Sounds Around**–hearing
5. **Poet-Tree**–imagination, wonder

STORYLINE Organisms have diverse characteristics that enable them to adapt to diverse habitats. Biological diversity is a critical requirement for all ecosystems.

6. **Picture This!**–diversity of organisms
7. **Habitat Pen Pals**–diversity of habitats
8. **The Forest Of S.T. Shrew**–diversity of roles within an ecosystem
9. **Planet Of Plenty**–importance of biological diversity
10. **Charting Diversity**–diverse adaptations
11. **Can It Be Real?**–species diversity

STORYLINE Trees and other plants are renewable natural resources that benefit humans in a variety of ways.

12. **Tree Treasures**–people derive various products from trees
13. **We All Need Trees**–trees support our lives in many ways
14. **Renewable Or Not?**–humans depend on different natural resources
15. **A Few Of My Favorite Things**–products are derived from different resources
16. **Pass The Plants, Please**–humans depend on various plants for food

STORYLINE All people have the same basic needs, but are diverse in lifestyles, cultures, and values.

17. **People Of The Forest**–diverse lifestyles

18. **Tale Of The Sun**–diverse cultures
19. **Values On The Line**–diverse values within a group
20. **Environmental Exchange Box**–sharing of information among diverse groups

INTERRELATIONSHIPS

Ecological, technological, and socio-cultural systems are interactive and interdependent.

STORYLINE Trees are interrelated with the environment in many ways.

21. **Adopt A Tree**–characteristics of a tree
22. **Trees As Habitats**–trees as home for other organisms
23. **The Fallen Log**–ecological importance of dead trees
24. **Nature's Recyclers**–organisms are important in decomposing organic material

STORYLINE Organisms have developed complex adaptations and interrelationships.

25. **Birds and Worms**–predator and prey relationships
26. **Dynamic Duos**–partnership and parasitic relationships
27. **Every Tree for Itself**–environmental requirements of plants
28. **Air Plants**–interaction between plants and air
29. **Rain Reasons**–influence of climate on the distribution of organisms

PROJECT LEARNING TREE is a program of the American Forest Foundation and the Council for Environmental Education.

AMERICAN FOREST FOUNDATION

John Luke, Jr., Chair

Laurence Wiseman, President

COUNCIL FOR ENVIRONMENTAL EDUCATION

Arva Jackson, *President*

Josetta Hawthorne, *Executive Director*

NATIONAL ASSOCIATE SPONSORS

National Association of Conservation Districts

National Association of Professional Forestry Schools and Colleges

National Association of State Foresters

Society of American Foresters

United States Department of Agriculture, Forest Service

World Forestry Center

PROJECT LEARNING TREE OPERATING COMMITTEE

Dr. Louis Iozzi, Rutgers University-Cook College, New Jersey, *Co-Chair*

Dave Mumper, Weyerhaeuser Company, Washington, *Co-Chair*

Bill Andrews, California State Dept. of Education, California

Kay Antunez, California Department of Forestry, California

William Banzhaf, Society of American Foresters, Maryland

Judy Braus, World Wildlife Fund, Washington, DC

Pam Godsey, USDA Forest Service, Washington, DC

Lynn Klein, Georgia-Pacific Corporation, Georgia

Jim Mallow, Dept. of Natural Resources, Maryland

Mike Powers, Procter & Gamble, Inc, Ohio

Dr. Darleen Stoner, California State University, San Bernadino, California

Terri Wildermuth, New Mexico State Forestry, New Mexico

Rick Zenn, World Forestry Center, Oregon

PROJECT LEARNING TREE STAFF

Kathy McGlauflin, *Vice President and Director*

Sheri Sykes Soyka, *Associate Director*

Caroline Alston, *Programs Manager*

Sue Shaddeau, *Field Support Manager*

Yolanda Jacobs, *Administrative Coordinator*

Elizabeth Erb, *Project Coordinator*

Adena Messinger, *Curriculum Project Assistant*

Leslie Comnes

Jody Marshall

Robin Myers

Jim Moore

Andy Pasternak

Luise Woelflein

Writers

Kay Antunez

Bob Samples

Pat Snyder

Deb Neuenschwander

Andrea Bosch

Kent Pond

Brenda Weiser

Andy Pasternak

Dr. Darleen Stoner
Art and Photography

Harriet Honigfeld

Cheri Horowitz

Stephanie Kim

Meg Lamm

Kerry Pasquarelli

Susan Smith

Takashi Togawa

Project Interns

Publications Professionals, Inc.
Copy Editing

Marty Anderson Design

Mediaworks, Inc.
Design and Layout

Dr. Tom Marcinkowski

Dr. Lou Iozzi

North American Association for Environmental Education's North American Commission for Environmental Education Research

Curriculum Evaluation

ACKNOWLEDGEMENTS

WE'D LIKE TO THANK EVERYONE WHO CONTRIBUTED TO THIS NEW EDITION OF the Project Learning Tree Environmental Education Activity Guide. Over the past three years an incredible number of dedicated professionals have volunteered their time to write, pilot test, field test, edit, and review activities for this guide.

We are especially grateful to the following companies and organizations who made special contributions to the development of our revised curriculum: Boise Cascade Corporation; Chesapeake Corporation; Consolidated Paper Company, Inc.; Finch, Pruyn & Company, Inc.; Fraser Paper Company; Gilman Paper Company; Georgia-Pacific Corporation; James River Corporation; Longview Fibre Company; MCI Telecommunications Corporation; Madison Paper Industries; Menasha Corporation; Monadnock Paper Mills, Inc.; Nalco Chemical Company; Plum Creek Timber Company, Inc.; Potlach Corporation; Port Townsend Paper Corporation; The Procter & Gamble Cellulose Company; Scott Paper Company; Simpson Fund; Technical Association of the Pulp and Paper Industry; Temple-Inland, Inc.; Union Camp Corporation; U.S. Department of Agriculture, Forest Service; U.S. Environmental Protection Agency; Virginia Fibre Corporation; Weston Paper and Manufacturing Company; Willamette Industries, Inc.; and Weyerhaeuser Company Foundation.

A special thank you goes to all the paper and forest products companies who, through their contributions to the American Forest Foundation, have supported Project Learning Tree for the past eighteen years. Without their continuing support, neither Project Learning Tree, nor this new activity guide, would have been possible.

Additionally, we'd like to thank all the current and past members of the Project Learning Tree Operating Committee (formerly the Planning and Advisory Council). Their vision and commitment to this program have been critical in helping us realize our goal of creating supplementary curriculum materials that truly help students learn how to think, not what to think about complex environmental issues.

And finally, we'd like to thank all of the state and provincial Project Learning Tree coordinators for their boundless energy and enthusiasm for Project Learning Tree. It's through their work that Project Learning Tree reaches educators throughout North America. Where we have made a difference in the classroom, they deserve a large measure of the credit.

Kathy McGlauflin
Director, Project Learning Tree

WRITING WORKSHOP PARTICIPANTS

MIDWESTERN WORKSHOP,
TOMAHAWK, WI

Karol Bartlett, Indianapolis, IN
Bonni Browning, Rockville, IN
Sam Carman, Indianapolis, IN
Lyle Clark, Columbus City, IA
Jeff Cummings, Crorydon, IN
Bob Dahl, Tomahawk, WI
Susan Fowler, Finland, MN
Barbara Glessner, Waterloo, IA
Candace Greenly, Fairfield, IA
Roger Gustafson, Belvidere, IL
Jim Halvorson, Spooner, WI
Sharon Kaufman, Burlington, IA
Judy Klippel, Milwaukee, WI
Sherry Klosiewski, Rhinelander, WI
Deloris Larson, Tomahawk, WI
Pat Marinac-Sanders, Appleton, WI
Judy Miller, Urbana, IL
Mike Miller, Rhinelander, WI
Shelley Mitchell, Indianapolis, IN
Beth Mittermaier, Jackson, WI
Carrie Morgan, Green Bay, WI
Patricia Murphy, Spooner, WI
Ray Nelson, Bemidji, MN
Deb Neuenschwander, Ossian, IN
Joe Panci, Eagle River, WI
Mary Rice, Wood Dale, IL
Patty Riggins, Edwardsville, IL
June Rusten, Ann Arbor, MI
Da ve Schiotz, W. Menomonie, WI
Bill Schultz, Columbus, OH

Glenna Jo Temte, Madison, WI
Peggy Stewart, Glencoe, IL
Joe Timmerman, Wisconsin Rapids, WI
Duane Toomsen, Des Moines, IA
Paul Torbert, Cedar Rapids, IA
Dennis Yockers, Madison, WI

SOUTHERN WORKSHOP,
NEW ORLEANS, LA

Kathy Ann Baucum, Picayune, MS
Mary Ann Hagerty, Philadelphia, PA
Bill Berry, New Orleans, LA
Dana Blanton, Washington, DC
Rei Boyce, Montgomery, AL
Hal Brown, Springdale, AR
Eglantina Canales, Saltillo, Coahuila, Mexico
Julio Carrera, Saltillo, Coahuila, Mexico
Karen Charles, Statesville, NC
Jim Culpepper, Baton Rouge, LA
Sharon Dolliver, Macon, GA
Jeff Doran, Tallahassee, FL
Connie Elpers, Wichita, KS
Janel Erickson, Kingsville, MO
Colleen Feist, Madison, WI
David Francis III, Athens, GA
Albert Hayward, Conway, SC
Ross Hobbs, Selma, AL
Lou Iozzi, New Brunswick, NJ
Sheri Jeter, Soper, OK
Paul Johnson, East Paltk, FL
Linda Kay, Jackson, MS
Don Kimberly, Waynesboro, TN
Patricia Layton, Philadelphia, PA
Sara Lee Simons, Florence, SC

Edward Macie, Atlanta, GA
Bob McKernan, Washington, DC
Jennie Morris, Columbia, SC
Susie Myers, Centerville, LA
Connie Nobles, Baton Rouge, LA
Devon T. Raddish, Clarksburg, WV
Barbara Reed, Lawrenceville, GA
Maxine Rudder, London, KY
Ann Seppenfield, Frankfurt, KY
Lynne Smith, Magnolia, AR
Cindi Smith-Walters, Nashville, TN
John Strickler, Manhattan, KS
Frank Truesdale, Baton Rouge, LA
Charles Walker, Livingston, TX
Brenda Weiser, Oklahoma City, OK
Larry Willett, Monticello, AR
Cindy Ybos, New Orleans, LA
Marilyn Young-Burrell, Goodman, MS

WESTERN WORKSHOP,
MILL VALLEY, CA
Kathy Anderson, Helena, MT
Bill Andrews, Sacramento, CA
Kay Antunez, Sacramento, CA
William Baker, Winnipeg, Manitoba, Canada
Howard Barbour, The Dalles, OR
Angie Bartholomay, Willow City, ND
Chuck Bell, Glendale, AZ
Lisa Bryce Lewis, Olympia, WA
Kathy Burcham, Berthoud, CO
Olga Clymire, Lakeport, CA
Larry Costick, Martell, CA
Carol Crosby, Lincoln, NE
Joel Davis, Olympia, WA
Tony Dietz, Salt Lake City, UT
Glenda Fauske, Bottineau, ND
Jean Fields, Phoenix, AZ
Dick Ford, Longview, WA
Jean Frederickson, Running Springs, CA
Sheila Gaquin, Ashland, OR
Susie Garber Ponce, Sheridan, WY
Jim Geiger, Sacramento, CA
Kristen Gottschalk, Wahoo, NE
Carol Heinricy, Carson City, NV
Amahra Hicks, San Francisco, CA
Repeka Howland, Pago Pago, American Samoa
Rex Johnson, Cheyenne, WY
Barbara Jones, Surrey, British Columbia, Canada
John Jones, Las Vegas, NV
Betty Joubert, Albuquerque, NM
Janann Kaufman, Anchorage, AK
Sue Kidd, Bozeman, MT
Cheryl Kollin, Berkeley, CA
Dorothea Kunz Shuman, Moscow, ID
Sharla Moffett, Portland, OR
Laura Noy, St. Paul, MN
Linda Rles, Spearfish, SD
Ralph Saperstein, Portland, OR
Daphne Sewing, Salt Lake City, UT
Marilyn Sigman, Douglas, AK
John Simpson, Guam, Marianas Islands
Sandra Urbaniak, Waubay, SD
Mike Way, Fort Collins, CO
Jeff Webster, Anderson, CA
Suzette Widergren, Oakland, CA
Jerry Wilson, Everett, WA
Lisa Worley, Post Falls, ID
Terri Zubchenok, Santa Fe, NM

NORTHEASTERN WORKSHOP,
HEBRON, CT
Virginia Anderson, Waterbury, VT
Stephen Bero, Liverpool, NY
Carroll Bond, Milford, ME
Diane Chisnall Joy, Hartford, CT
Paul Dolan, Chepachet, RI
Tom Driscoll, Augusta, ME
Dan Dziubek, Pittsburgh, PA
Steve Fish, Hartford, CT
Christine Flanagan, Boyce, VA
Chester Gillan, Charlottetown, Prince Edward Island, Canada

Margaret Gillespie, Holderness, NH
Marlena Gloff-Straw, Trenton, NJ
Roger Goldstein, Boston, MA
Shirley Griffin, Ashburnham, MA
Jane Hadley, Fredricton, New Brunswick, Canada
Brian Hearn, Charlottetown, Prince Edward Island, Canada
Gary Heath, Baltimore, MD
Ted Jones, Bristol, CT
Debbie Langille, Truro, Nova Scotia, Canada
Michele LeClair, Charlottetown, Prince Edward Island, Canada
Ken Mayhew, Charlottetown, Prince Edward Island, Canada
Colleen McNerney, Paul Smithe, NY
Paul Memmer, Fairfield, ME
John Miller, Cressona, PA
Karen Muir, Pasadena, MD
Patricia Neidhart, Annapolis, MD
Dick Obyc, Durham, NH
Tanya Oznowich, Trenton, NJ
Donna Peare, Troy, NY
Barbara Pietrucha, Neptune, NJ
Marsha Poindexter, Dorchester, MA
Celeste Prussia, Windham, CT
Nancy Pywell, Gainesville, FL
Linda Rapp, Rockfall, CT
Don Reeves, Charlottetown, Prince Edward Island, Canada
Juan Sanchez, Jr., North Windham, CT
Will Snyder, Amherst, MA
Lou Southard, Charlottesville, VA
Debbie Totten, Truro, Nova Scotia, Canada
Denice Upton, Hopewell, VA
Jeffrey Vroom, Truro, Nova Scotia, Canada
Kim Williams, Rumford, ME
Julie Winchester, Mehoopany, PA

REVIEWERS
Bill Andrews, California State Department of Education
Kay Antunez, California Department of Forestry
Terri Bates, National Association of State Foresters
Yvonee Beeler, Aluminum Association
Dana Blanton, American Forest and Paper Association
Judy Braus, World Wildlife Fund
Peter Bunten, American Forest and Paper Association
Bonnie Cornwall, California Energy Extension Service
Lester Decoster, American Forest Council
Jane Difley, American Forest Foundation
Fay Fiske, Stone Forest Industries
John Gahl, Western Regional Environmental Education Council
Frank Gallagher, Liberty State Park
Pam Godsey, USDA Forest Service
Brent Halsey Jr., James River Corporation
Josetta Hawthorne, Western Regional Environmental Education Council
Gary Heath, Maryland Department of Education
John Heissenbuttel, American Forest and Paper Association
Louis Iozzi, Rutgers University, Cook College
T.J. Jacob, Department of Forestry, University of Illinois
Barry Jamason, New York Department of Education
Larry Kotchman, North Dakota Forest Service
Paul Memmer, Scott Paper Company
Dave Mumper, Weyerhaeuser Company
Donna Peare, American Forest Council
Don Reeves, Forestry Canada, Prince Edward Island
Rudy Schafer, Environmental Education Consultant
Dan Sivek, University of Wisconsin - Stevens Point
Cindi Smith-Walters, Tennessee State Department of Education
Will Snyder, Cooperative Extension, University of Massachusetts
Lou Southard, Virginia Department of Forestry

Darleen Stoner, California State University, San Bernardino
Elena Tarailo, California Department of Fish and Game
Paula Tarnapol, Society of American Foresters
Karin Van Dyke, Mead Paper
Patti Vathis, Pennsylvania Department of Education
Brenda Weiser, Oklahoma Conservation Commission
Helena Wright, Smithsonian Institution
Terri Zubchenok, New Mexico State Forestry Division

PILOT TEST EDUCATORS
Aurelia Ellison Selma, AL
Liz Webb Selma, AL
Martha Jo Brook Selma, AL
M. Shuptrine Selma, AL
Irene G. Smith Selma, AL
Sherrill W. Parris Selma, AL
Joy Carchedi Selma, AL
Charlotte Griffith Selma, AL
Ann Thompson Selma, AL
Dionne M. Craig Selma, AL
J. Britton Selma, AL
Kay Antunez Sacramento, CA
Suzanne Scheidt Villa Park, CA
Andrea J. Catania Escondido, CA
Elma May Page Wilmington, DE
Regina Mathisa Lawrenceville, GA
Shirley Wright Pocatello, ID
Patricia K. Snyder Mundelein, IL
Gail Block Urbana, IL
Debbie Neuenschwander Ossian, IN
Shelly Mitchell Indianapolis, IN
Barbara Kinneerm Burlington, IA
Janice Harryman Girard, KS
Sherry Troegel Mansfield, LA
Glenrose T. Pitt Provencal, LA
Roger Smithson Bossier, LA
S. Kaye Lousseau Cotton Valley, LA
Sue Ann Charles South China, ME
Anthony Symasko East Hampton, MA
Jim Lafley Belchertown, MA
Jim Terruso Milton, MA
Shawna Zatinskey Hadley, MA
Patty Steinman Milton, MA
Sandra L. Nagle West Dennis, MA
Nancy M. Reynolds Winona, MN
Chris Collins Cottage Grove, MN
Patricia Livingston Madison, MS
Jarma D. Bridges Leakesville, MS
James D. Lane Sheridan, MT
Susan Glueckert Missoula, MT
Craig McCollin Bozeman, MT
Patty Dugan Henriksen Gorham, NH
Kathe Cussen Atkinson, NH
Barbara R. Pietrucha Neptune, NJ
Bernadette Vath Watchung, NJ
Barbara Doyle North Plainfield, NJ
Allison Brown Plattsburgh, NY
Carole Bjornson Cooperstown, ND
Carol L. Erwin Muskogee, OK
Delores Willoughby Choat Chikasha, OK
Pam Barnhill Conway, SC
Patricia G. Milley Loris, SC
Tom Rex Myrtle Beach, SC
Ruth Hayward Myrtle Beach, SC
Linda Singletonn Conway, SC
Karen Quinn Conway, SC
P. Strickland Conway, SC
Suzanne Cullen Conway, SC
Nancy Ray Green Sea, SC
Jennifer Hardee Conway, SC
Beverly DiMaio Aynar, SC
Raschelle M. Moss Conway, SC
Diane Parker Conway, SC
Jo Graham Kingston, SC
K. Johnson Conway, SC
Laura G. Wood Loris, SC
Tarlie D. Bryan Myrtle Beach, SC
Page Slate-Burns Conway, SC

Miltonette Clardy Conway, SC
Janet DeBow Buffalo, SD
J. Padgett Kelly Murfreesboro, TN
Jo Covington Monterey, TN
Connie L. Lillard Monterey, TN
J. Norrod Monterey, TN
Jill Ramsey, Monterey, TN
Debbie Schafer Millington, TN
Pauline Saville Townsend, TN
Cheri Dood Memphis, TN
Tilman D. Corum Jackson, TN
Carol F. O'Connell Halls, TN
Anne W. Smith Purcellville, VA
Sally Bien Leesburg, Virginia
Karen Blodgett Leesburg, VA
Dawn Caudell Leesburg, VA
Betty H. Phillips Leesburg, VA
Diana Townsend Vancouver, WA
Terre Rudgarden Blaine, WA
Rob Brown Vancouver, WA
Marlex Memmel Edmonds, WA
Lisa Worley St. John, WA
Catherine Thalhammer WI
Kathleen Adee Ashland, WI
Bill Worthman Poynette, WI
Linda Garcia Sankville, WI
Chester Gillian Charlottetown, Prince Edward Island, Canada

FIELD TEST EDUCATORS
Gina Karolan Fairbanks, AK
Jackie Martin Fairbanks, AK
Kim Aikers Bryant, AR
Cheryl Green Hickory Ridge, AR
Sheila Gardner Monticello, AR
Ann Cash Dover, AR
Anna Yarberry Bryant, AR
Debra Culpepper Prescott, AR
Linda Kellim Truman, AR
John Remmers Fayetteville, AR
Joane Doyle Payson, AZ
Laura Craft Tucson, AZ
Jean Fields Phoenix, AZ
Lynn Krigbaum Phoenix, AZ
Nancy Carter Carmichael, CA
Tammy Green-Sanchez Sacramento, CA
Daniel Backstrom Red Bluff, CA
Jean Crossley Winters, CA
Suzanne Scheidt Yorba Linda, CA
Betsy Olson Elk Grove, CA
Michael Lee San Francisco, CA
Faye L. Walton Carson, CA
Barbara Hickman Modesto, CA
John Zavalny San Pedro, CA
Patty Breece Colorado Springs, CO
Barbara Pratt Wilmington, DE
Doris Morris Wilmington, DE
Kay Tebbins Wilford, DE
Tonya Mead Ocean View, DE
Linda Litzkow Gainesville, FL
Myra Jeffres Panama City, FL
Leslie Egbert Idaho Falls, ID
L. Hyndman Rigby, ID
Ginger Lentz Indianapolis, IN
Bonnie Browning Russellville, IN
Kim Flake Indianapolis, IN
Katherine Asbell Russellville, IN
Laurie Allison Mooresville, IN
Merrilyn Goepal Altoona, IA
Diane Maddox Shawnee Mission, KS
Jo Graves Louisville, KY
Sharon Sloas Isonville, KY
Phyllis Warren Lexington, KY
Diane Derer Lexington, KY
Tracy Bourg Berwick, LA
Jeannie Windham Springfield, LA
Diane Chapman Hadley, MA
Beverly McGinley Concord, MA
Tom Hourihan Concord, MA
Debra Finn Midland, MI
Gena McCafferty Midland, MI

Gwaynel Dvorak Falcon Heights, MN
Donna White Apple Valley, MN
Sandy Macho Bloomington, MN
Jan Hatle Bloomington, MN
Lynda Pipkin Coffeeville, MS
Sue Bollwitt Utica, NY
Louise Wrobleski Madison, NH
Kathe Cussen East Hampstead, NH
Paulette Durkee Meredith, NH
Frank Kelley Wolfboro, NH
Sandy Kapela Ellenville, NY
Cindy Craft Napanoch, NY
James W. Clough South Glens Falls, NY
Wendy Henderson East Flat Rock, NC
Delyte Lee Williston, ND
Carol Erwin Coweta, OK
Beth Waugh, Buffalo, OK
Rita Wilson Frederick, OK
Betsy Zadorozny Woodward, OK
Tina Brazile Altoona, PA
Beverly Bruening State College, PA
Laura Barthmaier State College, PA
Shirley Donavan State College, PA
Mary Kerrick State College, PA
Diane Oyler State College, PA
Kimberly Granatire Pittsburgh, PA
Donna Dorey Lamar, PA
Rick Knepp Duncannon, PA
Judy Bamas Sharpsville, PA
Stephanie DeMott Oxford, PA
Lynn Alexander Spartanburg, SC
Stephanie Queen Columbia, SC
Karen M. Byrd Kadoka, SD
Jan Goodrich Spearfish, SD
Carol Greco Lead, SD
Jane Buxton Spearfish, SD
June Treber Lead, SD
Dorothy Erhart Deadwood, SD
Connie Lillard Monterey, TN
Jo Covington Monterey, TN
Joyce Norrod Monterey, TN
Jill Ramsey Monterey, TN
Brenda Barnett Ridgely, TN
Cheri Dood Memphis, TN
Mike Sanders Old Hickory, TN
Terry Cook Dyersburg, TN
Jackie Littleton Clarksville, TN
Linda Cottrell Nashville, TN
Jean Bond Guildhall, VT
Betty Phillips Leesburg, VA
Donna Henderson Roanoke, VA
Dina Richards Roanoke, VA
Dano Beal Veradale, WA
Beth Umlauf Ringle, WI
Donna Hahn Elm Grove, WI
Ann Walser Middletown, WI
Karen Yost Milwaukee, WI
Ann Dodds Milwaukee, WI
Karen Buchs Genoa City, WI
Barb Bauditz Truro, Nova Scotia, Canada
Karen Archibald Waugh Truro, Nova Scotia, Canada
Patricia Cochrane Truro, Nova Scotia, Canada

PROJECT LEARNING TREE COORDINATORS–1993

The following coordinators were instrumental in developing this revised curriculum:

Rei Boyce, Alabama Forestry Association

Peggy Cowan, Alaska Department of Education

Susan Rogers, Division of Forestry, Alaska

Mike Hart, Forestry Division, Arizona State Land Department

Chris Williams, Soil Conservation Service, Arizona

Jean Fields, USDA Soil Conservation Service & Arizona Association for Learning in and about the Environment

Susan Glaze, Arkansas Forestry Association

Dr. Larry Willett, Department of Forest Resources, Arkansas

Kay Antunez, California Department of Forestry

Mike Way, Colorado State Forest Service

Diane Joy, Connecticut Department of Environmental Protection

Linda Rapp, Connecticut Forest & Park Association

Juan Sanchez, Center for Environmental Education, Connecticut

Connie Zipterer, Delaware Department of Agriculture

Dr. Nancy Arny, Cooperative Extension Service, University of Florida

Jeff Doran, Florida Forestry Association

Sharon Dolliver, Georgia Forestry Commission

Laura Newbern, Georgia Forestry Association

Richard Osorio, Cooperative Extension Service, University of Georgia

Colleen Murakami, Hawaii Department of Education

Mike Bowman, Clearwater National Forest, Idaho

Dick Kay, Idaho Department of Education

Milt Williams, Idaho Department of Lands

T.J. Jacob, University of Illinois

Bonni Browning, Indiana Division of Forestry

Duane Toomsen, Department of Public Instruction, Iowa

John Strickler, Cooperative Extension Service, Kansas State University

Connie Elpers, Wichita Wild, Kansas

Ruth Jacquot, Murray State University, Kentucky

Doug McLaren, Cooperative Extension Service, University of Kentucky

Dr. Ron Gardella, Northern Kentucky University

Jim Culpepper, Louisiana Department of Agriculture & Forestry

Clyde Todd, Louisiana Forestry Association

Rick Kilpatrick, Cooperative Extension Service, Louisiana

Lisa Knauf, Maine Forest Service

Dr. Gary Heath, State Department of Education, Maryland

James Klunk, Maryland Forest Service

Will Snyder, Cooperative Extension Service, University of Massachusetts

Karin Van Dyke, Mead Paper Company, Michigan

Denise Seipke, Michigan State University

Laura Noy, Department of Natural Resources, Minnesota

Meg Hanisch, Department of Natural Resources, Minnesota

Bill Colvin, Mississippi Forestry Commission

Bruce Palmer, Department of Conservation, Missouri

Spencer Sartorius, Office of Public Instruction, Montana

Mike Cavey, Cooperative Extension Service, Montana State University

Bob Gibson, Society of American Foresters, Montana

Scott DeWald, University of Nebraska

Mark Kimbrough, Nevada State Parks

Pat Murphy, Division of Forestry, Nevada

Margaret Gillespie, Science Center of New Hampshire

Colleen Thomas, Department of Environmental Protection, New Jersey

Frank Gallagher, Division of Parks and Forestry, New Jersey

Terri Zubchenok, New Mexico State Forestry Division

Barry Jamason, New York Department of Education

Clint Rumrill, New York State Department of Environmental Conservation

Leon Harkins, Extension Forestry, North Carolina State University

Joe Hogue, North Carolina Forest Resources

Glenda Fauske, North Dakota Forest Service

Dr. John Hug, Ohio Department of Education

Bill Schultz, Ohio Department of Natural Resources

Bob Harrel, Oklahoma Forestry Service

Brenda Weiser, Oklahoma Conservation Commission

Barbara Middleton, Oregon State University

Ray Thiess, Oregon Department of Education

Patti Vathis, Pennsylvania Department of Education

Robert Merrill, Pennsylvania Bureau of Forestry

Paul Dolan, Division of Forest Environment, Rhode Island

Roger Greene, Department of Environmental Management, Rhode Island

Richard Harrington, Rhode Island Department of Education

Charles Moore, South Carolina Forestry Commission

David Erickson, South Dakota Division of Forestry

Beth Broyles, South Dakota Division of Forestry

Nancy Smith, Tennessee State Department of Education

Dr. Mike Walterscheidt, Cooperative Extension Service, Texas A&M University

Tony Dietz, Utah State Lands & Forestry

Joan Dolph, Utah State Lands & Forestry

Virginia Anderson, Vermont Department of Forest, Parks & Recreation

Lou Southard, Virginia Department of Forestry

Glenda Parrish, Virginia Forestry Association

Lynne Ferguson, Washington Forest Protection Association

Tony Angell, Washington Department of Public Instruction

Jon Wilcox, Washington Forest Protection Association

Bill Brown, West Virginia Forestry Association

Dick Waybright, West Virginia Forestry Association

Valeria Humphrey, Wisconsin Department of Natural Resources

Dr. William Futrell, Wyoming Department of Education

Rex Johnson, Wyoming State Forestry Division

Dr. Duane Keown, Wyoming University of Wyoming

Talosia Esau, Department of Education, American Samoa

Michael Harrington, Land Grant Program, American Samoa Community College

Ravi Chandran, North Marianas College, Commonwealth of the Northern Mariana Islands (Saipan, Tinian, Rota)

Estanislao Villagomez, Department of Natural Resources, Commonwealth of the Northern Mariana Islands (Saipan, Tinian, Rota)

Jacqueline Quirugua, Public School System, Commonwealth of the Northern Mariana Islands (Saipan, Tinian, Rota)

John Simpson, Department of Education, Guam

Carlos Noquez, Territorial Forester, Guam

Harvey G. Segal, College of Micronesia

Barbara Jones, British Columbia Forestry Association, Canada

Bill Baker, Manitoba Forestry Association, Canada

Dave Folster, Canadian Forestry Association of New Brunswick, Canada

Jeff Vroom, Nova Scotia Forestry Association, Canada

Randy Fulton, Nova Scotia Forestry Association, Canada

Barbara Bauditz, Nova Scotia Forestry Association, Canada

Claude Simard, Direction des Communications et de l'éducation, Ministère des Forêts, Quebec, Canada

Don Reeves, Forestry Canada, Prince Edward Island, Canada

Per Elof Bostrom, Natverket Skogen i Skolan, Finland

Shin-ichiro Yoshida, International Education Resource and Information Center, Japan

Julio Carrera & Eglantina Canales, Proteccion de la Fauna Mexicana A.C., Mexico

Boo Nilsson & Bil Berlof, Umea University, Sweden

Martin Smith, Munich International School, Germany

For a current listing of coordinators for Project Learning Tree, call 202-463-2462

Or visit our web site,
http://www.plt.org

Diversity

Overview
As humans we depend on all of our senses—touching, tasting, hearing, smelling, and seeing—to gather impressions of our environment. Our brain sorts out the diversity of sizes, colors, and shapes that we see. In this activity, students will focus their eyes on the many shapes that define both our natural and built environment.

Getting Ready
1. Before the activity, make "shape necklaces" by cutting out circles, ovals, squares, and triangles from construction paper. (There should be one shape for each student.) Punch a hole in each shape and thread string through the hole. Tie the string off so that it forms a loop big enough to fit easily over a child's head.

2. Cut an extra set of shapes.

3. For Part B, draw a circle, square, rectangle, and triangle on separate slips of paper. (Each slip should have only one shape.) Make enough slips for everyone in the group.

PART A
I SPY

Doing the Activity
1. Hold up each shape in turn and ask the students to identify it. Also ask if they can name something that has that particular shape.

2. Go for a walk with the students, making sure that each person wears his or her shape necklace. Also bring along the shapes you cut out earlier.

3. When you see an object obviously shaped like a circle, square, oval or triangle, hold up the appropriate cutout shape and say, "I spy something shaped like a _____" (fill in with the correct shape).

4. Give the students time to look for the object you're "spying." If they find other objects that also have that shape, acknowledge their observations and encourage them to continue looking for the object you have in mind.

5. After the students have identified one or more of the objects you've spied, encourage them to look for objects in the shape of the pieces of paper they're wearing around their necks. When someone sees that shape, he or she should say, "I spy!" Have the other students try to find the object the "spy" is observing. (If you're working with very young students, you might want to add colors to the list of things being spied. For example, you could say, "I spy something that is yellow and is shaped like a _____." Then have students look for a yellow object with "their" shape.)

6. When you get back to the classroom, hold up each cut-out shape in turn and ask the students to recall things they saw with each shape. Then have the students draw a picture of an object they spied with their shape.

PART B
SHOW 'N' TELL SHAPES (K-3)

Doing the Activity
1. Begin the activity by asking the students to name something round that they use every day. Also ask them to name everyday objects that are square, rectangular, or triangular.

2. Put the slips you made earlier in a sack or other container and have each person pick one. Tell the students to keep the identity of their shapes a secret.

3. Tell the students that they'll take a walk to look for shapes in the nat-

ural and built environment. During the walk, each person will

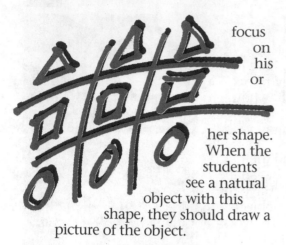

focus on his or her shape. When the students see a natural object with this shape, they should draw a picture of the object.

4. Before going outside, make sure each person has a crayon or pencil and paper. (The students can use either their notebooks or several sheets of paper attached to a clipboard. If you don't have enough clipboards to go around, give the students cardboard and have them secure the paper to the cardboard with rubber bands.)

5. Take the students on a leisurely walk around the school grounds or in a park or other natural setting. Stop as needed so the students can draw objects with the appropriate shape. Tell the students not to point out the objects to others; you will compare notes later on the different objects everyone saw.

6. Once you're back inside, ask for a volunteer to discuss which shape she or he was looking for. Ask the volunteer to show all pictures she or he created during the walk. Did any of the other students with that shape observe additional objects?

7. Talk about each of the remaining shapes in turn, allowing students to describe what they saw and to share their drawings.

8. To finish the activity, have the students use their drawings to create a "Shapes Around Us" bulletin board. (Give the students time to color their drawings or create new ones, if they want to.)

Enrichment
You can use this activity with primary and intermediate students as a "jumping-off" point for an activity focusing on birds, trees, or architecture. Many birds, trees, and buildings are identifiable at a distance by their overall shape, and field guides often provide silhouettes of trees and birds.

END NOTES...

ASSESSMENT OPPORTUNITY
Give each student a piece of paper and have each draw a tic-tac-toe grid on it. Students should draw three triangles on the first row, three squares on the second row, and three circles on the third row. Take students outside and have them look for shapes. The object is to find shapes in the environment that match the ones on the paper. When students find three in a row—up, down, or diagonal—they yell, "Shape Up!" and identify the three shapes they found.

RELATED ACTIVITIES
Get in Touch with Trees, The Peppermint Beetle, Sounds Around, Poet-Tree

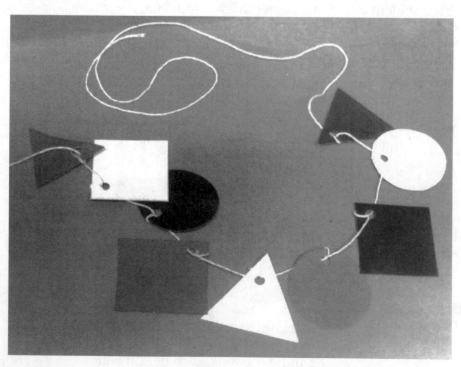

Overview
In this activity students will explore their sense of touch and discover why touch is important to animals, including themselves.

Background
Bark is a very important part of a tree. The outer bark acts as a suit of armor against the outer world. It wards off insects and disease, and it protects the inner tissues against damage from storms or extreme temperatures. The bark of certain species also protects the tree from fire. Bark descriptions are based on color, texture, thickness, shagginess, and other relevant details. The bark of some species changes significantly with age.

Getting Ready
1. Find an area where several different kinds of trees grow. Collect one or more objects from the ground underneath each of the trees. For example, you might collect several kinds of

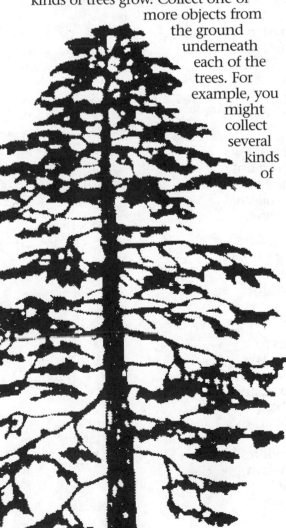

leaves (pointy edges, fuzzy underside, pine-needle clusters); bark (smooth, rough, crumbly); and nuts, seeds, or fruits (acorns, walnuts, pine cones).

NOTE—Do not tear living parts off the tree. Review guidelines for collecting objects from nature, Appendix 6. Again, remember to avoid harmful plants like poison ivy. You can also do this activity in urban settings without going outdoors by using tree products such as paper, wooden blocks, nuts, fruits, etc.

2. Cut a hole in the top of a box. The hole should be no larger than necessary for a hand to fit through comfortably. You can also sew or tape the top part of a sock to the hole to prevent peeking in. You may want to have the students decorate the outside of the box.

3. Put the objects you collected earlier into the mystery box.

PART A
FEEL THE DIFFERENCE

Doing the Activity
1. Ask the students what is important about the sense of touch. How do they use their sense of touch? What if they didn't have it? Ask them to give examples of how animals use the sense of touch for survival, and how people find touch important in their own lives. Have students imagine and describe what different parts of a tree might feel like. Have each student write down his or her description.

2. Take the students outside and divide them into groups of three. Give each group a blindfold.

3. Explain that each member of the group will take a turn wearing the blindfold. (Students can just close their

LEVELS
Grades PreK-6

SUBJECTS
Science, Language Arts, Visual Arts

CONCEPT
- Biological diversity results from the interaction of living and non-living environmental components such as air, water, climate, and geological features. (1.1)

SKILLS
Identifying, Attributes and Components, Observing, Making Analogies and Metaphors, Comparing and Contrasting, Classifying and Categorizing

OBJECTIVES
Students will ① become aware of how the bark of different trees varies in texture and ② describe a variety of textures found in leaves and other tree parts.

MATERIALS
Part A: Blindfolds (one for each group of three)

Part B: Medium-sized box (no smaller than a shoebox), natural objects (see mystery box directions on page 6 for ideas), and containers for collecting "tree parts"

TIME CONSIDERATIONS
Preparation: 30 minutes

Activity: 50 minutes

eyes if they're uncomfortable wearing a blindfold.) The blindfolded person will examine two or more trees, using only the sense of touch. If your school is in an area with few or no trees, you might want to arrange to take the students to a wooded park. You can also use objects other than trees, i.e., human-made objects, for this part of the activity.

4. Have the two "sighted" group members carefully lead the one blindfolded person to a tree. The blindfolded student should examine the tree's bark and, if possible, its leaves and other features. Students should be careful to avoid irritating plants such as poison ivy, oak, or sumac. Check with a local nature center to learn how to identify and avoid those plants. Such plants are often found on the ground next to trees. After they've spent a few minutes at the first tree, have students move on to another tree. Tell them to pay close attention to the differences and similarities between the two trees.

5. Have the students repeat the activity with each of the group members. (If possible, have the students choose new trees for each blindfolded person.)

6. When everyone is finished, bring the students together and have them describe the different trees they examined. Ask them to write a description of their experiences and to use similes, metaphors, and analogies (i.e., "pine bark has islands on it"). **Younger students** can give oral descriptions. Then see if the students can find their trees. If they can't find the tree, their group companions can show them.

7. Ask the students to join you in reviewing their original descriptions of a tree and its parts. Ask them which words they would still use (or add) if they were going to describe a tree to a classmate. Ask them to explain their answers.

8. Have the students use the bark of their particular trees to see if they can find more of the same trees in the area.

9. Older students should use a field guide to find the species of their tree.

Is the bark type a good indicator of this species? Does the bark texture or color change during the life of the tree? (See field guide references in the Bibliography on page 385.)

VARIATION FOR PART A

If you're working with preschoolers, try leading small groups or the entire group to different trees. You might also want to enlist the help of more adults or older students.

Enrichment
As a side topic, students could describe what it was like to be blindfolded. Were they scared? Were their other senses sharper? Also ask students how it felt to lead the blind person.

PART B
MAKE A MYSTERY BOX
Doing the Activity
1. Take the students to the place where you found the objects and give each person a bag or other container. Have each student reach into the mystery box you prepared earlier and feel as many of the items as possible. Then have students search for "tree parts" that match those in the mystery box. Tell them to put the tree parts in their containers.

2. Bring the students together and ask a volunteer to pull one object at a time from the mystery box . Have the students hold up the object they collected that matches the one from the box.

3. Older students can use field guides to try to identify which trees or plants the items in the box come from. Can these items be used to identify a particular species?

Enrichment
Have the students work in pairs to make their own mystery boxes. Ask another teacher to have his or her students also prepare mystery boxes, and have your students exchange boxes with them. After using the other class's mystery boxes for a period of time, have students from each class address the other class and say why an item they put in the box was special to them. (have them exhibit the object as well.)

Overview
In this activity students will explore their sense of smell and discover why smell is important to animals, including themselves.

Background
Taste and smell are chemically activated senses and are closely related. In fact, we are actually smelling much of what we think we are tasting. For a substance to be smelled and tasted, it must first be dissolved on the membrane of the olfactory area in the nasal passages (see diagram). That's why a person whose nasal passages are blocked because of a cold cannot smell or taste food very well.

The ability to respond to chemicals (smell or taste) is probably one of the earliest senses developed by organisms. It is especially important in the insect world. When foraging worker ants find food, they leave a scent trail for other ants. The ants touch their abdomens to the ground and secrete a substance that is detected only by members of the same species using their antennae. The better the food source, the more scent markings the ant will leave on the trail. If another animal accidently crosses the scent trail and breaks it, the ants become disoriented and confused.

Fish also rely heavily on odor for communication.

When one fish in a school is injured, it exudes an odor that scatters the school away from the source of injury and danger.

The champion odor-detector is probably the salmon. After salmon hatch in a stream, they swim downstream to the open ocean to live. Two to five years later, the salmon will unerringly trace its original path on a strenuous journey to its birthplace upstream. It is believed that this incredible homing behavior is due to its ability to remember the specific odor of the water where it was born, and to isolate that smell from all other odors in the water between its birthplace and the ocean.

To define an area or territory, many animals mark objects with scent from special glands. Scent-marking can be used for finding a mate or for establishing an area for family, shelter, and food supply. Animals often defend their territory from intruders, especially members of the same species.

Getting Ready
In preparation, flag or mark boundaries in a wooded area and "scent-mark" trees that lie roughly on the same line. Preferably, mark at least one tree per pair of students. Scent-mark the trees by moistening a cotton ball with peppermint oil (or other aromatic flavoring) and rubbing it on the bark around the tree at the nose level of a student of average height. Mark the trees close to the time the students will do the activity because the peppermint oil will evaporate. Cut lengths of yarn long enough to be tied around the tree trunks. Provide several lengths of yarn for each pair of students.

LEVELS
Grades K-6

SUBJECTS
Science, Social Studies

CONCEPT
■ Organisms adapt to changes in the environment according to the genetic and behavioral capacity of their species. (4.3)

SKILLS
Reasoning, Discussing, Identifying Relationships and Patterns, Concluding

OBJECTIVES
Students will ① describe various ways animals use their sense of smell, ② explain why some animals use scent marking, and ③ identify the importance of the sense of smell in our daily lives.

MATERIALS
Small bottle of concentrated flavoring (peppermint, cinnamon, wintergreen, etc.); cotton balls; a ball of yarn; flagging materials or rags to mark boundaries; several baby food or small jars with lids; cotton balls; and several organic liquids or substances with strong, distinctive smells *(Warning: Read the label on all items before deliberately inhaling them. Many substances such as nail polish remover, white-out, and rubber cement are harmful to inhale.)*

TIME CONSIDERATIONS
Preparation: 50 minutes

Activity: 50 minutes

Doing the Activity

1. Ask your students how their sense of smell is important to them. Did they ever have a cold and lose their sense of smell? How did it feel? Did it affect their sense of taste? (Explain how smell and taste are related. See Background.) Could your sense of smell save you from dangerous situations? (Yes, you could detct gas, smoke, or rotten food.) At this point you might want to have the students explore their sense of smell in more depth by doing the Enrichment.

2. Next, ask students how different animals rely on their sense of smell. Give examples. (Have students with pets give firsthand accounts.) Do these animals rely on smell more or less than people do? What purpose does smell serve for these animals? (It helps them find food, detect danger, find a mate, and identify another animal's territory.) You might want to allow the students time to go to the library and research how animals that interest them use their sense of smell.

3. Tell students to imagine an insect called the "peppermint beetle" (name it after whatever scent you are using, i.e., "licorice beetle" or "lemon beetle") living in the area they will visit. This flying beetle is famous for the peppermint scent it occasionally marks on the trunks of trees. They will work in teams to find the trees that the beetle has marked.

4. At the activity site, divide the group into pairs, and give each pair several lengths of yarn. (If your site has relatively few trees, use larger teams so that you have more trees than teams.) Tell each team to use their noses to find trees that the bee-

tle visited. If they find a tree that both team members agree is scent-marked, they should tie the yarn around the tree. Teams should continue searching for scent-marked trees; they need not check trees that have already been identified with yarn.

5. When all the scent-marked trees have been found, have the students walk the scent trail left by the peppermint beetle. Ask the students to consider why the peppermint beetle marked those trees. Could it be to attract a mate, or define a territory? Where might the peppermint beetle's trail lead? To a food source? Its home? Or nowhere in particular?

Enrichment

Make "mystery jars" to test how well students can recognize smells. Collect baby food jars or other small containers (film canisters are a safe choice for very young students). Put a wad of cotton in each jar. Collect liquids with strong distinctive smells such as perfume, vanilla, vinegar, or food flavorings. Pour a few drops of each liquid into different jars or place solid aromatic substances such as cloves, lemon peels, or garlic into film canisters or jars covered with paper. Poke a hole in the lid of each jar and screw lids down. Label the jars A, B, C, etc. Let the students smell each jar, and have them write down what they think each smell is and where they've smelled it before. You can also try putting the same scent in two different jars and see if the students can find the pair with the same scent. Afterward, ask the students if certain smells triggered certain memories.

END NOTES...

ASSESSMENT OPPORTUNITY

Ask the students to name animals (dogs, cats, ferrets, rabbits, deer) that also use scent to "mark" objects. How do they do this? (With urine or special scent glands.) Why might they do this? (To identify themselves to other members of their species, to attract a mate, to mark their territory.) Do animals publicize their territories using methods other than scent-marking? (Yes. For example, songbirds sing, howler monkeys howl.) What are animals trying to protect in marking their territory? (Food, water, shelter, family.) Do people mark their territory? How? (Fences, hedges, signs.) Why? (To protect themselves and their property.)

Ask the students to think of ways that people use their sense of smell. Ask them if they could use their sense of smell to find food. For example, could they find a pizza in the kitchen with the lights out? Why is the smell of a food important? (Makes it taste better, tells us if it's fresh.) Why do people use things like perfume or air freshener? (To make their environment more pleasant.)

RELATED ACTIVITIES

Sounds Around, Get in Touch with Trees, The Shape of Things, School Yard Safari, Trees as Habitats

REFERENCES

Background adapted from Ritchie, Donald D., and Robert Carola. BIOLOGY. Reading, MA: Addison-Wesley Publishing Company, 1979.

Overview
Our ears are constantly being bombarded with sound—so much so that we automatically "tune out" a lot of it. Some sounds are "music to our ears," while others can annoy us and even damage the delicate structures in our ears. Try this activity to help your students "tune in" to the sounds in their environment and to help them identify and lessen local noise problems.

Background
Sound is a form of energy that travels in waves. Sound waves can be transmitted only when molecules (like air or water) are present. Sound energy causes molecules to vibrate and bump into each other, creating a wave that travels through the "sea of molecules." When molecules are not present, like in outer space, sound waves cannot exist. That's why space explorers must use radio transmitters in order to communicate when taking a space walk.

When sound waves reach our ears, they are funneled down the ear canal to the eardrum (see diagram). The eardrum is a circular membrane that is stretched across the ear canal and vibrates when sound waves strike it. It separates the outer ear from the middle ear. The middle ear contains three tiny bones, the first of which is attached to the eardrum. Vibrations of the eardrum pass through these three bones. The third bone rests on the cochlea (KAHK-lee-uh), a structure in the inner ear. The cochlea is a fluid-filled tube that contains hairlike recep-

tors for sound. Sound vibrations are carried through this fluid causing the hairlike structures to bend. These receptors send impulses to the auditory nerve that connects the inner ear to the brain. Impulses from the cochlea are interpreted in the hearing center in the brain's cerebrum.

Getting Ready
For Part B, find an area in your community where noise (traffic or other sources) can be a problem. Within the area that you choose you'll need several locations—some that are in the open and very noisy, and others where the noise is muted by trees, shrubs, grass, buildings, walls, windows, parked cars, etc. The students will measure noise levels in several locations. The best way to measure noise is to use a noise meter—an instrument specially designed to measure the noise level in decibels. Try borrowing a noise meter from your state or city department of transportation, public works, or environmental protection. If you are unable to obtain one, a regular tape recorder will enable

LEVELS
Part A: Grades 1-6
Variation: Grades PreK-K
Part B: Grades 6-8
Part C: Grades PreK-K

SUBJECTS
Science, Language Arts, Social Studies, Math

CONCEPTS
- Biological diversity results from the interaction of living and non-living environmental components such as air, water, climate, and geological features. (1.1)
- Resource management and technological systems help societies to meet, within limits, the needs of a growing human population. (8.2)

SKILLS
Classifying and Categorizing, Organizing Information, Identifying Relationships and Patterns, Problem Solving

OBJECTIVES:
Students will ① identify sounds and map their location in the environment, ② explain how noise can be a problem in the community, ③ create and carry out a plan to lessen a local noise problem, and ④ study a Greek myth about sounds in nature.

MATERIALS
Paper, crayons or markers, clipboards (or cardboard and paper clips or notebooks), and a noise meter or tape recorder

TIME CONSIDERATIONS
Preparation: One hour and a half

Activity: Two 50-minute periods

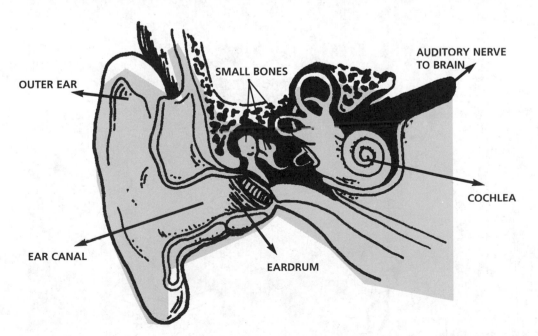

OUTER EAR

SMALL BONES

AUDITORY NERVE TO BRAIN

COCHLEA

EAR CANAL

EARDRUM

you to record noise at each location and compare the loudness of the recordings. Remember to use the same recording level at each location. Many tape recorders also have a meter that indicates noise level.

PART A
LISTEN UP!

Doing the Activity

1. Ask the students if they've ever tried to move around in a very dark place. How did they get around without being able to see? Did they rely on other senses? Did they notice sounds around them more than they might have otherwise? Ask for examples of animals that are active at night. Do they have special adaptations for seeing or for hearing? (Owls have large conical discs around their eyes that funnel sound to their ears, and foxes have large ears for picking up sounds.)

Explain that having ears on opposite sides of our head enables us (and other animals) to judge the location a sound comes from.

2. Pass out paper, crayons or markers, and a clipboard to each student. Have students find a place (indoors or outdoors) where they can sit comfortably, away from others. Then have them close their eyes and listen quietly to the sounds around them for several minutes. Tell them to try to remember all of the sounds they hear.

3. After they've listened for a few minutes, have students make a "sound map." They should put an X in the middle of the page to represent themselves, and then use pictures or words to show the location of the sounds around them. (They can use lines to show directions and approximate distances.)

4. Afterwards, lead the students in a discussion of their experiences. What were the sources of the sounds they heard? Were sounds caused by plants, animals, people, or machines? Which sounds did the students like? Which did they dislike? Call on students to demonstrate and explain their sound maps.

VARIATION FOR PART A

Have the students sit quietly in a circle with their eyes closed. After a brief interval, ask them what they are hearing and what they think is making each sound. You can have them point in the direction each sound is coming from. You can also have them imitate the sounds and draw pictures of what they think made the sounds.

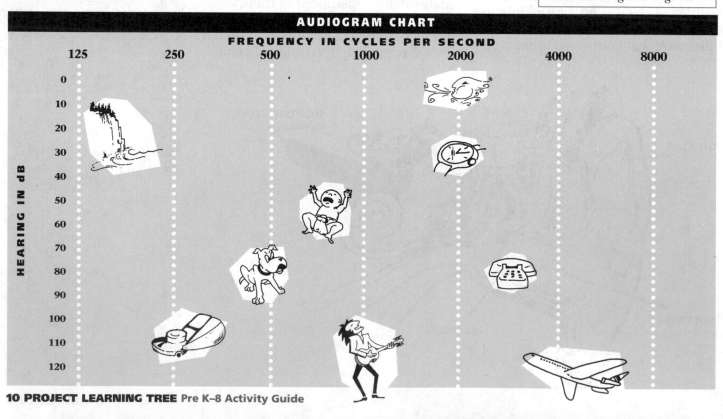

AUDIOGRAM CHART

FREQUENCY IN CYCLES PER SECOND

125 250 500 1000 2000 4000 8000

HEARING IN dB

0 10 20 30 40 50 60 70 80 90 100 110 120

PART B
NOISE BUSTERS

Doing the Activity

1. Ask the students to describe their concept of noise pollution and give examples. Discussion should reveal that there is no clear definition of noise pollution; rather, it is "in the ear of the beholder." Share with the class the decibel level of various noises and the possible damage they can cause. (See the chart on page 10.)

2. When visiting your selected site, ask teams of students to measure the noise level at two locations: one that is sheltered (by trees, walls, or objects) and one that is out in the open. If possible, both places should be about the same distance away from the main source of noise (i.e., traffic or construction). Students will want to determine if the buffer (shelter) helps to reduce noise pollution. Ask the students to consider what variables need to be controlled (recording equipment, time of day, wind) and what techniques should be used to measure the noise in both locations (number of measurements, distance from ground). Students may want to visit the site on additional days to gather more data.

3. Discuss the results with the students. If visits were made on different days and there were notable variations in the noise level at a particular location, discuss possible reasons for this. (A change in wind direction? An increased or decreased flow of traffic?)

4. If they used a noise meter or a tape recorder with a noise indicator, have the students create bar graphs comparing noise levels at different sites and on different days.

5. Using the results of their experiment, ask the students if it would be desirable or practical to reduce noise in locations where high levels were recorded, and if so, how this reduction could be accomplished. Help the students to identify a location in the community where it would be feasible to implement a noise reduction strategy. Trees are highly effective noise reducers. Tree barriers can reduce noise by over 50%–meaning that the noise level of a heavily travelled highway could be reduced to that of a suburban street in the quiet evening. Have them consider options such as planting a vegetation screen of trees, or shrubs to buffer noise. They could contact appropriate city officials to find out if such a project is possible and then contact foresters in their municipal, county, or state offices to find out what plantings are practical. If students work with local authorities and citizens' groups, such a project can be accomplished.

PART C
VOICES IN THE WATER

Until now, we have looked at sound scientifically, but people are not always scientific. In many cultures throughout human history, legends and myths have arisen that explain the story behind many sounds in nature. The following is a Greek myth that tells the story behind the soft murmur we hear in rushing water.

Doing the Activity

1. Read the story on page 12 aloud to the students.

2. After reciting the tale, discuss the story with your students using the following questions.

- What sound in nature inspired the creation of this myth? (The sound of a river.)

- What is special about the Marsyas River? (The spirit of Marsyas dwells in it.)

- When does the river sound like the music of Marsyas' flute? (When it flows peacefully.)

- When does the river "roar with wild threats"? (When it remembers Apollo's cruel revenge.)

- What other sounds might a peaceful or raging river remind you of? (Chimes, harp, cymbals, thunder.)

Enrichment

1. Students can make up their own myths to explain why things in nature sound the way they do. For example, why do trees groan? Why do leaves rustle? Why does the wind howl? Why do eagles scream?

2. Read to your students the excerpt from Maya Angelou's poem (page 10). In her poem, what is the message of the River's song?

END NOTES...

ASSESSMENT OPPORTUNITY

Assess the technique and accuracy of the students' recordings and measurements. Examine the accuracy of converting the data to a bar graph. Evaluate the students' understanding of noise pollution through their identification of noise problems in their community and the feasibility of their plan for mitigating one or more of these problems.

RELATED ACTIVITIES

Get in Touch with Trees, The Shape of Things, The Peppermint Beetle, Poet-Tree, Plant a Tree

REFERENCES

Stephanides, retold by Menelaos. *GREEK MYTHOLOGY SERIES: GODS AND MEN, VOL. 10—ORPHEUS AND EURYDICE.* Athens, Greece: Sigma Publications, 1989, pp. 30-32.

An excerpt from Maya Angelou's *ON THE PULSE OF MORNING* as delivered at the 1993 Presidential Inauguration of Bill Clinton.

KENTUCKY'S TREES: PUTTIN' ON AIRS, a fact sheet. Frankfort, Kentucky: Kentucky Division of Forestry Natural Resources and Environmental Protection Cabinet.

THE STORY OF MARSYAS

One day, the goddess Athena found the beautiful, long thigh bone of a deer. It was a pleasing object, and she wanted to make something both attractive and useful from it. She soon decided what she would make and began to work on the bone with great care and art. She cut off both ends, cleaned it out well inside, and then drilled holes down its length. Finally, she fashioned a handsome mouthpiece at the top. When she had finished, she placed the mouthpiece between her lips and began to blow, placing her fingers up and down on the holes. Lovely sounds came from the instrument she had created. It was the world's first flute.

The goddess was enchanted with her new creation and never tired of playing it. On one occasion, however, when she was playing for the other gods of Olympus, she noticed that Hera and Aphrodite were staring at her and exchanging secret giggles.

"If only you could see your face when you blow into that thing, you'd understand why we're laughing," replied the two goddesses.

"They must be jealous of me," muttered Athena, and she went off to play her flute by the banks of a river where she could see her own reflection as she blew. When she saw how her cheeks puffed out and her lovely face became distorted by the effort of blowing, she realized that Hera and Aphrodite could not be blamed for laughing behind their hands. In a sudden burst of anger, she hurled the flute away, shouting, "Miserable toy! Because of you I am insulted. A curse on anyone who picks you up and puts you to his lips."

The flute that Athena had thrown away was found by Marsyas. Suspecting nothing of the curse, he picked the flute up, liked the look of it, and decided to keep it. In time, he grew fond of the flute and learned to play it so well that whoever heard him said that not even Apollo could play so beautifully. How was unlucky Marsyas to know that the curse of Athena hung over him? He had never been one to boast, but now he began to tell everyone that he could make music even better than golden-haired Apollo.

It was not long before the great god of music appeared before the unlucky satyr. Apollo was magnificently attired, and under his arm he carried his golden lyre. The nine Muses accompanied the shining god. "How dare you call yourself a better player than I?" Apollo demanded. "Can there be anyone in the world, god or mortal, whose skill in music is a match for mine?"

"All we need do is put it to the test," replied Marsyas coolly. "Let your nine sisters judge which of us plays better. But whoever wins may impose any punishment he wishes upon the loser."

"Foolish Marsyas, what rash words were these? Did you imagine that a mere satyr could pit his poor skills against a mighty god? And did you not know that immortals are not to be insulted and are cruel beyond belief when they wish to exact punishment?" Apollo's answer was swift and terrible. "I shall defeat you and skin you alive for your insolence!" he screamed, as his face flushed with rage. But Marsyas seemed quite unconcerned and, putting the flute to his lips, began to play. The muses stood listening in awe. Even Apollo thought his ears were deceiving him. For the music that flowed from Marsyas' flute was so perfect that neither god nor man could better it. Next, it was Apollo's turn. Though his music was as good as Marsyas' in every way, it was not better. And so the Muses were unable to declare either of them the winner.

By now Apollo was boiling with rage. He was determined to be revenged on the satyr who had belittled him—by means fair or foul.

"Very well," he snarled, "now we shall play with our instruments upside down!"

And holding his lyre the other way up, he played it as superbly as before. But a flute, alas, cannot be played with its mouthpiece pointing downward, and poor Marsyas could not coax a single note from his instrument.

And so the Muses declared Apollo the winner.

The god's revenge came down on Marsyas like a thunderbolt, and the poor satyr died in hideous agony because he had dared to challenge an immortal.

The wood nymphs wept for Marsyas and buried him by a river. The muses felt sorry for the unlucky satyr and begged Zeus to take pity on him. The ruler of gods and men listened to their pleas, so Marsyas did not descend to the dark depths of Hades. Instead, his spirit was released into the waters of the river that flowed as musically as if the river were indeed playing a flute, and people listen to its song with pleasure. But when the river remembers Apollo's cruel revenge, its waters swell with wrath and roar wild threats, spreading fears and sorrow in their paths.

Overview

Writing and sharing poems will give your students an opportunity to express their feelings, values, and beliefs about the environment and related issues in creative and artistic ways.

Background

Poetic Forms

Haiku is a Japanese form of poetry that consists of three lines: the first line has five syllables, the second line has seven, and the third line has five again.

EXAMPLE

> The snow-covered tree
> Sparkles in the soft moonlight.
> The wind rushes by.

Cinquain poems consist of five lines, and each line has a mandatory purpose and number of syllables: ① the title in two syllables, ② a description of the title in four syllables, ③ a description of action in six syllables, ④ a description of a feeling in eight syllables, and ⑤ another word for the title in two syllables.

EXAMPLE

> Forests
> Graceful, growing
> Climbing among the clouds
> Calmly awaiting the sunrise
> Alive.

Diamante poems are diamond-shaped and consist of seven lines that follow the following pattern:

> noun
> adjective adjective
> participle participle participle
> noun noun noun noun
> participle participle participle
> adjective adjective
> noun

EXAMPLE

> seed
> small buried
> growing breathing living
> protection oxygen shade habitat
> dying rotting crumbling
> moist rich
> soil

In *acrostic* poetry the first letter in each line, when read vertically, spells out the name of something or conveys some other kind of message.

EXAMPLE

> **T**owering
> **R**eaching
> **E**xtending
> **E**mbracing the sky.

The words in *picture poetry* form a picture of what is happening in the poem.

EXAMPLE (a tree)

> branches
> shade rubber
> fruit clothes
> paper wind barrier fuel
> furniture resource nuts
> tree houses maple syrup parks
> multiple uses seeds oxygen
> lumber habitat energy
> building materials
> baseball bats leaves
> photosynthesis
> roots
> gum
> cork
> books
> paint
> cocoa
> sponge

A *windspark* poem has five lines with the following pattern: ① "I dreamed," ② "I was..." (something or someone), ③ where, ④ an action, and ⑤ how.

EXAMPLE

> I dreamed
> I was a tree
> On a hillside
> Playing with the wind
> Joyfully.

LEVELS
Grades 3-8

SUBJECTS
Language Arts, Science, Social Studies

CONCEPTS
- Humans throughout the world create differing social, cultural, and economic systems and organizations to help them meet their physical and spiritual needs. (3.2)
- Natural beauty, as experienced in forests and other habitats, enhances the quality of human life by providing artistic and spiritual inspiration, as well as recreational and intellectual opportunities. (3.4)
- Most cultures have beliefs, values, and traditions that shape human interactions with the environment and its resources. (9.1)

SKILLS
Observing, Composing, Discussing

OBJECTIVES
Students will ① express their feelings and attitudes about the environment using various forms of poetry and ② analyze their own and other people's poetry to discover its full meaning.

MATERIALS
Paper, pens or pencils, and clipboards (or cardboard and paperclips) for writing outdoors

TIME CONSIDERATIONS
Preparation: 15 minutes

Activity: 50 minutes

Free verse follows no set formula or style.

EXAMPLE

> I am
> the tree
> that overcomes
> all.
> I am
> the one
> that laughs
> at the wind.
> I am
> one with
> the wilderness.

Getting Ready
Make preparations to take students outdoors to observe a variety of trees.

Doing the Activity
1. Ask the students to name some of the benefits they derive from trees and forests. What experiences have they had with trees and forests? How do trees and forests make them feel? Do they have any favorite neighborhood trees? Any special wooded places they like to visit? Any favorite stories about forests or trees? Any forest issues that concern them? Come up with a group list of characteristics and attributes of trees or forests. Tell students they are going to have an opportunity to create a book of poetry expressing their ideas and feelings about trees and forests.

NOTES—① *This activity could be combined with "Adopt a Tree," on page 65, allowing students to explore their feelings about their tree.* ② *This activity can be used to explore parts of the environment besides trees and forests, i.e., art or architecture.*

2. Review with the students the major parts of speech (nouns, verbs, adjectives, participles, etc.). Write these on the chalkboard and have students generate a short list of examples under each category to make sure everyone understands.

3. Present the poetic forms described in the background information and give examples. Tell students there are many other types as well.

4. Take the students to visit nearby trees in the school yard, park, or forest to gather "tree impressions." (This can be done indoors through windows, if necessary.) Have each person sit quietly underneath a tree for at least 10 minutes. (Try to have students select different trees.) Tell students to write descriptive words about how the tree feels, smells, looks, and so on; sounds that come from the tree; living things they see on the tree; and the way they feel sitting underneath the tree.

5. While you're outside or once you're back inside, have the students write their own poems about trees and forests. Encourage them to try more than one poetic form. Then let the students share their poems with the rest of the group. Have them explain which poetic form they used and why they chose it.

6. Discuss some of the following questions with the students.

Point out how people see trees and forests differently.

■ Does your poem mention the influence people have on trees or forests? Does it mention the value of trees or forest products to people?

■ Does your poem speak of people's place in nature? How?

7. Have students review the poem or poems they wrote and choose the one they like the best. Then assemble everyone's favorite poems into a book. You may want to create just one class book, or you could run off enough copies of each poem so that each child can assemble his or her own book. You might make extra copies of the class publication to be distributed around the school and to parents.

8. Help students to identify and contact appropriate local, regional, and national organizations that might publish the students' poems in their publications, and encourage students to submit their work. (For example, Project Learning Tree publishes *THE BRANCH*, which often uses "poet-tree.")

VARIATION

Each student chooses a tree near school or home. Have students spend time with their tree, sitting against it, lying underneath it, walking around it, and observing it from various perspectives. During this time, they should write down words, feelings, ideas, and impressions that enter their heads. Later, they should convert these thoughts into a free verse poem. When the poem is finished, they should think of a word or phrase that sums up the "character" of their tree; this wording will serve as the title. Finally, they should take a photograph of their tree that visually captures the essence of their poem. Encourage them to be creative in choosing the right lighting and perspective for taking their picture. Through this activity, students can strengthen their writing skills and learn the magical power of photography.

Enrichment

Through class discussion, identify several environmental problems or issues (local, national, or global) that students are concerned about. List these problems on the chalkboard. Divide the group into teams of four, and have each team choose one of the issues to discuss. Team members should discuss their points of view with each other, making sure that each person gets a chance to talk. After about 10 minutes, students should write a short poem in any form that reflects their emotions or opinions on the issue. Afterward, discuss with the group poetry's value for getting in touch with your emotions. Ask if the opinions reflected in students' poems are based on facts and reasoning. How might their poems have distorted or exaggerated the issue?

Overview
In this activity, students can learn about the diversity of life on earth by looking at different plants and animals from around the world.

LEVELS
Grades PreK-3

SUBJECTS
Science, Visual Arts, Math

CONCEPTS
■ Plant and animal diversity results from the interaction of living and non living components in the environment. (1.1)

SKILLS
Observing, Classifying and Categorizing, Interpreting

OBJECTIVES
Students will ① identify similarities and differences between organisms by collecting pictures and categorizing them and ② comprehend the connection between diverse organisms and the diverse environments in which they live.

MATERIALS
Bag of mixed fruits and vegetables (see Getting Ready), magazines with pictures of plants and animals for cutting out (see Getting Ready), scissors, glue or paste, drawing paper or construction paper, and stapler

TIME CONSIDERATIONS
Preparation: 30 minutes

Activity: Two 50-minute periods

Background
No one knows for sure how many different kinds of plants and animals live on this planet. So far scientists have classified only about 1.5 million different *species*, but they estimate there may be from 40 to 80 million in the world. (For additional background see "Planet of Plenty," page 24.)

Getting Ready
1. Make a collection of fruits and vegetables that come in different colors, i.e., apples (green, yellow, or red); onions (white, yellow, or red); potatoes (red, white, or brown); or grapes (red, green, or black).

2. Gather a large supply of magazines with plant and animal pictures that you can cut up. *Ranger Rick*, *Big Backyard*, *National Geographic*, *National Wildlife*, *International Wildlife*, *Natural History*, *Audubon*, *Buzzworm*, and *Smithsonian* all contain good pictures. (Students can bring in magazines, or you can find back issues at libraries or museums.)

3. Find three or four large color pictures of different plants and animals.

Doing the Activity
1. Ask the students to name different kinds of plants and animals. (Guide them toward identifying species as different kinds.) Ask the students how many different kinds of plants and animals they think there are in the world. After the students have offered suggestions, tell them that no one really knows for sure, but scientists estimate that there are more than 40 million different species of plants and animals in the world. (Share with them the detailed breakdown on page 17.)

2. Begin the lesson by having the students help you to categorize a bag of mixed fruits and vegetables. Start by putting all the apples in one group, all the potatoes in one group, etc. Next, ask students to suggest other criteria for groupings, i.e., colors, with seeds, without seeds, thick-skinned, thin-skinned.

3. Ask the students to think about the kinds of plants and animals they're familiar with—ones they've seen in books, in zoos, in gardens, on television, in their backyard, and so on. Tell students that there are many ways these organisms can be grouped or classified. For instance, where do they live? (Do they live in the desert, ocean, or forest?) What kinds of things do they eat? (Do they make their own food, or eat grass, insects, fruit, or anything else?) How do the animals get around? (Are they stationary? Do they fly, walk, or swim?)

4. Tell the students that they are going to take a closer look at plant and animal life on Earth by going on a "picture safari." Then pass out the magazines you collected, and have the students cut out pictures of as many different kinds of plants and animals as they can find. You might want to give the students more direction in their search by having them look for different categories of pictures. For example, they could look for plants and animals they think are pretty; ones they think are strange; animals with two, four, many, or no legs; animals with fur, scales, and feathers; plants with broad leaves, needle-shaped leaves, and thorns; plants with beautiful flowers; big or little animals and plants and so on.

5. Once they've collected their pictures, have a sharing session. For example, they can each share their strangest animal or prettiest plant, and so on.

6. Have the students pretend their pictures are real animals and plants and that they need to organize them into exhibits for a new nature museum or zoo. Tell the students to think about ways they could group their animals and plants. For example, they might put all the large mammals together, all the birds together, and so on. Students might group animals by how they move (walkers, swimmers, fliers, nonmovers); what they eat (meat-eaters, plant-eaters); the number of legs they have; or even their color. Students might group the plants together with the animals that share their habitat (for example, desert plants and animals) or they might make special plant exhibits.

7. Have the students take turns explaining how they organized their museums or zoos and describing some of the plants and animals they put into each exhibit. After each person explains his or her exhibits, hold up one or more of the pictures you collected in Step 3 of "Getting Ready" and ask where these plants and animals would go in each museum or zoo. You might also want to have the other students hold up a picture from their own exhibit and say where the pictured item might belong in another person's exhibit.

8. Pass out drawing or construction paper. Have students name their exhibits, for example, "Life in the Forest," and create a visitor's guidebook for at least one exhibit. This book can be created simply by stapling several sheets of paper together and gluing pictures of plants and animals to each page. Afterwards, they can create a cover for their book that includes a title. Students can improve their guidebook by labeling each picture with a caption and adding artwork.

9. Discuss the following questions as a group. The students can consult their guidebooks during the discussion.

- How do the animals in your exhibit move around? How do you know?
- Look at one plant or animal in your exhibit. Where does it live? How do you know? What characteristics help it to survive in this area?

Enrichment

Have the students use their leftover pictures to create a changing bulletin board. For example, they might create a "Courageous Carnivores" bulletin board one week, then a "Wet and Wonderful" the next week, and so on. For each title the class chooses, have students select pictures from their own collections to include in that particular bulletin board. Here are some other possible bulletin board titles:

- Creepy Crawlers
- Getting By on Two Legs
- The Prickly Bunch
- Tremendous Trees
- Into the Deep (things that live under water)
- Home on the Range (things that live in grasslands)

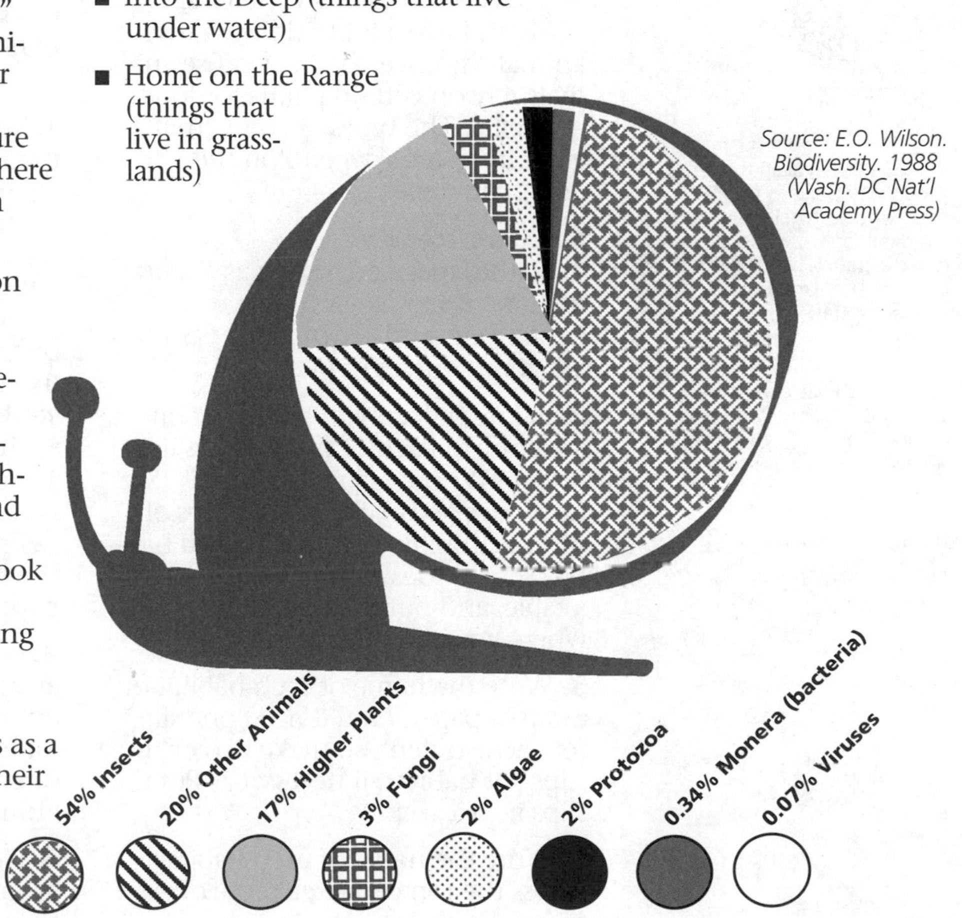

Source: E.O. Wilson. Biodiversity. 1988 (Wash. DC Nat'l Academy Press)
54% Insects
20% Other Animals
17% Higher Plants
3% Fungi
2% Algae
2% Protozoa
0.34% Monera (bacteria)
0.07% Viruses

END NOTES...

ASSESSMENT OPPORTUNITY

Have students select several different picture groups to put in a portfolio and include an explanation of why they chose those groups.

RELATED ACTIVITIES

Charting Diversity, Can It Be Real?, Planet of Plenty, School Yard Safari, Habitat Pen Pals

Overview
From icy tundra to scorching deserts to salty oceans, the world's habitats are diverse and fascinating. Each habitat, with its own special set of conditions, supports animals and plants adapted to living in it. By becoming "habitat pen pals," your students will learn about the diversity of habitats around the world, and will write letters from the perspective of organisms living in these habitats.

LEVELS
Grades 3-6

SUBJECTS
Science, Language Arts

CONCEPTS
- Biological diversity results from the interaction of living and nonliving environmental components such as air, water, climate, and geological features. (1.1)
- Forests, as well as other ecosystems, contain numerous habitats that support diverse populations of organisms. (1.2)
- The Earth's atmosphere, water, soil, climate, and geology vary from region to region, thus creating a wide diversity of biological communities. (1.3)

SKILLS
Researching, Classifying and Categorizing, Organizing Information, Comparing and Contrasting

OBJECTIVES
Students will ① explain the relationship between climate conditions and habitat, ② identify relationships between organisms within habitats, and ③ distinguish between kinds of animals that can and can't live in a particular habitat.

MATERIALS
Pictures of habitats and animals, easel or poster paper, tape, paper and pencils, and reference books (optional)

TIME CONSIDERATIONS
Preparation: 30 minutes

Activity: One or more 50-minute periods

Background
A *habitat* is defined as the place where an animal or plant normally lives, and is often characterized by a dominant plant form or physical characteristic (i.e., the forest habitat, the stream habitat). Some species are adapted to living in only one type of habitat. For example, you might see plenty of parrot species in a tropical rainforest, but most of these species probably wouldn't be able to survive in the temperate forests covering much of the United States.

Other organisms can survive within several habitat types. Opossums live in deciduous forests, tropical forests, and even tropical rain forests. They can also survive in suburbs and cities.

Plants have a lot to do with where animals can live. That's because animals rely on certain plants for food or shelter. The types of plants that grow in an area depend on the area's climate.

Getting Ready
1. Gather magazines such as *Ranger Rick, Big Backyard, National Geographic,* and *Natural History* that are good sources of pictures.

2. Before the activity, try to cut out a picture of each of the habitats listed under "Whose Habitat Is That?" (See next page.) Also cut out pictures of several animals that live in each habitat. Spread the animal pictures out on a table, and put the habitat pictures where you can easily get to them.

3. Write the name of each habitat on a slip of paper. (You'll need one slip for each student, so make two or three slips per habitat, if necessary.) Put the slips into a sack.

4. Write the name of each habitat across the top of a large piece of easel paper.

Doing the Activity
1. Have the students think about some nearby natural areas. Ask them to describe these areas. For example, they might mention a nearby park, pond, forest, river, meadow…even a vacant lot. Write these suggested habitats on the board as the students mention them.

2. Explain that each of these areas, and many others as well, make up all or part of an animal's habitat. Ask the students if they can describe what a habitat is. (An animal's habitat is the place where an animal lives, and where it gets what it needs to survive—food, water, shelter, and a place to breed and raise young.) Ask the students to name the types of animals that they would expect to live in the local habitats they mentioned.

3. Tell the students that there are many different kinds of habitats. Describe the habitats listed in "Whose Habitat is That?" on page 19 and hold up each of the habitat pictures you cut out earlier. Have the students try to identify where that habitat might be found and what the climate is like there. (Define words that the students may not be familiar with, such as **savanna** and **deciduous**.) Then have volunteers tape each picture to the appropriate piece of easel paper, right under the name of the habitat. Tape the pieces of easel paper around the room.

4. Have the students come up, one at a time, and choose an appropriate animal picture to tape under the habitat picture of their choice. Offer direction, as necessary, on which animals go with which habitats.

5. Depending on the level of your group, you might want to explain that there are similar kinds of habitats around the world. For example, tropical rain forests are found in South America, Africa, Australia, and elsewhere. Deserts are also found in many places around the world—and so are grasslands. Ask the students to explain the relationship between climate and habitat. (Regional climate determines the types of habitats the area provides—in other words, what kinds of plants and animals can live there.) But even though there are similar habitats around the world, there are differences in the animals and plants from one place to the next. For example, even though parrots are found in tropical rain forests throughout the world, different types, or species, are unique to certain areas.

6. Have each person pick one of the habitat slips out of a sack.

7. Tell the students to look at the completed habitat "posters" they created earlier. Have them imagine that they are one of the animals living in the habitat whose name they drew. Explain that they'll be writing a letter to a "pen pal" from the point of view of this animal.

8. Assign each person a pen pal, but don't tell the students which person represents which animal. Explain that the students should keep their "animal identities" and the identities of their habitats a secret.

9. Write the following questions and statements on the board:

- What's the climate like in your habitat?

- Name some other animals that live in your habitat.

- Describe some of the plants that grow in your habitat.

- Describe any special features of your habitat.

- What do you eat?

10. Tell the students that they should address each of these questions and statements in their letters. (They can also include other information, if they wish.) Encourage the students to be imaginative in the ways they address each point. For example, a parrot in a tropical rain forest might say, "It's been very hot here lately, but that's nothing new. It's hot here all year round!" And instead of simply saying, "I eat insects," a pen pal could say, "I had a delicious breakfast of ants and beetles this morning." Explain that, by addressing each point in an entertaining way, each "animal" will be providing hints about his or her identity and habitat.

11. Give the students time to research, as needed, and write their letters. Have them fold the letters in half and write the appropriate addresses on the outside.

12. Deliver the letters to the appropriate pen pals. Give the students time to read the letters they received and to try to figure out which animal and habitat their letter is referring to. Then have the students share the letters they received with the rest of the group. (If a student is unable to figure out which animal or habitat his or her pen pal represents, ask for opinions from classmates.)

Enrichment

After the students have figured out the animals and habitats that their pen pals represent, ask each person to act out his or her animal. Let each person in the audience try to guess which performer is his or her "habitat pen pal."

VARIATION

The activity could be done the same way using plant species instead of animal species.

Whose Habitat Is That?

TUNDRA	caribou, lemming, snowy owl
DESERT	jackrabbit, roadrunner, horned lizard
PRAIRIE	golden eagle, prairie dog, rattlesnake
AFRICAN SAVANNA	elephant, lion, gazelle
TROPICAL RAINFOREST	macaw, sloth, monkey
OCEAN	whale, plankton, shark
SALTWATER MARSH	heron, muskrat, fiddler crab
DECIDUOUS FOREST	deer, mole, raccoon
POND	frog, bass, dragonfly

Overview
By taking a "shrew's-eyeview" of life in the woods, your students will gain an appreciation for the variety of living things that make forests their homes, and for the variety of habitats within forests.

LEVELS
Grades 1-6

SUBJECTS
Science, Language Arts, Visual Arts

CONCEPTS
■ Biological diversity results from the interaction of living and nonliving environmental components such as air, water, climate, and geological features. (1.1)
■ Forests, as well as other ecosystems, contain numerous habitats that support diverse populations of organisms. (1.2)

SKILLS
Comprehending, Concept Forming, Comparing and Contrasting

OBJECTIVES
Students will ① identify microhabitats in the forest by drawing pictures or writing a story describing a microhabitat and ② describe some of the plants and animals that characterize several microhabitats within the forest.

MATERIALS
Copy of the story on pages 22 and 23, drawing paper, crayons or markers, and pictures of the animals mentioned in the story (optional; see "Background")

TIME CONSIDERATIONS
Preparation: 10 minutes
Activity: 50 minutes

Background
A habitat is the place an animal or plant lives and gets all the things it needs to survive, such as food, water, and space to grow, breed, and raise young. A deer's habitat might be a combination of forests and fields. A pitcher plant's habitat is a bog. And a humpback whale's habitat can be a stretch of ocean from Alaska to Hawaii. Within any habitat—a forest, field, coral reef, or sandy shore, for example—there are many smaller microhabitats in which temperature, humidity, light, and other conditions vary from those of the habitat as a whole. For example, a decaying log in a forest may be damper and cooler than the surrounding air or leaf litter. A small clearing in a forest may have more light and be drier than the surrounding areas. One part of a mountain may get more sunlight and less wind than other parts. And the deeper parts of a coral reef get less light than those closer to the surface of the ocean.

Plants and animals are often adapted to conditions within a microhabitat. For example, certain kinds of trees and other plants are adapted to growing in forest clearings while others are adapted to growing in the shadier (generally cooler and moister) parts of the forest. Mosses and fungi may be able to grow on one side of a tree or rock but not on the other because of differences in light, temperature, and moisture. And some animals that live in damp leaf litter couldn't survive above ground.

The following are biographies of animals in the story "In the Forest of S.T. Shrew"

■ The *shrew* is one of the smallest, but also one of the fiercest, mammals. It attacks and kills prey several times its size. The young, (four to five in a litter), are born in a hollow stump, log, or burrow, and can fend for themselves within a month. The life span is short–one and a half years at most. The short-tailed shrew, with its stubby tail, is one of the most common mammals of the eastern woods of the U.S.

■ The *millipede* is a slow-moving, elongated animal, usually with 30 or more pairs of legs. Generally, millipedes are found under bark, stones, or old boards, or in damp rubbish. Their food is decaying vegetable matter. The adult has a segmented body and an exoskeleton.

■ The *nuthatch* is a large-headed, short-tailed, short-legged, tree-climbing bird that eats insects from the bark of trunks and limbs. It is acrobatic and is equally at home climbing up, around, or down a trunk head first. Nuthatches often flock with chickadees and titmice. Their wings extend nearly to the tip of their tails. Their flight is jerky.

Getting Ready
1. For older students you may want to make copies of the story on pages 22–23 for them to read.

2. Try to find pictures of the animals described in the Background above (optional).

Doing the Activity
1. Ask the students to describe what a forest is and if they've ever visited one. What was it like in the forest? What kinds of things did they see while they were there? Did they enjoy being there?

2. Tell the students you are going to read them a story about a girl named Jackie who has quite an adventure in a forest. They should listen very carefully to the things that happened to her and the things she saw. Later they'll answer questions about the story.

3. Show the students pictures of some of the plants and animals in the story (optional).

4. Read the story on pages 22–23. Depending on the age group you're working with, you may want to read the story in different ways. For example, you might want to break the story into several segments so the students don't have to listen for such a long time. (We've broken the story into chapters, giving each one a subtitle.) You may want to have younger students do movements each time they hear a character's name. (S.T.: Hold fingers up to face and wiggle like whiskers. Millie: Hold base of hands against ribs with fingers out to the sides; wiggle fingers like legs and twist torso back and forth. Sitta: Put thumbs in armpits and flap arms like wings.) Or you may just want to have the students relax, close their eyes, and listen as you read the story from start to finish.

5. You can check for understanding using the assessment questions in the sidebar.

6. Pass out drawing paper and crayons or markers, and have the students draw pictures of the story. They might draw a picture of their favorite part of the story, the creature Jackie met that they thought was the most interesting, or a scene that depicts Jackie and many of the creatures in the forest. Have older students create a forest scene with flip-up windows that reveal the hidden life in the forest. First have students draw a picture of a forest with no animal life visible. Students should then cut flip-up windows in places where animals hide, and glue this picture along the edges to an equal-sized piece of blank paper. Students can then flip up each window, and draw the appropriate animal underneath. Students should be encouraged to use their flip-up pictures

to teach younger students or siblings about the hidden life of the forest. (See diagram for drawing a tree with flip-up windows on page 67.)

Enrichment

1. Take the students on a hike through the woods, a park, or a vacant lot, so they can take a closer look at some of the microhabitats Jackie saw on her adventures—a dead log, the bark of trees, leaf litter, and so on. If you want, pass out hand lenses so the students can get an even closer look at things. Can the students in your group find any of the same (or similar) kinds of creatures that Jackie saw? Can they find anything else?

NOTE—For more specific information about life in trees and dead logs, see "Trees as Habitats" on page 70, which has students examine all of the plants and animals that depend on a tree, and "The Fallen Log" on page 72, an activity that has students examine all of the plants and animals on a dead log as well as the decomposition process.

2. Have the students write the story of Jackie's next adventure. She will again shrink in size and explore a different microhabitat. Discuss different microhabitats with students, and have each student pick one and research its plant and animal life. Then have them make up a way for Jackie to shrink and to meet new animal friends who will guide her.

IN THE FOREST OF S.T. SHREW

Jackie sat down with a "humph." "I don't think anything lives in these woods," she thought. "I've been walking around for a long time, and I haven't seen anything except for a couple of squirrels." Squirrels didn't really count. She had squirrels in her front yard, and there were squirrels around school. She was supposed to be seeing all kinds of interesting, unusual animals to include in her report for school.

"Pick a place near school or home, and investigate what lives there. Then write a report about all the interesting and unusual things you find." That was the assignment. Too bad she didn't live near the pet shop, like Rene Navarro. Then she'd have lots to write about. But no, she had picked this patch of woods behind the playground thinking it would be loaded with animals.

"Now what am I going to do?" she wondered. She closed her eyes to think….

"So, you don't think anything interesting lives in these woods, huh?" she heard a high-pitched voice ask.

"What was that?" she gasped as she looked around. Sitting next to her, with its head poking out from under the leaves, was a small, furry animal with big whiskers and tiny little eyes. It repeated its question.

"You don't think anything interesting lives in these woods?"

"Well, I didn't…." she answered. "Who are you?"

"Everyone calls me S.T.," he answered. "I'm a shrew —a short-tailed shrew. Now, put your finger on my back."

"What?" she asked, surprised.

"Look, you would like to know about what lives in these woods, wouldn't you? So, c'mon. Hurry up!"

Slowly, Jackie reached out her finger and gently touched him on the back. There was a flash and she found herself standing next to S.T., looking him right in the eye. Then she realized that she was standing on four legs and

was covered with fur. She had turned into a shrew!

"There, that's much better," he said. "Now, follow me."

"Where are we going?" asked Jackie.

"A lot of creatures around here are pretty upset that you don't know they even exist. So I've been appointed to show you around. Besides, now that you're my size, you'd make a tasty meal for something, so you'll be safer if you follow me." And with that he turned and dove down the hole he had popped up out of earlier.

As Jackie stood there wondering what to do, she looked up and saw a large bird flying overhead. "Uh-oh!" she cried and dove into the hole after S.T.

In the Ground

Jackie had never crawled through the ground before and wasn't sure she liked it. It was dark and damp and smelled like dirt. And there were so many roots everywhere! Tiny roots were constantly brushing by her face. She and S.T. had to crawl up, over, and around larger roots over and over again. Then all of a sudden, S.T. stopped.

"Hey, everyone! We're here!" he yelled at the dirt walls of the tunnel. At first Jackie could hear and see nothing. Then she noticed a rumbling sound that seemed to be getting louder and louder. Suddenly, heads began popping out of the tunnel wall. There were earthworms and beetles and white grubs and many other creatures Jackie couldn't identify.

"Do you all live in the ground?" asked Jackie in awe.

"Uh-huh, and lots of others do too," said one particularly fat earthworm.

"But how do you live?" Jackie asked. "I mean…what is there to eat down here?"

"Well, you could say I eat my way through the soil!" replied the earthworm. "I make a tunnel by eating the dirt, then separating out bits of plants and other food from the dirt particles. It's not for everyone, but I love it!" he ended.

"We suck juices right out of roots," said three white grubs together. "And one day we'll crawl up out of the ground and become adults."

"Did you ever wonder what happens to animals that die in the woods?" interrupted a black beetle, waving its antennae back and forth. "It's thanks to me that they're taken care of."

"He means, thanks to all us carrion beetles," said another black beetle. "We eat them up. Keep the forest clean."

As Jackie thought about all this, S.T. thanked all the soil creatures for coming. Then he turned to Jackie and said, "Follow me. There's still lots more for you to see."

A Rotten Place to Live

Jackie followed S.T. through the soil for a short distance; then they climbed up to the surface and ran along the ground under a cover of leaves. As they traveled, the leaves crunched and rustled. Jackie could see spiders, centipedes, and other small creatures crawling around. She wanted to stop and talk to them, but S.T. kept moving and she knew she had to keep up with him. Finally, S.T. stopped at the end of a log. S.T. ran onto the top of it and Jackie followed. Most of the top of the log was covered with a thick, green carpet of moss.

"Oooh!" cried Jackie. "It's so soft. And look at all the other things growing up here." Jackie ran around on top of the log. She rolled in the soft moss, touching the cool, bright-orange fungi that were growing on one end of the log, and sniffing the tops of tall, red-capped lichens as though they were flowers and had a scent. There was even a tiny tree, only about three inches tall, growing out of the log.

"Want to see the inside?" asked S.T.

"OK," answered Jackie, following S.T. back over the end of the log. She waited as he called to someone named Millie. In just a few seconds a long, dark creature with dozens of legs came crawling out of the end of the log.

"I'm a little too big to go with you on this part of the trip," S.T. told her. "You go with Millie and I'll wait for you here."

"But I'm just as big as you are," said Jackie. But just then Millie reared up and touched Jackie's head with several of her legs. Just as before, there was a flash, and Jackie turned into a millipede just like Millie.

At first Jackie found it a little difficult to move all her legs in a coordinated way. But once she and Millie got inside the log, she was too busy looking around to think about how to walk and she didn't have any trouble at all.

Millie was pointing out things and explaining them to Jackie, who was having trouble absorbing all the information. But finally, she began to get the idea she was in a kind of factory— a factory that breaks logs down into soil. Everywhere they went there were things chewing, tunneling, and boring through the wood. There were wood roaches, small white termites, and hard-shelled pill bugs that rolled into tight little balls as she and Millie went by. There were also insect-eating hunters: huge, shiny-black beetles with giant jaws and centipedes with venomous fangs. And at one point, when they'd crawled deep inside the log, they saw a salamander resting in a dark damp hole in the decaying log.

Jackie had no idea there was so much activity inside a log and was really sorry when they headed back to S.T. But after Millie turned Jackie back into a shrew, Jackie and S.T. said goodbye to Millie and scurried off.

Life at the Top

Soon Jackie and S.T. stopped at the base of a tree. Immediately, a small, black-capped bird flew down and landed on the leaves next to them.

"I was beginning to wonder whether you were coming," said the bird. "Hello, Jackie—I'm Sitta. Ever felt like flying?" she asked, stretching one of her wings over Jackie's head. There was a flash and then Jackie slowly stretched out her own wings—she had become a nuthatch just like Sitta.

"Let's go!" cried Sitta, and she leaped into the air and flew off. "I'll wait here," S.T. called after them.

Of everything she had done that day, Jackie was sure flying was the best. First they flew up over the trees where Jackie could see many other birds flying in and out of the treetops. Then she and Sitta swooped into the top of one tree and darted in and out among its branches.

Jackie was amazed at all the insects she saw. There were grasshopper-like creatures and other "bugs" sitting on the leaves. There were wasps and flies buzzing around. And there were caterpillars crawling on many of the leaves. Then Sitta fluttered down and landed on the tree trunk. As Sitta led Jackie down the tree head first, Jackie looked closely at the trunk and was amazed at what she saw. There were caterpillars and ants crawling. She saw several spiders and a moth that was almost the same color as the bark—in fact, she almost missed it because it was so perfectly camouflaged against the bark. There were also pale greenish lichens and moss growing on the bark. Eventually, she and Sitta reached the bottom of the trunk.

"This tree is like an apartment building or something," said Jackie as she jumped onto the ground next to S.T. "There are different things living on it all the way from the leaves at the top to the base right here on the forest floor." she added. "I guess I should say right down into the dirt—I shouldn't forget everyone I met underground earlier!"

"Well, it's good to hear you talking about all the things that live in and on trees," said Sitta.

Then she held her wing over Jackie's head again and flew back up into the trees out of sight.

Home Again

As Jackie once more followed S.T. through the ground, she began wondering where they could be going next. It was dark and damp in the tunnel, and root hairs were brushing by her face. As they ran along, the smell of dirt filled her nose....

Suddenly, Jackie opened her eyes. She was back by the tree she'd sat down against earlier that day. Somehow she'd fallen over and was lying on the ground with her face resting on top of the leaves. Her nose was filled with the smell of dead leaves and dirt. Slowly, Jackie sat up.

Did I dream the whole thing? she wondered as she looked around. "There's a dead log over there like the one I went to with S.T. And the bark of this tree is covered with all kinds of things, just like the one I saw with Sitta," she said as she stood up. Still her adventure seemed impossible. But then Jackie looked at the ground near where she'd been sitting and reached over to the spot that seemed to be where she thought she had first seen S.T. As she carefully lifted up some of the leaves, she could see it: a small hole in the ground. Jackie laughed out loud. "Boy, do I ever have a lot to write about in my report!" she cried. Then she turned and ran all the way home.

Overview
In this activity, students will pretend they are visitors from outer space, viewing life on Earth for the first time. By describing, in minute detail, all the life they find in a small plot of land, they will become more aware of the diversity of life on Earth and will better understand its importance.

LEVELS
Grades 4-6

SUBJECTS
Science, Language Arts, Visual Arts

CONCEPTS
■ Biological diversity results from the interaction of living and nonliving environmental components such as air, water, climate, and geological features. (1.1)

■ Forests, as well as other ecosystems, contain numerous habitats that support diverse populations of organisms. (1.2)

■ Populations of organisms exhibit variations in size and structure as a result of their adaptation to their habitats. (10.1)

SKILLS
Observing, Organizing Information, Classifying and Categorizing, Concluding

OBJECTIVES
Students will ① investigate the diversity of plants and animals on a small plot of land and ② explain the value of a diversity of life forms in a particular ecosystem.

MATERIALS
Part A: None
Part B: (per team of four students) Clipboard or writing tablet, paper and pencil, measuring tape or yardstick, string or flagging tape for marking plot boundaries, and tweezers and magnifiers (optional)
Part C: (per team) Paper and poster board

TIME CONSIDERATIONS
Preparation: 15 minutes

Activity: Two 50-minute periods

Background
All organisms on Earth can be grouped into different species. A *species* is a group of organisms that resemble one another in appearance, behavior, chemical makeup, and genetic structure. Organisms that reproduce sexually must also be able to interbreed and produce fertile offspring to be considered the same species.

One of Earth's most valuable resources is its **biological diversity**, or **biodiversity**. This resource is made up of three components: genetic diversity, species diversity, and ecological diversity.

Genetic diversity is the variability in the genetic makeup among individuals within a single species. Species diversity is the variety of species on Earth. Ecological diversity is the variety of forests, deserts, grasslands, streams, lakes, oceans, and other biological communities that interact with one another and with their nonliving environments.

Biologists estimate that Earth's current biodiversity consists of 40 to 80 million different species, each having variations in its genetic makeup and living in a variety of biological communities. So far, biologists have classified only about 1.5 million species. They know a fair amount about one-third of these species and the detailed roles and interactions of very few.

Humans are dependent on this biological capital. Diversity within and among species has provided us with food, wood, fibers, energy, raw materials, chemicals, and medicines and has contributed hundreds of billions of dollars yearly to the world economy. Also, every species on Earth today represents stored genetic information that allows the species to adapt to certain changes in environmental conditions. We can think of

biodiversity as nature's "insurance policy" against disasters.

Over billions of years, new species have formed, and ones that could not adapt to changing conditions have become extinct.

Extinction is a natural process. The rate of species extinction has increased sharply as human settlements have expanded worldwide, the main reason for this being, the alteration of many organisms natural habitats.

Getting Ready
Find an area on or near the school grounds where groups of four students can set up study plots 20-foot (6-m) square. (You can adjust the size to suit your conditions.)

PART A
MISSION TO PLANET EARTH

Doing the Activity
1. Divide your group into teams of four.

2. Tell students to imagine that they're scientists from an overpopulated, polluted planet called Deevoid. Deevoid has a similar atmosphere, climate, and mineral composition to Earth but has very little diversity of life has (though it once had great biodiversity). Deevoid scientists have long hypothesized that planet Earth is rich with a variety of life forms. To test this hypothesis, several teams of scientists have been sent on an exploratory mission to Earth. By studying the life on Earth, the Deevoid scientists hope to discover ways to improve the biological diversity and the quality of life on their own planet.

3. Explain that each team of scientists will set up a plot and study it for its variety of life forms. They will record, describe, and try to classify all the life forms they find. They can also draw conclusions about the diversity of life on Earth.

4. Have team members work together to devise methods for sampling, recording, and organizing their data. For example, they can create a chart indicating whether an organism is a plant or animal, whether it can fly, how many legs it has, and so on. Or they can make an "explorer's journal" with notes about each organism, emphasizing detailed descriptions based on observation. One or more team members should be official recorders, or everyone can take notes. Encourage the students to make sketches as well. When the research is complete, the data sheets and sketches should be evaluated to see what trends emerge.

5. Explain that, when the scientists arrive back on Deevoid, they will present their findings at a scientific conference. Since Earth organisms are completely unknown to their colleagues back on Deevoid, the scientists must be careful to make detailed observations while on Earth. For example, they may want to record detailed information about what the organism looks like, its size, where they found it, how it behaved, and so on.

PART B
DIVERSITY DATA

Doing the Activity
1. Take the students outside and give each team a tape measure or measuring stick. Also give them string, ribbon, or other materials for marking the boundaries of their plots. (This material can be saved for use in other PLT activities.)

2. Assign each team an area in which to set up a 20-foot (6-m) square study plot. (You can scale the plot size up or down to suit location or time constraints. For younger students, use smaller plots.) Try to arrange teams so that they are spread out and cover a variety of **microhabitats.** For example, one team might be in a wooded area, another on a grassy lawn, and another right next to the school building.

3. Each team should first predict what forms of life, if any, they expect to find at which locations in their plot. They should write down their predictions.

4. When the students are ready to begin examining their plots, tell them to be careful not to pick up creatures like centipedes or wasps that could bite or sting. In fact, they should carefully avoid handling any creatures. They should keep their hands away from the underside of any rocks and logs that they turn over. Finally, remind the students to take care not to harm any plants or animals, and to leave things exactly the way they found them.

5. Allow students ample time to examine their plots and record their data.

PART C
BACK ON DEEVOID

Doing the Activity
1. Once the students are back inside (and back on Deevoid), they should hold a conference to discuss the Earth expedition. Give each team time to prepare its presentation. Encourage the students to use posters, data charts, drawings, movements, sounds,

or anything else to describe the life forms they encountered. They should also decide on a format for their presentations. For example, one team might hold a panel discussion, allowing the "scientists" in the audience to ask questions. Another might give a straightforward presentation with each team member describing certain organisms. In whatever format they choose, they should describe what kind of plot they were sampling (field, wooded plot, grassy area, and so on), and how their initial predictions compared with what they actually found.

2. Ask students to take notes on all the presentations and then compare and contrast other teams' data with their own. Did any organisms appear in several of the plots? Were any organisms unique to a single plot? Did any plots seem to have a wider variety of animals than other plots? If so, how might different environmental conditions have contributed to biodiversity? (Guide them toward discovering that, in general, areas with a greater variety of plants have a greater variety of animals. For example, a plot on the edge of a wooded area would tend to have a greater variety of insects than a plot on a lawn.)

3. After considering all the data and making comparisons, teams should try to draw conclusions about what factors influence the abundance or lack of biodiversity. What problems might be faced in areas lacking in biodiversity? Did the mission to Earth provide enough data for teams to draw conclusions? What future study missions do the teams recommend?

4. Ask the students how their predictions compared with their actual findings? Do they think their investigation and collection methods were thorough and accurate? How would they do things differently next time?

5. Have the students brainstorm ways that biodiversity on planet Earth benefits the lives of its people. How might the people of Deevoid begin to improve their planet's biodiversity for the future? Answers will vary, but could include ideas such as decreasing pollution, increasing the abundance and variety of vegetation, and so on. What additional information would they like to have about Deevoid to help solve this problem?

6. Ask the students to imagine a place on Earth that is teeming with plant and animal life, and have them share their reflections. Explain that Earth has many communities rich in biodiversity, such as rainforests, coral reefs, swamps, and everglades. Explain that every species is an integral part of a community (let students give examples) and that the stability of a community depends on the diversity of its species.

Enrichment
Interplanetary Pen Pals
Write names of plants and animals on separate slips of paper. Mix them up, and let each person pick one randomly. Tell the students to imagine they have a pen pal on a different planet. Have them write a letter to their pen pal describing the animal or plant they picked. Afterward, have the students read their letters to the rest of the group (being careful not to say the name of the animal or plant). The "audience" should try to figure out the name of the organism that each letter is referring to.

END NOTES...

ASSESSMENT OPPORTUNITY
Assess the thoroughness of team data collection, the organization and clarity of their presentation, the accuracy of their information, and whether their conclusions were supported by their data.

RELATED ACTIVITIES
Charting Diversity, Environmental Exchange Box, Habitat Pen Pals, Picture This! The Fallen Log, School Yard Safari

REFERENCES
Background adapted from Miller, G. Tyler, *LIVING IN THE ENVIRONMENT*. Belmont, California: Wadsworth Publishing Company, 1988.

Overview
By exploring the amazing *diversity* of life on Earth, your students will discover how plants and animals are *adapted* for survival. This activity provides a basis for understanding why there are so many different *species* and what is the value of biological diversity.

Background
See background for "Planet of Plenty" on page 24.

Getting Ready
1. Copy a blank chart, such as the one shown below, onto the chalkboard or a piece of easel paper.

2. Make enough copies of student page 29 for each student.

Doing the Activity
1. Ask students to name different types of environments in which animals live, and write these on the chalkboard (forest, ocean, desert, arctic, others). Ask students if the animals living in these environments have special characteristics that enable them to survive (fish swim, squirrels climb, antelope run fast, etc.). Tell the students they're going to play a game in which they'll look at animals and determine how each is different and how each has a special role in the environment.

2. Have students copy onto a piece of paper the chart you put up earlier .

3. Pass out copies of student page 29.

4. Divide the group into pairs.

5. Give each pair three lunch bags or other containers. Have the students write one of the following labels on each bag:

- Where It Lives
- How It Moves
- What It "Wears"

6. Make sure the students understand all the words on the student page. Have them cut out the individual squares in the first column and put the squares into the bag labeled "Where It Lives." The squares from the second column go into the "How It Moves" bag, and the squares from the third column go into the "What It 'Wears'" bag. Have them shake the bags to mix up the squares.

7. To start, have one member of each pair take a square from each bag. Have students write the word on the square in the appropriate column of the chart they made. They should take turns doing this until all the bags are empty and then should put the squares back into the appropriate bags.

8. Explain to the students that they will need to do a little detective work to complete their charts with the right animal names. For example, if a row lists the words *forest, flies,* and *exoskeleton,* the students should do research to find one or more examples of an animal that has all three of these characteristics. (A forest-dwelling insect such as a katydid has this combination of traits.)

9. Give the students time over the next week to

LEVEL
Grades 4-8

SUBJECT
Science

CONCEPTS

- Biological diversity results from the interaction of living and non-living environmental components such as air, water, climate, and geological features. (1.1)

- Organisms adapt to changes in the environment according to the genetic and behavioral capacity of their species. (4.3)

SKILLS
Researching, Identifying Attributes and Components, Evaluating

OBJECTIVES
Students will ① organize different species of plants and animals according to various characteristics and ② determine how certain characteristics help species adapt to environmental conditions.

MATERIALS
Chalkboard or easel paper; copies of student page 29 (one per pair); paper lunch bags or other containers (three per pair); and resources on plants and animals (encyclopedias, dictionaries, field guides)

TIME CONSIDERATIONS
Preparation: 15 minutes

Activity: 50 minutes

Where It Lives	How It Moves	What It "Wears"	Name of Animal

research animals and fill in their charts. For combinations that they can't identify (for example, if the characteristics in one row of their charts require them to find an animal with fur that hops and lives in the water), allow them to pick another characteristic from one of their bags.

10. After they've finished their research, have the students present their findings to the rest of the group. For each species they identify, students should be prepared to say how that species is especially suited for the environment it lives in.

VARIATION

1. Refer to the different environments listed in Step 1 above. Ask the students if plants are specially adapted for different environments as well. (Remind them to include trees, shrubs, fungi, and aquatic plants when thinking of "plants.") Give examples of adaptations such as air bladders to keep plants afloat (seaweed), tasty fruits for animals to eat and spread their seeds (apple tree), structures for storing water (cactus), and so on.

2. Keep the group in pairs. Tell pairs that they will play "Diversity Detectives" using plants instead of animals. Each pair will have to decide on three categories by which to identify plants (similar to the "Where It Lives," "How It Moves," and "What It 'Wears'" used for animals). You can suggest categories such as "Where It Lives," "How It Reproduces," "How It Gets Food," "How It Looks," "How People Use It," and "How It Protects Itself." They should relabel their three bags for the new categories they decide on.

3. Students then should make cards similar to those used for animals. They will identify four characteristics (four cards) in each plant category. For example, if they use the category "How It Reproduces," they may want to list characteristics such as "Has Tasty Fruit" (for spreading seeds), "Has Bright Flowers" (for attracting pollinators), and "Has Seeds that Float

or Flutter." They should put these cards in the appropriate bags.

4. Each team should make a blank chart as before but should identify plant categories instead. Each partner takes a turn drawing a set of three cards, while the other partner fills in the appropriate words on the chart. Together, they should try to think of a plant that has those three characteristics, i.e., for "woody," "tasty fruit," and "fields and yards," they might say "apple tree."

Enrichment

Have the students use the cards they made in the activity to play the "Spice of Life" game described below.

Here's How to Play

1. Teams of two play one another. Put the set of cards (plant or animal) into the appropriate bags.

2. Have the students create six "wild cards." They should add two wild cards to each bag.

3. Have each team take turns pulling a set of cards out of the bags (one from each bag). The opposing team must try to think of an animal or plant that has all of the characteristics printed on the cards. If a team pulls a wild card, they can pick any characteristic they want, provided it fits the category of the bag it came from.

4. To simplify the game for younger students, you may want to have them pick only one card per play and think of a plant or animal with that trait. They can alternate the bag they pick the card from each time.

5. Develop your own rules for dealing with disputes. For example, if one team feels that an answer another team gives is inappropriate, they can use books to look up the plant or animal in question.

6. Have the students keep track of their own scores. A "right" answer wins one point, and an inappropriate answer or no answer results in no points.

7. When the bags are empty, the game is over. Have the students add up their points to see which team is the winner.

CARDS FOR GAME

Grassland

Swims

Exoskeleton

Desert

Hops

Feathers

Forest

Crawls, Walks, or Runs

Scales or Slimy Skin

Water

Flies or Glides

Fur

Overview
A beetle that drinks fog. A flower that smells like rotting meat. A fish that "shoots down" its prey. Are these plants and animals for real? In this activity, your students will discover extraordinary plants and animals, and will gain insight on how they are uniquely adapted to environmental conditions.

LEVELS
Grades 4-8

SUBJECTS
Science, Language Arts

CONCEPTS

■ Biological diversity results from the interaction of living and nonliving environmental components such as air, water, climate, and geological features. (1.1)

■ Organisms are interdependent; they all depend on nonliving components of the Earth. (4.1)

■ Organisms adapt to changes in the environment according to the genetic and behavioral capacity of their species. (4.3)

SKILLS
Analyzing, Inferring, Predicting, Identifying Relationships and Patterns

OBJECTIVES
Students will ① study the characteristics of unusual plants and animals and ② describe how plants and animal species are adapted to a particular set of environmental conditions.

MATERIALS
Part A: Copies of student page 33 and pencils or pens
Part B: Research books on plants and animals, poster board, drawing paper, markers or crayons, and other art supplies; copies of student page 34

TIME CONSIDERATIONS

Preparation: 10 minutes

Activity:
Part A–Two 50-minute periods;
Part B–50 minutes

Background
Scientists estimate that we share this planet with 40 to 80 million different species of plants and animals, most of which are insects. So far, scientists have identified only about 1.5 million different species.

When an organism's environment changes, the organism must either move, adapt, or die out. The changing of an organism over time that makes it suited to its environment is called *adaptation*.

Adaptation is the result of the combined effects of variation and the selecting power of the environment. For example, plants in a population have differing capacities for producing cutin (a waxy, outer coating) on their leaves. Some individuals are heavily covered with this protective layer, and others are only thinly covered. If the *climate* becomes drier, as it did in the Sahara Desert, plants with thicker cutin will not dry as fast as those with thin cutin and may live to set a crop of seed. They have been "selected." Succeeding generations will also show variability, and those with the best protection against drying will be the only ones to live and reproduce. In this instance, only one feature, cuticular covering, has been pointed out, but in reality a plant would have to possess a whole range of features that work together. It is the species, not the individual, that adapts.

Getting Ready
Make copies of student pages 33 and 34.

PART A
STRANGER THAN FICTION

Doing the Activity
1. Pass out copies of student page 33. Introduce the word *fictitious*. Discuss how the creators of movies and comic books invent "mutant" and "alien" life forms by combining and/or exaggerating attributes of real plants and animals. Have the students give examples.

2. Tell the students that you're going to read descriptions of eight plants and animals whose pictures are on student page 33. They should listen carefully and try to decide if the plant or animal is real or fictitious. If they think it is real, they should check the box for "Real". If not, they should check "Fictitious." Explain that all of the animals and plants may be real, all of them may be fictitious, or there may be a mix.

3. Read aloud each of the descriptions under "Who's Who" on page 32. Read only the information that appears in italics. Do not tell the students the names of the animals and plants.

4. Once you have read all the descriptions to the students, review each picture and ask the students to raise their hands if they thought it was real. List on the chalkboard the class' majority opinion for each organism. Ask several students why they thought an organism was real or fictitious.

5. Tell students that all of the plants and animals on the page are real. Discuss each animal or plant using the additional information provided in "Who's Who."

6. Ask the students to describe animals or plants they have actually seen that have unusual characteristics. Encourage them to name local examples, not just exotic ones. Discuss how these life forms benefit from their unusual characteristics.

PART B
THE ADAPTABLES

Getting Ready

1. Brainstorm with the students to generate on the chalkboard a list of plants and animals with unusual characteristics. Give the students copies of "Amazing Animals & Plants," page 34, and have each student choose a species from the page. Explain that each species has unique adaptations that help it to survive in its environment. It is the student's job to find out what these adaptations are.

2. Tell the students that after researching their plant or animal, they should create a poster describing it. The poster should include a drawing of their plant or animal in its habitat and an explanation of how it is adapted to its environment.

3. Give students plenty of time to do their research and create their posters.

If they're having trouble finding information, you might suggest they look in books or encyclopedias about animals. (You may need to bring in your own books, borrow from the public library, or have your school librarian help you gather resources.)

4. Have the students display and explain their posters to the rest of the group, then hang the posters on the wall. After all the presentations, the students could make up special award categories such as "The Funniest Looking Animal" or "The Craftiest Plant," and vote for which entries should get these awards.

Enrichment

Have teams of students pretend that they are writers for a movie and they need to come up with a really outrageous alien creature. After each team has developed a creature, have students explain to the rest of the group what real-life animals inspired the various attributes of their fictional creature.

END NOTES...

ASSESSMENT OPPORTUNITY
Assess the students' presentations for understanding of the relationship between species adaptations and habitat conditions.

RELATED ACTIVITIES
Charting Diversity, Planet of Plenty, Picture This!

REFERENCE
Ritchie, Donald D. and Robert Carola. *Biology.* Reading, MA: Addison-Wesley Publishing Company, 1979.

WHO'S WHO

1. Ogre-faced Spider
When it's time to catch a meal, this spider has a special trick: first it spins a web of silk. Then it grabs the corners of the web with its four front legs. And then it hangs upside down and waits for insects to crawl by along the ground. When they do, the spider drops the web over them like a net and pulls up its meal. Ogre-faced spiders live in the southeastern United States and in tropical areas around the world. They're usually active at night. In addition to dropping their web over crawling insects, they may hold their web out in the air so that flying insects get caught in it.

2. Rafflesia
This plant with an enormous reddish, rotten-smelling flower is a parasite that lives inside the roots of a tropical forest vine. The flowers may be more than three feet (91 cm) across and weigh over 35 pounds (16 kg). They bloom for only three days and depend on flies to pollinate them. Rafflesias grow in the rain forests of Indonesia. Large, hoofed mammals in these forests transport the seeds from place to place on the bottoms of their hooves and push seeds into the soil as they walk. The plant's flowers may take two years to develop.

3. Satin Bower Bird
At breeding time, the male bird builds a house of sticks. Then he decorates the stick house with shells, feathers, flowers, clothespins, jewelry, and ther objects that he fancies. His favorite color is bright blue. He may also paint the inside of the stick house using berry juice and charcoal sticks. Female birds are attracted to the male's handiwork. These birds live in the forests and woodlands of Australia. Females are attracted to the bower, but once a female has mated with a male she goes off on her own to build a nest and raise her young.

4. Black-eyed Susan
These yellow and black flowers seem to be just like any other wildflower you might find in a field. However, they have special ultraviolet markings on their petals that can't be seen by human eyes. These markings serve as an illuminated landing pad for pollinating insects. Black-eyed Susans have colored markings that seem to advertise, or lead pollinators to, their food source. Patterns of lines, dots, or solid colors lure insects to the spot where they will inadvertently pollinate the flower. Markings on the petal reflect ultraviolet light, which is visible to many pollinating insects but not to humans. The petals of the black-eyed Susan appear to be solid yellow to people. To bees, however, the petals have two tones, with ultraviolet markings near the blossom's center, at the source of the nectar.

5. Archer Fish
When this fish wants a meal, it looks for insects above the surface of the water. When it spies one, the fish spits water up at it. The fish can hit an insect accurately at four feet (122 cm), knock it into the water, and gobble it up. Archer fish live in Southeast Asia in mangrove swamps and other areas along the coasts, as well as in rivers. They have a groove on the roof of their mouth that, with their tongue pressed against it, becomes like the barrel of a pistol. If an archer fish misses its first shot at an insect, it can adjust its aim quickly and fire again.

6. Tenebrionid (tuh-NEE-bree-AH-nid) Beetle
This beetle gets all the water it needs from fog. Standing on a dune in the desert where it lives, the beetle raises its back end into the fog. Droplets of water form on its body and run down toward its mouth. These particular tenebrionid beetles live in the Namib Desert in southwestern Africa. However, there are many other kinds of tenebrionid beetles throughout the world.

7. Skunk Cabbage
This plant is like an outdoor hot tub. The temperature inside its flowers is 36-63 degrees Fahrenheit warmer than the outside air. It gives insects a nice warm place to stay when it's cold out. Skunk cabbage flowers produce little pollen or nectar. Therefore, they rely on their warmth to attract pollinating insects. By successfully capturing warmth from the sun, the flowers attract insects without needing to use their own food energy to produce much pollen. The skunk cabbage provides insects with a warm place in the cold. In turn, the insects end up transporting pollen from one flower to another.

8. Strangler Fig
This tree starts out as a small, non-threatening seed that sprouts on the branch of another tree. Yet as it grows, its stems, roots, and leaves wrap completely around the host tree, stealing its water and blocking its sunlight. The host tree eventually dies a long, suffocating death. There are many different species of strangler fig (Ficus sp.) in the rain forest. The small seeds are dispersed by the many birds and monkeys that eat fruit. Now and again one of these seeds gets lodged in the branch of a tree and germinates. The seedling first sends out a long aerial root. When contact with the ground is made, the young fig starts to grow, putting out more roots from its perch to the ground, and developing stems and leaves. Eventually the host tree is smothered by the fig's foliage, the trunk is encased in its roots, and the tree dies. In this way, the fig avoids competition, taking the place of a tree that already stands tall.

WHO'S WHO

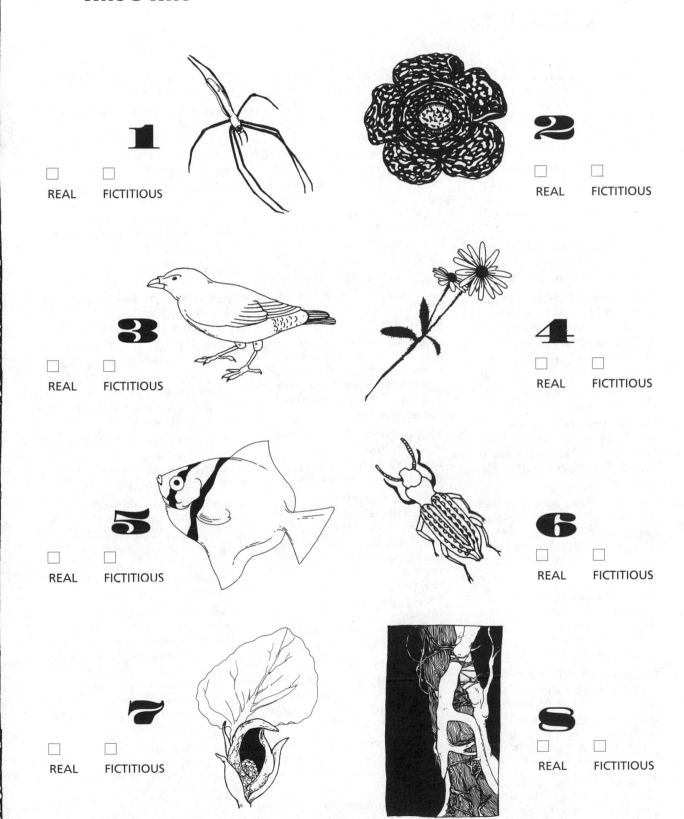

1
☐ REAL   ☐ FICTITIOUS

2
☐ REAL   ☐ FICTITIOUS

3
☐ REAL   ☐ FICTITIOUS

4
☐ REAL   ☐ FICTITIOUS

5
☐ REAL   ☐ FICTITIOUS

6
☐ REAL   ☐ FICTITIOUS

7
☐ REAL   ☐ FICTITIOUS

8
☐ REAL   ☐ FICTITIOUS

AMAZING ANIMALS AND PLANTS

Angler Fish—many different kinds in tropical and temperate seas around the world; has worm-like flap of skin on its first dorsal fin; uses flap to lure small fish close enough to catch for food

Aye-aye—mammal-primate; rain forests of Madagascar; bizarre-looking mammal that eats insects and has a similar role to wood-peckers of temperate forests

Axolotl—amphibian-salamander; lakes in Mexico; usually repro-duces while still in its larval state

Basilisk Lizard—reptile; rain forests of Latin America; can run across water on its hind legs

Bolas Spider—southeastern United States; eats only male moths, which it catches on the end of a line of silk that it swings through the air

Cleaner Wrasse—fish; coral reefs; feeds on parasites that live on larger fish and sets up "cleaning stations" to remove those para-sites

European Water Spider—lakes and ponds in Europe; creates an underwater, air-filled space to rest; can swim under water with an air bubble attached to its abdomen

Fringe-lipped Bat—mammal; forests in Latin America; feeds mostly on frogs it finds by detect-ing and recognizing the mating calls of male frogs

Golden Plover—bird; winters in South America, breeds in the Arctic; adult birds fly south for winter before young can fly; young make their first journey from the Arctic to Argentina alone

Hoatzin—bird; South America; bizarre-looking bird whose young can climb through trees using hook-like claws on their wings

Honey Guide—bird; forests of Africa; guides Pygmies to honey-bee nests; Pygmies break open nests and collect honey; bird feeds on the beeswax

Hooded Seal—mammal; in water and along coasts mostly in the North Atlantic; in displays of aggression, male may inflate a hood on his snout or force his nasal membrane through either one of his nostrils, creating a red "balloon"

Kangaroo Rat—mammal-rodent; deserts of North America; gets all the water it needs to survive from the seeds it eats

Leaf-cutter Ant—insect; rain forests of Latin America; ants grow their own food in gardens in their underground nests and col-lect leaves and other material to use as compost

Matamata—reptile-turtle; South America; bizarre-looking turtle that's perfectly camouflaged in river bottoms where it lives

Monarch Butterfly—insect; breeds in eastern North America and winters in Mexico and Central America; adults migrate north, lay their eggs, and die; then, at the end of the summer—and three or four generations later—adults of the last brood migrate south for the winter—to the same areas their "great-great-grandparents" came from

Nudibranch—mollusk-marine invertebrate; can transfer the stinging cells of its prey to its own skin and then use them to protect itself from predators

Pitcher Plant—bogs and wet-lands in North America; traps insects in long tube and then digests them

Platypus—mammal-monotreme; streams, rivers, and lakes in Australia; bizarre-looking mam-mal that lays eggs

Poison Dart Frog—amphibian; many different kinds; rain forests of Latin America; bright skin colors warn predators the frogs are poisonous

Starnose Mole—mammal; wet ground near lakes and streams in eastern North America; its bizarre-looking nose is divided into many fleshy tentacles

Suriname Toad—amphibian; lakes and ponds in South America; eggs develop in spongy skin on back and hatch as tiny toads after about three months

Thorny Devil—reptile-lizard; deserts of Australia; the scales on its skin form a network of canals; when dew gets on its skin, it trav-els through these canals directly to the animal's mouth

Welwitchia Plant—Namib Desert in southwestern Africa; has only two leaves and may live to be more than 1,000 years old

Brown Bee Orchid (genus Ophrys)—plant; resembles bee that attracts males of certain bee species who try (unsuccessfully) to mate with the flower; pollen sticks to the bee and is transferred to another flower

Bromeliad—spiky leaves channel water into the center of the plant, which may hold as much as 18 pints (8.5 liters); captures falling leaves, which rot, thus providing nutrients the bromeliad cannot retrieve from the soil; also pro-vides a habitat for a number of different animals

Bottle Tree—dry forest of Australia; swollen trunks are self-contained reservoirs that store water for long, dry spells

Overview
Students are often surprised to learn how many different products we get from trees. Use this activity to help your students learn just how much we depend on trees in our daily lives.

Background
See the background and student readings for "We All Need Trees" on page 39. See also "Would You Believe It Comes from Trees" on page 37.

Getting Ready
1. Gather old magazines with plenty of advertisements. Cut out pictures of products that are derived from trees (even partially). You'll need at least one picture per student. You should collect pictures that fit equally into three categories: paper products, food products, and solid wood products.

2. In different parts of the room, display a large picture or actual product to represent each of these categories. For example, a newspaper could represent paper products, a piece of furniture or a musical instrument could represent wood products, and an apple could represent food that comes from trees.

3. For the Assessment Opportunity, make copies of page 38 for each student.

Doing the Activity
1. Start with a brainstorming session. Ask students to name as many tree products as they can think of, and list them on the chalkboard. After a few minutes, look back over the list. Which products do students use every day? Which are made totally from trees? Which partially? If you're working with preschoolers, see Variation 2 on pages 36–37.

2. Tell the students that they are going to be "tree-tectives" (tree detectives). Each student will gather clues about a "mystery tree product" and try to figure out what it is. When students know what it is, they need to decide which category the product belongs in: food, wood, or paper.

3. Assign each person a mystery product by taping a tree-product picture to each student's back. (Have several students help you to speed up this step.) Tell students they must figure out the identity of the product on their back by asking each other questions. They can ask each person only two questions, and the questions must require a "yes" or "no" answer. For example, "Is this product used in our school?" For more advanced students, you can make this game more challenging by not allowing these questions: "Is it made from paper?" "Is it made from wood?" "Is it used for food?"

4. Give students time to mingle and ask questions. When they think they've identified their product, they should decide which category (wood, paper, food) it belongs to, and go to the section of the room designated for that category.

5. Allow additional time for the students in each category to discuss with the others why they think they belong in that group. If a student has misidentified his or her product or is standing in the wrong category, others in the group should provide more clues until the product's identity or category becomes apparent. Students should also discuss whether their product could fit in more than one category. Allow students to change groups if they see fit.

6. Afterward, revisit the list of tree products the group brainstormed earlier. Have the class identify categories each student belongs in. See if students can name other products that come from trees. Talk about unusual tree products such as chewing gum, turpentine, spices, medicine, and others. (See "Would You Believe It Comes From Trees" on page 37.) You may want to bring in samples of some unusual tree products.

LEVELS
Activity: Grades 2-6
Variation 1: Grades 4-6
Variation 2: Grades PreK-1
Enrichment: Grades PreK-5

SUBJECTS
Science, Social Studies, Visual Arts

CONCEPTS
- Humans use tools and technologies to adapt and alter environments and resources to meet their physical, social, and cultural needs. (2.1)
- Natural beauty, as experienced in forests and other habitats, enhances the quality of human life by providing artistic and spiritual inspiration, as well as recreational and intellectual opportunities. (3.4)
- All humans consume products and thereby affect the availability of renewable and nonrenewable natural resources. (6.4)

SKILLS
Identifying Attributes and Components, Classifying and Categorizing, Researching, Evaluating

OBJECTIVES
Students will ① identify and categorize products derived from trees, ② find out which forest products are recyclable or reusable, and ③ recommend actions for conserving forest resources.

MATERIALS
Activity and Variations: Assortment of pictures (cut from magazines) of products made all or in part from forest resources
Enrichment: A used Christmas tree, a live potted tree, or a tree branch, and a small sample of forest products
Assessment: Copies of page 38

TIME CONSIDERATIONS
Preparation: One hour
Activity: 50 minutes

7. Students may want to think about how they could use forest products in a way that helps to extend and conserve forest resources. Explore ways to remove forest products from the waste stream (i.e., reuse paper bags, recycle newspaper, etc.).

VARIATION 1—WHERE FROM ART THOU?

NOTE—You may want to have the students read pages 41-42 in "We All Need Trees" before doing this variation.

1. Follow the same procedures used above, but with slight modifications.

2. Make sure your collection of magazine pictures includes products derived (in part) from all parts of the tree (leaves, fruits, flower, wood, bark, sap, roots). (See "Would You Believe It Comes From Trees" on page 37 to find out what common products are made from these different parts.)

3. Label sections of the room according to these tree parts.

4. Tape pictures to the students' backs and have them guess their identities as in Part A. After guessing, they should go to the proper "tree part" section.

5. Within each section, students should discuss why they belong there. If they feel they have made an error in choosing a section, they can move to another.

VARIATION 2—TREE-TECTIVES

1. Hold up a small branch and a wooden object such as a block, pencil, or toy. Ask where each of these comes from. (Students will most likely recognize the branch as coming from a tree but might recognize other products as coming from a store, house, closet, etc.)

2. If possible, acquire a "tree cookie," a cross-section slice of a tree trunk or branch. Have students see and feel the texture of the wood. Can they identify similar texture and grain in various wood products? Do they recognize those products as coming from trees?

3. Ask the students if they know where paper comes from. Describe in simple terms the process by which trees become paper. (See "We All Need

Trees" on page 39.) You can have the students help you make paper. (See "Make Your Own Paper" on page 176.)

4. Ask students if they can think of other things that come from trees. Ask if they've used anything today that comes from trees.

5. Explain that paper, wood, and food are three of the main kinds of products people get from trees. Hand out the pictures you cut out earlier, one per person. (See "Getting Ready.") Explain that each picture shows one of these three important types of tree products. Tell the students to decide what type of tree product they have: wood, food, or paper.

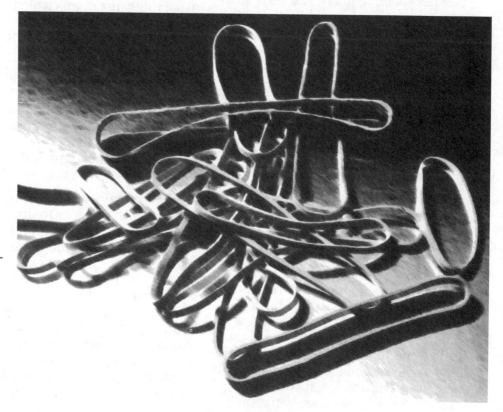

Would You Believe It Comes From Trees?

CELLULOSE PRODUCTS
- Carpeting
- Cellophane
- Rayon and other fabrics
- Thickening agent in shampoos
- Suntan lotion
- Shatterproof glass
- Cosmetics
- Paper products such as writing paper, magazines, books, toilet paper, newspaper, wrapping paper, building paper, industrial paper, and wallpaper
- Fiber board
- Imitation leather

BARK PRODUCTS
- Cork
- Tannin (used for curing leather)
- Dye
- Drugs and oils

SAP PRODUCTS (GUMS AND RESINS)
- Cosmetics
- Paint thinner
- Perfumes
- Soap
- Rubber products
- Sugar and syrup
- Varnishes
- Waxes
- Chewing gum
- Flavoring
- Printing ink
- Shoe polish
- Crayons
- Cleaning fluids
- Electrical insulation
- Adhesives

Many of the products listed aren't always—or exclusively—made from trees.

6. Make sure the students understand the kinds of products that each category includes. Then give them time to go and stand under the picture representing the appropriate category. (See "Getting Ready.")

7. Have each of the students name their tree product. Ask if anybody can think of other products that come from trees. Then refer to "Would You Believe It Comes From Trees" on this page to discuss some unusual tree products. Bring in some samples to pass around.

Enrichment
Make a Treasure Tree
Bring in a dead or pruned tree limb (with lots of branches), a used Christmas tree, or a small potted tree. Have the students decorate the limb (propped up), Christmas tree, or potted tree with pictures of tree products. They can draw their own pictures, cut pictures out of magazines, or use the pictures from the activity. They can also use actual small tree products, such as pencils, paper towel rolls, nuts, fruit, cellophane, etc., to decorate the tree.

END NOTES...

ASSESSMENT OPPORTUNITY
Conduct a survey of the forest products found in the classroom or home. For the classroom, divide students into small groups, with each assigned one of the following categories:
- paper products
- other school supplies
- building materials
- furniture or furnishings
- personal items (even chewing gum was once entirely made from the latex of a tropical tree)

Distribute a copy of "Classroom Forest Products" (page 38) to each group. Have each group identify the classroom forest products found within the selected category and record their information on the handout.

RELATED ACTIVITIES
We All Need Trees, A Few of My Favorite Things, Make Your Own Paper, Three Cheers for Trees!

REFERENCES
PLT poster "We All Need Trees" (ordering information in the Bibliography on page 386).

CLASSROOM FOREST PRODUCTS

Group Members

Forest Product Category Items

1 _____   **5** _____

2 _____   **6** _____

3 _____   **7** _____

4 _____   **8** _____

How the item is derived from the forest:

1 _____

2 _____

3 _____

4 _____

5 _____

6 _____

7 _____

8 _____

Overview
It is easy to see that items made of wood come from trees. However, many tree products are not obvious. In this activity your students will discover the diversity and multitude of products that are in some way derived from trees.

Background
Products are derived from all parts of a tree. Wood is the most obvious. It provides things such as lumber for houses, furniture, doors, picture frames, clocks, paintbrush handles, counters, cabinets, floors, spools for thread, etc. *Cellulose* is the major component of wood (and most other plant fiber). Paper is made from cellulose, and paper products include books, wrappers, cereal boxes, magazines, newspapers, food labels, etc. Besides being used to make paper, cellulose is an ingredient in many other products. (See student readings on pages 41-42.)

Getting Ready
1. Before doing this activity, collect as many of the following items as you can:

- Newspaper
- Toothpicks
- Candy bar with almonds
- Piece of lumber or plywood
- Tissue paper
- Sponge (synthetic, not natural)
- Article of rayon clothing or a piece of rayon cloth
- Baseball
- Wooden chopsticks or a wooden mixing or salad spoon
- Bottle of vanilla (flavoring)
- Book or magazine
- Cardboard box
- Can of paint thinner, turpentine, or mineral spirits
- Pack of chewing gum
- Can of paint

- Bottle cork
- Rubber gloves
- Apple or other piece of fruit that comes from trees
- Plastic comb or brush
- Piece of cellophane
- Wooden chair or other piece of furniture

Most of these items should be readily available around the house. Others may be available from your school's buildings and grounds department, shop, or art department. Scraps of plywood and lumber may also be available from a home improvement store.

2. You will be dividing your students into groups of four, so make enough copies of student pages 41-42 for each group of four students.

Doing the Activity
1. Place the items you collected around the room, and label each one with a number.

2. Divide the group into teams of four, and tell them that team members will work together to determine which of the products around the room are made from trees. All team members must agree with the team's decision about each product and must be able to explain why each product is on their team's list.

3. Have the students in each team number themselves from one to four. Tell all the "1's" that it's their responsibility to record the information that everyone on their team agrees on and that they'll have to report their group's findings to the rest of the class. Tell all the "2's" that they must make sure that everyone in the group has an opportunity to speak as the team tries

LEVELS
Grades 4-6

SUBJECTS
Social Studies, Science, Language Arts

CONCEPTS
- Successful technologies are those that are appropriate to the efficient and sustainable use of resources, and to the preservation and enhancement of environmental quality. (2.3)
- Natural beauty, as experienced in forests and other habitats, enhances the quality of human life by providing artistic and spiritual inspiration, as well as recreational and intellectual opportunities. (3.4)

SKILLS
Analyzing, Classifying and Categorizing, Interpreting

OBJECTIVES
Students will ① examine various products and determine which ones are made from trees, ② describe ways that trees are used to make products and ways that these products can be conserved, and ③ explore methods for recycling and reusing products.

MATERIALS
Various forest products (see Getting Ready Step 1) and copies of pages 41–42

TIME CONSIDERATIONS
Preparation: 30 minutes

Activity: Two 50-minute periods

to reach decisions. The "3's" must make sure the group stays on track and gets everything accomplished in the time allowed. And the "4's" are the only people who may leave the group to ask you questions.

4. Have the teams move around the room and examine the products. *(WARNING: Do not let them open any of the product containers.)* After they have decided if one item comes from trees in some way, they should record it on a list and move on to the next one.

5. Once teams have established their lists, give each team a set of the readings on pages 41–42. Each student should read the article that corresponds to his or her number. (Student pages can be cut in half).

6. After reading their articles, students should explain the contents to their team members. Each person is responsible for making sure everyone else in the group understands what his or her article says.

7. The teams should then re-evaluate the list of products they came up with in Step 4. Are there any products they want to add to or delete from their list? Once again, remind them that everyone on their team must agree with the changes and should be able to explain why each item is on their list.

8. Have the teams share their lists with the rest of the group. Discuss the diversity of products we get from trees. Check the students' understanding of the articles by asking them to explain why they included certain products. If they didn't realize it during the activity, they should realize by the end of the discussion that all the products you spread around the room came from trees in some way.

9. How will this new awareness of forest products affect student's lifestyles? Will they make any changes? Talk about conservation practices where their families use a forest product but could also ① recycle the product, ② reuse the product, or ③ reduce its use.

Enrichment

Have the students work in their groups to brainstorm a list of the ways they use paper. Then have them write down possible substitutes for the three or four items on the list that they think are the most important. Afterward have them compare the environmental and economic factors associated with these products and their possible substitutes by answering the following questions. (They will need to do research to answer some of the questions. Encourage them to divide the research among their group members.)

1. Would the substitute serve the same purpose as efficiently and cheaply as the tree product?

2. Is the substitute made from a renewable or nonrenewable resource?

3. Does the production of the substitute require more or less energy than the production of the original product? (They will need to research this.)

4. Is the substitute reusable or recyclable? Was the original forest product reusable?

5. What, if any, are the long-term implications for continuing to use the paper product or its substitutes?

END NOTES...

ASSESSMENT OPPORTUNITY

Wood furniture is an obvious tree product. But many common products such as toothpaste, which contains cellulose or wood fiber, are not. A scavenger hunt for tree products is a fun way to assess students' understanding of the concepts and information presented in this activity. The scavenger hunt can be done in school, outdoors, or in a supermarket or drug store.

1. Organize students into groups of three.

2. Provide each group with a list of items such as these to find :

■ two products derived from the gum of trees (rubber products, chewing gum)

■ two objects made directly from wood (furniture, toothpicks, spools)

■ two products made from tree resin (violin rosin, soap, varnish)

■ two products derived from fruits and nuts of trees (cider, dyes, spices)

■ two products extracted from the leaves or bark of trees (astringent lotion, cork, honey)

3. Challenge your students to find items that are not obvious tree products.

4. After a fixed amount of time, have the students share their discoveries and explain which part each product is from.

RELATED ACTIVITIES

Tree Treasures, A Few Of My Favorite Things, Three Cheers for Trees, Resource–Go–Round, Renewable or Not?

REFERENCE

Wright, Helena. *300 YEARS OF AMERICAN PAPERMAKING*. Washington, DC: Smithsonian Institution, 1991.

TREE READINGS

1 Look around you and chances are you'll see a lot of things made out of wood. People use wood to build houses and other buildings; to construct doors, floors, fences, and furniture; and to make many other products including bowls, boats, paddles, crates, baskets, and baseball bats.

To make wood products, you must first harvest trees and process them into lumber. In sustaining a renewable supply of timber, forest managers practice silviculture—the management and cultivation of forests. Young trees are usually re-planted or naturally re-seeded on the land where they were harvested. Openings created by harvests often improve the habitat for certain wildlife species.

After the trees have been cut down, the branches are removed, and they are cut into logs. Then, the logs are loaded onto trucks and transported to a sawmill. The first machine at the sawmill strips off the bark. The logs are then measured and then cut into lumber. Depending on how the wood will be used (whether for buildings, furniture, baseball bats, etc.), the trees will be cut in different ways. What products a tree is used for depends on the type of tree it is. For example, hardwood trees such as oak and maple are often used for flooring and high-quality furniture, while softwood (coniferous) trees are usually used for papermaking, lower-quality furniture, houses, and crates.

Plants contain a compound called cellulose to give them rigidity and support. Cellulose is the main component in wood and, in most cases, people use

this source of cellulose to make paper.

2 Paper was made by hand for nearly 17 centuries following its invention in China about 100 A.D. In the Orient, plant fibers were beaten into a pulp, suspended in water, and formed into sheets by draining the fibers through a screen. As knowledge of papermaking moved westward, papermakers began to use rags rather than plant fibers to furnish pulp.

Papermaking spread to Europe through the Middle East, reaching Spain from North Africa by about 1200. From Spain, the craft eventually was brought to the New World. The Spanish established a European-style paper mill in Mexico in about 1580, but little is known of that endeavor, and it did not mark the beginning of continuous production.

Paper mills use cellulose from three sources: recycled paper, wood chips and sawdust leftover from making lumber, and raw logs. When raw logs arrive at the mill, machines strip the bark off and chop the trees into chips. Then the chips (and other sources of cellulose) are "cooked" with chemicals until the mixture becomes a thick pulp.

Next, the pulp is "washed." During the washing stage, dirt and other impurities are filtered out, producing clean pulp and,

leftover waste and solids called sludge water. The sludge is separated from the water and either landfilled, burned, or applied to the land as fertilizer. The wash water goes into a waste water treatment system. The clean pulp then goes through a series of machines where the fibers get mashed apart so that the pulp will form smooth sheets when dried.

Eventually, the pulp is run onto screens where the water drains off, and the result is newly formed paper. The paper is compressed and dried. Depending on the chemical process used to refine the pulp and the amount of cleaning and flattening involved, people create different kinds of paper such as coffee filter paper, heavy writing paper, wrapping paper, and so on. They can also create cardboard, boxboard, paperboard, and other strong products.

TREE READINGS

3 All land plants contain a compound called cellulose, which provides them with rigidity and support—it's the number-one component in wood. People use cellulose from wood to make a variety of products besides paper. For example, cellulose can be mixed with certain chemicals and squeezed into fibers that are used to make carpets, wigs, and fabrics such as rayon for clothes and furniture. Cellulose is also used as a key ingredient in cellophane, sausage casings, explosives, shatterproof glass, sponges, shampoo thickeners, imitation leather, and many other products. Processed with certain chemicals, cellulose may also be used to produce molded plastics for eyeglass frames, hairbrush handles, steering wheels, and so on.

4 It would be hard—if not impossible—to find a part of a tree that people do not use in some way. The bark of many trees, for example, is used for many different products. Most bottle corks are made from the bark of cork oak trees, which grow in Europe and Africa near the Mediterranean Sea. The spongy bark of these trees is made into bulletin boards, the inner cores of baseballs, and many other products. Quinine, the drug used to cure and prevent malaria, comes from Peruvian bark and had been used by Native Americans long before the Europeans arrived. Some tree bark has an abundance of a chemical called tannin. People use tannin to process leather.

Some trees produce saps called gums and resins that are used to make paint thinner, chewing gum, medicines, and many other products. For hundreds of years, South American Indians have extracted the sap or latex from the rubber tree to make products such as rubber-soled shoes and containers. They processed it by heating the rubber and mixing it with sulfur to improve its strength. Maple trees produce a sap that people turn into maple syrup. Trees provide people with fruits and nuts such as apples, coconut, pecans, lemons, and olives, and spices such as allspice and nutmeg. Tree leaves, trunks, and other parts also provide ingredients for paints, road building materials, medicines, artificial vanilla, adhesives, inks, and hundreds of other products.

Overview
Students often do not know which resources are *renewable* and which are *nonrenewable*, or which are *recyclable* or *reusable*. In this activity, students will learn what these terms mean and discover why sustainable use of natural resources is so important.

Background
Natural resources are the raw materials we use for housing, clothing, transporting, heating, cooking, and so on. They include the air we breathe, the water we drink, the land we farm, and the space we use for living and recreation. In short, they are all the things we use in our physical environment to meet our needs and wants. We can put them into three categories: *renewable*, *nonrenewable*, and *perpetual* resources.

In a human time frame, perpetual resources such as solar energy, wind, and tides last forever. Nonrenewable resources, however, exist in fixed amounts and once they're used up, they're gone forever. For example, *fossil fuels* are formed through natural processes that take millions of years. If we use all the available fossil fuels, no additional amounts of them will ever be available to us–at least not for millions of years. Other nonrenewable resources such as copper and other metals were created billions of years ago during the explosions of giant stars. These nonrenewable resources are not created through natural processes here on Earth. The only way we could get more of them is to mine them on other planets.

Renewable resources are materials that can be replenished through natural and/or human processes. For example, even though trees die naturally or are harvested, new trees are naturally reseeded or can be replanted by humans. And even though people consume livestock, new animals are constantly being raised. It is important to realize that renewable resources need to be carefully managed. People can use a renewable resource in a way that it cannot recover itself. For example, in the early 1900s, the passenger pigeon was hunted so heavily

and irresponsibly that its numbers dwindled and it became extinct. *Grasslands* can become overgrazed to the point where the soil loses its ability to support plant life and the area becomes much like a desert. *Groundwater* supplies may be pumped out of the ground faster than *precipitation* can trickle down to replenish them.

The maximum rate at which people can use a renewable resource without reducing the ability of the resource to renew itself is called *sustainable yield.* For example, a sustainable yield of timber would mean harvesting only the amount of trees that the forest could grow. This term also applies to water and wildlife. The sustainable yield of any resource varies from region to region, and it can be altered through various management practices.

When people *recycle* or re-use natural resources, they decrease the demand on the resource and save energy. (Of course, the recycling process itself also consumes energy.) For example, when people recycle aluminum cans, less *bauxite* needs to be mined to create "new" aluminum. Recycling aluminum saves lots of energy as well. With paper products, the equation is more complicated since paper fibers cannot be recycled indefinitely and new fiber from trees must be added to the papermaking cycle. However, recycling keeps paper out of landfills and incinerators. Many resources, including renewable and nonrenewable ones, can be recycled and reused.

Getting Ready
Make a copy of student page 47 for each team of four students.

LEVELS
Grades 4-8

SUBJECTS
Science, Social Studies

CONCEPTS
■ The standard of living of various peoples throughout the world depends on environmental quality; the availability, use, and distribution of resources; and the societies' political structure and culture. (3.3)

■ Resource management and technological systems help societies to meet, within limits, the needs of a growing human population. (8.2)

■ Conservation technology enables humans to maintain and extend the productivity of vital resources. (8.3)

SKILLS
Discussing, Representing, Composing, Summarizing, Interpreting, Predicting

OBJECTIVES
Students will ① identify renewable, nonrenewable, perpetual, reusable, and recyclable resources and explain the differences among them and ② play a game that simulates society's use of renewable and nonrenewable resources.

MATERIALS
Part A: Copies of student page 47, pens or pencils, and paper
Part B: Large amount of popcorn (or nuts or candies), 88 cookies or crackers (demonstration #3 only), large jar or other container, 44 slips of paper, and 15 paper or plastic bags

TIME CONSIDERATIONS
Preparation: 20 minutes

Activity: Two 50-minute periods

PART A
SORTING WHAT'S WHAT

Doing the Activity

1. Write the terms "renewable resource," "nonrenewable resource," and "perpetual resource" on the chalkboard. Ask students to write a definition or give a few examples for each. Tell them not to worry if they're not sure what the terms mean. By the end of the activity they will have a better understanding.

2. Divide the group into teams of four. Explain that teams will be working together to come up with a one- or two-sentence definition for each of the three terms.

3. Give each team a copy of student page 47. Have them cut out the clues and give one to each team member.

4. Each student should read their clue card and share the information with the rest of their team. Then, each team should use these bits of information to synthesize a definition for "renewable," "nonrenewable," and "perpetual" resources. Everyone on the team should understand each of the clues and agree with their team's definitions.

5. Teams should then discuss the questions on student page 47, with one member designated to record their responses and one designated to report them.

6. Review each of the questions with the entire group, with each team reporting its answers.

PART B
DEMONSTRATIONS

Doing the Activity

Try these simple demonstrations to teach the students about sustainable use and to give them a better understanding of renewable and nonrenewable resources.

1. Divide the group into teams of four. Give each team 16 pieces of popcorn (nuts or candies can also be used). Explain that students will play a game in which the popcorn represents the team's supply of a renewable resource that is replenished after each round of play. Each student can take freely from the team supply; however, the team should keep in mind the following rules:

- At the end of the game, each team member will get to eat all the popcorn or candy that he or she amassed.

- Each team member needs to take at least one piece per round to be sustained.

- At the end of each round, the resource will be replenished by one-half of its existing amount.

2. Allow students to take freely from their team's popcorn pile. Students should record how many pieces they have taken and how many are left in the team pile.

3. Find out how many pieces each group has in its central pile, and give the group half that amount in new pieces.

4. Play three or four more rounds, stopping after each to find out if any of the students didn't survive. Then provide each group with the prescribed amount of new popcorn.

5. After four or five rounds, have the students share what happened in their teams. In which teams did all the students survive? Which students had the most popcorn in their personal supplies? Which team had the most popcorn in its collective pile? Which teams think they would be able to keep eating popcorn forever as long as the resource kept renewing itself? On these teams, how many pieces were these students taking each round?

ANSWERS TO THE QUESTIONS ON STUDENT PAGE 47
PART A

1. Renewable: corn, trees, tuna, salmon

Nonrenewable: oil, coal, gold, sand

Perpetual: sunshine, tides, hot springs, breeze, river

2. Answers will vary depending on what's in your classroom.

3. Answers will vary. For example, students may suggest that wood may be used as a substitute for plastic or metal in chairs and other equipment.

4. Answers will vary. Students may suggest that some materials are cheaper than others, that products made from renewable resources are better since the materials to make them can always be available, or that some materials from nonrenewable resources are superior to others because they're lighter in weight or have other properties.

5. If the students don't come up with answers to this question, don't worry. And don't give them an answer! The demonstrations in Part B should teach the students conditions under which this could occur.

6. Solar energy, winds, tides, etc.

6. Discuss these questions with the entire group:

- What are the advantages and disadvantages of using a resource in a sustainable way? (Advantage: It can last forever. Disadvantage: You need to control your use of it.)

- What advantages and disadvantages are there to using a resource in a nonsustainable way? (Advantages: People will have a large amount of the resource available when they want it; they can make a lot of money in the short term. Disadvantage: They can destroy the resource base for themselves and future generations).

- In this demonstration, the population of each group stayed same. In reality however, the human population is increasing rapidly. What would have happened if one or two or three additional people would have been added to your group?

NOTE—Some of the groups may run out of resources right away or after only two rounds. But one or more of the groups should figure out a way to collect at least one piece of popcorn each round and still have leftovers in their collective pile to be "renewed" each round. During the discussion, be sure to introduce the concept of "sustainable yield." (See Background.)

DEMONSTRATION 2—POPCORN GENERATION

1. Fill a large jar or other container with popcorn. Mark 14 slips of paper as follows: Two "1st Generation," four "2nd Generation," and eight "3rd Generation." Put the slips into a sack.

NOTE—You should have extra popcorn available after the demonstration is over for the students that don't participate directly in the demonstration.

2. Have 14 students each draw a slip of paper from the sack. They should not tell anyone what the paper says. Give these students a lunch bag and explain that they will be part of a demonstration.

3. Ask the two 1st Generation students to come up to the big jar of popcorn. Explain that the food in the jar represents the world's supply of a nonrenewable resource. Tell them they can take as much of it as they want. Let them fill their bags while the rest of the group watches.

4. When the 1st Generation students have gotten their fill, invite the four 2nd Generation students to go up and take as much of the remaining popcorn as they want. After they've finished, have the 3rd Generation students come up and take what's left.

5. Discuss with the students what is happening to the world's popcorn supply. What happened to the total amount of the resource? How much was left for each successive generation? Was anything left for a 4th generation? Did any of the students who were part of the demonstration think about those who might be eating after them, or were they only trying to get as much popcorn as they could?

6. What parallels do the students see between what happened in the demonstration and what happens in the real world?

NOTE—Students may eat as much of the popcorn as they can without any thought as to who will come after them. By the time the 3rd Generation students are finished, there should be little or no popcorn left for the 4th. Even if the students don't eat as much as they can, they will eat some and the 4th generation will have very little. The students should realize that as new generations come along, there will be less and less of the resource available to them, and eventually there will he nothing.

DEMONSTRATION 3—GLOBAL COOKIE JAR

1. Before your group arrives, label different parts of the room with signs saying Africa, South America, North America, Europe and the Middle East, Russia, and Asia. Prepare slips of paper, one for each student. For a group of thirty students, label eighteen "Asia," four "Europe and the Middle East," three "Africa," two "South America," two "Russia", and one "North America." (For different size groups, adjust these numbers, keeping approximately the same ratio.) Put these slips in a bag. You will also need to bring a jar or box of 88 cookies or crackers ("Global Cookie Jar.") You can also use individually wrapped candies.

2. When the students arrive, have each pick a slip and go to the section of the room assigned to that region. Display a large map of the world so students can see the regions they belong to. Tell them that they represent the relative population of the regions. Each group should appoint an "ambassador" to represent their region.

3. Tell the regions that they will receive a certain number of cookies, which represent their Gross National Product (the total value of goods and services that their region produces in a year). Give Africa two cookies, Russia three cookies, Asia nine cookies, Europe and the Middle East twelve cookies, South America twenty cookies, and North America thirty cookies.

4. Explain that each person must have at least one cookie to survive. Students can exchange cookies freely between regions but only the appointed ambassador can leave the group's designated area.

5. Allow the game to go on for 15 minutes. Let the students work out the inequalities of "wealth" any way they think. Take notes on what you hear and see happening.

6. Announce the end of the activity. Discuss students' experiences by using the following questions:

■ What was your overall experience?

■ What was your initial reaction?

■ How did you feel when you looked around the room and saw who had what?

■ Did you think you would survive?

■ Did you ask others for food? How?

■ What did you do with your food? Share it, hide it, eat it?

■ What choices are available to nations that do not have enough money to buy food from other countries?

■ What are some important ideas involved in this game?

■ What is missing from the game that would make it more realistic?

ASSESSMENT OPPORTUNITY

Have each student write in his or her own words what renewable and nonrenewable resources are. Then have the students answer these questions:

1. If a resource is renewable, does that mean it will continue to exist no matter what people do? Explain your answer.

2. What two factors would you say are most important in determining how fast natural resources are used? (This question may be difficult for some students. By recalling the demonstrations, though, they should be able to deduce that the number of people using a resource and the amount each person uses are very important in determining how fast resources get used.)

For Part A:
Listen to the teams' discussions and note how they work together in listening to different opinions and reaching some consensus answers.

RELATED ACTIVITIES

A Few of My Favorite Things, Tree Treasures, A Look At Aluminum, Resource-Go-Round

CLUES & QUESTIONS

CLUES

1
On Earth, there are only limited amounts of fossil fuels such as oil, coal, and natural gas. There are also only limited amounts of minerals such as iron, copper, and phosphates. These resources either cannot be replaced by natural processes or require millions of years to replenish.

2
Some nonrenewable and renewable natural resources can be recycled or reused. This process decreases the rate at which the supplies of these resources are depleted. For example, aluminum cans can be recycled and turned into new cans or other aluminum products many times over. Recycling reduces the need to mine bauxite, the mineral used to make aluminum.

3
Renewable natural resources include plants, animals, and water, when they are properly cared for. Minerals and fossil fuels such as coal and oil, are examples of nonrenewable natural resources.

4
Trees, wildlife, water, and many other natural resources are replaced by natural processes. Plants and animals can also be replenished by human activities. Water is continuously cycled and reused. Sunlight, wind, geothermal heat, tides, and flowing water are perpetual resources.

QUESTIONS

1. Categorize the following as renewable, nonrenewable, or perpetual resources:

- a field of corn
- oil in the Arctic tundra
- coal in the Appalachian Mountains
- sunshine everywhere
- tides in the Bay of Fundy
- trees in a forest
- tuna in the ocean
- gold mines in the western United States
- hot springs in Alaska
- sand on a beach
- a breeze over the Texas plains
- salmon in streams
- water in a river

2. Look around the classroom and list as many items as you can that are made from renewable natural resources. Make a separate list of all the items made from nonrenewable natural resources.

3. What renewable natural resources could be used to replace the nonrenewable ones used in the items you listed in Question 2? What nonrenewable resources could be used in place of the renewable ones?

4. What advantages and disadvantages might there be for using renewable natural resources in place of nonrenewable ones?

5. Under what circumstances, if any, would a renewable natural resource not be renewable?

6. Which resources, if any, would continue to be available no matter how much people used them?

Overview

Here's a way to give your students a better appreciation for how many *natural resources* they depend on in their day-to-day lives. By tracing the resources that go into making one item, they will learn how the manufacturing of just one product can have an impact on the environment.

LEVELS
Grades 4-8

SUBJECTS
Science, Social Studies, Visual Arts

CONCEPTS
- Humans use tools and technologies to adapt and alter environments and resources to meet their physical, social, and cultural needs. (2.1)
- The quantity and quality of resources and their use—or misuse—by humans affects the standard of living of societies. (6.2)
- All humans consume products and thereby affect the availability of renewable and nonrenewable natural resources. (6.4)

SKILLS
Discussing, Analyzing, Elaborating, Generalizing, Representing

OBJECTIVES
Students will ① explain how the different materials that go into making a product all come from natural resources, ② identify natural resources as being renewable or nonrenewable, ③ identify the steps that go into making a product, and ④ describe some of the impacts from obtaining and processing natural resources for making products.

MATERIALS
Paper and art supplies for presentations, and each student brings in a favorite object

TIME CONSIDERATIONS
Preparation: 10 minutes
Activity: Two 50-minute periods

Background

See background information for "Renewable or Not?" on page 43 and "Resource-Go-Round" on page 316.

Doing the Activity

1. Have each student bring in a favorite object such as a skateboard, book, or toy. Give students five minutes to write down as many of the materials that went into making it as they can. They should be able to generate a list of materials just by looking at the object (plastic, wood, aluminum, steel, leather, rubber, glass)

2. Ask several students to describe their possessions and the materials that went into making them. As they list the materials, write them on the board, without duplicating responses.

3. Explain to the students that all the products we use and the materials in them are derived from natural resources, resources that occur naturally on Earth. Go down the list of materials on the chalkboard and help the students to identify the natural resource from which each material is derived. Afterward, ask the students to identify the major groups of natural resources from which all of the materials are made (plant, animal, metal or mineral, petroleum).

4. Explain to the students that some natural resources can be renewed while others cannot. Ask them which of the resources that they've identified are renewable and which are not. (Plants and animals are renewable.) Which materials in their favorite thing come from renewable resources? Could the materials that are not from renewable resources be substituted with materials that are?

5. Explain that some materials can be recycled and some cannot. Have the students look at the list of materials on the board and decide which ones they think can be recycled and which ones cannot. (Glass, paper, aluminum, and some plastics can be recycled.) Does this mean that products made from these materials can always be recycled? (No, it is difficult to recycle products that contain different resource materials mixed together.) Can any of the items the students brought in be recycled? Can any of them be reused? How long will they last? Will they eventually get thrown in the trash?

6. Ask the students if they know what type of fuel or energy was used to make their favorite item and to transport the item to them. What energy is used to maintain it? Is this a renewable source of energy? How might the mass production and use of each item affect the environment? How might negative affects be minimized?

7. Have students look at their favorite thing again, think about all the materials and energy that went into making it, and decide whether these were derived from *renewable* or *nonrenewable natural resources*. For example, a skateboard might have a plastic board derived from petroleum, metal wheel supports from minerals in the earth, and rubber wheels from tree sap. So, in this example, the only material that might come from a renewable resource is rubber. In addition, nonrenewable *fossil fuels* (oil, gas, coal) were used to process raw materials for manufacture, and transport the skateboard.

8. Students should use poster paper and markers to create a visual representation of their favorite thing, showing the materials, resources, and energy that go into making it.

Enrichment

Now that the students have learned that most manufactured items are very difficult to recycle, have them find out what happens to those items when people throw them away. They probably end up in a landfill or incinerator.

Many times people throw away things that are still useful because they are no longer interested in them or don't want to have them repaired. This problem can be solved by giving items away, fixing them, or finding ways to reuse them.

Swap Shop

Students can practice reuse by setting up a classroom Swap Shop, which is a simple process.

1. Have students bring items from home that can still be used, but that their family no longer wants and would eventually throw out.

2. Have students put the items on a table in back of the room.

3. All the students should inspect the table and see if there's anything on it they want.

4. The group should discuss what rules should apply to the swap. One possibility is to have students sign out items on a first-come basis. If more than one person wants an item, students should take turns, with each person taking it for a certain period of time.

Trashion Show

1. Students should bring an item from home that is broken and would eventually get thrown out. All items should be put on a table in back of the room.

2. Students can come up and select what they would like to take and fix or have fixed.

3. Students could come up with new inventions or alternate uses for items that nobody wants to have repaired such as turning a broken aquarium into a planter.

4. Your class could have a Trashion Show in which students exhibit their new creations from trash.

END NOTES...

ASSESSMENT OPPORTUNITY
Examine each student's poster from Step 8 to assess how well each understands the type of resources, materials, and energy that go into making the favorite thing.

RELATED ACTIVITIES
Tree Treasures, A Look At Aluminum, Resource-Go-Round, Renewable or Not?

Overview
Chocolate candy. Apple pie. French fries with catsup. Tortilla chips with guacamole dip. Thanks to plants, these and many other favorite foods are ours to enjoy. Try the following activities to get your students thinking about just how big a part plants play in our daily diets.

LEVELS
Part A: K-8 Part B: 3-8 Part C: PreK-8

SUBJECTS
Science, Social Studies, Math, Language Arts

CONCEPTS
- Humans throughout the world create differing social, cultural, and economic systems and organizations to help them meet their physical and spiritual needs. (3.2)
- The standard of living of various peoples throughout the world depends on environmental quality; the availability, use, and distribution of resources; and the societies' political structure and culture. (3.3)

SKILLS
Discussing, Identifying Attributes and Components, Organizing Information, Researching, Analyzing

OBJECTIVES
Students will ① identify edible plant parts and give examples of each, ② describe how plants are used to make various kinds of foods, and ③ discuss the importance of plants in people's diets.

MATERIALS
Copies of student page 53, ingredients and utensils for snack recipes (see Part C)

TIME CONSIDERATIONS
Preparation: One hour

Activity: Two 50-minute periods

Background
People and other animals eat parts of many different plants. For example, people eat roots (carrots, parsnips); above ground and underground stems (asparagus, onions, potatoes); leaves (lettuce, spinach); leaf stalks (celery); flowers (broccoli, cauliflower); fruits (apples, peaches, tomatoes, cucumbers); and seeds (wheat, rice, corn, pecans, walnuts, beans).

Nutrition is something that all people should be concerned about. According to the U.S. Department of Agriculture, most nutritionists recommend that in our daily intake of food we have ① 2-4 servings of fruits (a serving would be one medium apple, orange, or banana; half a cup of small or diced fruit; three-fourths cup of juice); ② 3-5 servings of vegetables (a serving would be one cup of raw leafy greens, or half a cup of other kinds of vegetables); ③ 6-11 servings of grains, bread, cereal, rice, or pasta (a serving would be one slice of bread, or half of a bun, bagel, or English muffin; one ounce of dry ready-to-eat cereal; half a cup of cooked cereal, rice, or pasta); ④ 2-3 servings of dairy foods (a serving would be one cup of milk or yogurt, or about one and a half ounce of cheese); ⑤ 2 servings of meat, poultry, fish, legumes, eggs, or nuts; and ⑥ very sparing amounts of fats, oils, or sweets. (These servings may vary slightly among males, females, children, and adults.) Foods with complex carbohydrates and fiber such as fruits, vegetables, whole grains, breads, cereals, and legumes (peas or beans) should make up the majority of a person's diet. A diet too high in fat, especially saturated fat and cholesterol, could result in a number of health problems such as heart disease.

It also matters how food is prepared. For instance, a person should limit their intake of foods that have been heavily processed with added sugars and preservatives or fried in oils and fats. These foods are generally less nutritious.

Getting Ready
Make copies of student page 53. If you plan to use recipes in class, you may want to bring and prepare ingredients and utensils in advance. You can also ask students to bring ingredients and utensils, or you can take them on a field trip to the supermarket.

PART A
PLANTS IN THE PIZZA?
Doing the Activity
1. Have the students brainstorm a list of foods that come from plants. The foods can be either plants themselves (such as potatoes) or made from plants (such as french fries). Write the students' ideas on the board.

2. Point out that many plant foods are not obvious. For example, tortilla chips are made from ground corn. Bread is made from wheat or other grains. Even pizza, with its wheat crust and tomato sauce, is made mostly from plants. Ask the students if they can think of others, and add their suggestions to the list.

3. Examine the list and have the students try to identify the plant parts each food comes from. On the chalkboard, write the plant part categories in which the foods belong (see Background). What animals also eat these plant parts?

NOTE—It is important to make clear through discussion that not all parts of an edible plant are edible. Sometimes we may eat one part of a plant while another part is poisonous. Animals can often eat plant or plant parts that are inedible or even poisonous to people.

4. Pass out copies of page 53, "Veggie Plate," to each student. Have them fill in the name of the appropriate plant part on the blank line below the word identifying the food. If they want, they can also color the page. Afterward, go over the answers with the students (see Answers below).

5. Older students can research the vitamins and minerals provided by each of the veggies on the plate.

PART B
ANALYZE YOUR LUNCH

Doing the Activity

1. Have each student make a chart (see sample below), and tell the students that they are going to take a close look at their lunch from Monday through Thursday. They will fill in the chart with information about the plant foods they eat for lunch each day.

2. Go over the charts initially with the students. Each day after lunch, give them time to add information to their charts.

3. On Friday, discuss the data with the students. Did some plant parts show up in their lunches more often than others? If so, which ones?

4. Have the students create a bar graph showing the occurrence of different plant parts in their lunches during the week. How might this change from season to season? (summer fruits)

5. With older students, discuss what a balanced meal is (see Background). Have students create a balanced diet of plant foods. Students could be introduced to concepts about sound nutrition and human health.

PART C
TREE-LICIOUS TREATS AND OTHER SNACKS

Doing the Activity
Hold a plant foods feast! Page 52 has a few recipes you can try. Ingredients that come from trees and other plants are in italics. (You might want to have students bring in some of the ingredients.)

Enrichment
1. Take the students on a field trip to the supermarket. In addition to shopping for ingredients for Part C, have the students work in groups to gather data on the prevalence of plants in different products. Each group can focus on a particular aisle, reading food labels and writing down information about the plant ingredients in each product. Back in the classroom, the students could create charts depicting their data. Are products healthy just because they are made from plants? What factors go into deciding whether a food product is healthy? (Low fat, low sugar, low salt, high carbohydrate, high protein, vitamins, etc.)

2. Take students on a trip to a farm to see where their food comes from.

3. Have the students research some familiar spices used in different types of ethnic cooking such as Mexican, Indian, Italian, Middle Eastern, etc. Individuals or small groups could discover where and what plants these ingredients come from and other information, and then present their findings to the rest of the group. Bring in some ethnic foods and have students see how they like the flavor that spices give those foods.

SAMPLE CHART

	MON			
MON				
TUES				
WED				
THURS				

Answers for Veggie Plate

cashew	seed
onion	underground stem
asparagus	aboveground stem
cherry tomato	fruit
spinach	leaf
broccoli	flower
apple	fruit
celery	leaf stalk
carrot	root

RECIPES

Maple 'n' Walnut Spread
(Makes enough spread for about 25 people.)
8-oz. package of cream cheese, softened
1/2 cup chopped *dates*
1 1/2 cups nondairy whipped topping
1/4 cup *maple syrup*
1 cup finely chopped *apple*
enough bagel halves for everyone in your group
1 cup chopped *walnuts*

Combine cream cheese, whipped topping, and syrup in a large bowl. Add apple, walnuts, and dates. Stir until well mixed. Spread onto bagel halves and serve.

Guacamole
(Makes about 2 1/2 cups.)
1/4 cup sour cream
2 soft, ripe *avocados*
1/2 teaspoon *chili powder*
2 tablespoons *lemon juice*
dash *paprika* and *black pepper*
2 small *tomatoes*, chopped
1/4 cup *black olives*, chopped (optional)
2 cloves *garlic*, minced
corn chips
1 teaspoon salt

Mash the avocados in a small bowl. Thoroughly mix in the lemon juice. Chop the tomato and add it to the mixture. Blend in the garlic, salt, sour cream, black pepper, and chili powder. Sprinkle with paprika and serve with corn chips.

Hummus
(Makes about 4 cups.)
3 cups cooked *chick peas* (also called *garbanzo beans*)
1/2 to 3/4 cup *tahini (sesame seed paste)*
3 cloves *garlic*, minced
1 teaspoon salt
black pepper to taste
3 tablespoons *tamari (soy sauce)*
cayenne pepper to taste
1/4 cup *lemon juice*

Put all ingredients in a food processor or blender on a high setting and mix until ingredients are smooth and well blended. Serve with pita (pocket) bread.

Tree Treats
(Makes three to four dozen treats.)
1 cup dried *apricots*
1/2 teaspoon ground *cloves*
1 cup dried *figs*
1 teaspoon *cinnamon*
1 cup dried, pitted *prunes*
1 small package shredded *coconut*
2/3 cup *almonds*

Grind the apricots, figs, prunes, and almonds in a food grinder or processor. Stir in the spices. Mold the mixture into little balls and then roll the balls in the shredded coconut.

Sunflower Seed Cakes
(Adapted from an Iroquois recipe from about the time of the first Thanksgiving.)
2 cups shelled *raw sunflower seeds*
6 tablespoons *cornmeal*
1 1/4 cups water
vegetable oil or butter for frying
3/4 teaspoon salt

Put the sunflower seeds and water into a large pot. Bring the mixture to a boil and then simmer for an hour, stirring occasionally. Remove from heat and blend in the cornmeal, one tablespoon at a time. This will make a stiff, sticky dough. Add salt and pat into 3-inch by 1/2-inch cakes. Heat the oil or butter in a frying pan until hot. (If you don't have access to a stove at school, an electric frying pan can be used.) Add the cakes and brown on either side. Drain on paper towels, and serve with berry jam or cranberry sauce. (You could also make the batter the night before and refrigerate it until frying it the next day at school.)

VEGGIE PLATE

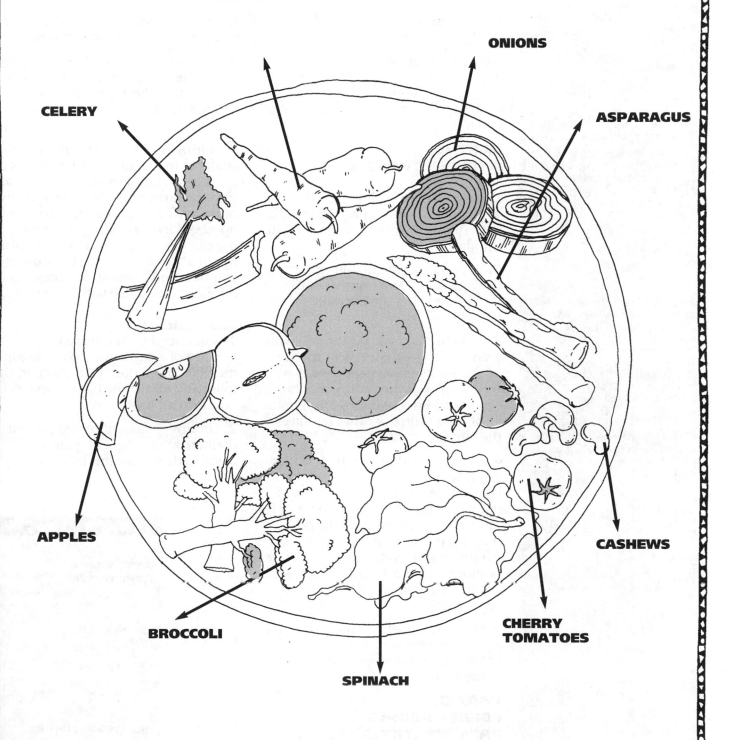

CARROTS

ONIONS

CELERY

ASPARAGUS

APPLES

CASHEWS

BROCCOLI

CHERRY TOMATOES

SPINACH

Overview

To the Mbuti Pygmies of Africa, the Yanomami and the Kuna of Latin America, and other peoples around the world, the forest is home. More than just a place to live, the forest provides for all of their needs. By comparing and contrasting different forest peoples, both past and present, your students can learn about some of the ways people have depended on forests throughout history.

LEVELS
Grades 5-8

SUBJECTS
Social Studies, Language Arts

CONCEPTS
■ Human societies vary greatly and inhabit many land forms and climates throughout the world. (3.1)

■ Humans throughout the world create differing social, cultural, and economic systems and organizations to help them meet their physical and spiritual needs. (3.2)

SKILLS
Comparing and Contrasting, Researching, Organizing Information, Representing

OBJECTIVES
Students will ① describe the lifestyles of several forest-dwelling peoples of the present or past and ways that they depend upon the forest, ② describe some of the effects forest people have on the their environment, and ③ write a story focusing on a day in the life of a member of one group of forest people.

MATERIALS
Copies of student page 55 (one per student), slips of paper (one per student), art supplies, and research materials (optional)

TIME CONSIDERATIONS
Preparation: 15 minutes

Activity: Two or three 50-minute periods

Background
See student page 55.

Getting Ready
1. Make copies of page 55 for each student. Try to get one or more copies of *THE FOREST PEOPLE* by Colin Turnbull (see Bibliography).

PART A
A DAY IN THE LIFE

Doing the Activity
1. Pass out a copy of page 55 to each student. Allow time for them to read through it.

2. Have a short discussion with the students about the Pygmies of the Ituri forest using the information on page 55.

3. Explain that each person will write a story that depicts a day in the life of a forest-dwelling people such as the Pygmies of the Ituri. Students can use additional information from *THE FOREST PEOPLE* or other resources they find.

4. Tell the students that their stories can take any of several perspectives. For example, a story can focus on a day in the life of a forest people, or it can trace the activities of the people through the seasons. The students can tell the story through the eyes of one or more community members, or they can narrate from the third-person point of view.

5. Give the students time to research and write their stories. Then have them share their stories with the rest of the group.

PART B
FOREST PEOPLE
PRESENTATIONS

Doing the Activity
1. Divide the class into teams and have each team research the lifestyle of a past or present forest people.

2. Have each team use the knowledge about their forest dwellers to develop a presentation. Each presentation can include displays, posters, and other exhibits.

3. During the presentations, have the students in the audience take notes on the various forest dwellers. Afterward, have each team use its notes and any other pertinent information to develop a booklet comparing and contrasting each group of forest dwellers. You might also want to have the students compare and contrast the forest dwellers' way of life with their own.

Enrichment
1. Students should assume the identity of a particular Pygmy group member and write a paragraph on the following idea: "The hardest lesson I ever learned in the forest was…"

2. Groups of students could present dramatizations depicting forest cultures they have studied.

FROM **THE FOREST PEOPLE**
by Colin Turnbull

In the Northeast Corner of the Belgian Congo (now Zaire), almost exactly in the middle of the map of Africa, lies the Ituri Forest, a vast expanse of dense, damp, and hospitable-looking darkness ...

The world of the forest is a closed, possessive world, hostile to all those who do not understand it. At first sight you might think it hostile to all human beings, because in every village you find the same suspicion and fear of the forest, that impenetrable wall. The villagers are friendly and hospitable to strangers, offering them the best of whatever food and drink they have, and always clearing out a house where the traveler can rest in comfort and safety. But these villages are set among plantations in great clearings cut from the heart of the forest around them. It is from the plantations that food comes, not from the forest, and for the villagers life is a constant battle to prevent their plantations from being overgrown.

They speak of the world beyond the plantations as being a fearful place, full of malevolent spirits and not fit to be lived in except by animals and the Mbuti, which is what the village people call the Pygmies. The villagers, some Bantu and some Sudanic, keep to their plantations and seldom go into the forest unless it is absolutely necessary. For them it is a place of evil. They are outsiders.

But the Mbuti are the real people of the forest. Whereas the other tribes are relatively recent arrivals, the Pygmies have been in the forest for thousands of years. It is their world, and in return for their affection and trust, it supplies them with all their needs. They do not have to cut the forest down to build plantations, for they know how to hunt the game of the region and gather the wild fruits that grow in abundance there, though hidden to outsiders. They know how to distinguish the innocent-looking itaba vine from the many others that closely resemble it, and they know how to follow it until it leads them to a cache of nutritious, sweet-tasting roots. They know the tiny sounds that tell where the bees have hidden their honey; they recognize the kind of weather that brings a multitude of different kinds of mushrooms springing to the surface; and they know what kinds of wood and leaves often disguise this food. The exact moment when termites swarm, at which they must be caught to provide an important delicacy, is a mystery to any but the people of the forest. They know the secret language that is denied all outsiders and without which life in the forest is an impossibility.

The Mbuti roam the forest at will, in small isolated bands or hunting groups. They have no fear, because for them there is no danger. For them there is little hardship, so they have no need for belief in spirits. For them it is a good world. The fact that they average less than four and a half feet in height is of no concern to them; their taller neighbors, who jeer at them for being so puny, are as clumsy as elephants–another reason why they must always remain outsiders in a world where your life may depend on your ability to run swiftly and silently. And if the Pygmies are small, they are powerful and tough.

PYGMY FACTS

- Mbuti [mm-BOO-tee] Pygmies live in small groups of several families. They dwell in the Ituri (ih-TUR-ee) Forest, a rainforest in Zaire (zi-EAR), Africa.

- When food becomes scarce, the group moves to another area within the forest.

- Women gather most of the group's food (fruits, vegetables, mushrooms, roots, nuts, and so on). Girls often help with food gathering.

- Men hunt small antelopes, monkeys, and other animals using bows and arrows. Boys often help with the hunt. Men and boys also gather honey, a favorite food.

- After a successful hunt, the Pygmies hold a feast. After the feast, they often celebrate by singing and dancing.

- Women build the group's dome-shaped huts out of saplings and leaves.

Overview
Every culture in the world has stories that are part of its history and tradition. These stories reveal the beliefs of the people who tell them. For example, many stories teach lessons in proper attitude and behavior. In this activity, your students can analyze a story told by the Muskogee (Creek) Indians of present-day Oklahoma. Later, students can read and discuss stories told in other cultures from around the world.

LEVELS
Grades K-6

SUBJECTS
Language Arts, Science, Social Studies

CONCEPTS
■ Human societies vary greatly and inhabit many land forms and climates throughout the world. (3.1)

■ Natural beauty, as experienced in forests and other habitats, enhances the quality of human life by providing artistic and spiritual inspiration, as well as recreational and intellectual opportunities. (3.4)

■ Organisms are interdependent; they all depend on nonliving components of the Earth. (4.1)

SKILLS
Comprehending, Discussing, Observing, Interpreting

OBJECTIVES
Students will ① describe how stories reveal the beliefs of the people who tell them and ② read or listen to an American Indian story to gain insight on the vital importance of the sun.

MATERIALS
Paper and pens or pencils, books of folktales, drawing paper, and crayons or markers (optional)

TIME CONSIDERATIONS
Preparation: 15 minutes

Activity: 50 minutes

Background
The traditions of a group of people include its stories, sayings, dances, songs, and customs. Many traditions are passed down orally from generation to generation. The stories of a people serve many purposes—they tell the history of the people, convey their religious beliefs, teach moral lessons, and entertain. The story in this activity reflects the traditional beliefs of the Muskogee people about how the world was formed—and it should be treated with the same respect as the creation beliefs of other cultures. Regardless of a person's faith, this story offers a valuable perspective on the relationships between plants, animals, people, and the sun.

Doing the Activity
1. Discuss with students their perceptions of what stories are. Explain the generally accepted definition that appears in the Background. Ask the students for a few examples of stories that reflect various cultures.

2. Tell the students you are going to read them a story told by the Muskogee (Creek) Indians of present-day Oklahoma about how the sun got into the sky. They must listen carefully to the story. Later they'll answer questions about it and the people who told the story.

3. Read aloud the story on page 57.

4. Discuss the story on two levels. On the first level, ask the students how the story, as a traditional creation story, explains why certain animals look the way they do. On the second level, ask them how the story can teach people a lesson in how to work and live together.

5. Have the students read another tale that relates to wildlife or the environment. (See the list of children's stories in the Bibliography on page 385.) What happens in the story? What does the story reveal about the people who told the tale? Does the story conflict with scientific explanations of nature? For example, according to scientists, can the wolf in "Little Red Riding Hood" really talk? What lesson for living can people learn from the tale?

Enrichment
Students can write their own short folktale incorporating information about plants and/or animals along with lessons that they think are important. Have the students illustrate their stories.

HOW GRANDMOTHER SPIDER STOLE THE SUN

A tale from the Muskogee (Creek) Indians

When the Earth was first made, there was no light. It was very hard for the animals and the people in the darkness. Finally, the animals decided to do something about it.

"I have heard there is something called the Sun," said the Bear. "It is kept on the other side of the world, but the people there will not share it. Perhaps we can steal a piece of it." All the animals agreed that it was a good idea, but who would be the one to steal the Sun?

The Fox was the first to try. He sneaked to the place where the Sun was kept. He waited until no one was looking. Then he grabbed a piece of it in his mouth and ran. But the Sun was so hot it burned his mouth and he dropped it. To this day all foxes have black mouths because the first fox burned his carrying the Sun.

The Possum tried next. In those days Possum had a very bushy tail. She crept up to the place where the Sun was kept, broke off a piece, and hid it in her tail. Then she began to run, bringing the Sun back to the animals and the people. But the Sun was so hot it burned off all the hair on her tail and she lost hold of it. To this day all possums have bare tails because the Sun burned away the hair on that first possum.

Then Grandmother Spider tried. Instead of trying to hold the Sun herself, she wove a bag out of her webbing. She put the piece of the Sun into her bag and carried it back with her. Now the question was where to put the Sun.

Grandmother Spider told them, "The Sun should be up high in the sky. Then everyone will be able to see it and benefit from its light."

All the animals agreed, but none of them could reach up high enough. Even if they carried it to the top of the tallest tree, that would not be high enough for everyone on the Earth to see the Sun. Then they decided to have one of the birds carry the Sun up to the top of the sky. Everyone knew the Buzzard could fly the highest, so he was chosen.

Buzzard placed the Sun on top of his head, where his feathers were the thickest, for the Sun was still very hot, even inside Grandmother Spider's bag. He began to fly, up and up toward the top of the sky. As he flew, the Sun grew hotter. Up and up he went, higher and higher, and the Sun grew hotter and hotter still. Now the Sun was burning through Grandmother Spider's bag, but the Buzzard still kept flying up toward the top of the sky. Up and up he went and the Sun grew hotter. Now it was burning away the feathers on top of his head, but he continued on. Now all of his feathers were gone, but he flew higher. Now it was turning the bare skin of his head all red, but he continued to fly. He flew until he reached the top of the sky, and there he placed the Sun where it would give light to everyone.

Because he carried the Sun to the top of the sky, Buzzard was honored by all the birds and animals. Though his head is naked and ugly because he was burned carrying the Sun, he is still the highest flyer of all, and he can be seen circling the Sun to this day. And because Grandmother Spider brought the Sun in her bag of webbing, at times the Sun makes rays across the sky which are shaped like the rays in Grandmother Spider's web, and it reminds everyone of what Grandmother Spider did for all the animals and the people.

This story is reprinted from Keepers of the Earth *by Michael J. Caduto and Joseph Bruchac (Golden, Colorado: Fulcrum Publishing, 1989) with permission of the publisher.*

END NOTES...

ASSESSMENT OPPORTUNITY

Check for comprehension by discussing these questions with the group:

- What happens to Fox and Possum when they try to carry the Sun? How does Grandmother Spider succeed in bringing the Sun to the dark side of the Earth?

- What does the story explain about Fox's mouth, Possum's tail, and Buzzard's head?

- Buzzard makes a great sacrifice to place the Sun high in the sky. What is this sacrifice? What would you do in Buzzard's situation?

- Could we live without the sun? Why not? What are the most important things the sun gives us? In what way was the sun important to the Muskogee Indians?

- What would happen to the animals if green plants were gone?

RELATED ACTIVITIES

People of the Forest, Values on the Line

Overview
Many people never take the time to explore the underlying assumptions they have concerning the environment. They often form an opinion without understanding all the sides of an issue. This activity is designed to get students thinking about their feelings and expressing their views. You may also wish to use this activity on a regular basis to give students a chance to evaluate their opinions as they learn more about environmental issues.

LEVELS
Grades 6-8

SUBJECTS
Social Studies, Science

CONCEPT
■ Cultural and societal perspectives influence the attitudes, beliefs, and biases of people toward the use of resources and environmental protection. (6.3)

SKILLS
Evaluating, Establishing Criteria, Discussing, Principle Forming.

OBJECTIVES
Students will ① examine statements regarding environmental issues and determine the degree to which they agree with them, ② share their views and opinions with others and gain awareness on the range of values related to environmental issues, and ③ identify the need for balanced information when forming opinions.

MATERIALS
Copies of page 60, and pens or pencils
Variation: Chalk, string, or masking tape

TIME CONSIDERATIONS
Preparation: 15 minutes
Activity: 50 minutes

Background
Students should learn to respect the processes of searching for truth. These processes involve identifying and assessing facts; distinguishing substantial from insubstantial evidence; separating the search for truth from the acceptance of propaganda; and examining in a constructive and unbiased manner controversial subjects such as politics, ethics, and religion.

To make decisions, students need to resolve ambiguities, balance the advantages and drawbacks of alternative solutions, and project the likely consequences of a particular choice. By combining such a decision-making procedure with pertinent scientific and technological information, students move toward achieving scientific literacy.

Getting Ready
Make a copy of page 60 for each student.

Doing the Activity
1. Pass out copies of "Value Statements" on page 60, and ask students to rank how much they agree or disagree with each statement. For each statement, they should circle a number, with "10" signifying strongest agreement and "1" for strongest disagreement.

2. Find an open space and have the students stand in line. Tell them that the line represents the scale of 1 to 10 that they used to rank the value statements (one end of the line being "strongly agree" and the other end "strongly disagree.")

3. Read aloud one of the value statements and have students reposition themselves in line according to how they ranked that statement. They will need to communicate with each other to make sure everyone is in the right place. Once they are settled, point out how the line reflects the range of opinions in the class.

4. Next, break the line at its midpoint, and have half the students stay in place while the other half moves down so that each student has a partner. (See diagram on page 59.)

5. Give each person in each pair one minute to explain to his or her partner the ranking he or she chose. Then give the other partner half a minute to paraphrase what the partner said. Have the partners switch roles, giving the other person a minute to explain his or her ranking and the partner half a minute to paraphrase.

6. Repeat Steps 3 through 5 for as many of the value statements as you like.

7. Discuss each value statement with the students, using the following questions as a guide:

■ What reasons did they have for the rankings they chose?

■ What reasons did their partner give for the rankings they chose?

■ Did any of them support their rankings using examples or specific information from real-life situations?

■ Did anyone feel like changing their ranking on a particular statement after pairing with someone else and hearing their opinion?

■ Did students feel they needed additional information to judge an issue? If so, what did they need?

■ Where do people's values come from? What kinds of experiences change or strengthen people's values?

VARIATION

Using chalk, string, or tape, create a scale of 1 to 10 on the floor or ground. Make the scale 10 yards or meters long with the numbers one yard or meter apart. For a particular value statement, have the students place themselves as close as possible to the ranking they chose. When everyone is settled, make a diagram on the chalkboard or easel paper of how students are distributed on the scale. Have them do the exercises in Steps 3 to 5, and allow them to change their ranking based on what they learn. Have students once again position themselves on the scale. Draw another diagram showing their revised positions. Compare the diagrams and discuss the changes with the entire group.

Original line:

Break the line here...

Have half the students move over...

...and pair with someone else.

END NOTES...

ASSESSMENT OPPORTUNITY

Have the students think about the following questions and write down their responses. Then have the group discuss each question.

■ What problems, if any, might there be in forming an opinion about an issue without knowing all the facts, related issues, and consequences of various actions?

■ How can people become better informed about all sides of an issue?

■ When people with different values end up on different sides of an issue, conflicts can arise. How can people on different sides of an issue reach a settlement?

RELATED ACTIVITIES

People of the Forest, A Look at Lifestyles

REFERENCES

Science Framework for California Public Schools— Kindergarten Through Grade Twelve. Sacramento, CA: California Department of Education, 1990

VALUE STATEMENTS

1 Natural resources should not be left untapped if using them could improve living conditions for a group of people.

1 2 3 4 5 6 7 8 9 10

2 It is important for people to preserve wilderness areas even if a vast majority of people will never visit them.

1 2 3 4 5 6 7 8 9 10

3 The world's natural resources exist for people to use. Preserving these resources as wilderness is a luxury we often cannot afford.

1 2 3 4 5 6 7 8 9 10

4 Environmental degradation is the biggest problem facing humanity today.

1 2 3 4 5 6 7 8 9 10

5 People will eventually develop new technologies to cope with environmental problems.

1 2 3 4 5 6 7 8 9 10

6 People have a responsibility to protect all life forms on Earth.

1 2 3 4 5 6 7 8 9 10

7 Protecting a country's natural resources and natural heritage is primarily the government's responsibility.

1 2 3 4 5 6 7 8 9 10

8 The government is doing a good job of protecting your country's environment.

1 2 3 4 5 6 7 8 9 10

9 Recycling is the most important thing people can do to help improve the environment.

1 2 3 4 5 6 7 8 9 10

10 People should be able to use their own land (i.e., farming, housing, logging, wildlife habitat) in whatever way they see fit.

1 2 3 4 5 6 7 8 9 10

11 All people have a legal right to clean air and water.

1 2 3 4 5 6 7 8 9 10

12 When a dilemma arises between protecting wildlife and protecting jobs for people, we should consider the needs of people first.

1 2 3 4 5 6 7 8 9 10

13 The fate of the human race is tied to the fate of other living things; if people are to survive, we must protect all species and their habitats.

1 2 3 4 5 6 7 8 9 10

14 Human overpopulation is the single greatest factor contributing to Earth's environmental problems.

1 2 3 4 5 6 7 8 9 10

15 The laws the federal government has passed to control pollution are sufficient to ensure safe air and water for future generations.

1 2 3 4 5 6 7 8 9 10

Overview

Preparing an environmental exchange box will give your students a chance to learn more about their own region and the things that are special about it. Then, when they receive an exchange box from another region, they can compare environments, people, and much more.

Getting Ready

Before doing this activity, you'll need to find another group to exchange boxes with—and we can help! Just fill out the form on page 62 and send it to us. We'll match you with another educator. Be sure to allow at least four weeks for a match.

Doing the Activity

1. Once you get the name and address of your "exchange partner," tell the students that they are going to exchange "environments" with students in another region. Explain that the students you're exchanging with will not know much about your local environment. It's the responsibility of your group to prepare items for the box that will teach your exchange partners about your region.

2. Brainstorm with the students a list of items to include in the box. Then have the students divide up the responsibilities of researching, collecting, and preparing materials for the box. The students might want to consider some of the following items for their box:

- Brief descriptions of your region written by the students

- A collage of pictures of local ecosystem types (beaches, marshes, deserts, urban environment, and so on)

- A book with drawings of some interesting local plants and animals or of many different plants and animals found in the region

- Photographs of your group and your school or meeting area

- A video of local ecosystems which also records the sounds of animals in those areas

- Stories written by the students about their favorite things to do or favorite places to go

- Samples of special regional foods such as maple syrup from Vermont, prickly pear jelly from Arizona, dates from California, or peaches from Georgia (see safety note on page 62)

- Descriptions and pictures of regional cultural events and celebrations

- Representative natural objects from your area such as tree leaves, nuts, and cones; pressed flowers; rocks; and shells (see safety note on page 62)

- Recordings of sounds of your area or oral reports on various topics prepared by the students

- A field guide, prepared by the students, to all the trees in the neighborhood (or to other natural things in your area)

- A description of local environmental issues and news articles on all sides of the issues

3. While you're waiting for the box from the other group to arrive, ask the students what they know or have heard about the region they're exchanging with. Can they name major cities, geographical landmarks, or other features of the region? What is the climate like there? Record the students' ideas on a chalkboard.

4. When the box arrives from your exchange group, open it with the students and examine its contents. Then have the students compare that region to their own. For example, how do the climates compare? What kinds of animals and plants (if any) live in both places? Are there differences in the ways people live?

LEVELS
Grades K-8

SUBJECTS
Science, Social Studies

CONCEPTS

- Biological diversity results from the interaction of living and nonliving environmental components such as air, water, climate, and geological features. (1.1)

- Forests, as well as other ecosystems, contain numerous habitats that support diverse populations of organisms. (1.2)

- Cultural and societal perspectives influence the attitudes, beliefs, and biases of people toward the use of resources and environmental protection. (6.3)

SKILLS
Observing, Formulating Questions, Representing, Comparing and Contrasting

OBJECTIVES
Students will ① discover some of the resources, products, and other characteristics of their region and ways that people in their region are trying to improve the environment and ② describe similarities and differences between their region and another region with respect to these characteristics.

MATERIALS
Books about the natural history of your region; markers, crayons, drawing paper, and other art supplies.

TIME CONSIDERATIONS
Preparation: One hour
Activity: Two 50-minute periods

5. As a wrap-up, have the students use the exchange box to create a representation of what they liked most about the other area or what they imagine it would be like to live there. For example, students could draw pictures that depict their favorite item from the box or that show a scene in the other region. Or they could write down their impressions of items from the box in creative ways. For example, they could write stories about their imaginary adventures in their partner's region.

Enrichment

1. The concept of conservation can be discussed using the exchange box your class made. What actions could be taken to conserve the resources used to make the products that they put in their exchange box?

2. Contact your local newspaper for coverage of the opening of your exchange box. Students could write a press release (see "Publicize It!" on page 209).

SAFETY NOTE—Many states have laws regulating the types of plant and animal materials that can cross their borders. Be sure to check with the state or county department of agriculture or a local office of the agricultural extension service to find out about restrictions in your exchange partner's state before you send any plant or animal materials.

ASSESSMENT OPPORTUNITY

1. Upon completing a successful exchange, help your students assess how well it went. How helpful were the information and artifacts included in the ex-change box that they received? How well did the box represent the ecological or cultural environment of your partner's region? How did their exchange box differ from yours? How was it worse? How was it better? How could either group have done things differently?

2. Have all students in your class write a short thank-you note to the exchange class, describing their impression of the box and what they liked best about it. Have the class formulate a list of questions they have about items in the box they received or a list of general questions about the partner's region. Perhaps they would like more information or clarity on certain items. They can send the letters and questions to their partner class and wait for a reply.

RELATED ACTIVITIES

Habitat Pen Pals, Planet of Plenty

VARIATION

Environmental Exchange Box on the Internet

Try using our "on-line" environmental exchange box as an alternative to sharing information with another school through the mail. Three times a year, the PLT web site will highlight a different school and their environmental exchange box. This on-line exchange box will feature the type of environment, wildlife, climate, and culture of a school's region. You and your class can use this information to compare with that of your own region and environment. This site will also allow you to share information about your environment and ask questions to the on-line exchange class through an on-line forum. Visit our web site at www.plt.org to learn more about how you can participate in PLT's on-line environmental exchange box activity.

Exchange Box Form

Name

School

School Address

City/State/Zip

Telephone Number (work and home)

Grade Level/Age of Students

Preferred U.S. state, territory, or region with which you would like to exchange:

Return this form by mail or fax to:
Project Learning Tree
American Forest Foundation
1111 19th Street, NW, Suite 780
Washington, DC 20036
FAX 202-463-2461

Interrelationships

Overview
This activity will encourage students' awareness of individual trees over time, as well as incorporate various other subjects. By adopting individual trees, students will gain greater awareness and appreciation of their local environments.

Background
See Backgrounds for "Tree Factory" on page 223 and "Plant a Tree" on page 95.

Getting Ready
Have students make "Adopt a Tree" notebooks for recording information. Students can fold a sheet of construction paper in half, insert blank pages, and staple the book along the folded edge. They can draw or paste a photo of their adopted trees on the cover. Make copies of student page 68 for each student.

Doing the Activity
1. Ask students to name something that is their very own or is special to them in some way. For example, someone might mention a pet. Someone else might mention a present received from a relative or close friend, and so on.

2. Explain that each person will choose his or her very own special tree to adopt. With **younger students**, you can have the whole group adopt a particular tree. Where there's a shortage of trees, you might have teams adopt trees. Students will observe their trees throughout the school year, or for however long you decide to conduct the activity. How they select their tree is up to them. Some students may choose the tallest or fullest tree. Others may choose the smallest, "cutest" tree. Some may pick a seemingly average-looking tree, only to discover that there's more to it than meets the eye. No matter which tree they pick, students should be able to say why they chose it. You might have students tie a colored piece of yarn around their tree to identify it.

3. Provide each student with a small notebook, and explain that students should use their notebooks to record observations and answer questions about their trees. You can also have them make and decorate their own notebooks.

4. Take students outside and let each choose a tree. If you're working with **older students**, or if there aren't trees near your school, you might have students choose trees near their yard or in their neighborhood. Students could briefly visit their trees before or after school.

5. Have students write the answers to the questions on the student page in their "Adopt a Tree" notebooks. For **younger students**, you will need to read and explain the questions to them.

6. You might give **younger students** "Adopt a Tree" certificates (page 69) to fill out after they've chosen their trees.

7. Have students visit their trees on a regular basis. Each time they visit, have

LEVELS
Activity: Grades 3-8
Variation 1: Grades PreK-1
Variation 2: Grades K-4

SUBJECTS
Science, Math, Language Arts, Visual Arts, Social Studies

CONCEPTS
- Organisms are interdependent; they all depend on nonliving components of the Earth. (4.1)
- While every organism goes through a life cycle of growth, maturity, decline, and death, its role in the ecosystem also changes. (13.3)

SKILLS
Observing, Concept Forming, Reasoning, Organizing Information

OBJECTIVES
Students will ① describe a chosen tree using personal observation and investigation, and organize information about the tree, ② identify relationships between their tree and other organisms, and ③ put together a book or portfolio about their tree.

MATERIALS
Activity: notebooks, pencils, drawing paper, crayons or markers, camera, copies of page 68, (optional), student page 69

TIME CONSIDERATIONS
Preparation: 15 minutes

Activity: 50 minutes (longer projects can be done throughout the year)

them write a few sentences or make sketches in their notebooks describing any changes they notice (broken branches, new leaves); animal or human activity taking place on or near the tree (nest, carved initials); or any other observations. You might make up additional questions as different seasons come and go. What color do the leaves become in the fall? When does the tree bloom in the spring? Have students guess the causes of these changes and predict future changes, or have them take photographs of their tree.

VARIATION 1—GROWING UP TOGETHER

1. Take the class outside to a grove of trees. Give students a few minutes to use their senses of smell, touch, hearing, and seeing to get acquainted with the area. Choose a particular tree to observe in different ways. For example, how does the tree look when you are sitting? When you are lying on your side? When you are lying on your back?

2. Ask students to volunteer to describe the tree, using their senses. Summarize each student's description by making comparative statements. You may structure students' comments by asking individuals to complete this sentence: "The tree is _____."

3. Ask students whether they think the tree is alive. Do not discount their answers but ask students how they know whether the tree is alive or not. (Trees need food and water to grow, just like people.)

4. Use these discussion questions: How are all the trees here alike? How are they different? Are they all alive? Are other plants alive in the area? What are the benefits these trees provide for them and the environment?

VARIATION 2—ADOPT AN OBJECT

Rather than limiting this activity to trees, allow students to adopt any special object (house plant, pet, statue, billboard, a store window) from their indoor or outdoor environments. Adapt the "Adopt a Tree" student page 68 so that it encompasses non-tree and human-made items. Include questions that relate the object to people. How did it get there? How does it benefit society? What is its special meaning to you?

Enrichment

1. Have students work in pairs to measure the height, circumference, and crown of their trees. (See "How Big Is Your Tree?" on page 239 for complete directions.) Afterward, have each pair use those measurements to design several math problems. Have the pairs share their math problems with the rest of the group.

2. Have students create a picture of a tree with flip-up windows portraying the life on their tree, in their tree, and among the tree's roots. (See the diagram on page 67.)

3. Raise money to buy a class tree. Take students to a nursery to pick out the tree; then hold a tree-planting ceremony. (See "Plant a Tree" on page 95 for complete directions.)

4. Create a "Whole Language Tree." Use a large, bare tree, painted or modeled in the classroom, as a focal point for various curriculum topics. Through the year, have students show how the tree is constantly changing: from green leaves and apples to changing colors and falling leaves; and from winter skeletons to bursting buds, flowers, and bees. You can also use the tree to demonstrate ideas associated with plants, wildlife, holidays, and social and environmental issues.

END NOTES...

ASSESSMENT OPPORTUNITY

1. Over short or extended periods, younger students can create books or portfolios about their adopted trees. On the first book page, each student can glue a picture of himself or herself standing next to the adopted tree. Students' books can also include drawings, poems, stories, pressed leaves, rubbings, flowers, or twigs.
2. Older students can write an essay about life from their tree's perspective. For example, a student who adopts a very old tree might write a story in which the tree "talks" about the days when small farms dotted the landscape or when horses and buggies crowded city streets. The tree could also talk about how it relates to the plants, animals, and people around it, and what problems it has.

RELATED ACTIVITIES

Trees as Habitats, Plant a Tree, We All Need Trees, Trees for Many Reasons, Tree Lifecycles, Trees in Trouble, Tree Cookies, Signs of Fall, How Big Is Your Tree?

DIAGRAM OF
FLIP–UP WINDOWS

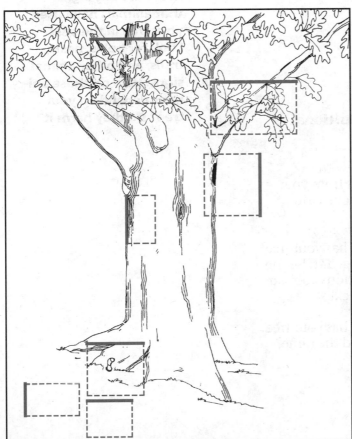

ADOPT A TREE QUESTIONS

On Your First Visit

Where is your tree? Draw a map to show its location.

Is your tree alive? How can you tell? Is it healthy? In what ways are people helping or hurting it?

Draw a picture of your tree from various perspectives: from a distance, from a high place, or from lying underneath looking up.

Write a paragraph or poem describing your tree.

Draw a picture of a leaf from your tree. How does the leaf smell? How does it feel?

Do you know what kind of tree you have adopted? Does your tree have any fruits, nuts, or seeds that help identify it? Use a field guide to look up your tree.

Make a rubbing of your tree's bark. How does the bark feel? How does it smell?

Are any animals on or near your tree? Don't forget to look for insects, spiders, and other small animals.

Are there any signs that animals have used your tree in the past? Look for holes, nests, trails, and other animal signs. How do those animals depend on your tree? Do they harm it?

On Additional Visits

1 Review the notes from your previous visit.

2 How has your tree changed? (Use the questions above as a checklist.)

3 How has your tree stayed the same?

OFFICIAL PLT
Adopt a Tree Certificate

_____

Official Tree Name

_____

Nickname

_____

Birthplace

_____

Circumference   **Height**   **Age**

_____

Identifying Characteristics

_____

Adopted By   **Date**

One Especially Interesting Thing About My Tree Is

_____

_____

_____

_____

Place Leaf Rubbing in the Space Above

Overview

From their leafy branches to their tangled roots, trees provide a habitat for a host of plants and animals. In this activity, your students will discover how plants and animals depend on trees in many ways.

LEVELS
Activity: Grades 3-8
Variation 1: Grades PreK-2
Variation 2: Grades 3-8

SUBJECTS
Science, Math, Social Studies, Visual Arts

CONCEPTS
■ Biological diversity results from the interaction of living and nonliving environmental components such as air, water, climate, and geological features. (1.1)

■ Forests, as well as other ecosystems, contain numerous habitats that support diverse populations of organisms. (1.2)

■ Organisms are interdependent; they all depend on nonliving components of the Earth. (4.1)

SKILLS
Observing, Organizing Information, Inferring, Identifying Relationships and Patterns, Predicting

OBJECTIVES
Students will ① take inventory of the plants and animals that live on, in, and around trees; ② identify ways those animals and plants depend on trees for survival and, in turn, influence the trees; and ③ for Variation 2; investigate how buildings provide a habitat for plants, animals, and people.

MATERIALS
Paper and pencil; clipboards or cardboard with paper clips (optional: field guides for trees, shrubs, insects, or birds; hand lenses; bug boxes; binoculars)
Variation 1: empty paper towel or toilet paper rolls for each student

TIME CONSIDERATIONS
Preparation: 15 minutes

Activity: 50 minutes

Background

A *habitat* is the place where a plant or animal gets all the things it needs to survive, such as food, water, shelter, and space for having and raising offspring. A habitat may be 100 square miles (259 km^2) of grassland for a lion or a single plant for an insect. A tree may serve as part of an organism's habitat, or it may be the organism's entire habitat. For example, an oak tree may provide food for squirrels and nest sites for crows. But lichens and moss get everything they need from growing right on the tree.

Getting Ready

Before this activity, find an area with several trees (any size) or shrubs that the students can examine. If the students have already adopted trees, have them use their trees for this activity. (See "Adopt a Tree" on page 65. If your activity area lacks trees or shrubs, see Variation 2 on page 71.)

Doing the Activity

1. Show the students a picture of a tree, and ask them to name some plants and animals that might depend on the tree. List their answers on the chalkboard.

2. Tell the students that they are going to study a tree to find out which plants and animals depend on it or use it in some way. Explain that they should try to determine which animals (including humans) only visit the tree, and which plants or animals actually live on it or in it. They should watch for clues and signs such as chewed leaves, holes in the bark, or carved initials. They should be sure to record where on the tree they find either living things or signs of life.

3. Pass out paper, pencils, clipboards, and hand lenses or bug boxes. Take the students outside and have them examine a tree. Students can work individually or in teams. Encourage them to draw pictures of all of the plants and animals they find, especially those they cannot identify. You may want to have field guides on hand to help them identify the organisms they find. You may also want to give them binoculars so they can get a closer look at life in the treetops.

4. Back in the classroom, have students organize their collected information into a booklet or portfolio, or in any other style. You might suggest organizing the data by plants, insects, or birds; by where on the tree the organism is found (roots, trunk, or leaves); by whether it lives on the tree or just visits; or by any other means. Have students identify how each plant and animal they observed in Step 3 benefits from the tree, and how it affects the tree. They may need to make more observations of their tree or collect more research about the plants and animals they observed. Encourage students to set up charts, tables, or graphs that illustrate their findings.

5. Have students or teams present their data to the rest of the group. You can record each group's data on the chalkboard and, set up tables or graphs that summarize the entire group's findings afterward. Discuss these questions with the students:

■ What did you find on the tree's trunk?

■ What did you see in the tree's branches?

■ How might the tree be affected by the plants and animals that live on it? Which of these organisms seemed to harm the tree? Why do you think so? Do any of the plants and animals you observed seem to benefit the tree? In what ways?

VARIATION 1—YOUNGER STUDENTS

1. Collect fallen leaves, twigs, bark, fruit, or nuts that show signs of plant or animal life. (Signs may be chewed holes, tunnels, scrapings, egg cases, webs, galls, moss, lichen, or fungus.) Show these to the students in the classroom. Discuss each sign with the students. Tell them that these examples show how animals and other plants depend on trees. In other words, trees provide a habitat for these plants and animals.

2. Have students make their own telescopes out of toilet paper or paper towel tubes decorated with tissue paper, paint, and glitter so they can study tree habitats. You might also provide hand lenses for students to use.

3. Lead students to a tree and have them describe what they see living on its trunk and branches with their hand lenses or telescopes. Give them plenty of time to make their observations. Ask these questions:

- Can you spot bird nests, chewed leaves, or other animal signs?

- Do you see any animals climbing around or in the tree, or flying to and from it?

- Do you see any other plants growing on the tree?

4. Have students look on the ground around the tree for fallen leaves, twigs, bark, seeds, fruits, or nuts that might also show signs of animal or plant life. Did students find any of the examples that you showed them earlier?

VARIATION 2—URBAN ENVIRONMENTS

If you do not have access to trees or shrubs, use buildings instead. Buildings are the predominant structures of an urban environment, and they provide a habitat for many plants and animals (especially people).

1. Have students consider buildings they are familiar with, such as houses or apartment buildings, a parent's office building, the school building, or a community center. Ask them to think of all the plants that grow on the inside (house plants, potted trees, mold, mildew) or the outside (moss, grass, lichens) of such buildings. Ask them to name all the animals that make their homes on the inside (people, cats, dogs, goldfish, cockroaches, mice, houseflies) or outside (birds, ants, bees) of those buildings. Have them consider how all those living things depend on the building and how those things, in turn, affect both the buildings and the people living in them.

2. Have the students work individually or in teams to investigate the plant and animal life inside and outside a building habitat (school, nature center, or home). They should consider what environmental conditions in the building attract and support those organisms.

3. Ask students to organize and present their findings as described in Steps 3 and 4 in the main activity. (Adapt the questions to suit building habitats.)

Enrichment

1. Have students examine their trees or buildings at other times during the year. Then ask them to compare their findings from season to season.

2. Have them draw pictures depicting ways that a tree provides a habitat for animals and other plants, or have the entire group work together on a "Tree Habitat" mural.

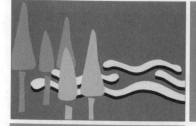

Overview
It's amazing how many things live in and on rotting logs. In this activity, your students will become familiar with some of those organisms. They'll gain an understanding of how *decomposition* takes place. And they'll gain a better appreciation for *microhabitats* and *communities*.

LEVELS
Grades 4-8

SUBJECTS
Science, Visual Arts

CONCEPTS
- Biological diversity results from the interaction of living and non-living environmental components such as air, water, climate, and geological features. (1.1)
- Forests, as well as other ecosystems, contain numerous habitats that support diverse populations of organisms. (1.2)
- Organisms are interdependent; they all depend on nonliving components of the Earth. (4.1)

SKILLS
Observing, Representing, Organizing Information, Analyzing

OBJECTIVES
Students will ① identify some of the organisms that live in, on, and under fallen logs and explain how those organisms depend on the dead wood for survival, and ② describe the process of decomposition.

MATERIALS
containers with lids (plastic tubs, glass jars, or plastic baggies); paper and pencils; clipboards or sheets of cardboard with paper clips (optional: field guides on insects, spiders, or nonflowering plants; hand lenses and bug boxes)

TIME CONSIDERATIONS
Preparation: 15 minutes
Activity: 50 minutes

Background
Throughout their lives, trees collect *nutrients* from the environment and use them to build new bark, wood, branches, leaves, and so on. When a tree dies, its nutrients are recycled back into the environment through *decomposition.* Animals, such as bark beetles, move into trees and start the process of decomposition even before a tree has died. These creatures may hasten the death of the tree. Wood-eating insects, as well as *fungi* and *bacteria*, invade a dead or dying tree, paving the way for other invaders. Here's a look at some common things your students may find on, in, and around dead wood.

Things Growing on Dead Wood
Any decaying wood is sure to have fungi, moss, lichens, and other plants growing on it. Wildflower, tree, and other plant seeds that land on a soft, decomposed log may also sprout and grow. Plants and fungi absorb nutrients from the decaying wood, and as they grow, they penetrate the wood and break it apart. Lichens, as they grow, release a weak acid that breaks down the wood. Moss keeps the log moist, making it a suitable place for other plants and animals to live.

Wood Munchers
Termites, sowbugs, carpenter ants, and wood roaches are all examples of creatures that eat or tunnel through wood. Many of those animals also eat other kinds of vegetable matter, such as dead leaves. As all of them chew their way through the wood, they help break down the log.

Bark beetles eat through the living tissue just under the tree's bark. Evidence of their work is easy to find on most dead logs. The tunnels of those tiny insects create intricate patterns in the wood underneath the bark.

Predators on the Prowl
Some animals, such as centipedes and spiders, feed on the sowbugs, millipedes, and other *scavengers* that feed on the decaying log. The predators, and then the scavengers in turn, become meals for birds, skunks, and other animals that tear into a log to find food.

Hideouts and Nurseries
Many creatures depend on decaying logs as places to hide from predators or to find shelter from the elements. Patent leather beetles, click beetles, and other animals may spend the winter inside a rotting log. Some beetles, wasps, slugs, and other animals lay their eggs in decomposing wood. Salamanders may wait in the relative coolness and dampness of a fallen log during the day and then hunt for food at night. As these animals burrow into the log, they also help to break it down.

Getting Ready
Before doing this activity, find a place that has several dead logs, large fallen limbs, decomposing tree stumps, or rotting pieces of lumber that are fairly close together. Optimally, the logs (or pieces) should be at least eight inches (20 cm) across and should be in different stages of decomposition. Since these materials are not readily available on most school grounds, you may want to use this activity during a trip to a park or nature center.

Doing the Activity
1. Begin by asking the students why forests aren't piled high with fallen trees, branches, and leaves. What happens to trees after they die? Tell the students that they're going to examine dead logs to find answers to those questions.

2. Divide the group into teams of three or four, and explain that the teams will each examine a rotting log. Team members will need to keep track of each different kind of plant or animal found, where it was found, what it looked like, and what it was doing. Each team should develop a data sheet to record this information. Here are some questions students should try to answer during their investigation:

- Is there bark on the log? What is its condition?

- What kinds of plants are growing on the log? (Examples are young trees, young shrubs, wildflowers, mosses, fungi, slime molds, and lichens.)

- What kinds of animals are on the bark? Under the bark? Inside the log? Under the log?

- What do the animals you found appear to be doing? What would you predict each one eats? What makes you think so?

- What evidence of animal activity do you see on or around the log? (Examples are insect holes, spider webs, woodpecker holes, animal dens, animal tracks, piles of sawdust, or patterns in the wood under the bark.)

- How might the tree have died? What evidence supports your ideas?

- Has the tree been dead a long time or a fairly short time? What makes you think so?

NOTE—If you're working with younger students, you might want to create a worksheet for them to use.

3. Take students to the area you picked in Getting Ready, and pass out materials. Then have each team choose a log to study.

NOTE—If there aren't enough logs available, have the teams double up on the same log. Explain that students should disturb their log as little as possible while they examine it. They should put any creatures they find into their containers only briefly for examination. Students must return the creatures to the places where they were found as quickly as possible. If students can't identify animals or plants in the field, they can make sketches to take back to school. They should make sure the log is in its original position when they finish. You may also want to establish rules such as "Don't stick your fingers into holes" and "Don't go beyond (a certain point)."

4. When they've finished examining their logs, have your students examine areas around each log. They might look in leaf litter, under rocks, around bases of trees, and so on. Have them record similarities and differences between these areas and the log. They should note which of the plants and animals that they found around their log also live in these areas.

5. Back inside, have the students use their notes and sketches to identify the creatures they were unable to identify in the field. Then have them present their findings to the rest of the group.

6. Have students work in their teams to answer the following questions. Afterward, discuss the answers as a group.

■ What similarities and differences were there between each of the logs? What might explain the differences?

■ Which animals and plants were found both on the log and in nearby areas, such as leaf litter? What do those areas and the log have in common?

■ How do the animals you found in the log interact with it? (The log provides habitat—shelter, food, a place to raise young, and space to live.)

■ Why is it important that logs like the one you studied decompose? (Decomposition recycles the nutrients stored in the log.)

■ How does the forest ecosystem benefit from a fallen log? (The log provides a habitat for plants and animals that are, in turn, food for other creatures. As animals and plants break down the log, its stored nutrients become available for other plants and animals.)

When access to parks or green spaces is difficult, you may study decomposers in other areas. In a city, any place where discarded items and other solid waste are lying on soil will offer a home to decomposers. You might find such (undesirable) dumping grounds on the sides and in back of buildings, roadsides, or vacant lots.

After studying the decomposers that live under garbage and discussing interrelationships between the decomposers, the garbage, and the urban environment, your students might decide that it would be best for the urban environment if people properly dispose of and recycle garbage, and refurbish the area. This cleanup could become a class action project.

Enrichment

1. Have students read the story "In the Forest of S.T. Shrew" on pages 22-23. Afterward, ask them to name all the things Jackie saw on her trip through the rotten log. List the items on a chalkboard. Put a checkmark next to the things your students also saw during their investigation of a rotten log.

2. If a field trip to a park or nature center is not feasible, you may want to get permission to put some logs on the school grounds. Place the logs on the ground, preferably in a moist shaded area, a week or two before you plan to use them to allow animals and other decomposers to become established on the logs. This log station can be monitored over time to see how the decomposition process progresses. The different organisms found at each stage can be recorded and compared to those found in other stages.

END NOTES...

ASSESSMENT OPPORTUNITY
To evaluate your students' understanding, tell them that a tree in the forest has just blown over during a terrible storm. Have them draw a series of pictures that shows what will happen to that tree over many years. In their finished pictures, look for representations of the tree with ① little living on it, ② many things growing on it or living in it, so less and less of the tree shows, and ③ as a final picture, only a small hump of material or a young tree growing where the decomposing log once was.

RELATED ACTIVITIES
Nature's Recyclers, The Forest of S.T. Shrew

REFERENCE
Lavies, Bianca. *Compost Critters*. New York, NY: Duttons Children's Books, 1993

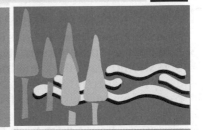

Overview
It's amazing how many organisms live off dead organic material and recycle those materials back into life. In this activity, your students will investigate the habits of one of these creatures. They will gain an understanding of how decomposition works and an appreciation for some of nature's less-heralded creatures.

Background
Turn over a rock or log, or lift up the leaf litter in a forest. Chances are you'll see small, gray, armored animals scurrying out of sight. These sowbugs (*Oniscus asellus*) and pill bugs (*Armadillidium vulgare*) are not "bugs" at all, or even insects. These relatives of crabs and lobsters are crustaceans, and they feed on dead plant material. By eating, digesting, and then excreting dead plant material, these little animals recycle nutrients back into the soil where they are reused by live plants.

Though sowbugs and pill bugs look almost alike, there's one very easy way to tell the difference between them: pill bugs can roll into a ball to protect themselves, but sowbugs cannot.

Both sowbugs and pill bugs are found in the forest as well as in the urban environment (gardens, roadside vegetation, garbage, wood piles, parks).

Getting Ready
Before doing this activity, collect sowbugs from under rocks, logs, leaf litter, and other debris. You will need at least eight bugs per team of students. Keep them in a large container with moist (not wet!) leaves until you're ready to use them. Also gather plastic containers or bags. You will need one container per team.

NOTE—Sowbugs and pill bugs cannot live indoors for a long time. You should collect them, have students make their observations, and then return the animals outdoors within a week.

Doing the Activity
1. Have the students pretend that they are teams of scientists who have been asked to solve a mystery. Someone has found a few strange-looking creatures and wants the scientists to identify what the animals eat. Give each team a couple of the sowbugs you collected earlier so students can look at them.

Ask students if they have ever seen the creatures, and, if so, what they know about the animals.

2. Tell students that the person who collected the animals found them under moist leaves around a house and under several large rocks in the back yard. Then have students brainstorm a list of foods the animals might eat, and write the foods on the chalkboard.

3. Have each team pick one of the foods listed in Step 2 to use in an investigation. If students came up with many possibilities in Step 2, they should form smaller groups, or each group should investigate two foods. If they came up with only a few possibilities, they should form larger groups, or more than one group could investigate a potential food source. Tell students that each team should set up a study container and record observations.

4. Give one container to each team. Have students collect the foods (leaves, dirt, vegetables, wood, grass, and so on) that they are going to investigate. Tell them to make sure their samples are moist, but not soaking wet. Have them label each container with the names of group members, the date, and the type of food inside. Then give approximately eight sowbugs to each team to put in its container. Place the containers in a cool place away from direct sunlight.

5. After the students have set up their containers, have them observe the creatures inside and record how they look and what they do. Teams should also record the type of food in the container, how much was put in, and what it looks like.

6. Have students observe their sowbugs and food several times over the next few days and write down what they see. As in Step 5, they should record what the creatures look like, what they're

LEVELS
Grades 1-6

SUBJECTS
Science, Language Arts

CONCEPTS
■ Biological diversity results from the interaction of living and nonliving environmental components such as air, water, climate, and geological features. (1.1)

■ Forests, as well as other ecosystems, contain numerous habitats that support diverse populations of organisms. (1.2)

■ Organisms are interdependent; they all depend on nonliving components of the Earth. (4.1)

■ In biological systems, energy flows and materials continually cycle in predictable and measurable patterns. (7.1)

SKILLS
Observing, Organizing Information, Identifying Relationships and Patterns, Analyzing, Inferring

OBJECTIVES
Students will ① understand and describe the process of decomposition, ② explain the function of scavengers and decomposers, and ③ experiment with sowbugs to determine what they eat and what their role is in the ecosystem.

MATERIALS
Activity: One plastic container with lid (or plastic wrap) or plastic bag per student or team, leaf litter and other organic material, eight sowbugs or pill bugs per student or team
NOTE: In temperate climates, sowbugs will be more difficult to find during the winter months. Schedule this activity for fall or spring.
Variation: An aquarium or large water-tight container, various types of organic wastes, soil (not potting soil), thermometer, trowel or large spoon, one to two dozen earthworms, rubber gloves

TIME CONSIDERATIONS
Preparation: Several hours

Activity: Two 50-minute periods over the course of a week

doing, what the food in the container looks like, and how much is left. After making their observations, team members should leave the container open for a while to keep it from becoming too moist, thereby making the food moldy. If the food does appear to be getting moldy, exchange it for fresh food. (You might also use the opportunity to discuss what mold is and its function as a decomposer.) If the container seems dry, students should sprinkle a little water over the food.

7. Have the teams organize and present their observations (data) to the rest of the group. After each team answers the following questions, discuss the answers with the entire group:

- What types of food did the sowbugs eat?

- Did they have a favorite food?

- Based on your experiments, what other foods do you think sowbugs eat in the "wild"? (Answers will depend on what foods students studied during the activity, but should include similar plant materials.)

- How might sowbugs be important to a forest ecosystem? (By eating dead leaves and plants, scavengers and decomposers such as sowbugs keep dead material from piling up on the forest floor. They recycle nutrients back into the soil, making them available for plants. Sowbugs are also eaten by other animals.)

- Sowbugs and other scavengers are often called the "garbage collectors" of nature. How does that name apply to them? Is it accurate? Explain your answer.

VARIATION

If you cannot find an adequate number of sowbugs, try this variation using earthworms. Earthworms are easy to find in urban soils. They are also available at many stores that sell fishing or pet supplies.

Food scraps, leaves, grass clippings, and other biodegradable organic wastes can be recycled by earthworms and other organisms that live in the soil. For this decomposition to occur, several components must be present: soil (including microorganisms), organic wastes, nitrogen, worms, water, air, time, heat, and mass. When we compost certain wastes, we create optimal conditions for decomposition to occur in a controlled setting.

1. Your group should assemble various organic wastes in the aquarium, including leaves, wood, vegetable scraps, and weeds. (Avoid meat scraps, dairy products, fats, and oils.) Chop wastes into small pieces. Leave some large pieces of the same materials so you can compare the rates of decomposition between large and small items. What would the difference be in the rates of decomposition?

2. Alternate layers of the materials as follows (amounts are approximate): one inch (2.5 cm) of soil, two inches (5.1 cm) of organic waste (add equal amounts of each type and keep a record of what you put in), a sprinkle of green grass clippings, and a sprinkle of water. Repeat.

3. Cover with one inch (2.5 cm) of soil. Water the pile enough to make it moist but not soggy. It should feel like a damp sponge.

4. Add the earthworms.

5. Place your mini-compost pile so that it will be at room temperature (not in the direct sun). Gently mix the compost once a week to aerate it.

6. Once a week, have a student with rubber gloves examine the compost pile to see the status of the organic material you put in. Have your class record the condition and approximate amounts of each type of organic waste. Continue the experiment until all of the organic matter has turned into rich soil. Draw conclusions about the habits of earthworms and their role in the ecosystem.

7. Use the rich soil that the worms made to grow beautiful plants in your classroom.

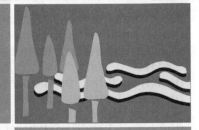

Overview
Camouflage is an important survival strategy in the animal kingdom. In this activity, students will discover the value of protective coloration as they pretend to be birds in search of colored worms or bugs.

Background
Many animals are "color coordinated" with their surroundings. For example, snowshoe hares and grouse-like birds named ptarmigans *(TAR-mee-guns)* change from brown in summer to white in winter. A box turtle's dappled shell and a fawn's white spots mimic blotches of sunlight on the forest floor. And the two-toned appearance of many fish, dark on top and light on bottom, helps them match differing levels of light in the water. When viewed from below, a fish's light-colored belly blends in with the sky. When viewed from above, the darker top blends in with the waters underneath. Any coloration, body shape, or behavior that helps an animal hide is called *camouflage*.

Blending in with the environment is a great way to avoid being eaten, but it's not an adaptation limited to prey animals. Many predators are also camouflaged: the better to avoid being spotted by a potential meal. For example, a lion's tawny coat matches the grasses of the African savanna and the leopard's spots match the patchy sunlight of the African forest.

Getting Ready
1. Assemble 60 small, colored objects consisting of equal amounts of at least three colors. Try to use easily biodegradable objects in outdoor settings (see Materials). You'll need 20 each of three colors, 15 each of four colors, 12 each of five colors, and so forth. If you use food items, remind students not to eat them. Those items represent "worms" or "bugs."

2. To play the game, find one or more large, open areas (indoors or outdoors) where you can scatter the worms or bugs.

3. Make sure you have at least one color that matches the playing surface (e.g., gray for asphalt, green for grass).

4. Scatter the worms or bugs (when students aren't looking) throughout the area.

Doing the Activity
1. Ask the class to think about advantages bullfrogs have because they're green and polar bears have because they're white. Introduce the concept of camouflage and ask if they've heard of it. Have them give examples of how camouflage helps both predators and prey.

2. Divide the group into two to four teams with the same number of students in each team. Take everyone outside to the area where the worms or bugs are hidden. Tell students that various types of tasty animals are scattered here and that the students are hungry birds. Describe to them what the worms or bugs look like. Ask them to predict what color worm or bug might have the best camouflage for this environment.

LEVELS
Grades K-6

SUBJECTS
Science, Math, Physical Education

CONCEPTS
■ Organisms are interdependent; they all depend on nonliving components of the Earth. (4.1)

■ Altering the environment affects all life forms—including humans—and the interrelationships that link them. (4.2)

■ Organisms adapt to changes in the environment according to the genetic and behavioral capacity of their species. (4.3)

SKILLS
Determining Causes and Effects, Analyzing, Identifying Relationships and Patterns, Predicting

OBJECTIVES
Students will ① simulate how predators use their vision to find prey, ② describe some different ways animals use camouflage for survival, and ③ invent a fictional animal that is camouflaged for its particular environment.

MATERIALS
60 small objects in assorted colors (e.g., pipe cleaner segments, colored pieces of yarn, paper clips, paper shapes, or punched holes) to represent the "worms" or "bugs" (for outdoor use, we recommend easily biodegradable items such as colored pasta, beans, popcorn, or dog treats); a large piece of butcher or white poster paper; crayons or markers; paper; pencils or pens; pictures of camouflaged animals

TIME CONSIDERATIONS
Preparation: 30 minutes
Activity: 50 minutes

3. Arrange the teams in relay race lines. Explain that the object of the race is to be the first team to get every bird fed. When you say, "Go," the first bird in each line should "fly" over the prescribed area and pick up the first worm or bug he or she sees. Each bird flies immediately back to the line and tags the next bird, who does the same thing. When the last bird returns, everyone on the team should sit down. The first team to be seated wins.

4. When all teams have completed the relay, spread a large piece of paper (at least poster size) on the ground. Make a chart with as many columns as there are students on each team. Each column will represent the student's position in line. The students should each place their worm or bug in the column that corresponds with their position in line.

5. Have students record which color worms or bugs were found in each round. Is there any pattern to the order in which the worms or bugs were found? Does this pattern have any significance?

6. Have students take back their worm or bug. Turn the paper over and make columns that correspond to the different colors. Have students place their worms or bugs in the appropriate color column. Have each student record the number of each color. What color was easiest to find? What color was hardest to find? What type of worm or bug has the best camouflage for this environment and why?

7. Have the teams line up again and repeat the game to find the remaining worms or bugs. Afterward, record the results in the same two ways as before, and discuss the results.

8. Before leaving the game area, make sure students have recovered all of the worms or bugs.

9. Back inside, have students help you record the data from both rounds in tables drawn on the chalkboard. Older students can create bar graphs to represent the information. Help students interpret the graphs.

Enrichment

1. Repeat this activity in a different environment that has predominantly different colors. If your first game was on grass, try asphalt, or vice versa. Discuss how the results differed and give reasons.

2. Have students use assorted art supplies to create make-believe "camouflaged" creatures. Have students suggest the advantages of their creature's camouflage and the environment that suits it best.

END NOTES...

ASSESSMENT OPPORTUNITY
To assess how well students understand the concept of camouflage, ask them to give examples of animals from around the world that depend on camouflage. For each example, they should explain how and why the animal benefits from it. They can also look through old nature magazines to find pictures of animals (including people) that demonstrate the use of camouflage. They can use these pictures to make a bulletin board display about camouflage.

RELATED ACTIVITIES
Charting Diversity, Habitat Pen Pals, Picture This!, Can It Be Real?

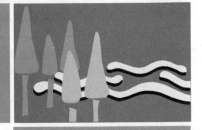

Overview
Organisms in an ecosystem depend on each other for food. But they may also depend on each other for protection, transportation, or shelter. A close, long-term relationship between two organisms is called *symbiosis* (sihm-bee-OH-sihs). In this activity, students will learn about several kinds of symbiosis.

Background
Many plants and animals have evolved *symbiotic* relationships. Sometimes these relationships are *mutualistic* (both species benefit). For example, many birds, insects, and bats get food by drinking nectar from flowers and, in the process, pollinate the flowers. Some fish get their meals by cleaning parasites from other fish. Many birds and mammals disperse plant seeds by eating the plant's fruit and excreting the seeds later.

Some relationships are defined as *commensal* (kuh-MEN-suhl) (one partner benefits, while the other is seemingly unaffected). For example, some frogs in rainforests carry their young to water-filled plants named bromeliads (bro-MEE-lee-ads) that grow attached to the trunks and branches of trees. The tadpoles get a safe place to develop but the bromeliad doesn't seem to be harmed by this use. Some moths feed on the tears of cattle and other animals without affecting them.

In *parasitic* relationships, one partner benefits but the other is negatively affected. For example, fleas and ticks suck blood from their hosts, but the hosts suffer itching and may also contract diseases from those parasites. Cuckoo birds lay their eggs in the nests of other birds. When they hatch, cuckoo chicks push the other chicks out of the nest and the host birds raise the young cuckoos as if those chicks were their own.

Getting Ready
Make copies of student pages 81 and 82, and bring in help-wanted ads from newspapers.

Doing the Activity
1. Start by asking the students to name some ways that we depend on plants. (Food, building material.) What are some things we do to support and maintain plants that are important to us? (Agriculture, forestry.) How do other animals depend on plants? (Food, shelter.) How do plants depend on animals? (Pollination, seed dispersal.) Explain that students will discover more about the ways some plants and animals help each other to survive.

2. Pass out copies of student page 81 titled "Classified Ads." Explain that the top portion of the student page represents fictitious want ads in a newspaper. (Show students where the want ad section is in the local paper, and read a few ads so they understand the concept.) At the bottom of the student page is information about several different animals or plants. The students should decide which animal or plant described at the bottom of the page would be likely to respond to each ad.

3. When the students are finished, go over the page using the answers on page 80 and the Background information. As you review each ad, ask students to describe what each partner gets from the relationship.

4. Ask students to describe other symbiotic relationships they know of. Do they know any other examples where both partners benefit? (Mutualism: see Background.) Do they know of partnerships in which one partner benefits and the other is unaffected? (Commensalism: see

LEVELS
Grades 5-8

SUBJECTS
Science, Language Arts

CONCEPT
■ Organisms are interdependent; they all depend on nonliving components of the Earth. (4.1)

SKILLS
Analyzing, Reasoning

OBJECTIVES
Students will ① examine close relationships that exist between different organisms and ② explain how partners in these relationships help each other to survive.

MATERIALS
copies of student pages 81 and 82, pencils and paper, want ads from the local newspaper (optional)

TIME CONSIDERATIONS
Preparation: 20 minutes

Activity: 50 minutes

Background.) Do they know of partnerships in which one partner benefits and the other suffers? (Parasitism: see Background.)

Enrichment
Pass out copies of student page 82 titled "Relationships," and go over the page with students. Have them identify what, if anything, each partner gets from the relationship. Use each example as a springboard for further discussion and as an introduction for local examples.

END NOTES...

ASSESSMENT OPPORTUNITY
Have the students think of (or research) a symbiotic relationship other than the ones described in the activity (preferably a local example), and write a newspaper-style want ad from the point of view of one or both of the partners.

RELATED ACTIVITIES
Charting Diversity, Can It Be Real?, Picture This!, Habitat Pen Pals

ANSWERS

A. Flora (Angraecum orchid) & 2 (hawk moth). Many plants rely on animals to pollinate their flowers. In some cases, plants depend on specific animals to pollinate them, and the animals are specially adapted to pollinate only those plants. The Madagascan hawk moth and the Angraecum orchid are an excellent example of this type of specialization. The moth, with its 12-inch (30.5-cm) feeding tube, is the only animal in the Madagascan forest that can reach the flower's nectar supply.

B. Acacia (uh-KAY-shuh) (bull's horn acacia) & 5 (Pseudomyrmex ant). Hollow thorns on acacia trees provide excellent places for ants to live and raise their young. For the adult ants, the trees provide food in the form of nectaries inside their stems. At the tips of their leaves, they also produce protein-rich food that the ants feed to their young. The ants, in turn, defend the tree against potential foes. They attack and chase away any insect that lands on the tree, cut down competing plants, and may even attack large, browsing mammals.

C. Mimosa (mee-MOH-sah) & 1 (Mimosa girdler beetle). Mimosa girdler beetles will lay their eggs only on mimosa trees. Mimosa trees usually live for about 20 years. However, trees that have been "girdled" by the beetles may live twice as long (the reason is not yet known).

D. Melly Ratel (RAD-uhl) (honey badgers) & 3 (honey guide). Ratels, or honey badgers, eat many different foods, including small mammals, birds, dead animals, and plants. If a ratel hears a honey guide making characteristic calls, it will follow the bird—and the bird will lead it to a beehive. Once the ratel has broken open the hive, it will eat the honey and the bees; the bird will eat the bee larvae and wax in the hive. Honey guides also lead people to bee hives.

E. Mr. Pits (fruit tree) & 4 (flying fox). Flying foxes are active at night and may fly long distances from their roosting trees to the trees where they feed. Once flying foxes have found trees laden with fruit, they will eat, rest, and digest their food before flying home. These large bats are important seed dispersers for many different fruit-bearing trees.

CLASSIFIED ADS

A
Pollen mover needed. Will give sweet, energy-packed nectar in exchange for carrying pollen to other flowers. Must bring a long tube to reach the nectar. Call Flora, 555-9377.

B
Desperately need protection from insects and climbing vines. Will provide protein-rich food for your young, a safe home, and nectar in exchange for guard duties. Call Acacia, 555-8733.

C
Pruning helps me live longer. Can provide safe area for your young to develop in exchange for cutting off the ends of my branches. Call Mimosa, 555-6672.

D
Extremely strong individual seeks partner to help locate nests of wild bees. Will rip open nests and share the contents in exchange for guide services. Call Melly Ratel, 555-2473.

E
Seeking individual to spread seeds around the forest. Offering juicy fruit in exchange for delivery services. Call Mr. Pits, 555-1234.

CRITTERS

 1 My eggs can hatch only in dead wood. I lay my eggs in the end of a tree branch. Then I cut through the bark all the way around the branch. This kills the end of the branch and my eggs have all the dead wood they need.

_____

 2 I'm active at night and feed using a straw-like tube that I can coil up like a hose. Uncoiled, my feeding tube may be 12 inches (30.5 cm) long.

_____

 3 I love to eat honey and beeswax. I can easily spot the beehives that are full of these delights, but I have no way to open the nests.

_____

 4 I can eat twice my weight in fruit every night. I chew the fruit, suck out the juices, and then spit out the pulp and seeds.

_____

 5 I live in a colony, and all of the members of my colony share the jobs. We take care of the young, collect food, take care of the queen, and defend our nest.

_____

RELATIONSHIPS

It's tough not to pick up leeches in the Nile, where this crocodile lives. Because the crocodile's skin is so tough, leeches usually attach themselves to the soft areas in the reptile's mouth. Birds called Egyptian plovers (PLUHV-uhrs) hop in and out of the crocodiles' mouths, making meals of the leeches and any food that's stuck between the crocodile's teeth.

These ants live in the hollow root balls of certain plants called epiphytes (EP-uh-fights). The hollow balls provide a protected nest for the ants. And the material that the ants carry into their nests creates a great nutrient-rich compost for the epiphytes.

Only a swordbilled hummingbird can drink the nectar of the Passiflora (PASS-ee-floor-ah) orchid. The birds need tremendous amounts of energy, which the flower provides. In the process of getting a meal, the birds pollinate the flowers.

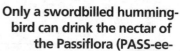

Some rain forest trees rely on very unlikely animals to disperse their seeds: fish! During certain times of the year, the Amazon River floods. Then fish swim into parts of the forest that they can reach only during flood season. As fruit falls from the trees into the water, the fish eat it. Later, they excrete the seeds in another area.

By trapping insects, plants like this bucket orchid get pollinated. Perfume lures bees to the flowers. When the bees crawl inside the flowers, they fall into a pool of liquid. By crawling out a special "side door," the bees save themselves from drowning. In this process, they become coated with pollen, which they carry to the next orchid they visit.

Overview
Try this activity to give your students an idea of the conditions that trees need to live and grow, and to help your students understand that trees must often compete for their needs.

Background
What do trees need so they can grow? Some of their needs are the same as those of people and other animals. For example, trees need plenty of water. They also need plenty of nutrients, which they get from food. But trees and people don't get food in the same way. Plants make their own food by using energy from the sun.

If trees don't get enough water, nutrients, or sunlight, they may grow slowly or die. Growth rings show this graphically. In general, wide rings indicate good conditions for growth (plenty of nutrients, water, and sunshine) while narrow rings often indicate less favorable conditions for growth (drought, insect damage, lack of nutrients, competition). (See additional Background in "Tree Cookies" on page 289, "Sunlight and Shades of Green" on page 137 "Air Plants" on page 85, and "How Plants Grow" on page 135.)

Getting Ready
Cut two 3" x 3" (7.6 cm x 7.6 cm) squares out of blue, yellow, and green construction paper for each student. To save time, you could use colored poker chips. Poker chips work much better than paper if you're doing the activity outdoors on a breezy day.

Doing the Activity
1. Pass out cross-sections from several 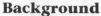 trunks or branches (tree cookies), and have your students examine the growth rings. (If you don't have an actual cross-section, draw a big one on the chalkboard.) Explain that the number of rings indicates a tree's age.

2. Give a large piece of paper (at least 8.5" x 11" or 22 cm x 28 cm) or a white paper plate to each student.

3. Tell students to imagine that they are trees. Have them draw a cross-section of themselves, representing their age in growth rings. (You might laminate these drawings for durability.)

4. Have students stand about three feet (91 cm) apart on their cross-sections.

5. Equally distribute the colored squares (or poker chips) on the floor around the students so the squares are about one to two feet (30-61 cm) apart.

6. Tell students that they'll be playing a game called "Every Tree for Itself." The object of the game is for the "trees" to gather as many squares as they can. Explain that each colored square represents a tree requirement. Blue represents water, yellow represents sunlight, and green represents a nutrient such as nitrogen, oxygen, or carbon dioxide. Make appropriate adjustments if you use poker chips.

7. Give a signal, to start the first round. Have student trees reach with their roots and branches (arms and legs) to gather their requirements. Tell students that one foot (their tap root) must remain planted on their cross-section at all times. They are not allowed to slide their cross-section along the floor or step off it; they will be disqualified for doing so.

8. Allow student trees to gather these requirements for one 30-second round. (They can either collect all types of requirements at once or one type of requirement each round.) Have students use a notebook to record how many of each color requirement they gathered. Use the following questions to discuss the results of the first round:

LEVELS
Grades K-8

SUBJECTS
Science, Math

CONCEPTS
■ The Earth's atmosphere, water, soil, climate, and geology vary from region to region, thus creating a wide diversity of biological communities. (1.3)
■ Organisms are interdependent; they all depend on nonliving components of the Earth. (4.1)
■ Altering the environment affects all life forms—including humans—and the interrelationships that link them. (4.2)

SKILLS
Determining Causes and Effects, Identifying Relationships and Patterns, Predicting, Interpreting

OBJECTIVES
Students will ① simulate how trees compete for their essential needs; and ② describe how varying amounts of light, water, and nutrients affect a tree's growth.

MATERIALS
8" x 10" (20 cm x 25 cm) pieces of paper or paper plates; pieces of blue, yellow, and green paper; markers or crayons (optional: tree trunk or branch cross-sections showing annual growth rings, often available from tree-trimming services or forest industries; three colors of poker chips)

TIME CONSIDERATIONS
Preparation: 15 minutes
Activity: 50 minutes

- How many requirements did each tree get?

- Do any trees lack a particular requirement?

- What might happen to a real tree that lacked one of its requirements? (It might grow slowly or eventually die. Point out to the students, though, that different species of trees have different requirements.)

- Is there such a thing as too much water, sunlight, or nutrients? (Yes, every species has optimum levels beyond which the tree becomes stressed.)

9. Have students stand on their cross-sections in groups of three to five. Gather the colored squares and spread them around the room again. Play another round and have student trees record their results.

10. Compare the results of this round with those of the first. In most cases, students will notice that each tree gathered fewer requirements. Ask if they can reach any conclusions about trees that grow close to each other. (Such trees compete for requirements. Often they don't grow as well as trees that are more widely separated from one another.) Ask if any trees "died" because they couldn't get a particular requirement. (You can allow trees to fall down or look tired and droopy if they haven't received their vital requirements.)

11. Ask students how foresters might use their knowledge of competition in caring for a stand of trees. (Foresters plant trees a certain distance apart so the trees will be able to get enough nutrients. The distance varies depending on the species of the tree. Foresters also thin young stands of trees).

12. Try several more rounds, comparing the results each time. Here are suggestions for setting up additional rounds. As before, each student should examine his or her results in each round. Older students can record those results and later graph or chart the results of each round and draw conclusions.

- Have all of the students stand closer together.

- Put students closer together, but have only half of the class participate.

- Use fewer water squares (representing a drought).

- Use fewer sunlight squares (representing lack of sunlight for young trees because of overcrowding).

- Use fewer nutrient squares (representing poor quality soil).

Enrichment
For a visual way to portray water absorption by roots, try the following:

1. Explain that, for many species of trees, the diameter of the spread of the tree's roots is roughly equal to the tree's height. Have students measure themselves and then make a circle (using chalk or string) with a diameter equal to their height.

2. Play the tree game with each student standing in the center of his or her circle. Tell the student trees they can gather water squares only within their circle of roots.

3. Play the game again using root circles, but this time have trees stand in clumps. Afterward, discuss the results of root competition.

Overview
Plants play a part in every breath we take. Use this activity to help your students understand how photosynthesis works and how humans depend on this process.

Background
Green plants, like animals, need food, but unlike animals, plants make their own food through the process of photosynthesis. In this process, plants use energy from the sun to convert carbon dioxide (gas) and water into carbohydrates (simple sugars). This process takes place in tiny chambers called chloroplasts that are found mainly in the plant's leaves. Chloroplasts contain a green pigment called chlorophyll, which enables plants to absorb the sun's energy.

One of the by-products of photosynthesis is oxygen, which is used by people and other animals. Plants release this gas through tiny openings called stomata underneath their leaves. As animals use energy, they exhale carbon dioxide gas, which can be picked up by green plants and used for photosynthesis.

Getting Ready
1. Cut string into 20-foot (6-m) lengths (one per student).

2. Make copies (one per student) of page 87 for the Assessment Opportunity.

Doing the Activity
1. Have your students brainstorm a list of ways plants are important to people and other animals. Write their ideas on the chalkboard.

2. If the students' list does not include the fact that plants provide oxygen for people and other animals to breathe, add that fact to the list. Ask students if they can think of ways that people help plants, and then make a list of their ideas. If it is not listed, add the fact that animals give off carbon dioxide, a gas that plants need to make food (photosynthesize).

3. At this point, you might have students do the Enrichment on page 86. This short experiment demonstrates how plants give off oxygen during photosynthesis.

LEVELS
Grades 3-6

SUBJECTS
Science, Math

CONCEPTS
■ Altering the environment affects all life forms—including humans—and the interrelationships that link them. (4.2)

■ The structure and scale of an ecosystem are influenced by factors such as soil type, climate, availability of water, and human activities. (10.2)

SKILLS
Representing, Analyzing, Predicting, Verifying

OBJECTIVES
Students will ① demonstrate and describe the general process of photosynthesis and ② explore the relationship between the amount of oxygen produced by plants and the amount of oxygen used by humans.

MATERIALS
Activity: Copies of student page 87, large ball of string, crayons or markers (optional)
Enrichment: Clear, tall drinking glass; large bowl of water; water plant from a tropical fish store; 1 teaspoon baking soda; lamp with a 75-watt bulb

TIME CONSIDERATIONS
Preparation: 30 minutes

Activity: Two 50-minute periods

4. Using the background information, discuss with students the basic steps of photosynthesis.

5. Ask students to consider how much oxygen they need each day and how much of that amount grass produces through photosynthesis. Explain that studies have shown that a person requires a minimum of 360 liters of oxygen per day, or 210 ml per breath. (You might show them a one- or two-liter bottle.) A 25-square-foot (2.25-square-meter) plot of grass can, on average, produce that much oxygen in one day.

NOTE—If you do not have access to a large, grassy area, use the Variation.

6. Tell the students they're going to measure plots of grass that represent their oxygen needs for a day. Take them outside to a large, grassy area and give each person one of the pieces of string. (Depending on the level of your group, you may want to have students figure out on their own how long their string must be if it must enclose a 25-square-foot (2.25-square-meter) plot, or a square that is 5 feet (1.5 meters) on each side.

7. Have students use their 20-foot (6-m) lengths of string to form their individual 25-square-foot (2.25-square-meter) plots. You might arrange all of the plots in a grid to show the total area needed by the group for one day's oxygen supply.

8. Later, you may want to have students calculate the total area needed to produce the daily oxygen requirement for your entire school. How many football fields would it take to provide this much oxygen?

VARIATION

If a large, grassy area is not available, you can use trees instead. An average tree along a street releases enough oxygen each day to support one person, while that person, in turn, exhales enough carbon dioxide to support the tree. Have the students each draw a diagram showing the mutual relationship they have with a street tree. How many trees would it take to support their entire family? How many for their entire school?

Enrichment

This experiment lets your students watch a plant make oxygen. Since the plant is under water, oxygen will be visible as bubbles.

1. Fill a bowl with fresh water.

2. Mix baking soda into the water. Baking soda (bicarbonate of soda) will provide the carbon dioxide that a plant needs to produce oxygen.

3. Place a water plant inside a drinking glass.

4. Lower the glass sideways into the bowl of water until the glass fills with water and no air bubbles are left in the glass. Then turn the glass upside down in the bowl without letting in air. The glass should rest on the bottom of the bowl.

5. Aim light from the lamp toward one side of the glass.

You will see small bubbles forming on the leaves in the water. Most bubbles will come from the side of the plant nearest the light. After about an hour, you will see that a large bubble has accumulated on top of the water inside the glass. This bubble contains the oxygen that the plant has made.

END NOTES...

ASSESSMENT OPPORTUNITY

To evaluate the students' understanding, pass out copies of page 87. Have students cut out and arrange the shapes according to their understanding of photosynthesis. They can present the information any way they like, but must be able to explain each step and its place in the process.

RELATED ACTIVITIES

Sunlight and Shades of Green, Air to Drive, Plant a Tree, Waste Watchers

AIR PLANTS

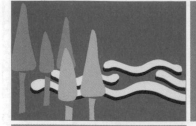

Overview
Rainfall, sunlight, and temperature are important factors influencing where plants can grow and, in turn, where animals can live. In this activity, students will design experiments to see how these climatic factors influence the growth and lives of plants. They will use the learned principles to explore how varying climate conditions have resulted in an astounding variety of forest types in Puerto Rico.

SUBJECTS
Science, Math, Social Studies

Levels:
Grades 6-8

CONCEPTS
- Biological diversity results from the interaction of living and nonliving environmental components such as air, water, climate, and geological features. (1.1)
- Organisms are interdependent; they all depend on nonliving components of the Earth. (4.1)
- Altering the environment affects all life forms-including humans-and the interrelationships that link them. (4.2)

SKILLS
Solving problems, Observing, Determining Causes and Effects, Predicting, Verifying

OBJECTIVES
Students will ① explore how variations in water, light and temperature affect plant growth and ② describe how precipitation and geography can affect the plant and animal species that are found in a particular region.

MATERIALS
Part A: small containers, potting soil, fast-growing seeds (mung bean or radish), water, measuring sticks, graph paper, pencils
Part B: copies of pages 90-92, markers or paper pencils [optional: clear plastic sheets for map overlays, PLT Forests of The World Map (see Bibliography, page 386)]

TIME CONSIDERATIONS
Preparation: 30-60 minutes

Activity: Part A: Two 50-minute periods over several weeks;
Part B: 50 minutes

Background
Puerto Rico is a subtropical island about the size of Delaware. Because of regional variations in elevation, temperature, and, most important, rainfall, Puerto Rico has a tremendous variety of forest types—from dry, open woodland to lush rainforest. (See student page 91 for more information on forest types. Also see Background for "How Plants Grow" on page 135.)

Getting Ready
1. Make copies of student pages.

2. Prepare materials for experiments in Part A.

PART A
EXPERIMENTAL SPROUTS

Doing the Activity
1. Begin by asking the students what plants need for growth (water, light, nutrients). List their suggestions on the chalkboard.

2. As they consider these requirements, ask students how the climate conditions of rainfall, sunlight, and temperature affect the growth of plants and trees. Divide the group into teams of two, and challenge each team to design an experiment using live plants that will demonstrate how climatic factors influence plant growth. Teams should follow certain guidelines such as ① testing for one variable at a time (water, sunlight, or temperature); ② labeling containers clearly; and ③ having a control group. (See "Trees in Trouble" Part B on page 294 for more detailed information on experimenting for plant requirements.)

3. Have teams predict the outcome of their experiments.

4. Tell each team to first grow the sprouts they will use in their experiments. They should use fast-growing seeds in small paper cups or egg cartons filled with potting soil. When the seeds have sprouted, students should record the height and appearance of the plants before beginning their experiments.

5. Have students observe their plants each day, and record any changes, especially size and appearance.

6. After several weeks, have students present the results of their experiments to the rest of the group. Did any team get results it didn't expect? How did team members interpret those results?

PART B
ISLAND PARADISE

1. Point out the Commonwealth of Puerto Rico on a world map. Have any students or their relatives been there? Identify for students the different forest types they could see on a trip to Puerto Rico. (See Map D on page 90.) Ask students to use experiments they did in Part A as they consider how climatic factors have affected the development of those different forest types. (For example, more rainfall supports lusher forests.) Would climate also affect where particular animals can live? (Yes, animals depend on food sources that are specific to certain climate conditions.) Tell students they will study the relationship between climate and forest types in Puerto Rico.

2. Divide the students into teams of four, and distribute copies of student pages 90-92 to each student. Each person on a team will study the materials to gain information on how one of the following is distributed on the island: ① rainfall, ② temperature, ③ elevation, or ④ forest types.

Afterward, have teams work together to answer the questions on page 92. Students should hypothesize about what types of plants and animals might be found in the different forest types of Puerto Rico. Point out to students that classifying a "forest type region" does not mean that region is presently covered with forest. Much of Puerto Rico's originally forested areas has been replaced by farmland. But, if this farmland were left alone, it would eventually return to the forest type of that region.

Enrichment

1. Each student should select a common local plant or animal species, then look it up in a field guide that shows the range for that species. Most series of field guides such as GOLDEN GUIDES, THE PETERSON FIELD GUIDE SERIES, OR AUDUBON SOCIETY FIELD GUIDES AND NATURE GUIDES show these ranges (see References). Students should compare the species' range with a map showing average precipitation for regions of North America. Many encyclopedias have precipitation maps. Students should consider whether the range of their species is limited by precipitation or vegetation type. Then, students should read more about their species to verify their conclusions.

2. Plan a class trip to a nursery, plant shop, or greenhouse. (Ask the owner for permission first. You may want to set certain rules: "Don't handle plants.") Have students roam about in pairs. They should select a plant that interests them; they should write down its name and carefully read the directions for taking care of it (usually on a card attached to the plant or stuck in the soil). Each card will tell what level of temperature, soil moisture, and sunlight the plant requires, and perhaps what continent the plant comes from. Using this information, students should imagine a natural habitat where the plant might be found (e.g., desert, grassland, swamp, dry forest, moist temperate forest, tropical rainforest). Remind students of the relationships they studied between plants and climate factors in Puerto Rico. Perhaps someone working at the nursery or greenhouse can give students more information about the plants they selected.

3. Ask a local **silviculturalist**, **horticulturalist**, or **botanist** to visit your classroom and bring several plants from distinctly different climate areas. (These experts may work at universities, greenhouses, arboretums, botanical gardens, plant nurseries, or research institutes.) Let students guess where plants may be from by recalling characteristics they have learned. The experts can discuss students' guesses, tell students where the plants occur naturally, and point out each plant's special adaptations.

END NOTES...

ASSESSMENT OPPORTUNITY
Evaluate how well the students used maps to gain information for answering the questions on page 92. Evaluate the students' understanding of what all living things need to survive, and what factors influence where particular plants and animals can live.

RELATED ACTIVITIES
Environmental Exchange Box; Tropical Treehouse; Planet of Plenty; How Plants Grow; Field, Forest and Stream

REFERENCES
AUDUBON SOCIETY FIELD GUIDES. New York: Alfred A. Knopf.

AUDUBON SOCIETY NATURE GUIDES. New York: Alfred A. Knopf.

Ewel, J.J. and J.L. Whitmore. THE ECOLOGICAL LIFE ZONES OF PUERTO RICO AND THE U.S. VIRGIN ISLANDS. Rio Piedras, Puerto Rico: Institute of Tropical Forestry, USDA Forest Service, 1973.

A FIELD GUIDE TO NORTH AMERICAN BIRDS. Washington, D.C.: National Geographic Society.

GOLDEN GUIDES. New York: Golden Press.

THE PETERSON FIELD GUIDE SERIES. Boston: Houghton Mifflin Company.

Wiley, James W. and Gerald P. Bauer. "Caribbean National Forest, Puerto Rico," AMERICAN BIRDS 39(1): 12-18. (Spring 1985)

ANSWERS TO QUESTIONS ON PAGE 92

1.a) Higher elevations correspond to lower temperatures.
b)Yes, it usually gets colder as you go up a mountain, because the atmosphere is thinner and retains less heat.

2.a) Mountainous regions tend to have more rainfall.
b)When warm, moist air reaches a mountain range, it is forced to rise. In doing so, it cools and condenses, losing most of its moisture as precipitation.

3.a) Lower temperatures correspond with more rainfall.
b) Lower temperatures cause water vapor to condense and cause rain.

4.a) The northeast and west corner.
b) High.
c) e.g., Sierra palm trees, tabanuco tree, colorado tree, ferns, vines, bromeliads.
d) e.g., Puerto Rican parrot.
e) Rainforest, upper montane rainforest, lower montane rainforest, or lower montane wet forest.

5.a) Southern Coast.
b) Higher
c) Dry forest
d) e.g., crazy ants, hummingbirds; ucar, gumbo-limbo, aleli
e) e.g., cactus plants have spines; gumbo-limbo trees shed leaves during the dry season.

6.a) Foothills.
b) Average.
c) Average.
d) e.g., prickly and royal palm, bananaquit, gray kingbird.

MAPS OF PUERTO RICO

A. TEMPERATURE MAP

- 76° F
- 74° F
- 72° F
- 70° F
- 68° F

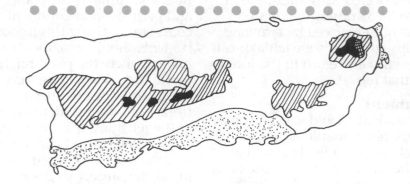

B. TOPOGRAPHY MAP

- 0–500 FEET
- 500–2000 FEET
- OVER 2000 FEET

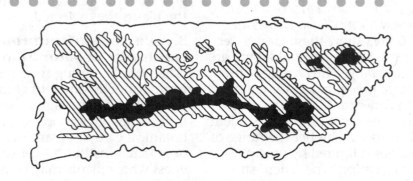

C. RAINFALL MAP

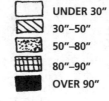

- UNDER 30"
- 30"–50"
- 50"–80"
- 80"–90"
- OVER 90"

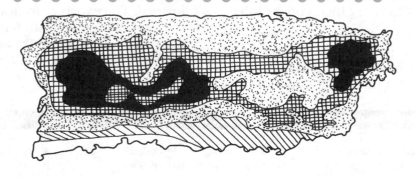

D. FOREST TYPE MAP

- DRY FOREST
- MOIST FOREST
- WET FOREST
- UPPER MONTANE RAINFOREST
- LOWER MONTANE RAINFOREST

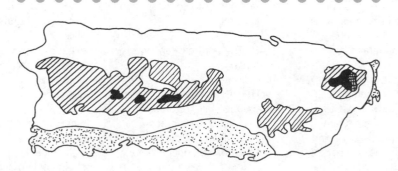

FOREST TYPES

Dry Forests

Ucar (OOH-KAR), gumbo-limbo (GUHM-boh-lim-boh), aleli (AH-lay-LEE), turpentine, and guaya-can (GWEYE-uh-kan) are some common trees adapted to climate conditions in the dry forests of Puerto Rico. Gumbo-limbo trees, for example, shed their leaves during the dry season and slow their growth at times when little moisture is available.

The trees provide homes for other plants and animals living in the dry forest. For example, mistletoe, a parasitic plant growing right out of tree branches, derives most of its nutrition directly from trees. Many birds, such as hummingbirds and bullfinches, depend on trees in dry forests for building their nests. In turn, the melon cactus depends on the hummingbird to pollinate its brilliant pink flowers and on the bullfinch to eat its pink fruits, thereby dispersing its seeds throughout the forest. Cactus plants (cacti) are adapted to dry conditions since their leaves (spines) have little surface area; for cacti, photosynthesis happens in their stems instead of leaves. (With less surface area, cacti lose less water than leafy trees through transpiration.) The stems (green, fleshy part of the cactus) store water for drier times. Also, the broad, shallow root system of cacti gathers water over a large area.

As one of the dry forest's recyclers, "crazy ants" break down leaves, dead insects, and other debris. These ants, in turn, become food for many different lizards that live there, such as the ameiva (uh-MAY-vah), with its long, iridescent tail.

Moist Forests

In Puerto Rico moist forest covers more area than any other forest type, but almost all of it has been cleared at one time or another for growing crops. As a result, grasslands are a dominant feature of this zone today. Trees up to 20 meters (65.6 feet) tall with rounded crowns like the mango are characteristic of areas where deforestation has not occurred. Common trees of the moist forest are prickly and royal palms, white and Spanish cedars, grandleaf sea grapes, and shortleaf figs. In coastal areas, mangroves grow much taller in the moister forests than in the drier forests. Common birds in the moist forest include the bananaquit, the grey kingbird, and the greater Antillean (an-TILL-ee-uhm) grackle. Reptiles such as the ground lizard are common there, as well as the Jamaican fruit bat.

Wet Forests

In the wet forests, you are likely to see tabanuco (TAB-uh-NEW-ko) or candlewood, trumpet, balsa, and sierra palm trees growing. Those trees support many vines and epiphytes (EP-uh-fights) (plants that use other plants for support). One epiphyte, the red-flowered bromeliad (bro-MEE-lee-ad), catches water in its tank-shaped leaves, providing a moist home for insects like centipedes. The ground of the wet forest is typically covered with ferns and mosses. In a wet forest, where there is no need to retain water because of the constant rainfall, plants have large, green leaves that transpire a lot of water. In addition, many plants are ever-greens, meaning that they retain their leaves and photosynthesize all year long.

Birds of the wet forests include Puerto Rican tanagers (TAN-ih-juhrs), hawks, owls, pigeons, quail doves, and the endangered Puerto Rican parrot (a beautiful green, blue, and red bird about one foot or 30.5 cm long). However, fewer birds are in the wet than in the dry forests because large lizard and frog populations in the wet forests compete for the same insect food. Puerto Rico is famous for its coquis (KO-key), or tree frogs, most of which live in the wet forests and climb trees for food and shelter.

Rainforests

Within the wet forest are several types of rainforests, which vary on the basis of elevation. Below 2,000 feet, the lower montane (mountain) rainforest is dominated by the tabanuco tree whose spreading crowns create a semi-dark environment. Tabanuco tree trunks are clear of branches for more than half the tree's height, creating an open midsection in the forest. On the forest floor grow ferns and other lush vegetation. Above 2,000 feet, the lower montane rainforest is dominated by colorado trees, which are mostly short, gnarled, and twisted. When they grow old, these trees develop cavities that are used by birds, insects, and the Puerto Rican parrot.

The upper montane rainforest is dominated by Sierra palm trees. On the trees and floor of this forest grow ferns, mosses, and the red-flowered bromeliad. With rainfall nearly every day, the rainforest at the highest elevations supports great numbers of vines and bromeliads.

QUESTIONS

1
a Look at Maps A and B. What is the relationship between elevation and temperature in Puerto Rico?

b Does this relationship occur in other parts of the world?

2
**a** Study Maps B and C. What is the relationship between elevation and rainfall in Puerto Rico?

b What makes you say this?

3
**a** Study Maps A and C. What is the relationship between temperature and rainfall in Puerto Rico?

b What might cause this relationship?

4
**a** Using Map C, find the regions with the most rainfall.

b Are these areas at a high, medium, or low elevation?

c Use the student page 91 to find out what types of plants grow there.

d What types of animals live in these forests?

e What are these forests called?

5
a Find the region with the least rainfall.

b Is its temperature higher or lower than other regions?

c Look at Map D to find out the name of this type of forest.

d What kinds of plants and animals would live in this region?

e How are the animals and plants that live there adapted to this type of forest?

6
a On Map D, find the regions that have moist forests. Do these regions occur in the coastal lowlands, foothills, central mountains, or coastal valleys of Puerto Rico? (See Map B)

b How does the amount of rainfall in this region compare to the rest of Puerto Rico?

c How about the temperature?

d What kinds of plants and animals do you think live in this region?

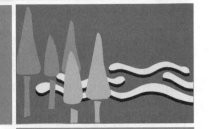

Overview
It's easy to take for granted both trees and the many benefits they provide. Here's a way to start your students thinking about how much trees add to people's lives.

Background
(See background for "Plant a Tree" on page 95.)

Doing the Activity
1. Write the following list where everyone can see it:

>**playground**
>**school grounds**
>**city street**
>**neighborhood**
>**park**
>**zoo**
>**highway**
>**picnic area**
>**backyard**
>**farm**

2. Have each person or team choose and draw one of the areas on the list. Explain that students can draw the area any way they like, with one exception: They must leave trees out of the picture. (You might work on one big mural with each team drawing a different section.)

3. When students have finished their drawings, have them draw the same scene again, but this time use as many trees as they wish.

4. Display the drawings (or murals) where everyone can see them. Ask students in which environment they would rather spend their time, and if trees have anything to do with their preferences.

LEVELS
Grade 1-6

SUBJECTS
Science, Social Studies, Visual Arts

CONCEPTS
- Resource management technologies interact and influence environmental quality; the acquisition, extraction and transportation of natural resources; and all life forms. (5.1)
- While technological advances decrease the incidence of disease and death, the ever-increasing world population is placing heavy demands on the finite resources of the Earth. (5.2)

SKILLS
Discussing, Evaluating, Comparing and Contrasting, Identifying Attributes and Components

OBJECTIVES
Students will ① describe the ways in which trees benefit people and ② make pictures or models depicting how trees may be used to improve the human-made environment.

MATERIALS
Activity: drawing paper, crayons or markers
Variation: 8" x 10" (20 cm x 25 cm) white paper, 8" x 10" (20 cm x 25 cm) overhead transparencies, pencils, colored markers for drawing on transparencies

TIME CONSIDERATIONS
Preparation: 20 minutes

Activity: 50 minutes

5. Discuss the benefits of trees in public places. For example, trees not only look nice; they also provide shade, protection from wind, and a habitat for wildlife. Trees help to improve the quality of air and to reduce noise.

VARIATION

1. Give each student or team an 8.5" x 11" (215 mm x 279 mm) piece of paper and an 8.5" x 11" (215 mm x 279 mm) blank overhead transparency.

2. On the piece of paper have students draw a familiar scene (their house or building, street, school, playground, downtown) without its trees, bushes, grass, flowers, or plants of any kind.

3. Then have them place the transparency over the picture and tape it to one edge.

4. On the transparency, have them use colored markers to draw any trees, bushes, and plants that they remember being in the scene.

5. When they've finished, they can flip up the transparency and compare the pictures with and without trees and plants.

6. Afterward, they can continue drawing on the transparency. Maybe the added trees, plants, or flowers represent the way students would like to see the scene some day.

Enrichment

Plan a planting event (trees, bushes, plants, flowers) for your school, group, or community. Use this opportunity to publicize all the benefits that trees and plants provide for us. (See "Plant a Tree" on page 95.)

END NOTES...

ASSESSMENT OPPORTUNITY

Create a "Three Cheers for Trees" bulletin board showing the benefits of trees in public places. Have the students brainstorm a list of tree benefits. Then have them draw or cut out pictures and write slogans that depict these benefits (products, shade, wildlife, beauty, fresh air, and so on). With your guidance, allow them to design and arrange the bulletin board.

RELATED ACTIVITIES

Air Plants, Improve Your Place, Trees in Trouble, Plant a Tree We All Need Trees, Publicize it!

Overview
Never underestimate the power of a tree! Besides giving us an amazing array of paper and wood products, trees provide a host of other benefits—from shading our backyards to assisting in the maintenance of the global climate. Students can express their appreciation of trees by planning and carrying out their own tree-planting program.

Background
Industrialized societies depend on carbon-based fuels such as gasoline, oil, coal, and natural gas to heat homes and to power factories, vehicles, appliances, and other machinery. Burning those fuels releases enormous amounts of carbon into the atmosphere. On the average, every person in the United States is responsible for 2.3 tons (2.1 metric tons) of atmospheric carbon each year. Some scientists believe that these emissions can cause climatic changes that, in turn, could lead to severe storms, droughts, floods, and times of famine. (See Background for "Waste Watchers" and "Air to Drive" on pages 274 and 325.)

Tree planting is an important strategy for reducing this potential threat. An average young tree stores about 25 pounds (11.3 kg) of atmospheric carbon a year. At present, 1.5 billion trees flourish in American cities and towns.

According to Dr. Rowan Rowntree of the U.S. Forest Service's Urban Forest Ecology Research, a 12-year-old child needs to plant and maintain 65 trees in order to offset the amount of carbon that child will put in the atmosphere during the rest of his or her lifetime. Planting 65 trees is lot of work, so the time to start is right away! As an alternative, students can care for trees that have already been planted, since those trees often die from damage or neglect.

Below is a list of some other benefits trees provide, particularly those planted in urban or residential areas:

- Help settle out, trap, and hold small particles (dust, ash, smoke) that can damage lungs
- Absorb sulfur dioxide and other pollutants
- Replenish the atmosphere with oxygen
- Hold soil with roots, preventing erosion
- Provide homes and food for birds and other animals
- Serve as a windbreak, keeping buildings warmer
- Provide shade, keeping buildings cooler
- Lower energy bills by providing shade and serving as a windbreak
- Muffle traffic noise
- Provide beauty and enjoyment

Getting Ready
Find out which agencies or organizations are responsible for tree planting and maintenance in your community. Parks departments, urban forestry departments, and independent garden clubs are possibilities. Students can write to those agencies or organizations for tree-planting information.

Doing the Activity
1. Ask students to name some areas in the community (such as along city streets and in other public areas, including the school grounds) where trees have been planted. Then have them work in small groups to list the benefits trees provide to people and wildlife in those areas.

2. Use the groups' lists to develop a class list, and add any other benefits you can think of (see Background). Have everyone make a copy of the list.

3. Tell the students that planting trees is a great way to do something good for the community—and for planet Earth! Then have them work in small groups over the next week or so to identify areas in the community (or on the school grounds) that would be improved by the presence of one or more trees. Remind students to refer to

LEVELS
Grades 1-8

SUBJECTS
Science, Social Studies

CONCEPTS
- Organisms are interdependent: they all depend on nonliving components of the Earth. (4.1)
- Altering the environment affects all life forms—including humans—and the interrelationships that link them. (4.2)
- Resource management technologies interact and influence environmental quality; the acquisition, extraction and transportation of natural resources; and all life forms. (5.1)

SKILLS
Researching, Defining Problems, Formulating Questions, Making Decisions, Evaluating

OBJECTIVES
Students will ① identify ways that urban trees enrich our lives, ② determine how people care for urban trees, ③ identify areas in the community that would benefit from having more trees, and ④ organize and execute a class tree–planting project in a local area.

MATERIALS
Paper and pencils, copies of "Planting Recommendations" on student page 97

TIME CONSIDERATIONS
Preparation: 60 minutes

Activity: Two to five 50 minute periods

their lists of tree benefits as they consider different planting sites. If you're working with younger students, take them on a walk around the school to locate an area or areas that would be improved by adding a tree.

4. After the students have identified possible sites, have a group discussion about the feasibility of each site. Have students decide which site (or sites) should be the focus for their tree-planting campaign. With proper supervision, teams can work on different sites.

5. If you're working with older students, ask them whom they think they should contact to get permission to plant in the area(s) they've chosen. Then help them compose a letter to the appropriate people, agencies, or organizations. You might also suggest that the letter include several general questions about tree planting in the community, such as the following:

■ How much money is spent annually on tree care in the community? How many trees are planted, and where?

■ Which species are most often chosen for planting?

■ Do any criteria exist for selecting the species that will be planted? If so, what are they? Whether or not such criteria exist, you may want to suggest to students that they consider many different factors before deciding on which trees to plant. For example, depending on where they'll be planting, they may want to consider species that are resistant to air pollution, drought, and so forth.

■ What are some hardships that urban trees face? What is the average life span of a city tree?

■ How can citizens become involved in planting and maintaining trees on public property?

6. After the students have received a reply, have them detail plans for their tree-planting campaign. For instance, they may decide to raise money to buy trees from a local nursery, or they might ask people to donate trees.

7. Have students plant trees and take care of them. See the planting recommendations on student page 97, and get directions from the nursery on how to plant and care for the particular species of tree.

Enrichment
1. Students could arrange for a special tree-planting ceremony, possibly in conjunction with a special occasion such as Earth Day or Arbor Day. Students should plan the event and send out news releases to publicize it.

2. As discussed in the background, students need to plant and maintain about 65 trees each to absorb all the carbon they put in the atmosphere during their lifetime. Ask students to list all the opportunities they have for tree planting throughout the year. What is the total number of trees they could plant in a year if they took advantage of all those opportunities? Is the total close to 65? If not, what other action could they take to keep carbon out of the air? (They could cut back on fuel consumption.)

END NOTES...

ASSESSMENT OPPORTUNITY
Your group could put together an information booklet that other groups could use to plan, execute, and publicize a community tree-planting project. Teams of students can work on different sections of the booklet. It should include sections on learning the benefits of tree planting, selecting a site in your community, getting permission and advice for planting on a site, finding volunteer help and funding, determining what species to plant, learning how to plant and care for the trees, and arranging for publicity. Students can include photos, diagrams, drawings, and videos.

RELATED ACTIVITIES
Air to Drive, Waste Watchers, Three Cheers for Trees, We All Need Trees, How Plants Grow

REFERENCES
Baumgardt, John Philip. *How to Care for Shade and Ornamental Trees.* Kansas City, Missouri: Intertec Publishing, Corporation, 1974.

Lipkis, Andy and Katie. *The Simple Act of Planting a Tree: A Citizen Forester's Guide to Healing Your Neighborhood, Your City, and Your World.* Los Angeles: J.P. Tarcher, 1990.

Pirone, Pascal Pompey. *Tree Maintenance.* New York: Oxford University Press, 1988.

Rowntree, Rowan. *How Many Trees Does It Take to Store the Carbon You Produce? A Guide to Help You Contribute to the Prevention of Global Climate Change.* Washington, D.C.: U.S. Forest Service.

PLANT A TREE

CHOOSE YOUR SITE CAREFULLY.

Look up, around, and down. The tree you plant today could eventually reach 40 to 100 feet (12 to 30 meters) in height (depending on the tree type). Give your tree plenty of room—its roots will grow wide and deep.

Plant it well away from buildings and powerlines, so that it won't do any damage,

or need disfiguring or harmful pruning later in its life. Plant the tree where its roots will not grow into sewers and pipelines, or under driveways and sidewalks.

Look at the tree. Make sure it's suited to the environment you are planting it in, so that it has the best chance of surviving.

TAKE CARE BEFORE AND DURING PLANTING.

Keep the tree cool and shaded, and keep its roots moist until

planting. During planting, try not to handle the tree's roots. Tamp the dirt firmly, but don't pack it too tightly or the roots won't be able to either reach out for water and nutrients, or anchor the tree. Soak the soil around the tree with water to encourage deep rooting.

If you're planting a sapling—
Dig a hole twice as wide and as deep as the rootball. Build a mound of soil, and place the sapling on top of the mound so that it is two inches (five cm) above the hole's bottom. If the roots are wrapped, remove the burlap. Fill the hole with dirt, tamping it down with your foot and wetting it with water as you fill the hole.

If you're planting a seedling—
Dig a hole a little deeper than the roots' length. Fill the hole around the seedling with dirt. Then gently pull the trunk of the seedling up slightly to straighten out the roots.

GIVE SPECIAL CARE DURING THE EARLY, DEVELOPMENTAL YEARS.

A tree is most vulnerable during the first years of its life. Protect it from pests and animals. Water it frequently. *Then sit back and enjoy!* If cared for properly, each tree you plant will grow and flourish, providing you and all of us with benefits and beauty for generations.

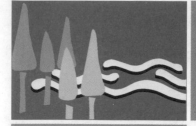

Overview
Privately and publicly owned forests are often managed to some degree to provide several different resources. In this activity, students will learn how forests are managed to meet a variety of human and environmental needs.

LEVELS
Activity: Grades 5-8
Variation: Grades 1-4

SUBJECTS
Science, Social Studies

CONCEPTS
■ Resource management technologies interact and influence environmental quality; the acquisition, extraction and transportation of natural resources; and all life forms. (5.1)

■ All humans consume products and thereby affect the availability of renewable and nonrenewable natural resources. (6.4)

■ The structure and scale of the natural resources in a given area shape the economy upon which the society and its culture is based. (12.1)

SKILLS
Classifying and Categorizing, Analyzing, Discussing, Evaluating

OBJECTIVES
Students will ① identify ways that people use forest resources, ② explain that forests are managed to satisfy a variety of human needs, and ③ explore how different forest uses can be balanced with each other.

MATERIALS
Activity: art supplies
Variation, Step 1: pictures of various forest animals and forest-related activities

TIME CONSIDERATIONS
Preparation: 20 minutes
Activity: 50 minutes

Background
The United States has 731 million acres (296 million hectares or ha) of forestland that make up about one-third of the total land base. Canada has 1,119 million acres (453 million ha). To be classified as forestland, the area must be at least one acre (.4 ha) and contain about 10 percent tree cover. About 487 million acres (197 million ha), or two-thirds, of U.S. forestlands are also classified as commercial timberland (forests capable of growing commercial crops of trees). In the United States, commercial timberlands are owned by three sectors of society: Private individuals own 57 percent; public agencies (federal, state, county) own 28 percent; and forest industries own 15 percent. To varying degrees, those forests are managed to provide several resources at the same time, such as timber, wildlife habitat, and recreational areas. This strategy is called multiple use management.

Law mandates that the U.S. Forest Service will manage its commercial forests for multiple use. Although the Forest Service manages 142 million acres (57 million ha) of national forests, timber harvesting is allowed on only 57 million acres (23 million ha). Those forests are also managed to protect watersheds, conserve soil, protect wildlife habitat, and provide public recreation.

Private forests are also managed for multiple use. For example, forests owned by a forest product company can be used for hiking, fishing, and camping while being managed for timber production and ecosystem protection as well.

Multiple use management involves making choices about the types of activities that can take place in particular areas. Some forest ecosystems cannot support certain activities, and certain activities cannot take place in the same area at the same time. For example, few people would want to hike alongside a strip mine or camp next to a logging operation. Loggers would have a tough time doing their jobs if people using off-road vehicles were driving through an area where they worked. And protecting a watershed or a commercial fishery might mean carefully planning other activities, such as roadbuilding or mining.

Getting Ready
For Variation Only
Gather pictures of forest animals, of recreational activities that people do in forests, and of products that people get from forests. (Look in nature, outdoor, recreation, or tourist magazines.) Pictures you might use include salamander; centipede; mouse; spider; deer; raccoon; woodpecker; people hiking, camping, fishing, skiing, snowmobiling, picnicking, or cutting trees; paper and wood products; oil rig, gas station, or car (runs on gas); and strip-mines, coal, or metal objects.

Doing the Activity
1. Ask students to think of what they use, or how they benefit, from forests. Have them put the list on a piece of paper.

2. Ask students to name animals that live in forests, and record their answers on a chalkboard under the heading "Wildlife." (Encourage students to come up with less obvious examples such as fish, insects, worms, and microorganisms.)

3. Ask students in which kinds of recreational activities they or their families have participated in forests. Record their answers on the chalkboard under the heading "Recreation." Then ask students what needs are satisfied by each activity listed under "Recreation," for example, exercise, solitude, or fun.

4. Have students list products that people get from forests, and record their answers on the chalkboard under the heading "Products." If students don't mention them, be sure to add oil, natural gas, and minerals to the list, because they are also extracted from forest lands. Then ask students what needs are satisfied by each product on the list (e.g. wood for construction, paper, and other products; maple syrup for food; minerals for industry; hydroelectricity for energy; watershed protection for ecosystems; gas and oil for cars and other vehicles).

5. Explain that forests may be managed with an emphasis on different needs. For example, some may be managed to meet the needs of wildlife, others to meet recreational needs, and still others to meet the need for forest products. Or, if possible, one forest can be managed to meet all of the needs above.

6. Divide students into teams of four. Tell team members to pretend they are forest managers and need to manage a forest for wildlife. What strategies would they use to promote wildlife? What would wildlife need to survive in the forest? Examples include food, water, shelter, and space. Have each group share its ideas and record them on the chalkboard in a column next to "Wildlife."

7. Next, have students pretend they must manage a forest for recreational use. Have them brainstorm what a forest manager would need to do to promote recreation. What types of activities might go on in the forest? What would the manager need to provide for these activities? (e.g. roads, trails, parking, bathrooms, campgrounds, picnic areas) Ask them to share their ideas and record them on the chalkboard next to "Recreation."

8. Finally, have students pretend that, as forest managers, they must manage a forest to provide products for people. What things would they need to consider to manage the forest in this way? Which resources will be removed from the forest, how will they be taken out, and what will be needed so the resources can be removed? Once again, record the group's ideas on the chalkboard in a column next to "Products."

NOTE—As a time-saving alternative to doing Steps 6-8, you can divide your group into three teams and have each brainstorm a list of ideas for one category ("Wildlife," "Recreation," or "Products").

9. Explain that, in many cases, forests today are managed for more than one use at a time. Have your students look at the lists they created and ask them these questions:

- Which activities listed can go on at the same time in the same forest?

- Which activities on the list might conflict with one another if someone tried to manage both at the same time?

- Would those activities always conflict or conflict only at certain times and under certain conditions?

1. Show students the collected pictures of forest animals and have them identify each one. Ask if they've ever seen this animal in real life. If they have, ask where. (Many will have seen the animal only in a zoo.) If they haven't seen the animals, discuss why not. (Some may never have been in a forest, and usually when you are in a forest, you do not see animals.) Tack the pictures on a bulletin board or tape them to a chalkboard under the heading "Wildlife." You may also want to have students name other animals that live in forests.

2. Show students the collected pictures of people doing recreational activities. What are people doing in each picture? Have any students done those activities? Which activities could be done in a forest? (all) Again, place the pictures on a bulletin board or chalkboard, and ask students to name other activities people could do in forests.

3. Show students pictures of products from forests, and have them identify what's in each picture. Ask which items they use. (Depending on the pictures you gathered, you may need to explain what some items are.) Place those pictures on a bulletin board or chalkboard, and have students name other examples of forest products.

4. Have students look at all the pictures you've placed on the bulletin board, and explain that there are people who manage forests so that the forests can provide homes for wildlife and people, recreation places for people, and products people need and want. Ask students to identify activities listed on the bulletin board that might go on in a forest at the same time. For example, people may hike through a forest where animals in the "Wildlife" column are living. Other people may hike, birdwatch, and ski in the same areas. People may reach camping areas by driving on the same roads that go to areas of the forest that are being logged. Some animal species may do well in forests that have be opened up by logging.

Enrichment

Students will enjoy putting on mystery dramas to show multiple uses of a forest area. Divide students into teams of four. Explain that each team will perform a silent skit depicting a particular forest use. Secretly assign each team a forest use such as hiking, camping, logging, skiing, mining, or living in a wildlife habitat. Have teams go to different areas to quietly discuss or practice their skits. After about 20 minutes, bring teams back and have each team silently present its skit. After each skit, have other teams guess what forest use was being portrayed.

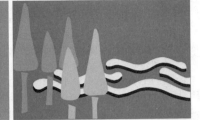

Overview
Few issues, if any, have simple solutions—and resolving them usually involves compromise. In this activity, your students will learn about some of the effects that human activities can have on a forest. They will explore some of the trade-offs involved in working out a land-use issue.

Background
Just like forest ecosystems, forest issues are varied and complex; solutions to forest problems are not always obvious or satisfying to everyone. In most conflicts involving forests, many individuals, organizations, and agencies have different perspectives and beliefs on how forested land should be managed.

The conflict is often heightened when all or part of the forest involved is considered an **old-growth** area. What is an old-growth forest? The answer depends on where the forest is, what tree species it contains, and what criteria we use. For example, by some definitions, a white pine forest in Maine would have to be over 100 years old to be considered old-growth, while a Douglas fir forest in Oregon would have to be over 200 years old. The Forest Service estimates that the United States has about 13.2 million acres (5.3 million ha) of old-growth forests. Approximately 8.0 million of these acres (3.2 million ha) are protected within national parks and wilderness areas.

People have many different views about what laws and regulations, if any, should govern the use of the remaining 5.2 million acres (2.1 million ha) of old-growth forest in the United States. Here, we present two positions that are on opposite sides. However, there are many compromise positions in between.

Many people feel that old-growth forests should be left untouched and that logging in those areas should be prohibited. Those people believe that too much old-growth has already been cut and that the remaining old-growth habitat must be preserved to ensure the survival of plants and animals living there, some of which are already endangered.

Others feel that enough old-growth forest has already been set aside in parks and wilderness areas, and that harvesting and replanting should be allowed on the remaining lands. They believe that closing off old-growth forests will seriously hurt the economic stability of many regions and that whole communities will disappear. They claim that when old-growth is harvested and replanted, new forests will be capable of meeting the demands for forest products, wildlife habitat, clean water, and recreation.

This is a simplification of an issue that has complex legal, political, ecological, economical, and social ramifications. In most situations like these, the people are not "good" or "bad"; they merely have their own needs, emotions, biases, and beliefs. In many situations, people feel that they have compromised enough, and they refuse to consider any more compromises. Such a position makes it harder to find a solution that will satisfy everyone.

Getting Ready
Make copies of student page 104.

Doing the Activity
1. Have students imagine that they have been given a large piece of forest land on the outskirts of town. They can do anything they want with it. What would they do? Give students, or teams of students, time to think. Then have them share their ideas.

LEVELS
Grades 6-8

SUBJECTS
Science, Social Studies, Language Arts

CONCEPTS
- Forests, as well as other ecosystems, contain numerous habitats that support diverse populations of organisms. (1.2)
- Human societies and cultures throughout the world interact with each other and affect natural systems upon which they depend. (6.1)
- Cultural and societal perspectives influence the attitudes, beliefs, and biases of people toward the use of resources and environmental protection. (6.3)
- Governmental, social, and cultural structures and actions affect the management of resources and environmental quality. (12.2)

SKILLS
Analyzing, Discussing, Defining Problems, Making Decisions, Solving Problems

OBJECTIVES
Students will ① evaluate the options for managing or using a piece of forested land and ② make a land-use decision and explore the consequences of that decision.

MATERIALS
copies of student page 104, chalkboard or flipchart

TIME CONSIDERATIONS
Preparation: 15 minutes

Activity: One or two 50-minute periods

2. Ask students what consequences their plans might have on the neighboring community and environment. Did they consider those consequences when they decided on a plan? Explain that they will take a closer look at a particular situation as they explore the consequences of various land-use decisions.

3. Read aloud the scenario written in italics on student page 104.

4. Divide students into teams of four, and explain that members of each team should work together to decide what the Morristown City Council should do. Each team member should agree with the team's decision and be able to explain it to the rest of the group.

5. Pass out copies of student page 104, which contains written proposals of different interest groups on how the land should be used. As the teams read through each proposal, they should ask themselves the questions below. Afterward, they should decide either to accept one proposal or to make a compromise or alternate proposal.

- What facts presented in the proposal support that land use?

- What opinions are presented in the proposal?

- What will it cost the town to adopt the proposal?

- What are the advantages of adopting the proposal?

- What negative effects could result from adopting the proposal?

- Who benefits most from the proposal?

- If you adopt the proposal, what changes, if any, would you want to make to it?

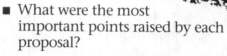

6. Give students plenty of time to work out a solution. Afterward, have each team present its decision to the entire group. After all teams have presented their decisions, discuss the following questions:

- Was it difficult or easy to decide what to do? Explain your answers.

- What were the most important points raised by each proposal?

- Did you have enough information to make a good decision?

- If you knew the city of Morristown was in a severe economic recession, would it have changed your team's plan? If yes, how? If no, why not?

- If you knew that a rare plant grew in several sections of the forest, would that fact have changed your team's plan? If yes, how? If not, why not? What if a rare species of squirrel lived in the forest? What if a rare species of mosquito lived there?

- What differences might exist between the way you made your decision and the way a real city council would have made a decision like this?

- There is a saying that people should consider the effects of their actions to the seventh generation. Did you consider future generations when you decided on a land management plan, or were you concerned only with how Morristown would be affected now? How strongly do you agree with this saying?

7. How do the proposals relate to one another? What would you do if two of the proposals could be accepted? What would be the compromises, advantages, and disadvantages involved?

VARIATION

1. Divide students into groups of ten. Four students within each group will become the City Council that has to decide what to do with Morris Woods. The six other students will work in pairs to present each land-use proposal: one pair represents the developer; one pair, the lumber company, and one pair, advocates of creating a wilderness park. In their groups, have students present their proposals to the City Council. The council must decide to accept one proposal, but members can also make amendments to it. Afterward, call all teams together and have the various City Councils present their decisions.

2. You can also set up a public hearing. Select seven students to serve as a panel of judges. Divide the rest of the students into five teams. Using the three proposals for reference, each team should come up with its own proposal for what to do with Morris Woods. Each team will have the same amount of time to present its proposal to the judges. Each judge then votes for one proposal out of the five that he or she prefers. The proposal that gets the most votes wins. In the case of a tie, the judges should vote again to break the tie.

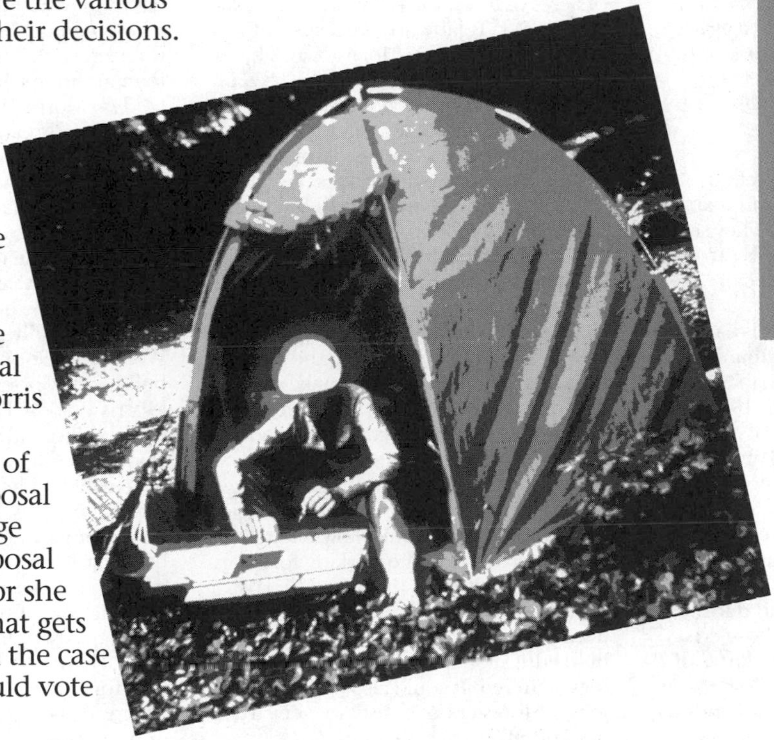

Enrichment

Students can put together a special class newspaper, or a radio or TV broadcast, that features the Morris Woods controversy. Students can write a news story, or opinion piece for the project. (Make sure there is a good mix.) For radio or TV broadcasts, encourage students to work in groups and try some live interviews or play-acting.

END NOTES...

ASSESSMENT OPPORTUNITY

1. Examine the students' answers to the questions in Step 6 of the activity to assess how well they grasp the dynamics of issues presented in the Morris Woods controversy.

2. Discuss with your students the old-growth controversy in the Pacific Northwest using background information on page 101. Ask students what similarities or differences this controversy has with the Morris Woods situation? How would you feel about this issue if you lived in the Pacific Northwest? What personal factors (job, interests, home, family) influence the way you feel about the old-growth controversy? Assess students' answers to determine how well they understand the complexity of issues in the Morris Woods situation.

RELATED ACTIVITIES

A Forest of Many Uses, 400-Acre Wood, Who Works in this Forest? I'd Like to Visit a Place Where..., Forest for the Trees, Loving It Too Much

MORRIS WOODS

Last month someone donated 250 acres (101 hectares) of nearby land to the town of Morristown. The land, known as Morris Woods, is completely covered with forest, including about 100 acres (40.5 ha) of old-growth forest that is over 150 years old and has very large trees. A nice stream flows through the forest and has good places for swimming. Deer, raccoon, frogs, salamanders, foxes, many different birds, and other animals live in the forest.

Morristown is a medium-sized, middle-class town. Many people who live there work for a local lumber company, but a lot of people also work at a computer-parts plant in a neighboring town. Many people work in Morristown itself at the schools and library and in all sorts of small businesses.

There are no zoning restrictions on Morris Woods, and the City Council has to decide what to do with the land. Some people want to preserve the entire area with all of its animals and plants so that it can provide people with a "wilderness" experience close to home. A developer has offered to buy the land and build a shopping mall and luxury homes. The local lumber company has offered to buy the forest land and manage it to provide forest products, wildlife habitat, and scenic hiking trails. If you were a member of the Morristown City Council, what would you vote to do?

Proposal #1

Proposal: Morristown should retain ownership of Morris Woods and manage it as a protected natural area. They should build and maintain hiking trails through it so the people of Morristown can enjoy it.

Perspective: Morris Woods is a unique area. Giant trees, some more than 100 feet (30.5 m) tall and more than 30 feet (9 m) around, make up about 100 acres (40.5 ha) of the forest. Some of these trees are almost 200 years old and were growing long before Morristown even existed. Walking among them is an incredible experience. Many other plants and many different kinds of animals also live in Morris Woods.

If we allow trees to be cleared for development, the habitat of those creatures will be destroyed. Several kinds of fish breed in the streams that flow through Morris Woods. Studies conducted in the woods just a year ago showed that those fish depend on cool water and gravel bottoms to lay their eggs. If parts of the forest are cleared, the fish may not be able to breed because (a) soil and other debris from the cleared land will wash into the streams and cover the gravel; and (b) with fewer trees to shade the stream and condition the air, temperatures in the stream will increase. Similar problems may result if parts of the forest are man-

aged for timber production.

Morristown doesn't need a mall. It has all the shops the townspeople need right in town. And if we did build a mall, what would happen to all those business owners downtown? They'd go out of business!

There are no forests as old and as large as Morris Woods anywhere in our region. Why should the people of Morristown sacrifice their natural heritage so some business people can make a lot of money? Setting the land aside and maintaining hiking trails will be the best thing for the people of Morristown today, and for future Morristown residents.

Proposal #2

Proposal: Morristown should sell Morris Woods to the L.T. Lumber Company, which would manage the forest for multiple uses.

Perspective: L.T. Lumber Company now manages much of the forest land near Morristown. In fact, the company has harvested and replanted thousands of acres of forest for 125 years. Trees harvested on L.T. land are processed into lumber at the mill in Morristown. That lumber is in high demand and is used in most local construction jobs.

We, at L.T. Lumber, offer to buy Morris Woods and manage it for commercial as well as ecological values. We plan to set aside an area of old-growth forest and to establish a buffer strip of forest around the stream to protect those important habitat areas. In the "working" part of the forest, we will practice selective cutting or clear cutting, depending on which is the best technique for managing the forest for all its resources. We will make sure that tree harvesting takes place under carefully controlled circumstances and will make every effort to minimize the visual affects of tree harvesting. Our regular practice is to immediately replant harvested areas, and we will allow hiking and other recreation in the working forest.

The money from the sale of Morris Woods will provide a much-needed economic boost to Morristown and could help education and social programs that have suffered. It could also provide new jobs for foresters, scientists, loggers, truckers, and mill workers.

Setting aside the entire forest as a wilderness park would lock up an important and needed supply of inexpensive, high-quality wood—and we already have several parks in and around Morristown. Like other natural resources, forests should provide economic, social, and ecological values at the same time. If the land is developed for a mall, valuable resources and wildlife habitat will be lost indefinitely.

The Morristown area has plenty of retail business, and forestland is too precious to waste.

According to our management plan, there will be minimal environmental trade-offs, and L.T.'s long history of responsible forest management speaks for itself.

Proposal #3

Proposal: Morristown should sell Morris Woods so developers can build a shopping mall on a large tract and new homes on the remaining portion while preserving its "forest character."

Perspective: Shopping malls are very convenient places for people to shop; all the stores are together under one roof and people can go from one store to another without going outside—a big plus, especially in bad weather. Malls often contain many national chains, offering shoppers more choices and very competitive prices. Malls draw people from a wide area, and their shopping can mean big money. So far, no one has built a shopping mall in Morristown, or anywhere near it. The closest mall is more than an hour's drive away.

The Morris Woods shopping mall would be a great convenience to the people of Morristown and surrounding communities. The money generated from the sale of the land and from property taxes could be used to improve Morristown schools and the town library, and to provide social services such as medical care and affordable housing.

After building the mall, we at Morris Woods Development Company would build luxury houses in another area of Morris Woods. Those houses would provide families with beautiful homes in a wooded setting near town. Their property taxes would help the above-mentioned social programs. Morris Woods Development Company plans to leave a buffer strip of forest around the stream and to preserve an area of old-growth forest. The roads through our development will be pleasant for walking or bicycling.

Locking up the entire woods as wilderness for a handful of nature enthusiasts is not in the best public interest. Our development plan will make the land more accessible for many different uses: recreation, leisure, shopping, commerce, and homes. And why should L.T. Lumber Company be the sole beneficiary of land that belongs to all of us? It is only fair that Morris Woods is developed in a way that benefits the most people possible, and our proposal offers those benefits.

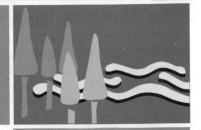

Overview

All kinds of people work in the forest—from foresters to loggers, from scientists to naturalists. Everyone depends on properly managed forests for recreation, essential products, and a healthy environment. This activity provides students with an overview of forest-related careers.

Background

Forestry is more than just planting trees and fighting forest fires, although those tasks may be part of a professional forester's responsibilities.

In nature, forest ecosystems are controlled by sunlight, rain, and soil fertility. Wind storms, insect infestation, tree disease, and lightning also have a role in regulating forest ecosystems.

We cannot depend on nature alone to take care of forests and provide the timber, wildlife, clean air, water, and other forest products that we need today and in the future. In the profession of forestry, people care for forests in ways that mimic nature. Urban foresters specialize in caring for the nearly 70 million acres (28 million hectares) of forests that grow in and around metropolitan communities. They pay close attention to factors that affect those forests, such as limited growing space, poor air, lack of water, poor soil quality, and vandalism. Urban foresters try to increase the average life span and maintain the aesthetic quality of trees in those city parks or forests.

Forestry activities can also affect surrounding communities. For example, when trees are harvested or pesticides are used, the water quality in nearby streams must be protected. Foresters are trained to care for all the systems in and around the forest.

While foresters are trained in managing all forest resources, foresters often call on other professionals who specialize in individual parts of the forest, such as soils, water, or wildlife. Some specialists work in computer modeling, mapping, and statistical or budget analysis. Usually, a team of foresters and specialists work together to decide how to care for the forest so that it provides all the things people need and want from it.

Getting Ready

Make copies of student page 107 and gather magazines for cutting out pictures.

Doing the Activity

1. Ask students if they have either visited or seen pictures of a forest. Do they think those forests require people to take care of them? If so, what kind of work is necessary? Record their answers on the chalkboard.

2. Discuss with students how forests provide plant and animal habitats; paper and wood products; places for recreation; and air, soil, and water protection. Explain that people must manage forests to enhance all of these. See if students can add more jobs to their list by drawing on this discussion.

3. Pass out copies of page 107, and tell students the page will describe several people who do particular types of work. Students should read the brief descriptions and decide which jobs are necessary in caring for a forest. If they think a job is necessary, they should check "Yes," and explain their choice underneath; otherwise, they should check "No," and explain their choice.

4. Go over page 107 with students. Have them share their choices and the reasons for those choices. By the end of the discussion, all students should realize that every job on the page is helpful in conserving and caring for forests. Also use background information as you discuss some other kinds of people who work with forests.

5. Write the following occupations on the chalkboard: logging truck driver, cardboard box maker, nature guide, wildlife biologist, bird-watcher, newspaper deliverer, wildlife artist, angler, sawmill operator, campground manager, and garden supply store owner.

LEVELS
Grades 3-6

SUBJECTS
Science, Social Studies

CONCEPTS
- Successful technologies are those that are appropriate to the efficient and sustainable use of resources, and to the preservation and enhancement of environmental quality. (2.3)
- The extracting, processing, transporting, and marketing of natural resources provide employment opportunities for many people. (6.5)
- Evolving technologies require well-educated and skilled workers who are dedicated to the conservation ethic. (14.3)

SKILLS
Identifying Attributes and Components, Representing, Formulating Questions, Discussing

OBJECTIVES
Students will ① explore a variety of jobs that are directly related to forest resources and ② describe how various professionals work together to care for forests.

MATERIALS
Copies of student page 107, art supplies, magazines for cutting out pictures (optional)

TIME CONSIDERATIONS
Preparation: 15 minutes
Activity: 50 minutes

6. Ask students how each of those workers could benefit from having forests managed by the people they've learned about. Which workers depend on forests in some way to do their jobs? (all of them) Be sure students explain how each person depends on forests.

Enrichment

Invite several people whose jobs (forester, wildlife biologist, logger, sawmill worker, and so on) are related to the forest to come and speak to your group. Have students prepare questions to ask each person about the work he or she does. Here are some possible questions:

- What kind of training do you need?

- What's a typical day like?

- How many other people do you work with?

- What other kinds of people do you depend on to do your job?

- What kinds of clothes do you wear to work?

- What special equipment do you use on the job and what does this equipment enable you to do?

- What are the most rewarding things about your job?

- What aspects of your job pose the biggest challenges?

Afterward, have students draw pictures or write stories about the people and their jobs.

ANSWERS FOR STEP 6

logging truck driver—Work depends on the availability of logs.

cardboard box maker—Work depends on wood to make cardboard.

nature guide—Forested land is pleasant place to hike and study.

wildlife biologist—Forests contain wild creatures to be studied.

birdwatcher—Forests provide a habitat for many different kinds of birds.

newspaper deliverer—Papers are made from trees.

wildlife artist—Artist may use forests and the animals and plants that live there as subjects for pieces of art.

angler—The forest protects streams, the habitat of fish.

sawmill operator—Business depends on a supply of logs.

campground manager—Nearby forests draw people to certain campgrounds.

garden supply store owner—Bark from trees provides mulch for people's gardens.

END NOTES...

ASSESSMENT OPPORTUNITY

Using magazines, have each person create a collage showing how people depend on forests. It can include pictures of forests, trees, people living near forests, forest products, and people using forests or products, and people working in forests. Have the students explain their collages to you verbally or in writing.

RELATED ACTIVITIES

Tree Treasures, We All Need Trees, Plant a Tree! A Forest of Many Uses, 400-Acre Wood

WHO WORKS IN THIS FOREST?

1 Juanita

Many of my friends call me "Wild Woman." That's because I'm a wildlife biologist. I help make sure that wild animals and plants have all the things they need to survive, such as food, water, and space.

Is this job necessary? ☐ **YES** ☐ **NO**
Explain

_____

_____

_____

_____

_____

3 Brigitte

How would you like to decide how a forest should be cared for? That's what I do all the time. I'm a forester. Being a forester can be tricky: I have to find the right balance between all kinds of needs, including the needs of people, plants, and animals.

Is this job necessary? ☐ **YES** ☐ **NO**
Explain

_____

_____

_____

_____

_____

5 Haley

Like all hydrologists (high-DRAHL-uh-jists), I'm interested in water. I look at water supplies, study watersheds and water cycles, and try to solve water pollution problems.

Is this job necessary? ☐ **YES** ☐ **NO**
Explain

_____

_____

_____

_____

_____

2 Max

When people ask me what I do, I tell them I have a "dirty" job. I'm a soil scientist. One thing I do is monitor soils to make sure they don't get smashed down, or compacted. I know that soil can absorb a lot of water from snowmelt and rain. But if the soil gets compacted, rainwater and snow melt can rush right off, causing erosion problems.

Is this job necessary? ☐ **YES** ☐ **NO**
Explain

_____

_____

_____

_____

4 Jerome

I love numbers. And I get to deal with them each day: I'm a budget analyst. (A budget is a kind of outline of the money an organization expects to spend during a year.) I review the budgets people set up to make sure they're not spending too much money or money on the "wrong" things, and to make sure they're spending enough money on the "right" things.

Is this job necessary? ☐ **YES** ☐ **NO**
Explain

_____

_____

_____

_____

6 Takashi

Are some living things more resistant to diseases and pests than others? Do some living things grow faster than others? Can these abilities be transferred to other living things, creating things that are "better"? These are the kinds of questions I'm trying to answer. I'm a geneticist (juh-NET-uh-sist).

Is this job necessary? ☐ **YES** ☐ **NO**
Explain

_____

_____

_____

_____

Overview
National parks are the treasures of any nation. Yet national parks today struggle with serious dilemmas. By looking at problems in America's national parks, students can begin grappling with some tough environmental issues that affect parks locally and globally.

LEVELS
Grades 6-8

SUBJECTS
Science, Language Arts, Social Studies

CONCEPTS
■ While technological advances decrease the incidence of disease and death, the ever-increasing world population is placing heavy demands on the finite resources of the Earth. (5.2)

■ Cultural and societal perspectives influence the attitudes, beliefs, and biases of people toward the use of resources and environmental protection. (6.3)

■ Demographics influence environmental quality, government policy, and resource use. (12.3)

■ Ecosystems change over time through patterns of growth and succession. They are also affected by other phenomena such as disease, insects, fire, weather, and human intervention. (15.4)

SKILLS
Comprehending, Analyzing, Representing, Interpreting, Predicting

OBJECTIVES
Students will ① explain how increased numbers of park visitors and activities outside park boundaries affect ecosystems within national and local parks and ② offer possible solutions to problems facing national and local parks.

MATERIALS
Graph paper, pencils, copies of student pages 110, 111, and 112 .

TIME CONSIDERATIONS
Preparation: 15 minutes

Activity: Two 50-minute periods

Background
According to 1993 figures, the National Park Service oversees 80 million acres (32.4 million hectares) of the National Park System thereby preserving much of our country's historical and natural heritage. Large parks, lake shores, seashores, battlefields, memorials, recreational areas, and historic homes are all part of the system. According to the act that created the National Park Service, all areas in the National Park System are to be managed "to conserve the scenery and the natural and historic objects" in them, and to enable people to enjoy those objects in ways that "will leave them unimpaired for the enjoyment of future generations."

Wilderness Areas are federal lands specially designated by Congress; and they are different from National Parks (although National Parks may contain Wilderness Areas). Wilderness Areas are governed by strict guidelines, which for the most part, prohibit road building, logging, hunting, fishing, mineral and oil exploration. At present, 92 million acres of forested and unforested land has been set aside–an area the size of Montana. Each federal agency manages Wilderness Areas: About 49% of US Park Service lands have been set aside as wilderness, about 10% of Bureau of Land Management lands, about 24% of Fish and Wildlife Service lands, and about 15 % of US Forest Service lands.

Since the end of World War II, more and more people have been visiting national parks. Our increased population, standard of living, leisure time, and better transportation have fueled this explosion. Many parks have been overused by the increasing volume of visitors. The number of souvenir shops, hotels, restaurants, and other developments within the parks has ballooned and so has development outside park boundaries. The latter can bring air and water pollution, even to remote parks. (See "Problems in Paradise" on page 112 for specific examples of park problems.)

What can be done to protect our parks so that people today and generations tomorrow can visit them and have enjoyable experiences? Many ideas have been put forth, and different strategies work better for different parks. Here are a few solutions people have suggested that are already being implemented in some parks:

■ Determine the carrying capacity for each park and limit visitors to that number at any given time.

■ Limit and reduce automobile access to parks. Establish buses, trams, and other mass transit systems within parks to move people around.

■ Close many shops within the parks and move them to areas outside park boundaries. Re-evaluate other concessions (e.g., restaurants, gas stations) within the parks and possibly move some out as well.

■ Restrict the types of activities people can do within or adjacent to certain parks. Or, to conserve the park ecosystems, restrict the times of the year for such activities.

■ Increase the Park Service's budget for science and conservation programs.

■ Educate the public about the need to protect parks already in the system and to increase the number of protected areas.

Getting Ready

1. Make copies of student pages 110, 111, and 112.

2. If possible, obtain PLT's Federal & Forest Land Map. See References.

3. Show your students how to plot a graph on graph paper.

Doing the Activity

1. Begin by asking students how many of them have visited a national park in the United States or abroad. Talk about some local or famous national parks using the chart on page 113. Have students share their experiences in the parks. Where did they go? What was it like? What did they see? Were there very many people there?

2. Ask students which of the following activities they think are allowed in America's national parks: mining, logging, oil and gas drilling, or livestock grazing. (none) Discuss with your students the fact that although some public lands such as national forests are managed for multiple uses (wildlife, recreation, timber), national parks allow more restricted use. (Use Background for explanation of the National Park Service's mission.)

3. Divide your group into teams of two, three, or four. Pass out copies of pages 110 and 111, graph paper, and a pencil to each student. Have teams use the statistics to draw a bar or line graph of U.S. population growth since 1800 and a graph of park visitation from 1950 to 1990. You can also have them create their graphs using a computer. Depending on the level of your group, you may need to give them help in setting up and plotting their graphs.

4. Have students work in their groups to answer the questions. Afterward, go over the questions using the answers on this page.

5. Pass out copies of "Problems in Paradise" on page 112. While students are reading this page, write the following questions on the chalkboard. Have students work in their groups to discuss the reading and answer these questions:

- What problems have been caused by an increase of visitors to national parks?

- What other problems do national parks face?

- Do any of the same problems affect your local or community parks as well?

- What solutions would you recommend to combat those problems?

- What other information would you like to know before making recommendations?

- What problems might your recommendations solve?

- What problems might your recommendations create?

- Would your recommendations work for all parks or for only some?

- What can be done when the best action to protect resources inside a park would have a negative effect on communities outside the park?

6. Discuss problems facing the Park Service. What solutions did students recommend? How do other students feel about those recommendations? What are the pros and cons of each recommendation? Discuss some options presented in the background section. Do students think parks should charge entrance fees that adequately reflect the fair market value of a park experience? Why or why not?

Enrichment

Invite a local park employee (manager, forester, naturalist, ranger, police officer) to visit your group and address the students' concerns about how the park is managed and cared for, what its rules are, and how the rules are enforced. Have students discuss their ideas for solving park problems. They might also find out how to present suggestions to the appropriate person in the park's administration.

END NOTES...

ASSESSMENT OPPORTUNITY

Have students prepare written arguments stating what should be done about problems facing national or local parks. Tell students that each person's argument should explain the problems, as well as what causes the problems. Students should clearly state one or more recommendations for solving the problems and explain why their suggestions would be effective.

RELATED ACTIVITIES

I'd Like to Visit a Place Where…, 400-acre Wood, Who Works in This Forest?, A Forest of Many Uses

REFERENCES

Statistical Abstracts of the United States, 1993

SOURCES OF THREATS, State of the Parks. National Parks Service.

PLT FEDERAL AND FOREST LAND MAP. Write to PLT, American Forest Foundation, 1111 19th St NW, Washington DC 20036

ANSWERS

1. Both population and visits have regulary increased; visits have been increasing at a faster rate than population growth.

2. Students should realize that both will continue to rise.

3. Answers will vary. Possibilities could include (a) crowded cities and suburbs that cause people to want to visit open spaces in parks, (b) increased amounts of leisure time, and (c) increased ease of access because of improved highways and other roads and because of the popularity of automobiles and recreation vehicles.

4. Answers will vary. Students should realize that more support services (roads, rest rooms, and visitor centers) will be needed for increasing numbers of visitiors. Don't give students any answers at this point. They'll discover more problems when they look at the reading on page 112.

5. Answers will vary. Some students may realize that increased population growth can create problems around park boundaries or in the parks themselves. Don't give students any answers yet. When they read page 112, they'll discover more problems that increased population creates outside the parks.

STATISTICS

U.S. POPULATION

YEAR	POPULATION
1800	5,308,483
1820	9,638,453
1840	17,069,453
1860	31,443,321
1880	50,155,783
1900	75,994,575
1920	105,710,620
1940	131,669,275
1960	179,325,798
1980	226,545,805
1990	248,709,873

Source: Statistical Abstracts of the United States

RECREATION VISITS ALL NATIONAL PARK SERVICE AREAS

YEAR	VISITS (IN MILLIONS)
1950	33.0
1955	56.6
1960	79.2
1965	121.3
1970	172.0
1975	238.8
1980	300.3
1985	263.4
1990	258.7

Source: Statistical Abstracts of the United States

LAND AREA ALL NATIONAL PARK SERVICE AREAS

YEAR	LAND (IN 1,000 ACRES)
1950	24,598
1955	24,646
1960	25,704
1965	26,549
1970	28,543
1975	29,091
1980	70,936*
1985	75,749
1991	80,275

*Includes 41,845 million acres of Alaskan lands added to the system in 1978. To convert to hectares, multiply acres by .4047 hectares.

Source: Statistical Abstracts of the United States

QUESTIONS

1 Based on the graphs you drew, what trends do you see in the size of the U.S. population? What trends do you see in the number of visits to national parks?

2 What do you predict will happen to the size of the U.S. population, and how will that change affect the number of visits to national parks in the future?

3 What circumstances might explain changes in the number of visits to national parks since 1950?

4 What changes do you think were made in parks to accommodate the increasing numbers of park visitors? What problems, if any, might the increasing numbers of visitors have caused?

5 If the number of park visits stopped increasing, could continued population growth cause problems in the parks? If so, how? If not, why not?

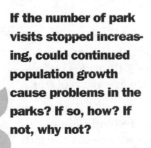

PROBLEMS IN PARADISE

Our nation's "crown jewels." That's how some people have described our national parks. Unfortunately, our parks face some big problems. Many people feel that if we don't take steps soon, our parks will suffer.

Inside Pressures

In 1990, more than 250 million visitors spent time in the historic homes and forts, recreation areas, seashores, memorials, and parks that make up our National Park System. That's about eight times as many people as visited the parks in 1950. And park visitation is expected to rise. In fact, some people estimate visits may double in the next 15 years.

Cars, campers, and motor homes already jam the most popular parks. Hikers often crowd trails. Visitors have destroyed trailside vegetation in many areas. Vandalism is a problem in almost every park: People steal Native American artifacts, plants, and other pieces of the parks to sell them to collectors; people spray graffiti on park rocks and walls; and vandals have even used park-protected items for target practice.

Accommodating so many people has put additional pressures on our parks. For example, more roads have been built to handle the increased traffic. New campgrounds have been built and existing ones have

been expanded. More concessions, including snack bars, hotels, and souvenir shops, have been built in many parks. All of these developments mean less habitat for plants and animals that live in the parks.

Outside Pressures

Aside from the problems being caused by increasing numbers of park visitors, other problems are caused by activities outside the park boundaries. As the population increases, civilization creeps closer and closer to park boundaries. Wild animals, whose natural ranges extend beyond park boundaries, are being squeezed together for living space as people develop land outside parks. In addition, resource extraction and management activities have brought pollutants into the parks. Let's look at a few threats facing certain parks:

■ On some days, air pollution can be a problem in Acadia National Park (Maine) and in Shenandoah National Park (Virginia).

■ Copper smelters near Glacier National Park (Montana) have caused fluoride contamination in some parts of the park.

■ Extensive development in Florida has drained, diverted, or polluted water necessary for the survival of many plants and animals in Everglades National Park. In the past 60 years, many wading birds that once nested in the Everglades have disappeared.

Finding Solutions

Fortunately, many problems in the parks are being addressed and solved. For example, studies in Cape Cod National Seashore (Massachusetts) have led to a management plan that allows off-road vehicle use and protects nesting seabirds and beaches where people swim. In the past few years, stream conditions in Olympic National Park (Washington) have improved. And people are working hard to reverse the changes that diverted water away from the Florida Everglades. However, it's going to take more action to completely protect all of our parks.

National parks belong to all people: young and old, able-bodied and disabled, those seeking complete solitude and those seeking a nice view. Most important, the parks belong to future citizens. Meeting the needs of people today while protecting our resources for the future is a big challenge for the National Park Service. How well it meets this challenge will determine whether, and in what condition, our parks survive.

NATIONAL PARKS, BY STATE

PARKS	ACREAGE	OUTSTANDING CHARACTERISTICS	PARKS	ACREAGE	OUTSTANDING CHARACTERISTICS
ALASKA			**MAINE**		
DENALI	4,716,726	CONTAINS N. AMERICA'S HIGHEST MOUNTAIN (20,320 FT)	ACADIA	41,408	RUGGED SEASHORE ON MT. DESERT ISLAND AND ADJACENT MAINLAND
GATES OF THE ARCTIC	7,523,888	DIVERSE NORTH CENTRAL WILDERNESS; CONTAINS PART OF BROOKS RANGE	**MICHIGAN** ISLE ROYALE (1931)	571,790	LARGEST WILDERNESS ISLAND IN LAKE SUPERIOR; MOOSE, WOLVES, LAKES
GLACIER BAY	3,225,284	PARK POPULAR FOR WILDLIFE, WHALE-WATCHING, GLACIER-CALVING, AND SCENERY	**MINNESOTA** VOYAGEURS	218,035	WILDLIFE, CANOEING, FISHING, AND HIKING
KATMAI	3,716,000	KNOWN FOR FISHING, 1912 VOLCANIC ERUPTION, BEARS	**MONTANA** GLACIER	1,013,572	ROCKY MOUNTAIN SCENERY WITH GLACIERS AND LAKES
KENAI FJORDS	669,541	MOUNTAIN GOATS, MARINE MAMMALS, BIRDLIFE	YELLOWSTONE	2,219,790	WORLD'S GREATEST GEYSER AREA; ABUNDANT FALLS, WILDLIFE AND CANYONS
KOBUK VALLEY	1,750,421	NATIVE CULTURE AND ANTHRO-POLOGY CENTER AROUND THE BROAD KOBUK RIVER IN NORTH WEST ALASKA	**NEVADA** GREAT BASIN	77,109	EXCEPTIONAL SCENIC, BIOLOGIC, AND GEOLOGIC ATTRACTIONS
LAKE CLARK	2,636,839	PARK PROVIDES SCENIC AND WILDERNESS RECREATION ACROSS COOK INLET FROM ANCHORAGE	**NEW MEXICO** CARLSBAD CAVERNS	46,755	THE WORLD'S LARGEST KNOWN CAVES
WRANGELL-ST. ELIAS	8,331,604	LARGEST PARK SYSTEM AREA HAS ABUNDANT WILDLIFE, SECOND-HIGHEST PEAK IN U.S. (MT. ST. ELIAS); ADJOINS CANADIAN PARK	**NORTH CAROLINA** GREAT SMOKY MTS.	520,269	HIGHEST MOUNTAIN RANGE EAST OF BLACK HILLS; LUXURIANT PLANT LIFE
ARIZONA GRAND CANYON	1,218,375	MILE-DEEP GORGE, 4 TO 18 MILES WIDE, 217 MILES LONG	**NORTH DAKOTA** THEODORE ROOSEVELT	70,416	SCENIC VALLEY OF LITTLE MISSOURI RIVER; T.R. RANCH
PETRIFIED FOREST	93,532	EXTENSIVE NATURAL EXHIBIT OF PETRIFIED WOOD	**OREGON** CRATER LAKE	183,224	DEEP BLUE LAKE IN HEART OF INACTIVE VOLCANO
ARKANSAS HOT SPRINGS	5,839	47 MINERAL HOT SPRINGS SAID TO HAVE THERAPEUTIC VALUE	**SOUTH DAKOTA** BADLANDS	243,244	ARID LAND OF FOSSILS, PRAIRIE, BISON, DEER, BIGHORN, ANTELOPE
CALIFORNIA CHANNEL ISLANDS	249,353	AREA IS RICH IN MARINE MAMMALS, SEA BIRDS, ENDANGERED SPECIES, AND ARCHAEOLOGY	WIND CAVE	28,292	LIMESTONE CAVERNS IN BLACK HILLS; BUFFALO HERD
KINGS CANYON	461,901	HUGE CANYONS; HIGH MOUNTAINS; GIANT SEQUOIAS	**TENNESSEE** GREAT SMOKY MTS.	520,269	HIGHEST MOUNTAIN RANGE EAST OF BLACK HILLS; LUXURIANT PLANT LIFE
LASSEN VOLCANIC	106,372	EXHIBITS OF IMPRESSIVE VOLCANIC PHENOMENA	**TEXAS** BIG BEND	802,541	MOUNTAINS AND DESERT BORDERING THE RIO GRANDE
REDWOOD	110,132	COASTAL REDWOOD FORESTS; CONTAINS WORLD'S TALLEST KNOWN TREE (369.2 FT.)	GUADALUPE MTS.	86,416	CONTAINS GUADALUPE PEAK (8,751 FT.)
SEQUOIA	402,482	GIANT SEQUOIAS; MAGNIFICENT HIGH SIERRA SCENERY, INCLUDING MT. WHITNEY	**UTAH** ARCHES	73,378	UNUSUAL STONE ARCHES, WINDOWS, PEDESTALS CAUSED BY EROSION
YOSEMITE	761,170	MOUNTAINS; INSPIRING GORGES AND WATERFALLS; GIANT SEQUOIAS	BRYCE CANYON	35,835	AREA OF GROTESQUE ERODED ROCKS, BRILLIANTLY COLORED
COLORADO MESA VERDE	52,085	BEST PRESERVED PREHISTORIC CLIFF DWELLINGS IN U.S.	CANYONLANDS	337,570	COLORFUL WILDERNESS WITH IMPRESSIVE RED-ROCK CANYONS, SPIRES, ARCHES
ROCKY MOUNTAIN	265,200	SECTION OF THE ROCKY MOUNTAINS; 107 NAMED PEAKS OVER 10,000 FT.	CAPITOL REEF	241,904	HIGHLY COLORED SEDIMENTARY ROCK FORMATIONS IN HIGH, NARROW GORGES
FLORIDA BISCAYNE	173,039	AQUATIC CORAL REEF PARK SOUTH OF MIAMI	ZION	146,597	MULTICOLORED GORGE IN HEART OF SOUTHERN UTAH DESERT
EVERGLADES	1,508,938	SUBTROPICAL AREA WITH ABUNDANT BIRD AND ANIMAL LIFE	**VIRGINIA** SHENANDOAH	195,382	TREE-COVERED MOUNTAINS; SCENIC SKYLINE DRIVE
HAWAII HALEAKALA	28,655	WORLD-FAMOUS 10,023-FT. HALEAKALA VOLCANO (DORMANT)	**WASHINGTON** MOUNT RANIER	235,404	SINGLE-PEAK GLACIAL SYSTEM; FORESTS, FLOWERED MEADOWS
HAWAII VOLCANOES	229,117	SPECTACULAR VOLCANIC AREA; LUXURIANT VEGETATION AT LOWER LEVELS	NORTH CASCADES	504,780	ROADLESS ALPINE LANDSCAPE; JAGGED PEAKS; MOUNTAIN LAKES; GLACIERS
IDAHO YELLOWSTONE	2,219,790	WORLD'S GREATEST GEYSER AREA; ABUNDANT FALLS, WILDLIFE AND CANYONS	OLYMPIC	921,942	FINEST PACIFIC NORTHWEST RAINFOREST; SCENIC MOUNTAIN PARK
KENTUCKY MAMMOTH CAVE	52,419	VAST LIMESTONE LABYRINTH WITH UNDERGROUND RIVER	**WYOMING** GRAND TETON	309,993	PICTURESQUE RANGE OF HIGH MOUNTAIN PEAKS
			YELLOWSTONE	2,219,790	WORLD'S GREATEST GEYSER AREA; ABUNDANT FALLS, WILDLIFE AND CANYONS

SOURCE: THE NATIONAL PARKS: INDEX 1989, U.S. DEPARTMENT OF THE INTERIOR, 1989.

Overview
Here's a way for your students to take a closer look at pollution: what it is, what its sources are, and what are some things people can do to reduce it.

LEVELS
Activity: Grades 2-6
Variation: Grades PreK-2

SUBJECTS
Science, Social Studies, Math

CONCEPTS
■ Altering the environment affects all life forms—including humans—and the interrelationships that link them. (4.2)

■ Pollutants, which are harmful by-products of human and natural systems, can enter ecosystems in various ways. (7.3)

■ Ecosystems possess measurable indicators of environmental health. (7.4)

■ The application of scientific knowledge and technological systems can have positive or negative effects on the environment. (8.1)

SKILLS
Observing, Comparing and Contrasting, Organizing Information, Solving Problems

OBJECTIVES
Students will ① identify forms of pollution and describe the effects that various pollutants can have on people, wildlife, and plants and ② describe relationships between various forms of pollution and human actions.

MATERIALS
Magazines, scissors, tape, poster board or paper, copies of student page 118, *The Cat in the Hat Comes Back* by Dr. Seuss

TIME CONSIDERATIONS
Preparation: 20 minutes
Activity: 50 minutes

Background

Thick, brown haze wraps around a city. Unwanted tires, appliances, and other refuse float in a stream. Oil washes up on a beach. All of these are examples of **pollution**. Human-generated chemicals, trash, noise, and heat can all be pollutants, but so can ash spewing from an erupting volcano or smoke spreading from a forest fire. Pollution is any contamination of air, water, or land that affects the environment in an unwanted way. Here's an overview of three types of pollution-air, land, and water—and a look at pollution controls.

Air Pollution: Automobiles, incinerators, coal-fired power plants, and factories send carbon dioxide, sulfur oxides, soot, and other pollutants into the air. Fireplaces and wood-burning stoves add carbon dioxide, ash, and other pollutants to the atmosphere. Other major forms of air pollution include *chlorofluorocarbons (CFCs)*, which are used in products such as refrigerators and air conditioners; smog; and toxins (benzene, asbestos, and lead).

Air pollutants can cause health problems for people and other living things. Smog can make people's eyes burn and can damage their lungs. *Acid rain*, caused when sulfur and nitrogen oxides in the air combine with water, has poisoned lakes in certain regions to a point where little life can survive in them. CFCs destroy ozone in the upper atmosphere, which allows more of the sun's harmful ultraviolet rays to reach Earth, possibly leading to increased rates of skin cancer. Increased amounts of carbon dioxide and other *greenhouse gases* in the atmosphere may affect world climate.

Water Pollution—Years ago, it was common for sewage treatment plants and industrial plants to discharge polluted waste water directly into rivers, bays, and oceans. Known as "point-source pollution," this practice continues unabated in many parts of the world. In the United States, government regulations, voluntary pollution prevention by industry, and citizen awareness have helped improve waste disposal methods. As a result, in parts of the US., many rivers and streams that were once severely polluted have been revived.

Non-point source pollution is pollution that is wide-ranging: for example, fertilizers, pesticides, and oil from cars wash into waterways from streets and agricultural land. Students should be aware that any pollutant released in a *watershed* or into the atmosphere will eventually find its way into the water cycle.

Land Pollution—Everything we throw away needs a place to go. Solid wastes that do not contain hazardous materials can be moved to sanitary landfills (about 80% of our solid waste ends up here) or burned to ash in an incinerator and then landfilled; many other items (glass, aluminum, paper, etc.) can be recycled (the U.S. currently recycles about 17% of its solid waste); and items like food scraps and yard waste can be composted, turned into dirt-like organic material that can then be recycled throughout a yard or garden. (See "Talking Trash, Not!" on page 119 for more information about landfills and incinerators, including problems associated with them.)

Hazardous wastes—flammable liquids, volatile or corrosive chemicals, and radioactive by-products—pose special disposal problems. Certain hazardous materials can be incinerated; others must be sealed in long-lasting, leak-proof drums; and others, like radioactive waste which may remain hazardous for generations, must be secured underground in complex, concrete reinforced structures.

Pollution Controls—By definition, pollution is bad. However, some pollution is also unavoidable. Natural events that we can't control can generate pollution. And much of our basic lifestyle generates pollution: producing goods, washing clothes, driving to work, watching television, growing food, rinsing things down the sink, fertilizing lawns, and so on. However, we can reduce the amount of pollution we produce by changing our lifestyles and by adopting new pollution-reducing technologies and other measures. For example, scrubbers in the smokestacks of coal-burning power plants can greatly reduce the amount of sulfur and nitrogen oxides such plants release. Using a little "elbow grease" instead of harsh chemicals to clean sinks and tubs can keep those harsh chemicals out of water supplies. Wastes stored in properly designed and maintained facilities can also be kept out of water supplies. Fuel-efficient cars burn less fuel, thereby releasing less pollution as well as consuming less energy. By riding bikes or walking instead of driving, people can further reduce the pollution they generate.

We also control and reduce pollution through laws. The United States has some of the strictest pollution control laws in the world. The Clean Air Act and the Clean Water Act (the Federal Water Pollution Control Act) are probably the two best-known examples. Under those laws, the Environmental Protection Agency (EPA) sets ① standards for which pollutants and, how much of each, can be dumped into waterways by sources such as industries and sewage plants; ② maximum levels of particular pollutants in the air; and ③ the amount of pollution that motor vehicles can produce. Other pollution control laws ① protect public drinking water supplies (Safe Drinking Water Act); ② regulate

pesticide use (Federal Insecticide, Fungicide, and Rodenticide Control Act-FIFRA); ③ control solid waste and hazardous waste disposal (Resource Conservation and Recovery Act-RCRA); and ④ regulate ocean dumping (Ocean Dumping Act).

Getting Ready
For Part A, make plans to take your students on a walk through the school neighborhood to look for signs and sources of pollution. For Part B, get a copy of *THE CAT IN THE HAT COMES BACK* by Dr. Seuss. For the Assessment section, make copies of student page 118.

PART A
NEIGHBORHOOD PATROL

Doing the Activity
1. Ask students to imagine what life would be like without clean air. What about life without clean water?

2. Ask students to list as many things as they can that might contaminate, or make unsafe, the air we breathe or the water we drink. List their ideas where everyone can see. Ask students if they know what word people use to describe the types of things they've listed. ("pollutants" or "pollution") Discuss what the term "pollution" means.

3. Take students on a walk (outdoors or indoors) to look for pollution or pollutants. During your walk, have students identify pollution they can see (litter, smoke); hear (honking horns, airplanes); or smell (diesel fumes, fresh paint). Alternatively, have students find examples of pollution on land (litter), in the air (car exhaust), and in water (pollutants that could wash into storm drains). As students spot different examples, have them explain how each one could pollute. What kinds of plants or animals (including people) could be affected by each one? Also ask students what might have caused each form of pollution. For example, how did a piece of litter get on the ground? How did oil get on the pavement? Record what they find outside, or have some students be recorders. Students can create bar graphs depicting the number of pollutants they have recorded in each category.

4. Back inside, have students draw pictures of pollution they spotted on the walk or things that might cause pollution. They can continue their search by looking through magazines for examples of pollution. (See Step 1 in Enrichment.) They should try to find at least one example for each category identified earlier: sight, smell, and sound; or air, land, and water.

5. Create a large chart on poster board or butcher paper with columns for each different category of pollution identified in Step 3. Have students take turns placing the pictures they drew into the pollution categories.

6. As a group, review and discuss the finished chart. Depending on the level of your group, ask students some of these questions:

■ Do any of the same items appear in different categories? If so, do you agree with where those items were placed? Can something pollute two different things, such as air and water, or land and water? How?

■ Can people always see, hear, or smell pollution?

■ Which examples on the chart might affect people's health? Which ones might affect plants or animals? In what ways?

■ One at a time, point out several examples on the chart and ask students how each form of pollution might be prevented. (To prevent litter, people could dispose of their trash properly; to prevent oil leaks, they could keep cars in good running order; and so on.) Depending on the level of your students, you might also have them discuss the fact that we can't prevent all pollution. Explain that we have developed technologies to reduce the amount of pollution we generate, and people are constantly working to develop newer technologies.

PART B
CAT WITH AN ATTITUDE
Doing the Activity

1. Tell students they are going to hear a fable about pollution. A fable is a story that teaches an important lesson.

2. Read aloud *The Cat in the Hat Comes Back*, making sure to show the pictures. (The story may be available on film or video.)

3. Tell them that, besides being funny, the story can teach us something about people's attitude toward pollution.

■ Ask students what represented pollution in the story. (the pink stuff)

■ Where did the pollution come from? (the cat)

■ How did the cat deal with the pollution first? (moved it from one place to another)

■ Did this solve the problem? (no)

■ Who did the "big cat" call on to help him solve the problem? (little cats)

■ What did the little cats do? (broke the pink stuff into little pieces and spread it around)

■ Did this help? (no)

■ Who finally cleaned up the mess? (little cat "Z")

■ Could we see him? (no)

■ What did he use to clean it up? (a "voom")

■ Could we see it? (no)

■ Do we know how it works? (no, just that it "cleans up anything")

4. After analyzing the story, discuss with students how *The Cat in the Hat Comes Back* demonstrates a common attitude people have toward pollution: We can deal with pollution by moving it from one place to another, for example, burying it or shooting it into space. Many people also feel we can simply break it up and spread it over a large area (pumping it into the air or dumping it into the ocean). In the end, many people simply feel that technology will solve all of our pollution problems. (This is like believing in the invisible "Z" cat with his invisible "voom.")

5. Ask students what they can do today to make their world a cleaner, safer, and healthier place instead of waiting for someone else to clean up their messes. Encourage them to learn more about what causes different types of pollution and what they can do to lessen it or clean it up.

Enrichment

1. For homework, have students look through newspapers or magazines and bring in pictures of pollution or potential pollution problems. They should each write a sentence or two about the pollution represented in their pictures. Have them mount their pictures and writing on a piece of construction or poster paper. The students should each tell how the pollution represented on their posters fits into categories they identified in Step 3 of Part A.

2. Now that your students are more aware of pollution, have them take action to help clean up their environment. Here are some projects your group may want to do:

■ Join forces with local cleanup operations.

■ Adopt an area—a nearby roadway, local park, or school—and keep it litter free.

■ Sponsor a pollution awareness week in your school. Have people take steps to reduce pollution all week long. Then encourage them to follow those steps all year long.

■ Organize a stream, beach, or neighborhood cleanup.

3. Younger students can decorate a pair of rubber gloves with nature images, slogans, colors, and so forth. Then, wearing their enviro-gloves, they can pick up litter in the forest, park, or school grounds. When they have collected a bag full of trash, children can sort it into piles, deciding what can be reused, recycled, composted, or thrown away.

END NOTES...

ASSESSMENT OPPORTUNITY
Pass out copies of page 118. Have each student circle items in the picture that are potential sources of pollution. On the back of the page they should explain how each item they circled might cause pollution and what can be done to prevent this form of pollution. See answers below.

RELATED ACTIVITIES
Air We Breathe, Every Drop Counts, Talking Trash, Not!, Energy Sleuths, Waste Watchers, Improve Your Place

REFERENCE
Dr. Seuss (Theodore Geisel). *THE CAT AND THE HAT COMES BACK.* New York: Beginner Books/Random House Inc., 1958.

ANSWERS TO ASSESSMENT

A person fertilizing the lawn—When used improperly, lawn chemicals may contribute to nonpoint source pollution. Students may want to consult with their garden center or local environmental agencies to learn about some of the potential hazards of certain lawn fertilizers and pesticides. Students can encourage adults to read chemical labelling carefully to insure that these products are used properly.

Six-pack rings—If improperly discarded, plastic six-pack rings may entangle and harm wildlife, both on the land and in the water. To protect these organisms, six-pack rings should be cut into smaller pieces and disposed of properly.

Person pouring motor oil down a drain—Some individuals who change their own motor oil contribute to nonpoint source pollution by not following proper oil disposal guidelines. Students can encourage adults to dispose of this potential pollutant properly and inform them to drop off their used motor oil at nearby service stations equipped with waste collection facilities.

Car driving on a road—Automobiles and other combustion engines contaminate the air with various air-borne pollutants. In order to limit this type of pollution, students can limit their use of automobiles by carpooling, taking mass transportation (buses and subways), and exploiting alternative means of transportation (such as walking or riding a bicycle). Students can also encourage adults to buy fuel-efficient cars and to keep all automobiles properly serviced.

Person walking a dog—Improperly discarded dog wastes are not only an unsightly form of litter, but may be a potentially harmful environmental pollutant, as well. Students can encourage dog owners to always clean up after their pets.

A person blasting a portable stereo—Loud music can sometimes contribute to noise pollution. To limit this pollutant, students can encourage people to wear headphones or to keep their music at a volume that is not bothersome to others.

POLLUTION SCENE

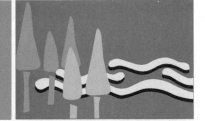

Overview
By taking a look at their own trash, your students can learn a lot about how and why they throw things away. They can find ways to cut down on the waste they produce and to improve the way waste is managed in their community.

Background
More and more people are involved in reusing, recycling, or recovering materials that people previously referred to as "trash." In fact, this "trash" is composed of valuable raw materials. Consequently, your community may sponsor recycling or composting programs, or have a waste–to–energy facility to decrease the amount of material disposed as waste.

Loving the Landfill—Many communities depend on landfills to take care of their garbage. In sanitary landfills, wastes are spread in thin layers, compacted, and covered with a fresh layer of soil each day. In modern landfills, methane gas is sometimes collected and used as fuel. Although landfills take up a lot of space, once they're filled and allowed to settle, it is possible to grade them for use as a park, a golf course, or a wildlife area.

Many existing landfills are filling up. Some communities are already exporting their waste to other areas, including other states and countries. Landfills are not designed to biodegrade or break down wastes. Some older landfills have been known to leak hazardous materials (motor oil, paint thinner, pesticides, etc.) and contaminate underground water supplies. However, newer landfills have special liners to help prevent this.

Up in Smoke—Incinerators can turn huge piles of garbage into much smaller piles of ash, which take up a lot less space in the landfill. In some communities waste is burned to produce electricity for community use. Incinerators can emit harmful materials from their smokestacks (especially when mercury batteries are burned). However, newer, cleaner incinerators and waste–to–energy plants are making these options more acceptable.

Getting Ready
For this activity, you will need some kind of large container (or containers) to hold a week's worth of classroom trash. Large cardboard boxes, a large trash barrel, or several plastic trash bags will all work well. (See Step 3 of the procedure for more about how you'll use the container and what to consider in choosing it.) You will also need to make arrangements so that no one collects trash from your room during the week.

Doing the Activity
1. Read aloud "Voyage of the Mobro" on page 120. On a map of North and Central America, have students trace the boat's voyage. What warnings should we receive from this bizarre story? (The urgent need for diverting and recovering materials from the waste stream.)

2. Discuss with students whether it is really possible to throw something away. Where is "away"? Do these things somehow disappear? Can trash continue to affect us even after we've thrown it away?

3. Tell students that for one week they will not throw anything away while in school. Explain that everything they want to throw away during the week should go into the large container you prepared earlier.

NOTE—Food wastes can be messy and unsanitary to keep. You might have students collect food waste in a separate container, weigh it, and record the contents before they throw it away. Have them predict how full the trash container will be by the end of the week. You might also have them predict the types of items that will make up the greatest proportion of the trash.

4. At the end of one week (or at the end of each day), have students look

LEVELS
Grades 1-6

SUBJECTS
Science, Social Studies, Math

CONCEPTS
■ By reducing waste and recycling materials, individuals and societies can extend the value and utility of resources and can promote environmental quality. (5.4)

■ All humans consume products and thereby affect the availability of renewable and nonrenewable natural resources. (6.4)

■ The application of scientific knowledge and technological systems can have positive or negative effects on the environment.(8.1)

SKILLS
Observing, Classifying and Categorizing, Researching, Analyzing, Predicting, Solving Problems

OBJECTIVES
Students will ① analyze the solid waste that they generate over a period of time, ② describe what happens to various types of waste when it's discarded, and ③ develop and implement a plan for reducing the amount of waste they generate.

MATERIALS
large box; boxes, pails, or other containers for sorted waste; rubber gloves; map of North and South America; bathroom scale (optional)

TIME CONSIDERATIONS
Preparation: 15 minutes

Activity: Several periods over the course of a week

at their trash. Did more or less accumulate than they'd predicted? You can sort through the trash and hold up items for them to see, or you can have one or more students sort through the trash. Be sure that whoever sorts wears rubber gloves. Record on the chalkboard the quantity and type of each item.

5. Older students can make tables, charts, or graphs that show volume, weight, number of pieces, and types of trash collected. They can figure the percentages of particular items or categories of items (e.g., paper, plastic) in the trash.

6. Using the following questions, discuss what usually happens to trash:

- What usually happens to classroom trash at the end of each day? (Someone collects it and takes it to a dumpster. You might want to take the students to see the dumpster.)

- Where does the trash end up? How often is it picked up? Have students guess. (In most cases, someone collects it from the dumpster and takes it to a local landfill where it is buried or to an incinerator where it is burned. Recyclable materials that are separated are often taken to a recycling facility.)

- What are the pros and cons of burning trash? (Greatly decreased the volume of waste. May put harmful pollutants in the air.)

- What are the pros and cons of landfills? (Provide easy disposal for large amounts of waste in a relatively sanitary fashion. Landfills are filling up and new landfills are difficult to site.)

- Where do the materials come from to make the items in their trash? (Paper comes from trees, metal cans from minerals in the earth, plastics from fossil fuels, fruit from trees and other plants.)

- When people use things only once and then throw them away, what are the effects on our supply of natural resources? (We have to use more minerals and fossil fuels for energy to create new products.)

7. Have the students look at the list on the chalkboard and try to think of what actions they could take to keep some items out of the trash and, therefore, out of the landfill or incinerator. As you go through the list, ask students to think of ways they could either reduce, reuse, or recycle each item on the list (i.e., recycle glass bottles and aluminum cans, reuse and recycle paper, use lunchbags over again, or compost food waste.)

8. Have the students develop an action plan to reduce the amount of trash they generate, then carry out the plan. Here are some suggestions of things your group can do. The students may also have other ideas.

- Set up a scrap box. Have the students put papers which they've only used one side of in the scrap box. When someone needs paper for scratch work or a short assignment, he or she can use a piece from the scrap box.

- Set up a "recycling center" in one corner of your room for the class (or for the whole school). You might collect aluminum, glass, plastics, and/or paper. Be sure to discuss what you're going to do with the collected material before you begin! (Find out what your school, community, or city is already doing. Consult the blue and yellow pages of the telephone book to locate recycling centers.)

- Create a compost pile outside your building. (Contact your state environmental agency for composting regulations.) Food scraps from your class, other classes, and the cafeteria can all be collected and then dumped in the compost pile. Building maintenance crews can also dump grass clippings and other yard waste into the compost pile. (*LET IT ROT!* by Stu Campbell has more about composting.)

- If composting outside is not an option, consider setting up a worm

THE VOYAGE OF THE MOBRO

During the spring of 1987, the small town of Islip, New York, hit national headlines. The media focused not on the people of the town, but rather on its garbage—nearly 3,200 tons (2,902 metric tons) of it. The landfills near Islip were filled beyond capacity, so Islip officials made a deal with Jones County, North Carolina, to handle Islip's trash.

When the Mobro—the barge transporting those tons of garbage from Islip—reached its destination, Jones County officials refused to accept the trash after determining that the cargo held hospital waste and other nonpaper trash as well. Fearing contamination of county water supplies, the North Carolina county sent the Mobro away.

For four months, the barge traveled along the Atlantic Coast to the Gulf of Mexico trying to find a state willing to dispose of the garbage. Unsuccessful, the Mobro even approached Mexico, Belize, and the Bahamas, but to no avail. The barge returned to dock at New York Harbor after a frustrating 6,000-mile (9,654-kilometer) voyage and awaited word from New York officials as to exactly what would become of its smelly cargo. A Brooklyn, New York, incinerator finally burned the garbage, reducing the volume from 3,200 tons (2,902 metric tons) to about 400 tons (363 metric tons) of ash, which was then dumped into a landfill back in Islip.

box in your classroom. All you need is a sturdy, ventilated box; some soil and shredded newspaper for "bedding" material; and some worms. Then add your food waste (but not meat or bones), keep the material moist, and turn everything once in a while to aerate it. Soon you'll have rich compost that's great for gardens and indoor plants. (For more information about setting up a worm box, read *WORMS EAT MY GARBAGE* by Mary Applehof.)

■ Have students bring in rags or old, worn-out clothes that can be turned into rags. Keep those rags in a handy place for cleaning up spills and other messes. These rags should be washed periodically.

■ Set up a swap table. If students have useful items they no longer want, such as old books, games, or clothes, they can bring in items to put on the swap table for others to take. (See "Reduce, Reuse, Recycle" on page 320 for more ideas.)

(See "Reduce, Reuse, Recycle" on page 320 for more ideas.)

VARIATION—DON'T BLOW YOUR ALLOWANCE

1. Let your class determine the amount of paper they think they will need for one week and allot them that amount.

2. Have class members manage their "allowance" in order to make the supplies last for the entire week.

3. At the end of one week, have students answer questions such as these: "Did we have enough paper?" "How much paper and pencils do we normally use in a week?" "Can we cut back?" "How much do we waste?"

4. The following week, let students further reduce their allotment of paper and try to stretch their resources by reusing and recycling.

Enrichment
Combine this activity with a field trip to a landfill, incinerator, or recycling center. Or have either a representative from one of those facilities or a professional from a solid waste management company speak to your students and answer their questions and concerns.

END NOTES...

ASSESSMENT OPPORTUNITY
For one week, have students keep a record of what goes into their garbage at home each day for a week. They could weigh it each day on a bathroom scale. Find out the total weight of a week's worth of family garbage. Calculate the "family average" for the class. Based on this figure, calculate the amount of garbage an average family would produce in a year. Compare this with the weight of an African bull elephant: 6.0 tons (5.4 metric tons). Have students write down 10 actions their family can take to cut down on this amount.

RELATED ACTIVITIES
We All Need Trees; Reduce, Reuse, Recycle; Pollution Search; Make Your Own Paper

REFERENCES
Applehof, Mary. *WORMS EAT MY GARBAGE.*
Campbell, Stu. *LET IT ROT!*

Overview

It's easy to waste water and even easier to take water for granted. Water pours out of our faucets as though it were endlessly available. But the truth is that fresh water supplies are dwindling. Fortunately, it's just as easy to conserve water as it is to waste it. Try this activity to help your class (and maybe the whole school) cut back on water waste.

LEVELS
Grades 4-8

SUBJECTS
Science, Social Studies, Math

CONCEPTS

■ Organisms are interdependent; they all depend on nonliving components of the Earth. (4.1)

■ By reducing waste and recycling materials, individuals and societies can extend the value and utility of resources and can promote environmental quality. (5.4)

■ Conservation and management technologies, when appropriately applied to the use or preservation of natural resources, can enhance and extend the usefulness of the resource as well as the quality of the environment. (11.2)

SKILLS
Predicting, Estimating, Organizing Information, Analyzing, Solving Problems

OBJECTIVES
Students will ① monitor their daily actions and estimate the amount of water they use in a day, ② describe how water is wasted and why it is important to conserve it, ③ design and implement a water conservation plan, and ④ determine the amount of water and money saved through their plan.

MATERIALS
Empty beverage container (1/2-gallon or 2-liter bottle), paper and pencils, measuring cup or other container, art supplies, copies of student page 125

TIME CONSIDERATIONS
Preparation: 15 minutes

Activity: Three or four 50-minute periods

Background

It's amazing how much water each of us uses every day. A seven-minute shower uses about 35 gallons (132.5 liters) of water. An average of six gallons (22.7 l) goes down the drain with each flush of a toilet. Washing a load of laundry requires at least 35 gallons (132.5 l) of water, and the list goes on. The U.S. public consumes about 36 billion gallons (136 billion l) a day. To that figure, add the water used by utilities, industry, and agriculture; thus the United States consumes 394 billion gallons (1,491 billion l) a day. That's nearly 2,000 gallons (7,570 l) for each person every day, which is the highest per capita use of any nation. Canadians come in second at about 1,200 gallons (4,542 l) per capita. (See the statistics below.)

Only about 0.003% percent of Earth's water is available for use; the rest either is saltwater, locked up in polar ice caps and glaciers, or located too deep in the ground to extract. If the world's water supply were represented by 26 gallons (98.4 l), then our usable supply of fresh water would be only one-half a teaspoon (0.003 l). Although natural systems can continually recycle this fresh water, the rate at which we use it is a problem.

Much of what we use every day is groundwater, which is water that fills the spaces between rocks and soil particles underground. The biggest source of groundwater supplies is precipita-

WATER USE

Breakdown of the 394 billion gallons* (1491 billion liters) of water used daily in the United States:

Thermoelectric Utilities	187 billion gal./day
Irrigation	137 billion gal./day
Public Supply	36 billion gal./day
Industry	26 billion gal./day
Rural & Livestock	8 billion gal./day
TOTAL:	**394 billion gal./day**

Daily water use:

Flushing the Toilet	**1.5-7 gal.
Taking a Shower	25-50 gal.
Taking a Bath	36 gal.
Washing Clothes	35-60 gal.
Washing Dishes (machine)	10 gal.
Brushing Teeth	2 gal.
Washing Hands	2 gal.
Watering the Lawn	5-10 gal./min.

*To convert gallons to liters, multiply by 3.785.

**Water-saving toilets are now available that use as little as 1.5-3.5 gallons (5.7-13.2 l) of water.

tion that has trickled down into the soil. This trickle-down process takes time; deep groundwater may require hundreds of years to be replenished. In many areas, the rate at which groundwater is able to replenish itself cannot keep pace with the rate at which it is being used.

Whether our water supplies come from groundwater (as does half of the drinking water in the United States) or from lakes, streams, reservoirs, or other surface water sources, using too much water too fast or contaminating water sources can cause problems for people and wildlife.

Through dams, reservoirs, and wells, people constantly try to increase the availability of fresh water. But, if everyone made an effort to conserve water by making a few changes in their daily routines, huge amounts of water could be saved. For example, by installing a water-saving shower head, each person could save 5,000 gallons (18,925 liters) a year!

Getting Ready
Make copies of "Water Use Chart" on page 125.

PART A
WATER WATCH

Doing the Activity
1. In the morning, show the students an empty beverage container (1/2-gallon or 2-liter bottle) and tell them how much water it holds. Have each student predict how much water he or she will use at school that day. Do the students think they will use less than the amount in the container? If more, how much more? Discuss ways in which students use water at school.

2. On the chalkboard, make a chart like the one below for recording the students' predictions. Depending on the level of your group, you may want to have the students work in pairs to figure the percentages of students who fell within various "prediction ranges."

3. Tell students that they'll monitor their water use for the rest of the day. To do that, they'll need to record the ways they use water and the number of times they used the water in that way. In some cases, such as when they wash their hands, get a drink from the water fountain, or take a shower, they'll need to record the length of time (or average) the water was running. (See student page 125.)

4. The next day, have students calculate the rate at which water comes out of the water fountain and wash basin. Time how long it takes the water to fill a container of known volume, and convert this rate to gallons or liters per minute. (For **younger students**, you may want to figure these rates for them in advance.) Have students use these rates to help them calculate the amount of water they used at school. Be sure to tell them the average amount of water used per toilet flush, shower, etc. (See chart on page 122, or have them contact their state water conservation department.)

5. Have students compare their calculations to the predictions they made earlier. Discuss the differences between the two.

6. Using the background information, lead a discussion about the importance of conserving water. Have students brainstorm a list of ways that they can consistently cut down on water waste at school and at home.

Gallons	5	10	15	20	25	30	35	40	45
(Liters)	(19)	(38)	(57)	(76)	(95)	(114)	(132)	(151)	(170)
Number of Guesses									

7. Once again, have students monitor their water use during the school day, this time practicing methods of saving water. The next day, have them calculate how much water they used. Have them determine their "water savings" and discuss it with the rest of the group.

8. Have students work in small groups to estimate how much water could be saved in one day if everyone in the school (including the staff) tried to conserve it. Consider installation of water-saving devices, and consider conservation practices in maintaining school grounds and fields.

PART B
ACTION PLANS

Doing the Activity

1. Have students create posters to help others learn about water conservation. They might present a program on water conservation to the rest of the school. After a discussion focusing on problems caused by wasting water, they might present their findings from Part A and the estimates they made on how much water the school could save by using simple water conservation practices.

2. Have students work in small groups to create an action plan to encourage water conservation in the school. For example, one group could research the feasibility of installing faucet aerators in restrooms. Another could look into toilet dams (objects that take up space in the toilet tank) or other water-saving devices.

NOTE—To do this part of the activity, you need a toilet with a tank.

A third group could focus on water waste (from leaky faucets, running toilets) and work on solutions to these problems.

3. Have students estimate the savings, of both water and money, that their water conservation action plan will produce. They can use their estimates to sell the plan to school administrators or to their parents.

WATER USE CHART

	Rate (Gals per Use or per Min)	# of Times or Mins per Day	Total Gals or Liters	Price per Gal or Liter	Total Price
Washing Hands					
Brushing Teeth					
Taking a Shower					
Taking a Bath					
Flushing the Toilet					
Dripping Faucet					
Using Water Fountain					
Washing Clothes					
Total:					

* To convert gallons to liters, multiply gallons times 3.785.

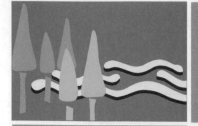

Overview
Important issues revolve around our use of energy. One issue is the growing scarcity of some energy resources. Another is the threat to our environment caused by our current energy systems. In this activity, your students will learn about different sources of energy, as well as how energy is used in their daily lives.

LEVELS
Grades 6-8

SUBJECTS
Science, Social Studies

CONCEPTS
■ Resource management technologies interact and influence environmental quality; the acquisition, extraction and transportation of natural resources; and all life forms. (5.1)

■ While technological advances decrease the incidence of disease and death, the ever-increasing world population is placing heavy demands on the finite resources of the Earth. (5.2)

■ By reducing waste and recycling materials, individuals and societies can extend the value and utility of resources and can promote environmental quality. (5.4)

■ Conservation and management technologies, when appropriately applied to the use or preservation of natural resources, can enhance and extend the usefulness of the resource as well as the quality of the environment. (11.2)

SKILLS
Researching, Defining Problems, Organizing Information, Identifying Attributes and Components, Summarizing, Establishing Criteria, Evaluating

OBJECTIVES
Students will ① identify different energy sources; ② discuss the pros and cons of various energy sources from economic, social, and environmental perspectives; and ③ describe some of the ways people use energy in their daily lives.

MATERIALS
paper and pencils, resource materials, art supplies, copies of student pages 128-130 (optional)

TIME CONSIDERATIONS
Preparation: 15-60 minutes

Activity: Two to four 50-minute periods

Background
Energy sources are classified as renewable or nonrenewable. *Nonrenewable energy* sources exist in fixed amounts; once they're used up, they're gone forever. For example, fossil fuels are formed through natural processes that take millions of years. If we use all available fossil fuels, no additional amounts will be available again for millions of years.

On the other hand, *renewable energy* sources can be replenished through natural, or resource management practices. For example, even though trees die naturally or get harvested, new trees are naturally re-seeded or are replanted by humans. It is important to realize that such renewable sources need to be carefully managed, because people can use them in such a way that human efforts of renewal management would still be unable to maintain the resources. Renewable sources of energy include *perpetual sources*, such as solar energy, wind, and tides, which, in human terms, last forever.

When we determine the degree of use of any energy alternative, the major factors are the energy source's estimated short-, intermediate-, and long-term supplies; its *net yield* of useful energy; its cost; and its potentially harmful environmental and social impacts. Each energy alternative has certain advantages and disadvantages. (See the "Energy Primer" on pages 128-130 for specific information on different energy sources.)

Getting Ready
Make a copy of the "Energy Primer" on pages 128-130 for each group you set up in Part A. You may want to gather library materials on energy resources.

PART A
ENERGY ROUND-UP
Doing the Activity
1. Make a list of the following energy sources where everyone can see them: coal, oil, natural gas, nuclear, solar, geothermal, biomass, wind, hydropower, synthetic fuels (e.g. hydrogen), and so on.

2. Divide the class into small groups, and from the list assign one energy source to each group.

3. Give the groups time to research their energy source and to develop a report containing information on the following:

■ Its availability

■ The technologies for extracting or processing it

■ Its economic potential and the feasibility of its small—and large—scale use

■ Pros and cons of its environmental and social impacts

■ The history of its use

■ The sustainability of its use

■ Its potential as a future energy source in the United States or other countries

(Students can use the "Energy Primer" and can supplement it with other research.)

4. Have the groups present their reports to the entire class. Students should take notes on each group's report.

5. After all groups have reported, each group should briefly outline a national energy policy that they'd like to see enacted. Such a policy should address issues such as energy conservation and alternative fuels. (Have students include federal, state, and local policies they would like to see enacted.)

6. Have the students share their energy policies. Discuss the pros and cons of each. You may give the groups time to revise their policies after they hear all reports.

PART B
FINDING OUT ABOUT FUEL

Doing the Activity

1. For one day, have students keep track of all the activities they do that directly or indirectly require energy. Tell them to make a list of those activities.

2. The next day, use individual lists to create a group list of activities that require energy. Add any other activities the students think of.

3. Assign students to small groups. Then assign three or more of the listed activities to each group.

4. Have each group find out the following:

■ What type(s) of energy is used for each activity? (fuel for heating or cooling, electricity for lights and appliances)

■ Where does the energy comes from? (oil, coal, nuclear, natural gas, solar, hydropower, wind)

■ How does it get from its source to where it is used?

■ What are the environmental consequences of using the energy for that particular activity?

Enrichment
Assign each student group to examine particular provinces, states, regions, or foreign countries. Students can then research what main energy sources those areas produce and what types of energy the people consume. As an alternative, have students find out which areas produce and consume the energy source assigned to their student group in Part A. Students can begin by researching the state or country, or by researching the energy sources themselves.

END NOTES...

ASSESSMENT OPPORTUNITY
Have the groups design posters or other visual displays portraying the information they found in Step 4.

RELATED ACTIVITIES
A Look at Aluminum, Waste Watchers, Pollution Search

REFERENCES
Miller, G. Tyler. *LIVING IN THE ENVIRONMENT: AN INTRODUCTION TO ENVIRONMENTAL SCIENCE*, 7TH ED. Belmont, CA: Wadsworth Publishing Company, 1992.

National Energy Education Development Project. *ENERGY ENIGMA*.

World Resources Institute. *THE 1992 INFORMATION PLEASE ENVIRONMENTAL ALMANAC*. Boston: Houghton Mifflin Co., 1992. [contains information on energy production and consumption arranged by state and country.]

World Resources Institute. *WORLD RESOURCES 1992-93*. New York: Oxford University Press, 1992.

ENERGY PRIMER

A. Nonrenewable Energy Sources

1. *Conventional crude oil,* or petroleum, is a fossil fuel that requires a very long time to form. The petroleum we use today formed from tiny sea organisms that sank to the bottom of the ocean millions of years ago, became buried by layers of sand and silt, and then were subjected to the right conditions of pressure and heat.

Since World War II, petroleum has replaced coal as the United States' leading source of energy. Petroleum is used primarily in transportation (63 percent) and industry (25 percent).

The major oil-producing states in the United States are Texas, Alaska, Louisiana, California, and Oklahoma. However, domestic oil supplies only about half of the U.S. demand for over 17 million barrels each day. The Middle East and the former Soviet Union are other regions rich in crude oil.

The advantages of petroleum are its easy transportation throughout the world, its relatively low cost and versatility as fuel, and its high net yield of useful energy. However, at current rates of consumption, affordable supplies may be depleted during the early part of the 21st century. Further, burning oil releases carbon dioxide into the atmosphere and could alter the global climate. Drilling for increasingly scarce supplies can threaten wildlife or people who live in the area and depend on the land.

2. *Conventional natural gas* formed millions of years ago when the remains of plants and marine organisms were buried under sand and rock.

Industry is the major consumer of natural gas in the United States. About half the nation's homes use natural gas for heating.

More than 95 percent of the natural gas consumed in the United States is produced domestically, most coming from Texas, Oklahoma, and New Mexico. The remaining 5 percent comes from Canada. The former Soviet Union has the world's largest share of natural gas.

Propane is a by-product of natural gas or (not as often) petroleum. Because it can be liquified, propane is easily portable. It is used mostly in rural or suburban areas not served by natural gas pipelines.

Natural gas burns hotter and cleaner than any other fossil fuel. It is versatile and relatively cheap, and it has a high net yield of useful energy. Propane-fueled engines emit cleaner exhaust than gasoline engines. However, supplies of natural gas may be depleted during the early 21st century, and the burning of natural gas produces carbon dioxide, which causes air pollution.

3. *Coal* comes from the remains of plants that lived 100 to 400 million years ago, that fell into swampy water, and that were later subjected to heat and pressure.

Over 85 percent of the coal in the United States is used by electric utility companies. Only a tiny portion is used for heating buildings and homes.

The United States has the world's largest share of known coal deposits (27 percent). At the 1990 consumption rate, the United States has about a 300-year supply. Major coal-producing states are Wyoming, Kentucky, West Virginia, Pennsylvania, and Illinois. The former Soviet Union, Colombia, Poland, and South Africa are also large producers.

The advantages of coal are many. It is the world's most abundant conventional fossil fuel, it is an efficient producer of electricity, it burns at the high temperature needed for industrial processes, and it is fairly cheap. But coal is an extremely dirty, hazardous, and environmentally harmful fuel to mine and burn without adequate (and costly) air pollution control devices, improved mine safety, and reclamation of strip-mined land. Coal releases more carbon dioxide per unit of energy produced than the other fossil fuels. And coal cannot conveniently be used to fuel vehicles or heat homes unless converted to gaseous or liquid fuels. Coal-derived fuels burn more cleanly, are more versatile, and can be transported more conveniently than solid coal. However, they have low net yields of energy, require large amounts of water for processing, release large quantities of carbon dioxide, and lead to greatly increased land disruption from surface mining.

4. *Conventional nuclear fission* is generated from uranium, a naturally occurring element found in rocks. After uranium is mined and processed, it is used to generate electricity. When atoms split, they release heat energy that is harnessed to change water into steam. The steam then turns a turbine, or generator. Although uranium is found in rocks all over the world, it is concentrated in certain areas such as New Mexico and Wyoming. During the 1950s and 1960s, it was projected that by the year 2000, almost one-fourth of the world's commercial energy would be produced by nuclear fission. However, by 1988, nuclear power was providing only 4.5 percent of Earth's commercial energy, and high costs have led many countries to abandon their plans to increase their use of this energy alternative. U.S. use of nuclear power peaked in 1988 at 19.5 percent.

Major advantages of conventional nuclear fission are ① unlike coal-fired plants, nuclear reactors do not release air pollutants such as carbon dioxide, particulate matter, and sulfur and nitrogen oxides;

ENERGY PRIMER (CONT)

② with current rates of use, it is unlikely that the supply of uranium would run out in the foreseeable future; and ③ water pollution and disruption of land are low to moderate if the entire nuclear fuel cycle operates normally. Major disadvantages are ① construction and operation costs of nuclear plants have been much higher, and construction much lengthier, than projected, even with massive government and consumer subsidies; ② conventional nuclear power plants can be used only to produce electricity (as opposed to fuel); ③ there is always a risk of large-scale accidents from nuclear plants (although extremely unlikely, some have already occurred as a result of mechanical and human errors); ④ the net yield of useful energy from nuclear power is low; ⑤ safe methods for storing high-level radioactive waste for several years to several hundred thousand years have not yet been developed; and ⑥ the use of nuclear energy spreads knowledge and materials that could be used to make nuclear weapons.

Some experts hope that either high-temperature or cold *nuclear fusion* will eventually be able to provide an inexhaustible supply of energy to generate electricity. However, after 45 years of research, high-temperature nuclear fusion is still at the laboratory stage, and no one has been able to get more energy out of the process than must be put in to initiate the fusion reaction. However, preliminary experiments in 1989 suggested that cold nuclear fusion might be possible. If so, it will take several decades to determine whether it can be used on a commercial basis. Even if everything goes well (a very big "if"), nuclear fusion is not expected to be a significant source of commercial energy until between 2050 and 2150, if ever. Although the process would produce less radioactive waste than conventional nuclear fission, there are still similar safety and waste issues associated with nuclear fusion.

B. Renewable Energy Sources

1. *Geothermal energy* comes from the heat deep within the earth. When water comes in contact with the heated rocks, steam is produced. This steam can be used directly to generate electricity or to heat buildings. These deposits of steam are close enough to the ground's surface for energy use in only 10 percent of the world's land mass. Currently, 20 countries use geothermal energy. In the United States, most usable sites are in the Western states; the world's largest project uses the geysers in California.

These sources of geothermal energy are technically nonrenewable and can provide a 100- to 200-year supply of energy for surrounding areas at a moderate cost. They have a moderate net yield of useful energy and don't emit carbon dioxide. However, there is not an abundance of accessible deposits; the energy cannot be transferred into a liquid fuel to power vehicles; and without pollution control, use of geothermal energy results in moderate to high air and water pollution.

There are also vast perpetual sources of geothermal energy in the form of molten rock, dry hot rock, and warm rock deposits. However, those deposits lie so deep under Earth's crust that with present technology they are too costly to develop on a large scale.

2. *Solar energy* is created in the sun when hydrogen atoms combine to form helium. During this process of nuclear fusion, a small amount of mass is lost and converted into heat and radiant energy. Less than one percent of the energy radiated from the sun reaches Earth.

Solar energy can be used to provide low temperature heat for heating spaces and water. Passive solar design, which uses architectural features for heating, cooling, and lighting, is the cheapest and most energy-efficient way to use solar energy on a lifetime basis with very low environmental impact. Examples of features that harness the sun's energy are large areas of south-facing glass, awnings to keep sun out, high insulation to prevent rapid heat fluctuations, and brick walls or other collectors to absorb solar energy. Stones, water, and other materials can be used to store solar energy for the time of day when the sun is unavailable or too weak to use.

An active solar energy system—one that collects, concentrates, and directs solar energy—can be a cost-effective way of providing heat and hot water to a residence on a lifetime basis. Solar systems were widely used in California and Florida in the 1920s and 1930s, and they revived again in the 1970s. Today, most are used for heating pools. Direct solar energy can also be concentrated to produce electricity in solar power plants or to produce high-temperature heat for industrial processes. The sun's rays can be concentrated on pipes to heat water and turn it into steam that is used to turn a generator, as with other conventional power plants. However, with present technology, the costs are too high.

Without use of any mechanical equipment, photo-voltaic cells can convert direct solar energy into electricity. Familiar examples include hand calculators and road signs. Environmental impact from this method is low, but costs need to become more competitive.

3. *Wind energy* is caused by the sun's uneven heating of Earth's surface. Wind is created when hot air rises and heavier colder air rushes in to take its place.

Before 1935, windmills were used primarily for grinding grain or pumping water. Today, large numbers of modern wind turbines in wind farms are used

ENERGY PRIMER
(CONT)

to generate electricity, primarily for local utilities. California has 95 percent of U.S. wind machines (80 percent of the world's total).

Because the wind does not blow constantly, wind machines operate only around 25 percent of the time. Most wind energy (80 percent) is produced between April and October. The advantages of wind power are its low environmental impact, competitive prices, and short installation time.

4. *Hydropower* is when the force of water flowing from higher to lower ground is used to turn turbines and generate electricity.

Hydropower was the first fuel used to generate electricity. In the 1950s, it generated 40 percent of U.S. electricity. In 1990, about 2,000 dams in the United States generated about 10 percent of the nation's electricity. In California, as much as 30 percent of the state's electricity is produced by hydropower.

Hydropower is the cheapest way to generate electricity and does not create air pollution. However, hydro-power facilities are expensive to build, and the dams can disrupt or destroy wildlife in the area that is flooded for the reservoir.

5. *Biomass* is fuel made from plant material. During photosynthesis, plants use the sun's energy to make carbohydrates from water and carbon dioxide. Those carbohydrates, in turn, can be burned to release energy. Burning wood accounts for almost 90 percent of all biomass energy; burning garbage and agricultural waste accounts for about 7 percent. Until the 20th century, biomass energy was used to run everything from steel mills to railroads.

Wood is still widely used as fuel for cooking, space heating, and water heating throughout the world, especially in lesser-developed countries. However, fuelwood supplies are decreasing as forests are being stripped of trees without adequate replanting.

Burning wood and wood wastes can be a cost-effective way for the forest products industry to co-generate steam and electricity and for individuals to heat residences. However, without adequate air pollution control, burning wood to heat houses produces unacceptable levels of indoor and outdoor air pollution.

Large quantities of fast-growing plants and trees on biomass energy plantations may become a source of biomass fuel.

Agricultural and urban wastes can be burned to co-generate steam and electricity for nearby industries, homes (district space heating), and local utility companies, as has been done in Europe and Japan for decades. Some analysts argue, however, that

more energy would be saved by recycling or composting such organic wastes. Further, burning garbage can cause serious air pollution.

Useful but limited amounts of methane-rich "biogas" fuel can be produced by bacterial decomposition of ① plants, ② organic wastes buried in large landfills, ③ manure collected from animal feedlots, and ④ sludge from sewage treatment plants. These anaerobic digesters are widely used in China.

Ethanol, or ethyl alcohol, which is produced from sugar and grain crops such as corn, is one form of liquid biomass. It is used to power automobiles in Brazil and is mixed with gasoline to produce super unleaded gasoline in the United States. However, prices are fairly high without government tax breaks. Another liquid biofuel, *methanol,* can be produced from wood, agricultural wastes, sludge from sewage treatment plants, and garbage, although coal and natural gas are its main sources today. Methanol has half the energy content of gasoline, but its high oxygen content allows it to burn efficiently. However, with present technology, it is far too expensive and can be burned only in modified automobile engines.

6. Because *hydrogen fuel* occurs only rarely in nature, it must be produced synthetically by the decomposition of water. Some believe that hydrogen gas, which burns very cleanly, may be used to fuel cars, heat homes, and produce electricity when oil runs out sometime in the next century. However, its negative net yield of useful energy means that its widespread use depends on having a large and affordable supply of energy available from some other source, perhaps from special cells powered by solar energy.

C. Conservation

The easiest and cheapest way to make more energy available, as well as to reduce the environmental impact of present use, is to reduce or eliminate unnecessary energy waste in industry, transportation, and commercial or residential buildings. This change requires modifying energy-wasting habits; increasing energy efficiency so that less energy is needed to do the same amount of work; and developing new devices that waste less energy than existing ones. Recent studies show that there exists the potential to cut U.S. electricity consumption by over 50 percent through cost-effective investments. In Germany and Japan, it takes only half the energy to produce the same amount of goods in as it does in the United States. Ultimately, energy efficiency will be the cheapest and cleanest source of energy *supply.*

Overview
If your community is like most others, it's now quite a bit different than it was 100, 50, 25, or even five years ago. This activity will help your students to understand how we, as people, affect and alter the environment in which we live.

Background
(See Background section for the activities in "Did You Notice?" on page 366 and "In the Good Old Days" on page 349.)

Getting Ready
If possible, obtain pictures or drawings of your community, township, or city from various stages in its past. (Municipalities or counties often have publicity pieces that feature these pictures.) If you're unable to bring in pictures, arrange to have your group visit a facility with such pictures, perhaps a local museum, heritage landmark, historical societies, or library. For the variation, you will need to know of several historical changes in your community, but you will need no special materials.

PART A
THE WAY IT WAS

Doing the Activity
1. Ask students if they've noticed any changes in their community recently. For example, have any new malls been built? Are there housing developments or schools? Has any land been put aside as a park or wildlife sanctuary?

2. Ask students how those changes make them feel. Discuss the pros and cons of how those developments affect people and communities. Talk about how such changes might affect wild animals and plants in the area.

3. Show students the old pictures of your community. If possible, identify each photo's location and have students describe what the site looks like now.

PART B
ASK THE ELDERS

Doing the Activity
1. Tell students that they'll interview an older person who has lived in the community for many years. This person could be a parent, grandparent, neighbor, or anyone who has lived in the area long enough to see many changes.

2. Have each person develop a list of interview questions. Here are a few suggestions for questions students might ask:

- How long have you lived in the community?

- How has the landscape within the community changed during that time?

- Have the changes helped you in any way?

- Have the changes hurt you in any way?

- How have the changes helped or hurt the community?

3. Give students time to conduct their interviews. Tell them not to feel bound by their list of questions. Encourage them to ask other questions that they may think of during the interview. Students will need to take notes during the interview or to tape record it and make notes later.

LEVELS
Activity: Grades 5-8
Variation: Grades 3-6

SUBJECTS
Social Studies, Science, Language Arts

CONCEPTS
- The quantity and quality of resources and their use-or misuse-by humans affects the standard of living of societies. (6.2)
- Cultural and societal perspectives influence the attitudes, beliefs, and biases of people toward the use of resources and environmental protection. (6.3)
- Increased public knowledge of the environment and the need for conservation of natural resources have resulted in lifestyle changes in many cultures. (15.5)

SKILLS
Researching, Formulating Questions, Comparing and Contrasting, Generalizing, Solving Problems

OBJECTIVES
Students will ① describe the environmental changes that have occurred in their community over the course of time, ② discuss whether those changes have been positive or negative for the community, and ③ discuss ways to remedy negative changes.

MATERIALS
paper and pencils, historical pictures of your community

TIME CONSIDERATIONS
Preparation: 20 minutes
Activity: 50 minutes

Instead of using pictures or visiting a museum, take your students back in time through an imaginary time machine. Have them close their eyes, imagine stepping into the time machine, and pretend they're going back 25, 50, 100, or 200 years. At each stop of the time machine, have the students step out and visit familiar places around town. Describe to the students what they might see. After returning from this imaginary journey, do Step 2 of Part A with your students.

NOTE—Your imaginary descriptions should be based on your actual knowledge or research about your community's past.

Enrichment

1. Brainstorm with the group to list areas in the community that have more or less been left in their natural states, for example, parks, wildlife sanctuaries, or private holdings. Then assign the students into small groups and have each group choose one area from the list. Have the groups research the area to find out the following information:

- What is the history of the area?

- Why has the area not been developed?

- Who lives in or uses the area (including wildlife)?

- Are there plans to change the area in any way?

Have members of each group prepare and present a report about their natural area.

2. Tell students to imagine they have traveled into the future. Have them write stories about how their community might be different 25, 50, or 100 years from now.

Systems

Overview
A plant is a biological system with these basic requirements for functioning and growing: sunlight, water, air, soil, and space. This activity allows students to explore what happens when a plant's basic needs are not met.

Background
A plant is a living system. To function and survive, it needs sunlight, air, water, soil, and space in the amount suitable to that plant.

Green plants get their energy from the sun. In a process called photosynthesis, sunlight activates the chlorophyll in leaves to convert raw materials from soil and air into carbohydrates (starches and sugars), which are the plant's food. Plant leaves draw carbon dioxide from air and combine it with water to make carbohydrates. (See "Air Plants," page 85, for more information.)

Water is essential to plants for several reasons. Besides being a main ingredient for photosynthesis, water is a primary component of protoplasm, the basic material that constitutes the plant's structure. Water also helps transport nutrients from the soil to the plant's roots.

Plants depend on soil to sustain and support them as it provides water and nutrients. How well soil sustains a plant depends on its texture (compact or porous), its water-holding capacity, its acidity, and its population of beneficial soil organisms. Different plants depend on different soil types for their particular needs. (See "Soil Stories," page 252, for more information.)

Plants also need space to grow. If they do not have enough space and if they must compete with neighboring plants for nutrients, light, and water, plants may find it difficult to grow or survive.

We should learn everything we can about plants because they provide us with food and drink (fruits, vegetables, grains); shelter (wood or grass houses); clothing (cotton, flax); products (paper, cellulose, wood furniture); and medicine (cough syrup, aspirin).

Getting Ready
Approximately three weeks before beginning the activity, place about 50 bean, pea, or alfalfa seeds in a clear jar on a layer of damp paper towels and put the jar near a window. Monitor the seeds daily, and keep the paper towels moist. Discuss with students what seeds need to sprout and develop. Seedlings will be ready for experimentation when they have developed leaves and roots.

Doing the Activity
1. Divide the students into five research teams. Ask what factors they think are necessary for plants to grow. Invite the teams to devise experiments to test whether or not plants really need those elements to grow. Help teams to think through each step of their experiment and to predict what might happen; then, help them conduct their experiment. Alternatively, have teams use the following experiment model. (See "Trees in Trouble," on page 293, for additional plant experiments.)

Control
Plant four seedlings in four separate containers of potting soil. Label these containers "Control." Place them near a window or other light source. Water as needed.

Test for Light
Plant four seedlings in four separate containers of potting soil. Label the containers "No Light." Place them in a dark cupboard or closet. Water as needed.

Test for Water
Plant four seedlings in four separate containers of potting soil. Do not water. Label the containers "No Water." Place them near a window or other light source.

LEVELS
Activity: Grades 4-8
Variation: Grades K-2

SUBJECTS
Science, Math

CONCEPTS
- In biological systems, energy flows and materials continually cycle in predictable and measurable patterns. (7.1)
- Populations of organisms exhibit variations in size and structure as a result of their adaptation to their habitats. (10.1)
- Organisms are interdependent; they all depend on nonliving components of the Earth. (4.1)

SKILLS
Observing, Predicting, Organizing, Analyzing Results

OBJECTIVES
Students will ① set up an experiment to determine what factors are necessary for plant growth and ② measure and compare plant growth under different environmental conditions.

MATERIALS
50 pea, bean, or alfalfa seeds; a large jar; paper towels; 20 planting containers (small pots, cups, plastic baggies, or egg cartons); potting soil; masking tape and pens

TIME CONSIDERATIONS
Preparation: 45 minutes plus time to sprout seeds for use in experiments

Activity: two 50-minute periods over four weeks

Test for Soil

Put four seedlings in four separate containers on a wet paper towel. Label the containers "No Soil." Place them near a window or other light source. Add water to keep the towel wet.

2. As the plants begin to grow, graph their heights. Older students can measure the plants' heights with rulers and transfer the measurement to graph paper. Younger students can use construction paper strips to find the height of the plant and can glue the strips onto poster board to make a bar graph. Graph the plants daily or weekly.

3. Discuss these questions:

- Which plants grew the most? Which grew the least?

- What other differences did you observe among the plants?

- What does a plant need to grow? How do plants get those needs?

- What happens if a plant doesn't get enough sunlight? Water? Soil?

- Which parts of the plants seemed most affected by lack of sunlight? Water? Soil?

- If you were going to plant a tree on the school grounds, where might you plant it? Why? (Look for a place with the right conditions: sunlight, air, water, soil, room to grow.)

- If you were to plant a tree on the school grounds, how might you benefit from it? (It looks nice, attracts animals, provides fruit, blocks wind, and provides oxygen.)

VARIATION—GROWING UP GREEN

1. Ask students what plants require for growth. Let them choose one requirement to test: light, water, soil, or space (see above).

2. Using two plants or seedlings of the same size and species, allow one to have a single requirement, while denying that requirement to the other (as described in Step 1 of the main activity).

3. At set intervals, let students measure the seedlings. After a period of time, have students measure and compare the plants. Ask students whether the plants look different, and if they do, what causes the difference?

4. Follow the same procedure to test another requirement suggested by the students.

Enrichment

1. Help students compare their own growth to that of the experimental plants. Measure student heights at the beginning and end of the experiment.

2. Arrange to visit a nursery or orchard to see trees in various stages of growth and to find out about the needs of different trees.

3. Have students try propagating seeds from their "adopted tree" (see "Adopt a Tree," page 65). If possible, collect a number of seeds. Experiment with planting and caring for the seeds under various conditions. For example, try different soils, some from near the parent plant and some from other areas; or try different amounts of water. After a seedling is well established, plant it in an area suited to the tree's needs.

4. Have older students make a small "flip-it" book that shows plant growth in animation. Give each student four 3" x 5" (7.6 cm x 12.7 cm) index cards. Have students cut each card into quarters so that they have 16 small rectangular cards. On the far right edge of each card, have students draw a small picture of the plant as it grows from a seed to a mature plant. For example, card #1 can show a seed, cards #2-15 can show the seed sprouting and gradually growing until it's full grown in card #16. Tell students to stack the cards in numerical order and hold them on the left side with their thumb and forefinger. By flipping through the cards on the right side, students will see the seed sprout and continue to grow. (Create and illustrate a sample booklet to show students before they begin their flip-it books.)

ASSESSMENT OPPORTUNITY

Ask students to draw a series of pictures showing the development of a seedling under different environmental conditions. Below each picture, have students use symbols to show what the plant has or lacks in each situation.

RELATED ACTIVITIES

Trees in Trouble, Have Seeds-Will Travel, Sunlight and Shades of Green, Adopt a Tree, Every Tree for Itself, Plant A Tree

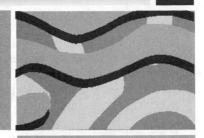

Overview
This activity introduces students to photosynthesis, the process that enables trees and other green plants to use sunlight to manufacture their own food.

Background

Plants and animals share certain characteristics: both are composed of *protoplasm* (mostly water and protein), both have *cells* and tissues of various kinds that serve different functions, both consume and store energy, and both can reproduce themselves. Plants have one significant difference from animals—most plants can manufacture their own food.

Trees and other green plants make their food through photosynthesis, which literally means "putting together with light." Many parts of the tree are involved in photosynthesis, and the process requires the elements of sunlight, air, water, and nutrients.

Tree roots absorb water and minerals and carry them to leaves, where they come into contact with *chlorophyll* (the green pigment in leaves and stems) and air. Sunlight passes into a leaf, strikes the chlorophyll, and gives it energy to break water molecules apart. The hydrogen from a water molecule combines with carbon compounds from carbon dioxide, which comes from air. The resultant carbohydrates (starches and sugars) are the plant's food. The leaf releases or "exhales" oxygen from the broken water molecule through the process of transpiration. (See illustration of photosynthesis in "Air Plants" on page 85.)

When something prevents a plant's leaves from getting the needed sunlight, photosynthesis stops or is slowed down. Therefore, the plant's growth is affected. If part of a leaf is covered, the plant stops producing green chlorophyll in that area, causing the spot to turn yellow. If an entire leaf gets no light, it will eventually turn brown and fall off. (See "Signs of Fall," page 299.) If a plant loses too many leaves, it will not be able to make enough food and will die.

Getting Ready

Choose a tree, shrub, or green plant with leaves that students can easily reach. Make sure the tree or plant you choose is safe to touch. You can do the activity indoors using a house plant.

Doing the Activity

1. Have students cut out several circles or squares of cardboard, each just large enough to make a good-sized "patch" on a leaf of a shrub, tree, or plant.

2. Take students outside and show them how to use paper clips to attach a cardboard circle or square to each of several leaves.

3. After four days, remove the pieces of cardboard and have the class observe the lighter-colored spot on each leaf where the cardboard deprived the leaf of sunlight.

4. Engage the students in a discussion of what they observed. What caused the light spot to appear on the leaf? Ask if any student has ever seen this happen before. (When sunlight was blocked from the spot, the leaf stopped producing chlorophyll. Some students may have seen this effect before when they moved objects that had been left on growing grass for a time.) Ask students for their ideas about how important leaves are to plants and how sunlight might affect plant leaves.

5. Ask students whether they have heard the word *photosynthesis* before. What do they think this word means. Explain that photosynthesis is the process by which plants make their own food with the help of sunlight and chlorophyll, the green pigment in leaves.

6. As a class, summarize the elements necessary for photosynthesis. Discuss these questions:

LEVELS
Grades 2-8

SUBJECTS
Science, Language Arts

CONCEPTS
■ In biological systems, energy flows and materials continually cycle in predictable and measurable patterns. (7.1)

■ Populations of organisms exhibit variations in size and structure as a result of their adaptation to their habitats. (10.1)

SKILLS
Observing, Forming Concepts, Inferring, Concluding

OBJECTIVES
Students will ① test the effects of lack of sunlight on plant leaves and ② describe the process of photosynthesis and how it enables a plant to survive.

MATERIALS
small scraps of cardboard, several large paper clips

TIME CONSIDERATIONS
Preparation: 20 minutes

Activity: two 45-minute periods over one week

- What different parts of a tree work together in photosynthesis? How is each part necessary? (Roots absorb water; trunk or stem holds the leaves up to the sun; leaves absorb sunlight, exchange gases, and make sugar.)

- What would happen if the sun stopped shining? (Green plants would die.)

- Does photosynthesis take place at night? (Not to a significant degree.)

7. To help students better understand the process of photosynthesis, lead them on the following imaginary field trip. Tell them to relax and close their eyes. When they are quiet, read the following passage aloud.

Imagine that you see a very tall tree in front of you. Look carefully at the tree, and then imagine spinning slowly around in a circle. As you spin, imagine yourself becoming the tree.

Feel your large taproot grow down from your hips and into the soft soil beneath you. Feel it sink 25 feet (7.6 m) into the ground. Then feel your lateral roots spread out just below the surface of the ground. They will spread farther and farther until they reach 30 feet (9 m) from your trunk. (pause)

Now imagine your branches rising from your trunk. Stretch your limbs. Feel your large branches divide into smaller and smaller branches. See the leaves at the ends of the branches. What do they look like? Are they large or small? Pointed or round? (pause)

See how green your leaves are and how your leaves contain tiny bursts of a green-colored matter called chlorophyll. Your leaves also have tiny holes that allow you to breathe the air. Imagine taking in some air through your leaves.

Deep in the ground, gather water with your roots. Feel the water pulsing up through your roots, up through your trunk, and out to your leaves.

Now feel the sun's warm rays on your leaves. Bring the sunlight into your leaves. Imagine the chlorophyll in your leaves trapping the sunlight. Use the energy from sunlight to change carbon dioxide (from

the air) and water (from the soil) into food for you. Your food is called carbohydrates, which means starches and sugars. As you make carbohydrates, your leaves exhale oxygen.

Send some of the food to your branches so they can grow bigger, to your trunk so it can get wider, and to your roots so they can grow longer. Feel yourself growing greener and larger with the sun's help. (pause)

When you are ready, open your eyes.

8. Observe students as they react differently to this imaginary field trip. Some will be eager to share their ideas and experience, while others will be reflective and quiet. Encourage those who wish to share their thoughts.

Enrichment

1. To learn more about what happens in tree leaves, test for starch (a sugar produced in photosynthesis). Place a broad-leafed plant, such as a geranium, in full sunlight and cover part of one leaf with a narrow strip of aluminum foil clipped at both ends to the leaf. After several days, remove the leaf from the plant and soak the leaf in a saucer of ethyl (rubbing) alcohol for a few hours to remove some of the chlorophyll.

NOTE—Keep alcohol away from flame or heated surfaces.

Next, place a few drops of diluted iodine on both the previously covered area and the area not covered. If starch is present, the iodine will change from reddish-brown to blue-black. Help students draw conclusions from their observations.

2. Consider why plants that live in shade are usually more green rather than less green. Compare plants (outdoor or house plants) that grow in shade with those that grow in sun. You may want to visit a plant shop, greenhouse, or botanical garden. Which plants are a deeper shade of green? Why are they greener? (Usually plants that grow in shade require more chlorophyll to absorb enough sunlight to make food, which results in a deeper green.)

3. Ask groups of students to create a skit to portray the process of photosynthesis. Allow time for groups to perform before the entire class. After each skit, ask students to interpret what they saw.

Overview
A plant is a biological system. Its processes and components enable it to grow and reproduce. This activity will introduce your students to one aspect of a plant's reproductive system: its seeds.

Background
Living organisms are made of systems that enable them to grow and reproduce. All living things have some system for reproducing members of their species.

Most plants reproduce using a system that includes flowers and seeds. In general, seeds develop within the ovary of the plant's flower after either being fertilized by pollen from another plant of the same species or being self-fertilized.

For a seed to germinate and grow into a mature plant, environmental conditions must be just right. Each plant needs a certain amount of sunlight, air, water, and nutrients from the soil. If a seed simply drops from the parent plant, it might compete with the parent for those essentials and have difficulty growing. Therefore, most seed-bearing plants have developed a way to disperse seeds away from the parent, giving the new plant a better chance to find what it needs to grow.

Some plants produce very light seeds with sail-like or hairy outgrowths that enable them to be carried by the wind. For example, a maple seed has papery wings that flutter like a helicopter, while a dandelion seed has a fuzzy parachute that carries it on air currents. Some plants, like beech trees and Queen Anne's lace, produce seeds with spines, hooks, or gooey coatings that catch on an animal's fur or people's clothing and are carried to distant places. Some plants, like black cherry trees and raspberries, develop seeds within an attractive, tasty fruit. Those seeds are eaten by animals, carried in the animals' digestive systems, and deposited in a different location when the animal defecates. Still other plants, like locust trees, violets, and witch hazel, have seeds that are ejected away from their parent plant. For example, witch hazel seeds develop within a pod that squeezes the seeds as the pod dries. When the seeds finally shoot out, they can travel up to 40 feet (12.2 m)!

Getting Ready
If students are to collect seeds from a vacant lot or natural area, be sure to obtain any necessary permission. Also, keep in mind that autumn is the best time for collecting seeds.

Doing the Activity
1. Ask students what seeds are and what they do. Ask for examples. (Don't worry about misconceptions at this point. Step 5 should clarify those ideas.) Tell students they are going to learn more about seeds by gathering and sorting them.

2. Ask your class to gather a collection of seeds. Students might bring in birdseed or seeds saved from fruits, collected from food in kitchen cabinets, or gathered from trees or other plants in their garden. You might also take students to a nearby field or vacant lot full of seed-bearing plants. They can collect seeds in one or more of the following ways:

■ Have students walk around the area, pick up any seeds they find on the ground, and collect the seeds in a cup or other container.

■ Help students drag an old blanket or other piece of fuzzy cloth through the area. Or have them wear large, old, wool socks over their shoes and walk around the area.

■ Have younger students wear bracelets of masking tape with the sticky side out so they can stick small seeds or seed parts directly on their seed bracelets.

LEVELS
Grades K-8

SUBJECTS
Science, Visual Arts

CONCEPTS
■ In biological systems, energy flows and materials continually cycle in predictable and measurable patterns. (7.1)

■ Populations of organisms exhibit variations in size and structure as a result of their adaptation to their habitats. (10.1)

■ Biological diversity results from the interaction of living and nonliving environmental components such as air, water, climate, and geological features. (1.1)

SKILLS
Observing, Classifying and Categorizing, Organizing Information, Inferring

OBJECTIVES
Students will ① sort or classify plant seeds they have collected, ② identify varying methods of seed dispersal, and ③ model or design seeds that use varying methods of dispersal.

MATERIALS
class collection of seeds gathered during Step 2 of activity, cups or other containers (optional), blanket or other piece of cloth (optional), pieces of cardboard (optional), masking tape (optional), binoculars (optional)

TIME CONSIDERATIONS
Preparation: one day to collect seeds

Activity: 50 minutes

- Encourage students to invent other simple seed-gathering techniques that do not harm the environment.

3. Put all seeds into a class collection. Divide students into groups of two to five, and give each group an assortment of seeds from the collection. Ask groups to examine their seeds and invent a system for sorting or classifying. (Younger students may simply sort seeds into two groups so that those in each group are alike in some way.) Invite students to share their methods for sorting.

4. Lead a discussion about the structure and function of seeds. Ask these questions:

- What are seeds? (A seed is a "plant egg." It contains a baby plant and a supply of baby plant food wrapped in a protective covering. You may slice open a plant with a large seed, such as an avocado, to show the parts as depicted in the diagram below.)

- Where do seeds come from? (The plant's ovary, or female part, is located in its flowers or cones.)

- Is there a reason for so many different kinds of seeds? (Every type of plant has a special type of seed designed for the plant's particular habitat and method of distribution—see background information.)

5. Ask students why it might be important for seeds to be dispersed away from parent plants. Invite students to share different ways they have noticed that plants disperse their seeds. Write those ideas on the board. If students have trouble thinking of various ways, you might mention particular seeds to stimulate more ideas. Ask students whether any of the ways they have observed seem similar. For example, they might have said that dandelions blow in the wind and that milkweed floats in the air. If appro–priate, help students compile groups of similar dispersal systems so the class ends up with a set of about five to eight categories. Remember there

is no one right way to group the seed dispersal systems. Use students' examples to help them create their own categories (see examples of categories).

6. Ask students to group their seeds according to the dispersal categories they identified.

7. With older students, discuss these questions:

- How do a seed's shape and size affect its dispersal?

- What other parts of a plant help it reproduce? (Flowers that have male and female parts, and fleshy fruits that encase seeds.)

- Why is it important for seeds to be dispersed in different ways? (Plants have different requirements that are served best by different seed-dispersal systems.)

- How far can a seed be dispersed? (Seeds can glide on the wind for several miles, float on the water for hundreds of miles, or travel on a bird for thousands of miles.)

- Can some seeds go farther than others? (yes) How is distance important? (It reduces competition for a plant's needs in a particular area. Widespread plants increase the species' chances of survival.)

- What value might seed dispersal have for plants, wildlife, and humans? (food, medicine)

Enrichment
1. Suggest that students plant some of the seeds they collected so they can observe plant germination in action.

2. Challenge students to design their own seeds with specialized dispersal mechanisms. Students can use a dried lima bean as the base of

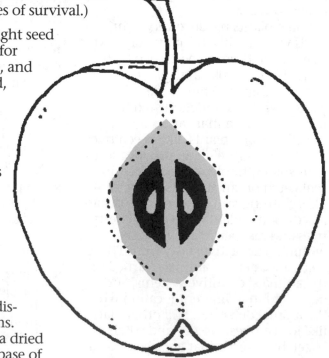

CATEGORIES OF SEED DISPERSAL

Floats on air
milkweed, dandelion, cottonwood

Flies through air
maple, ash, tulip poplar

Floats on water
mangrove, coconut, cranberry

Bounces or rolls
acorn, pecan, black walnut

Eaten by animals
cherry, apple, pyracantha

Stored by animals
acorns, hickory, beech

Thrown
locust, violet, witch hazel, lupine, jewelweed

Sticks to animals
beard grass, burdock, cocklebur, foxtail, goldenrod, wild barley

their design, along with "junk" materials (such as popsicle sticks, toothpicks, cardboard, egg cartons, cotton balls, string, and rubber bands), to design a seed that:

- Floats in water for at least five minutes

- Attracts an animal to carry it away

- Floats in air for at least 5 feet (1.5 m)

- Sticks to an animal and can be carried at least 10 feet (3 m)

- Is thrown at least 2 feet (.6 m) away from the parent plant

3. Drop seeds in front of a fan to demonstrate what effect moving air has on various seed designs. Note differences in movement, direction, speed, and rotation. Graph the distance each seed flies.

4. Many animals, including many of our favorite backyard birds, depend on seeds as their food source. By setting up a bird feeder, students can learn which birds like which seeds best. Students can either build or buy a bird feeder. They can make feeders from milk containers, aluminum pie tins, or other used materials. Set a feeder on a window sill or attach it to a tree or post where students can closely observe the birds. Bring to class a bag of mixed birdseed (usually sunflower seeds and millet). Give pairs of students a small handful of birdseed to study. Have them describe the different kinds of seeds. Ask what types of birds might like to eat the different seeds. Then, have students fill the feeder with birdseed and spend a little time each day observing it (try to have a pair of binoculars on hand). They should try to find out ① which birds prefer which seeds, ② what method each bird uses to eat seeds, and ③ the reason the bird uses that method. For instance, a chickadee will usually take one sunflower seed, fly to a nearby branch, and hammer the seed with its beak until the seed opens. Students can periodically check to see which seeds are eaten most often.

5. Not all plants reproduce from seed pollination. Use library resources to find out about plants that don't bear seeds, such as algae, ferns, fungi, mosses, and horsetails, which generally use spores or buds. Compare the reproductive systems of such plants to those of seed-bearing plants. Find out about seed-bearing plants that have additional vegetative methods of reproduction, such as potatoes ("eyes"), strawberries (runners), or roses (cuttings). Some trees reproduce vegetatively when their roots or stump sprout new trees. You can demonstrate vegetative reproduction in the classroom by growing new plants from pieces of carrots, potatoes, turnips, onions, or willow sticks (see illustration below).

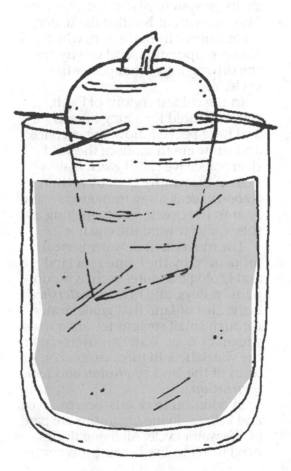

Overview
The water cycle is the system by which Earth's fixed amount of water is collected, purified, and distributed from the environment to living things and back to the environment. Plants play a large part in the cycle by absorbing water with their roots and transpiring it as vapor through their leaves. This activity will introduce students to the various steps of the water cycle and to the various paths water can take. They will also make connections between the water cycle and all living things.

LEVELS
Grades 4-8

SUBJECTS
Science, Language Arts, Physical Education

CONCEPTS
■ In biological systems, energy flows and materials continually cycle in predictable and measurable patterns. (7.1)

■ Conservation technology enables humans to maintain and extend the productivity of vital resources. (8.3)

■ Populations of organisms exhibit variations in size and structure as a result of their adaptation to their habitats. (10.1)

SKILLS
Organizing Information, Predicting, Comparing and Contrasting, Inferring

OBJECTIVES
Students will ① simulate the paths that water takes in the water cycle, ② describe the importance of the water cycle to living things, ③ conduct an experiment to discover how plants affect the movement of water in a watershed, and ④ describe how plants are important in maintaining water quality.

MATERIALS
Part A: strips cut from student page 146; copies of student page 147; seven envelopes, label for each of seven stations, watch or stopwatch
Part B: two long planter boxes filled with soil, several small plants, bricks or scrap wood (optional), watering can with spray head or coffee can with nail holes poked in the bottom

TIME CONSIDERATIONS
Preparation: 30 minutes (Part A) several hours (Part B)

Activity: 50 minutes (Part A) 50 minutes (Part B)

Background
Water covers 71 percent of Earth. It constitutes 50-70 percent of the weight of all plants and animals, including humans. Water consists of two parts hydrogen to one part oxygen. It can exist in liquid, vapor, or solid (ice) forms. Its unique physical properties enable life to exist on Earth. Those properties include water's ability to remain liquid in a wide range of normal Earth temperatures and its ability to dissolve and transport other substances.

Water is constantly moving. In general, it evaporates from oceans into the atmosphere (air), condenses into clouds, falls as rain or snow, and eventually returns to oceans through a drainage system of streams and rivers. This movement is called the **water cycle**. Energy from the sun, which allows evaporation, and gravity are the driving forces that power the cycle.

In the coldest regions of Earth, water is stored for a long time as ice and hard-packed snow. But even ice and snow are in motion; the solid rivers of ice we called **glaciers** slowly melt as they move inch by inch. **Icebergs** break away from glaciers and float in the ocean, slowly melting as they move toward the equator.

The movement of water is greatly influenced by the contour of land and geologic features such as mountains, valleys, and hills. A **watershed** is the area of land that guides water through small streams toward a major stream or river. Water's movement in the watershed, in turn, creates contours of the land by **erosion** and **sedimentation**.

In addition to clouds, oceans, rivers, and valleys, living organisms are part of the water cycle. All living things need water to live because it is essen-

tial to their bodily functions. Plants and animals take in water and return it to the atmosphere as vapor (breathing, transpiring) or to the soil as liquid (excreting).

Forests greatly affect watersheds. Trees, small plants, and forest litter absorb rainwater, reducing erosion and runoff. When rain falls on bare ground, the full force of raindrops can wash soil into streams, making them muddy. But when rain falls on the forest, it drips down through leaves and branches to the forest floor. The forest's canopy, as well as layers of plant litter under trees, protect the soil from the full force of rain. Tree roots hold the soil in place so that it doesn't wash away.

Forests also help improve water quality by filtering out impurities that could be potentially harmful in streams or **groundwater**. As water is absorbed by tree roots and then **transpired** as **vapor** through leaves, impurities (many of which are good for a tree) remain in the tree.

Although the gradual wearing down and erosion of soil is a natural process, without proper management human activities such as clearing vegetation for development, logging, dam building, farming, and draining wetlands will increase the rate of erosion in watersheds and can reduce water quality. By the same token, reforestation, certain types of farming and landscaping, and restoring wetlands can reverse those trends.

Getting Ready
For Part A, photocopy page 146 and cut the strips apart. Also copy student page 147 for each person. Using paper and marking pens, make a large label for each of seven stations: Cloud, Mountain, Stream, Groundwater, Ocean, Plant, and Animal. Use those labels to set up seven stations around

the room. At each station, put an envelope filled with the strips designated for that station.

For Part B, on or near the school grounds, find two sloped sites with about the same angle of slope: one should have little or no vegetation on the soil (a roadway cutbank, or steep bare slope, works well), and one should be covered with plants (grass, shrubs, or trees). Alternatively, you can build two boxes about 16" long x 12" wide x 4" deep (40.6 cm x 30.5 cm x 10.2 cm). Make them water-tight by lining with plastic material or aluminum foil. (You may use planter boxes, cake pans, or aluminum foil roasting pans with the approximate dimensions.) At one end of each box cut a v-shaped notch about 1.5" (3.8 cm) deep, and fit it with a spout of stiff paper so water is directed into a container (see diagram on page 145). Put a piece of sod (cut from a pasture, field, fence row, or lawn) in one box, and place bare soil (preferably from the same location) in the other. Set both boxes on a table so the spouts extend over the edge; place boards under the opposite ends to give both boxes the same slope. Place jars on stools underneath the spouts.

PART A
GO TO THE HEAD OF THE CLOUD

Doing the Activity

1. Ask students, "What is a cycle?" (A sequence of recurring events.) Invite them to name some cycles that are part of their life (morning, afternoon, night; fall, winter, spring, summer). Ask students whether they have heard of the water cycle before. Divide the class into pairs. Ask pairs to write down words that describe what they know about the water cycle or what they think the term water cycle might mean. Then ask them to write their own description of the water cycle. Ask volunteers to share their descriptions with the whole class.

2. On the chalkboard, draw a sketch of the water cycle as shown on this page. Make sure that students understand the terms evaporation, ground-water, and condensation (see "Glossary"). Use the following questions to focus their attention:

- If every living thing needs so much water, how come water isn't used up?

- Where does the water go when a puddle dries up?

- Why don't oceans and lakes dry up like puddles do?

- Where does rain come from?

- Do you think water always follows the same path as shown in the water cycle?

3. Explain that the water cycle is really a simplified model for looking at the "journey" of a water molecule. So students may learn more about the different paths water might take, invite them to play a game in which they each will be a water molecule. Have them use the score card on student page 147 to record the path they followed in the game. Later, they will compare score cards.

4. Divide students into seven approximately equal groups, and have each group begin at one of the stations.

5. Have students each remove a strip from the envelope at their station. They should read the strip and write on their water cycle score card, their current station stop, what happens to to them, and their destination. They should return the strip in the envelope. When you call out "cycle", students should go to the next station as directed on their strip.

6. Repeat Step 5 about 10 times or until most students have cycled through the Cloud station a couple of times.

7. Ask students to go back to their seats, and write a brief story from a water molecule's point of view that describes the journey they just took through the water cycle. For example, a student whose journey was Mountain→Groundwater→Plant →Cloud→Ocean→Ocean→Cloud →Stream→Animal→Mountain might start a story, "I was a lonely water molecule frozen in ice on top of a mountain. When the spring came and the ice thawed, I slid down the mountain and sank deep into the earth."

8. On the chalkboard, write the names of the seven stations. Beginning with Cloud, ask students to share all the different ways they got to Cloud. (For example, they evaporated from the ocean and transpired from the plant.) On the chalkboard, show each response by drawing arrows to Cloud. Repeat with the other stations.

9. Discuss the following questions:

■ Even though individual molecules took different paths, was anything similar about the journeys they took?

■ In the game, which stations seemed to be visited by the most water molecules, regardless of their particular journey? What can we infer from this?

■ Can you think of other parts of the water cycle that were not included in the game? (lakes, reservoirs, rivers, wells, puddles) Where might they be included in the cycle?

■ The water cycle is usually shown like this (point to sketch from Step 2). Do you think this is a useful way to show the cycle, even if the sketch doesn't include all the paths water might take?

■ What makes water move through the cycle? (sun, gravity, physical properties of water) What would happen if the sun's energy were blocked from Earth?

■ What might happen if all of Earth's water stayed in the oceans? In the clouds?

■ How is the water cycle important to plants and animals? (It moves water to them; it makes water available at different times.)

PART B
DON'T MUDDY THE WATER

Doing the Activity
1. Ask students, "Have you ever wished water didn't act the way it does? For example, you might have wished that it didn't rain on a day when your family was going to the zoo, that a puddle didn't evaporate because you enjoyed stomping in it, or that snow didn't melt because you wanted to ski." Discuss these questions:

■ Is there anything people can do to control or alter the water cycle? (build dams, cover reservoirs, seed clouds, make snow)

■ Do you think plants have any effect on the water cycle?

2. Explain to students that the class will conduct an experiment to find one way that plants might affect the water cycle and protect soil from erosion. Take them to the slopes you identified in Getting Ready, or use the two boxes. Describe the experiment to students (see Step 3). Then have them predict whether there will be any difference in what occurs on the two slopes.

3. Fill the watering can or coffee can with water. Help students hold the can at the same height so they can pour or sprinkle water at the same rate over the same point of each slope. Have students look for the following:

- The plants' effect on the water's speed

- The amount of run-off on each slope

- The appearance of the run-off water

- The water's effect on the contour (shape of the surface) of each slope

4. As you lead class members in a discussion about what they observed, ask questions such as these:

- What happened to the water on the bare slope? What do you think will be the water's next stop in the water cycle? (probably a stream)

- What happened to the water on the planted slope? What do you think will be the water's next stop in the water cycle? (plants, groundwater, or stream)

- In what ways do plants affect the movement of both water and sediment (soil carried in water) through the water cycle? (They slow down the water so more of it can soak into the ground and plants rather than running off into streams. They hold soil with their roots so it doesn't wash away.)

- What effect did the two slopes have on the quality of the water? How did the change occur? (Water on the bare slope might have been muddier.)

- How are forests important for maintaining the balance of water in a watershed?

Enrichment

Build a terrarium to observe the water cycle in action. (See Appendix 8 for instructions.) Put a small cup filled with water (to simulate a pond) in the center, and surround it with a 2" (5-cm) layer of soil. Place small potted plants (like ferns or house plants) in the soil. Then moisten the soil and plants lightly using a spray bottle. Cover the container tightly with plastic wrap and place the terrarium in indirect sunlight. What do your students observe happening as time passes? What causes the changes? (Plants should thrive. Moisture should condense on the underside of the plastic and the side of the container. The water level in the pond may rise if water drips into it.)

END NOTES...

ASSESSMENT OPPORTUNITY

Ask students to revise their definition of water cycle (from Part A) to reflect any new understanding they've gained from the activity.

Give students the following scenario to write about individually or in groups: Imagine that two pieces of land are exactly alike, except one area is bare and the other is covered by a forest. Now imagine a stream running through each piece of land. What are the differences in the way the stream might move through each piece of land? How would the water quality of the stream differ in each area? What physical changes might take place in each area?

RELATED ACTIVITIES

Rain Reasons, Soil Stories, Air Plants, Every Drop Counts

GO TO THE HEAD OF THE CLOUD

(Make two copies; then cut strips apart.)

STATION 1—CLOUD

You fall as rain onto a mountain. Go to Mountain.

You fall as snow onto a mountain. Go to Mountain.

You fall as rain onto a stream. Go to Stream.

You fall as rain onto an ocean. Go to Ocean.

You fall as snow onto an ocean. Go to Ocean.

You fall as rain onto a parking lot. Go to Stream.

STATION 2—MOUNTAIN

You evaporate into the air. Go to Cloud.

You soak into the ground and become part of the groundwater. Go to Groundwater.

You soak into the ground and get absorbed by a plant's roots. Go to Plant.

You roll downhill and become part of a stream. Go to Stream.

You roll downhill and become part of a stream Go to Stream.

You get frozen in ice and stay there. Stay at Mountain.

STATION 3—OCEAN

You are one of countless water molecules in an ocean and you stay there. Stay at Ocean.

You are one of countless water molecules in an ocean and you stay there. Stay at Ocean.

You evaporate into the air. Go to Cloud.

You evaporate into the air. Go to Cloud.

A kelp plant takes you in, releases you through its leaf, and transpires you into the air. Go to Cloud.

Go to Plant, but do not draw a card. Then go directly to Cloud.

STATION 4—STREAM

You evaporate into the air. Go to Cloud.

You evaporate into the air. Go to Cloud.

An animal comes to the stream and licks you up. Go to Animal.

You continue rolling downhill and become part of an ocean. Go to Ocean.

You continue rolling downhill and become part of an ocean. Go to Ocean.

STATION 5—GROUNDWATER

You become part of an underground stream that flows to an ocean. Go to Ocean.

You become part of an underground stream that flows to an ocean. Go to Ocean.

You become part of an underground stream that flows to a spring, where you become part of a stream. Go to Stream.

You become part of an underground stream that flows to a spring, where you become part of a stream. Go to Stream.

A plant takes you in through its roots. Go to Plant.

You are pumped out of the ground from a well to irrigate a farm. Go to Plant.

STATION 6—ANIMAL

After using you to process food, the animal urinates and you end up on the ground. Go to Mountain.

After using you to process food, the animal urinates and you end up on the ground. Go to Mountain.

You are exhaled from a human's lungs into the air as vapor. Go to Cloud.

You are exhaled from a human's lungs into the air as vapor. Go to Cloud.

A person uses you for brushing his or her teeth. Go to Stream.

STATION 7—PLANT

The plant transpires you through its leaves into the air as vapor. Go to Cloud.

The plant transpires you through its leaves and you evaporate into the air. Go to Cloud.

The plant transpires you through its leaves and you evaporate into the air. Go to Cloud.

The plant uses you to grow. Stay at Plant.

The plant stores you in its edible fruit. Go to Animal

WATER CYCLE SCORE CARD

WATER CYCLE SCORE CARD

STUDENT'S NAME:

STATION STOP	WHAT HAPPENS	DESTINATION
EXAMPLE		
Cloud	Fall As Rain	Mountain
1		
2		
3		
4		
5		
6		
7		
8		
9		
10		

Describe your entire journey on the back of the card.

Overview
In this activity, students will take a close look at one particular ecosystem (a forest) and will discover the ways that plants and animals are connected to each other. By substituting the appropriate information, you can also use the activity to study other ecosystems, such as oceans, deserts, marshes, or prairies.

LEVELS
Grades 4-8

SUBJECTS
Science, Language Arts, Visual Arts

CONCEPTS
■ Plant and animal populations exhibit interrelated cycles of growth and decline. (7.2)

■ Ecosystems posses measurable indicators of environmental health. (7.4)

SKILLS
Researching, Discussing, Identifying Relationships and patterns, predicting

OBJECTIVES
Students will ① collect information about various organisms in an ecosystem, ② create a mural that depicts the interdependence of various organisms with other components in an ecosystem, and ③ create a simulated web of life using a ball of string.

MATERIALS
enough large sheets of cardboard from boxes (or heavy paper) to construct a mural 4' x 8' (1.2 m x 2.4 m), tape, glue, pins, a ball of string or yarn, resource materials about forest plants and animals, folders (optional)

TIME CONSIDERATIONS
Preparation: 30 minutes

Activity: two 50-minute periods

Background
A forest is a living community dominated by trees. Each plant in the forest, from tiny mosses to giant trees, has its own specific needs for things like sunlight and moisture. Because environments vary tremendously, a specific location will be better for certain plant species than for others, and those species will grow more abundantly as a result. The most *dominant* tree species in a forest usually determines the forest's appearance and suitability as a habitat for plants and animals. For example, in some forests, large, dominant trees may reduce sunlight and monopolize soil moisture and nutrients, thus limiting the types of plants that can grow beneath them.

While trees and plants are usually its most conspicuous elements, the forest ecosystem also depends on animals. Animals are vital to most plants because they help pollinate flowers and disperse seeds. At the same time, animals such as deer, rabbits, and insects may eat certain plants, greatly reducing their presence. Some insects can substantially damage a forest ecosystem if their numbers get too high. Insect-eating birds play an important role in keeping insect populations in check.

Another way that forest plants and animals are connected is through a web of eating relationships. One primary function of a forest, like any other ecosystem, is to produce and distribute energy. All life depends on the ability of green plants to use sunlight to synthesize simple sugars from carbon dioxide and water. Through this process, called *photosynthesis,* plants take energy from sunlight and make it available to animals. Plant eaters, or herbivores, eat the plants directly; animal or flesh eaters, carnivores, in turn eat both herbivores or other carnivores, thus forming a *food chain.* A food chain is a simplified way of showing energy relationships between plants and animals in an ecosystem. For example, a food chain of sun→sunflower seed→mouse→owl shows that a seed is eaten by a mouse, that in turn is eaten by an owl. However, rarely does an animal eat only one type of food. A food web describes the interconnection of the food chains in an ecosystem and gives a clearer picture of how plants and animals in an ecosystem are related to each other.

In this activity, students will create a "web of life" to depict the relationships among members of a forest ecosystem. This web includes eating relationships (as in a food web), but also shows the various other kinds of relationships found in a forest (shelter, reproduction). The web of life suggests that all living things are connected to all others. No matter how unrelated organisms may seem, they are, in fact, connected.

Getting Ready
(Optional) For each team, begin a folder of information on a specific forest animal or plant. Folders might include pictures you cut from magazines or calendars, and articles or other information you glean from nature journals or other sources. If possible, select a variety of plants and animals so folders include at least two of each type: mammal, arthropod (insect or spider), bird, reptile, amphibian, trees, and other plants (see Step 2 of the activity for specific suggestions). Students will also need access to resource materials about forest plants and animals.

Doing the Activity
1. Ask students to work in pairs or teams to brainstorm all the components they think they would need to make a healthy forest. Invite them to share their ideas with the rest of the class.

2. Afterward, make a class list of animals that live in the forest. Some examples are bark beetle, bat, beaver, bear, box turtle, butterfly, chipmunk, deer, earthworm, field mouse, red fox, tree frog, grasshopper, king snake, lizard, mosquito, hawk moth, opossum, barred owl, rabbit, raccoon, skunk, snail, red squirrel, tick, or woodpecker.

3. Make a class list of plants that live in the forest. Some examples might be azalea, clover, columbine, cottonwood, honeysuckle, lichen, maple tree, Douglas fir, paintbrush, pine tree, poison ivy, shelf fungus, or violet.

4. Divide class into teams of two to four students. (You can use the same teams as before.) Have each team select a forest organism to study. (Or choose one of the folders prepared earlier.) Make sure the groups select a variety of plants and animals. For instance, try to have at least two groups that study each of the following kinds of organisms: mammal, insect, bird, reptile, trees, and other plants.

5. Instruct groups to collect as much information as possible about their chosen organism.

Animal groups should answer these questions:

■ Where does the animal live? (on the ground, in trees, at the edge of the forest, in the forest)

■ What does it need to survive?

■ What shelter does it require? Where does it perch, hibernate, breed, and sleep?

■ Does it migrate? If so, when and where?

■ Where and how does it get its water?

■ What animals does it prey on? How much does it eat?

■ What animals prey on it?

■ With what animals does it live? What plants?

■ How does the animal influence its environment?

Plant groups should answer these questions:

■ Where does the plant live?

■ What does it need to survive?

■ How does it reproduce? Does it have seeds? If so, how are they dispersed?

■ How much sunlight and water does it require?

■ Does it live near other plants? If so, what kinds?

■ What animals live with this plant?

■ What animals eat this plant?

■ How does this plant influence its environment?

6. Ask groups to find photographs or drawings of their plant or animal. (They can draw their own pictures or take their own photos.) If possible, pictures should show the organism in its natural habitat.

7. Ask the class to create a forest mural on large cardboard or paper sheets. Students can use pictures from magazines or their own drawings to show hills, valleys, streams, homes, plants, animals, and other features. The mural should show important elements like sun, water, soil, and atmosphere. The mural can show various forest areas: wet, urban, young, or mature. Each team can work on a separate panel and focus on a particular type of forest area.

8. When the mural is finished, each team should send a representative to place a picture of the organism (plant or animal) they studied into its appropriate habitat. The student should explain the team's reasons for placing each organism in a particular spot. When all organisms are in place, you might discuss the following questions:

■ What did you discover about your plant or animal that surprised you the most?

■ Why did you select the species you did? Have you ever seen the plant or animal you selected? Would you know where and when to look for it? Did you know before you studied it?

■ Is it a ***threatened*** or ***endangered*** species? If so, for what reasons is it endangered? Is anything being done to help or harm it? (See "Life on the Edge," page 335, for background on endangered species.)

9. When all animals are in place, introduce the web of life concept (see background, page 148).

10. Place a push pin next to each plant or animal. Then use yarn to connect each animal to other animals and plants with which it directly or indirectly interacts (for example, "eats," "is eaten by," or "depends on for shelter"). Students can help by acting as experts on the species they researched.

11. Ask each team to make sure that its organism is *appropriately* attached to other components in the ecosystem depicted on the mural. The completed mural forms a web of life for this ecosystem.

12. Discuss these questions:

- What would happen if one element of the ecosystem were missing? (You can demonstrate by removing a push pin.) What will happen to other organisms?

- What important elements are not included in our web?

- What are some webs of life within your school or community? (Students go to school -> teachers teach them -> cafeteria workers feed them -> parents pay taxes so teachers and cafeteria workers can buy food.)

- What are some global webs of life?

VARIATION—ALL TIED UP

1. After they research the organisms (in Step 5 above), have the teams each make a name tag for their forest plant or animal, including a picture. Ask one person from each group to sit on the floor in a circle. (If you have a small group, each student may research an organism, make a name tag, and sit in the circle.)

2. Starting with one "plant," ask that student to hold the end of a ball of string. Ask the team that studied the first plant to name another organism in the circle with which that plant interacts (for example, is eaten by or depends on). Pass the ball to this second student, who will wrap the string around one hand and pass the ball to the student representing an organism that the second team chooses to connect with. This

process will continue until each "organism" is linked to the ecosystem, and the ball is returned to the first student.

3. Now, have students slide back until the string is taut. Tell students to keep still. But if they feel a tug, they should tug in response. When everyone is still, tell the student holding the original end of the string to gently begin tugging. Keep reminding everyone that if they feel a tug, they should tug in response. Through this mechanism, vibration will spread through the food web until everyone is tugging and the whole web is shaking.

4. Ask students how the tugging demonstration might illustrate what happens when one of the links in an ecosystem is damaged through natural or human-made stress. (The rest of the ecosystem feels the effects.)

5. Ask students to pick one organism in the system that seems less important than the others, and have it drop out. Ask if any other organisms should drop out because they depended on that organism. After one or more have dropped out, ask the students again to identify an organism that seems less important, and repeat the procedure. Continue playing for a few more rounds; then ask the following questions:

- What happens when we remove a link in the forest ecosystem? (Organisms that depend on it are affected.)

- Were the changes more dramatic when the system was composed of many parts or when it had fewer parts? (fewer)

- What can we say about the relationship between how many parts the system has (its complexity or diversity) and how stable it is? (In general, complexity makes it more stable.)

Enrichment
Make food web mobiles. Have each student select a plant or animal that is part of the forest ecosystem or another ecosystem. Students should research their organism's place in the food web and make a cutout of all the food web organisms from construction paper and colored markers. Using a clothes hanger and

thread to hang cutouts in the proper arrangement, students can construct a mobile that represents their food web.

Overview
Every organism requires a place to live that satisfies its basic needs for food, water, shelter, and space. Such a place is called a habitat. In this activity, students will go on a safari to explore a nearby habitat, the school yard, while looking for signs of animals living there.

Background
Habitat refers to the place where an organism lives. Its habitat provides an organism with everything it needs to survive, including its specific needs for food, water, shelter, space, and reproduction.

Habitats vary tremendously in terms of size and appearance. For example, a field is home both to many types of grasses and to mice and rabbits that live among the grasses, a tree is the entire habitat for many tiny animals that live in its bark and among its leaves, and a crack in a sidewalk is the habitat for the dandelions and ants that live there.

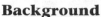

Even in the most sterile-looking environment, you can usually find some signs of animal life. In an urban school yard, for example, students can find things such as spider webs, ants underneath pieces of cement or rock, or insects buzzing around. Students need to understand that all animals, large and small, need food, water, and shelter from their environment. Remind students that people are animals too. Around the school yard they'll find plenty of signs of "people life."

While most students enjoy looking for animals, some may be afraid of certain animals like spiders or worms. Be prepared for some students to act timid or scared during the activity. You might help by briefing students in advance on the kinds of animals they are likely to see, and by assuring them that most animals will be scared of them. However, tell them it is smart to be cautious and warn them about animals they should not touch or pick up. (See Appendix 6 on page 379)

Getting Ready
You may want to do the activity at a time of year when students are most likely to see animals outdoors, such as spring or fall.

Always check an outdoor study site before taking students out. Look for potential hazards and risks. Either remove potential dangers or caution students about them. For younger students, arrange to have at least one or more parents, aides, or older students to help with the safari.

Doing the Activity
1. Invite students on a safari of the school grounds. They will look and listen for signs of animals living or visiting there. Tell students that they will need to search carefully to find animals, and that they will be more likely to find an animal if they are quiet. Ask students for ideas about where they might look. Their suggestions might include on the bark and leaves of trees, on shrubs, in the cracks of sidewalks, among blades of grass, on utility wires, in the soil around plants, along the edges of buildings, under leaves, and on walls and fences. List their suggestions on the chalkboard. You might stimulate their imagination by having them pretend that buildings are mountains and cliffs, that the lawn is a jungle, or that the sewer is an underground river.

2. Tell students that in addition to actual animals, they should look and listen for signs of animals. Remind

LEVELS
Grades PreK–5

SUBJECTS
Science, Language Arts

CONCEPTS
- Plant and animal populations exhibit interrelated cycles of growth and decline. (7.2)
- Organisms are interdependent; they all depend on nonliving components of the Earth. (4.1)

SKILLS
Observing, Concluding, Interpreting

OBJECTIVES
Students will ① find signs of animals living in the school yard and ② describe ways the school environment provides those animals with what they need to live.

MATERIALS
(all optional), clipboards or writing surfaces, drawing paper and colored pencils or markers, hand lenses

TIME CONSIDERATIONS
Preparation: 20 minutes

Activity: 50 minutes

students that people are animals too, and they can record signs of "people life." Ask students what kinds of signs they might find. Possibilities include insect-egg masses, spider webs, feathers, nests, animal tracks, bird or insect sounds, candy wrappers, cigarette butts, and leaves that have been nibbled. Talk with students about how they should leave animals where found.

3. Divide students into pairs. Take them outside and allow pairs 5-10 minutes to find two animals or signs of animals. Set boundaries so that students don't roam too far.

4. (Optional) Distribute clipboards or writing surfaces and drawing materials. Ask students to sketch the animals or signs they find. You might also give students hand lenses to increase their powers of observation. They can set up a table, and record the number of each animal they find. Later, they can make a graph using these numbers.

5. Bring the group together, and have students share their experiences and compare their findings. Focus them on the following questions:

- What animals did you observe living in our school yard?

- What evidence did you find of other animals?

- What do these animals need to live? (food, water, air, shelter, space)

- What kinds of food might animals find on the school grounds?

- Where do those animals get water?

- What kind of shelter might animals find on the school grounds?

- Did you see any damage to habitats or unhealthy conditions for plants, animals, or people? Were those conditions natural?

For younger students, you may want to ask these questions:

- What were the largest and smallest animals you found?

- What surprised you the most?

- How are those animals harmful or helpful to you?

Enrichment

1. Extend the safari to a larger outdoor setting, such as around the block or neighborhood. Students might focus their investigations by ① looking for birds and tallying the numbers of different kinds of birds, ② looking for evidence of animals eating or being eaten by something else, ③ looking for evidence of animals using water, or ④ sketching trees and looking for evidence of how trees help animals (including people).

2. Help students learn more about the animals they found in the school yard. For example, they could research different animals found and create a class chart showing a picture of each animal and information about what it needs to survive.

3. Ask students what kinds of animals they would like to have (or have more of) on their school grounds (birds, bees, butterflies, squirrels, rabbits). Have them do some research to find out what could be done to the school yard habitat to attract those animals. (Provide bird feeders or baths, shelters for mammals, or plants as food for wildlife.) They can find information in the library or get advice from experts such as the state wildlife agency. Have students develop a proposal, get permission from administrators, and then put their plan into action. (See Appendix 7, "Setting Up an Outdoor Classroom.")

4. Compare the school grounds habitat with that of a local forest. Do both have any of the same trees or animals?

END NOTES...

ASSESSMENT OPPORTUNITIES

Students can draw a picture or diagram, write a story, or make a diorama showing an animal that lives on the school grounds and how it gets the food, water, and shelter it needs to live. Alternatively, they could act out the behavior of an animal they observed, while other students guess what they are.

Students can select an animal they observed and can draw a picture of what the world looks like from its perspective.

Members of each pair can make analogies between the animals they found (actual or signs of) on the school grounds and animals from other parts of the world. For example, a centipede is like a lion because it is a voracious predator! Students can also describe analogies between animals they found and various jobs in the human community. For example, a sowbug is like a garbage collector or recycler because both keep the ecosystem clean and healthy.

RELATED ACTIVITIES

Field, Forest, and Stream; Web of Life; Trees as Habitat; Are Vacant Lots Vacant?

Overview
Look closely and you will see that a vacant lot is not so vacant! Plants of all kinds thrive in vacant lots, along with a host of animals such as insects, birds, and mammals. In this activity, a nearby vacant lot, overgrown strip, or a landscaped area will provide a rich laboratory for students to examine elements of an ecosystem.

Background
In an ecosystem, living and nonliving elements constantly interact. For example, most plants depend on soil for water and nutrients, and they need sunlight to manufacture food. Some plants also depend on animals to pollinate their flowers, disperse their seeds, and fertilize the soil in which they live. Animals, in turn, depend on plants for food and shelter. Some animals may also depend on other animals for food and protection.

A vacant lot, garden, or natural site near your school can provide a wonderful outdoor classroom for students to explore ecological relationships. By looking at a real ecosystem in action, students will begin to understand how the intricate parts of that system work together to support plants and animals living there.

The residents of a vacant lot that are easiest to observe are plants. Young trees and shrubs may have grown from seeds carried to the site by the wind or dropped by birds. The ailanthus (ay-LAHN-thus), or tree of heaven, is common in vacant lots across temperate North America. It produces many seeds that are carried by the wind and that germinate in many extreme conditions. Other common wild plants that students may find include butter-and-eggs, burdock, chickweed, clover, daisy, dandelion, goldenrod, wild mustard, oxalis, plantain, poison ivy, wild strawberry, Virginia creeper, yarrow, and many grasses.

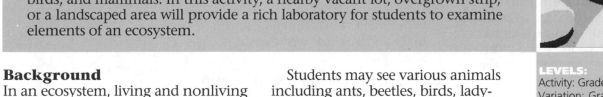

Students may see various animals including ants, beetles, birds, ladybugs, centipedes, earthworms, slugs, snails, spiders, squirrels, and sowbugs. Some plants and animals are native to your research area while others are exotics that have become established. Most field guides will contain information on this (see the Bibliography on page 384).

Students will probably find evidence of a particularly large mammal, the human. Students can often find garbage people leave behind or a path made by people's trampling feet.

Getting Ready
Locate a study site for conducting the activity, such as a vacant lot, a landscaped area of the school, or a nearby park. If students will visit a vacant lot, get permission from the owner so students can conduct a study project there. Locate any safety hazards such as ditches or broken glass, and either remove them or mark them as off limits. You might want to get extra supervisors for this activity. (See Appendix 6, for tips on teaching out-of-doors.)

Doing the Activity
1. Explain to students that they will visit a "living laboratory" to learn about plants and animals and how they live. Describe the site they will visit, and ask them to name plants and animals they think they might see. Ask what ways they might see plants and animals interacting.

2. Take students to the study site. Divide the class into teams of three to five students and have each team stake out a plot 12 feet (3.7 meters) square. (You can scale down the size, if necessary.)

LEVELS:
Activity: Grades 4-8
Variation: Grades K-3

SUBJECTS
Science, Math, Visual Arts

CONCEPTS
- Plant and animal populations exhibit interrelated cycles of growth and decline. (7.2)
- Ecosystems possess measurable indicators of environmental health. (7.4)

SKILLS
Observing, Organizing Information, Identifying Relationships and Patterns, Analyzing

OBJECTIVES
Students will ① describe plants and animals that live at and around the study site, and ② give examples of and describe ecological relationships between biotic and abiotic elements at the study site.

MATERIALS
stakes and rope, string, or strips of cloth for marking study plots; paper; clipboards or other writing surfaces; drawing paper; drawing materials

TIME CONSIDERATIONS
Preparation: 10 minutes
Activity: 50 minutes

3. Before investigating, ask each team to list the plants and animals they expect to find in their study plots.

4. Ask each team to examine its plot for signs of animal life such as burrows, tracks, anthills, and spider webs. Ask students to inventory the kinds of plant life they find. Suggest that they record their findings by sketching each type of organism and tallying the types. Make clear that they do not have to know the names of what they see; they can sketch, describe, or create their own names for the plants or animals they observe.

5. As students observe their plots, focus their attention using the following questions. You might give each group a different suggestion, or ask all groups to focus on the same question at the same time.

- Is there evidence that the plot is used by animals?

- Is there evidence of animals that eat (prey on) others?

- Do certain plants grow better in certain locations?

- Do certain animals stay close to certain plants?

- Have the plant and animal populations changed from previous times? Have their numbers and ratios to each other changed?

- How do the plants or animals get the water they need to live?

- How did the plants originally get there?

- In what ways have people used this site before?

- Are there any signs of pollution?

6. Back in the classroom, or at the site, ask each team to prepare a visual presentation of what was observed during the investigation. Provide drawing materials, flip charts, overhead transparencies, or whatever media equipment you can. Then allow time for students to plan and prepare their presentations.

7. After all teams' presentations, discuss their findings with the entire group. Include these questions to help with the presentations:

- What plants and animals seem to live in or pass through the study site?

- What elements of this site help support animals living there? Plants? What would happen if one of those elements were missing?

- Were there plants or animals that you expected to find but didn't? Did another group find them? What could be the reasons those organisms were not found?

- What are the positive and negative aspects of this site for people?

- What do you think would happen if people decided to erect a building on this site?

- What might be done to the site to make it better for plants? Animals? People?

VARIATION—MINI SAFARI

1. Give each pair of students a 3-foot (.9-m) piece of string and two hand lenses. Have pairs place their strings on the ground somewhere in the study site. Alternatively, you could give each pair a wire hanger stretched into a circular shape, and have students place it on the ground.

2. Invite students to take a mini-hike along the mini-trail created by their string or within the hanger. To "hike," they should sit or kneel next to the string or hanger and "walk" with their fingers.

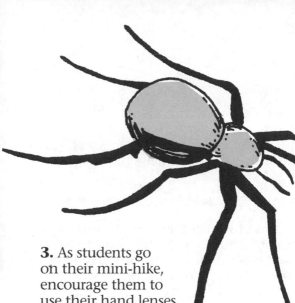

3. As students go on their mini-hike, encourage them to use their hand lenses to look for plants, animals, or interesting features along the way. Ask these questions:

- What are the plants like? Are they close together or far apart?

- What are the animals doing? Do you see any animals eating plants? How else do animals use the plants?

- What do you see animals doing with other animals?

4. Consider what might be done to the site to make it a better place for plants, animals, and people to live. Have students draw pictures of what the site might look like if all of their suggested improvements were carried out.

Enrichment
1. Ask each group to use the collected data to draw a map that indicates locations of plants and animals (or their signs) on its plot. These group maps could be combined to create a map of the entire vacant lot or site.

2. With the owner's permission, help the class conduct these further investigations of a vacant lot:

- Dig out a block of soil, and find leaves and stems that are disintegrating to become part of the soil.

  - Compare soil samples from different areas of the lot.

  - Examine old logs or pieces of wood being decomposed by fungi or insects. Decomposition frees the nutrients in the wood and returns them to the soil. (See "The Fallen Log" page 72.)

- Use a field guide to identify some of the plants.

- Catch insects by brushing the tops of grasses and weeds with an insect net; use a field guide to identify the insects.

- Collect seeds and soil from the lot, and try growing seeds in your classroom.

- Begin a journal noting feeding, nesting, or singing birds that the students observe in the lot.

3. Working in small groups or individually, ask students to prepare presentations that illustrate the value of vacant lots (or other areas) in providing plant and animal habitats. Their presentations might take the form of ① guided tours for younger students, ② oral reports along with plant and animal maps for adults in the community, or ③ recommendations to city officials for care of these community areas.

END NOTES...

ASSESSMENT OPPORTUNITIES
1. Use group presentations to evaluate student understanding. Assess the clarity of information presented and the validity of conclusions drawn. Also, see how well students addressed the questions in Step 7.

2. Ask students to consider improvements to the areas they are learning about, and have them draw pictures of what the site might look like if all suggestions were carried out. Those pictures can be used as part of the project outlined in Step 3 of enrichment.

RELATED ACTIVITIES
Schoolyard Safari; Have Seeds-Will Travel; How Plants Grow; Field, Forest, and Stream; Web of Life

Overview
In this activity students will examine three different environments as they focus on sunlight, soil moisture, temperature, wind, plants, and animals, in each environment. By comparing different environments, students will begin to consider how nonliving elements influence living elements in an ecosystem.

LEVELS
Activity: Grades 4-8
Variation: Grades 1-3

SUBJECTS
Science, Math

CONCEPTS
- In biological systems, energy flows and materials continually cycle in predictable and measurable patterns. (7.1)
- Plant and animal populations exhibit interrelated cycles of growth and decline. (7.2)
- Ecosystems posses measurable indicators of environmental health. (7.4)

SKILLS
Observing, Organizing Information, Comparing and Contrasting, Identifying Relationships and Patterns

OBJECTIVES
Students will ① investigate and measure components in three different ecosystems, ② describe similarities and differences they observe among three ecosystems, and ③ identify ways that the abiotic components of an ecosystem affect the biotic components.

MATERIALS
butcher paper, marking pens, paper for recording observations, trowel or stick, photographic light meter or photosensitive paper, thermometer, small strip of paper, compass

TIME CONSIDERATIONS
Preparation: 60 minutes

Activity: one or more 50-minute periods

Background
An ecosystem is a community of different species interacting with each other and with the chemical and physical factors making up its nonliving environment. It is a system of interrelationships among organisms, and between organisms and the physical environment.

Plants and animals in an environment interact with each other in various ways. For example, plants may depend on insects or birds to pollinate flowers and on earthworms to aerate the soil; animals may depend on plants for food or shelter. However, plants and animals also interact with the nonliving elements of their environment. In a local environment, physical factors such as sunlight, moisture, temperature, and wind influence the suitability of an area for particular organisms. Those factors determine the kinds of plants and animals that live there. Physical factors may be determined by the environment's geography, such as its proximity to water, its elevation, or its geological features. In addition, the resident organisms (particularly plants) may affect the sunlight, moisture, temperature, and wind of the area. For example, the tall trees of a redwood forest tend to block sunlight and thus create a dark, moist environment, or microclimate on the forest floor that is suitable for shade-loving plants but is too shady for other kinds of plants. Microclimate refers to special conditions of light, moisture, and temperature that occur in a narrowly restricted area within an ecosystem, for example, under a bush or in a small woodland opening.

Getting Ready
Find three study sites that are somewhat different from each other in terms of sunlight, air temperature, soil moisture, wind, and number and types of plants and animals living there. If possible, select one site that is open, like a field or lawn; one that has trees; and one that contains water. Possible study sites include a school lawn; a park, playground, or other area with many trees; a flower bed or vegetable garden; a vacant lot; a pond, stream, or marsh; an open field; and a forest.

Plan to visit the sites on the same day or on different days (at about the same time each day). Obtain any necessary permission to take students to visit the sites you have chosen. Check the sites beforehand to identify and possibly remove any safety hazards.

Arrange to have at least one parent volunteer, aide, or older student to help supervise students during outdoor investigations. This person will help the activity go more smoothly, ensure students' safety, and prevent damage to the sites.

Photocopy student page 159 for each team to record their observations.

Using butcher paper and marking pens, prepare a large chart for compiling each team's data.

Doing the Activity
1. Ask students to think of a place they enjoy visiting. (It might be a park, a grandparent's house, or the library.) Ask them to think about these questions:

- What did you particularly enjoy about the place? Was it the people? The physical space?

- What did you do?

- What living things made your place enjoyable? (plants, animals)

■ Name any nonliving things that made your place enjoyable. (water, mountains, climate)

Help students see that any place has both living and nonliving parts that work together to make an ecosystem. Explain that students will investigate ecosystems at three different study sites to find out how living and non-living elements affect each other.

2. Divide your group into six teams. Explain that each team will investigate and record observations of a different component of three different study sites. (If you have a large group, divide students into twelve teams, with two teams studying each component. Then average their data.) Give students instructions, a copy of student page 159, and materials as described below. Later, teams will transfer their observations to the class data chart.

Team 1—Soil
Ask this team to determine the soil moisture at the study sites. Students can use a trowel or stick to scrape the surface of the ground and to obtain a small sample of soil from underneath the surface. By feeling the soil, they should be able to tell whether it is wet, moist, or dry. (Moist soil will stick together.) They should examine the soil for other characteristics such as texture, color, and smell. They should also note plant material or organisms in the soil. (See "Soil Stories," page 252, for more information.)

Team 2—Sunlight
Ask this team to determine how much sunlight penetrates the ground at each study site. Students may determine light intensity at each site by using a photographic light meter or photosensitive paper. If these items are not available, they can use relative terms such as shady, dark, medium light, or bright; or "Site 1 is brighter than site 2, and site 2 is brighter than 3."

Team 3—Wind
Ask this team to use the small strip of paper to determine the wind movement at each site. One student can hold the paper away from the body, while the others observe whether it hangs straight down or blows at an angle. Ask students to use the compass to determine from which direction the wind seems to be blowing.

Team 4—Temperature
Ask this team to measure each site's temperature at ground level, 1" (2.5 cm) deep in the soil, and at 1 yard (.9 m) above ground. If one site is a pond, stream, or lake, have the team measure the temperature at just above the water, at 1" (2.5 cm) deep, and at 1 yard (.9 m) above.

Team 5—Plant Life
Ask this team to observe the various kinds of plants at each site (large trees, small trees, shrubs, small plants, grasses—no need to identify species). Suggest that students record the most common types of plants found in each location and that they note especially where each grows relative to the others.

Team 6—Animal Life
Ask this team to note the various kinds of animals at each site (insects, birds, reptiles, fish, frogs, or tadpoles). Students should note evidence of animals such as scat, tracks, burrows, or leaves that have been chewed.

3. After teams have had sufficient time to investigate each location, have them all come together to present their findings and share what they have learned.

4. Each team should listen to the reports of the other teams, and use the information to complete their team chart on page 159.

5. Ask teams to enter their data on the large class chart you prepared. Use this chart as a basis for discussing differences between the locations and any interactions students observed among the elements. Ask the following questions:

■ Which ecosystem had the greatest number of plants? Animals? Which has the least of each? How do you explain this difference?

- How are plants and animals the same at different sites? How are they different?

- Which site had the highest air temperature? The lowest? The most wind? The least?

- Which has the wettest soil? The driest?

- Do plants seem to affect the light intensity, air temperature, and soil temperature in an area?

- How does water seem to influence the soil temperature, air temperature, and soil moisture?

- What relationship does light seem to have with air temperature? With soil moisture? With plants?

- Which of the six elements we studied seems most important for determining the character of the environment at each site? What makes you say so?

VARIATION—STAKE YOUR CLAIM

Using index cards attached to sticks or stakes, prepare enough markers so that each pair of students has two. Write one of the following labels on each marker. For younger students, you may use simpler words or the suggested symbols: Most Soil Moisture (faucet gushing), Least Soil Moisture (faucet dripping), Most Sunlight (sun), Least Sunlight (sun covered by cloud), Highest Temperature (thermometer with high mercury), Lowest Temperature (thermometer with low mercury), Most Wind (fluttering flag), Least Wind (limp flag), Most Plants (several plants), Least Plants (one plant), Most Animals (several insects) and Least Animals (one insect).

After choosing a study area such as a vacant lot, mark it off with string or rocks. Divide the class into pairs, and give each pair "most" and "least" markers for each environmental factor listed above. Invite teams to explore the study area and determine which location has the most and the least of each factor. For example, a team studying plants should decide which

site has the most plants and which has the least. Students will indicate their choices by placing their markers in the ground.

After all students have marked their choices, examine the entire area to see where the markers of each type are located. According to the markers, which spot had the most or least sunlight? Moisture? Heat? Which spot did most animals seem to prefer? What makes you think animals prefer that spot? Did that spot have the most or least of any other factors? Which spot did most plants prefer? What makes you think plants prefer that spot?

Enrichment

1. Visit each site again at a different time of year and repeat your investigations. Compare your results: How has the soil changed? The temperature? The wind? The plants and animals? What factors influenced each change?

2. Revisit each location to look for ways humans have affected it. Students might look for things such as litter, damaged plants, new animal arrivals, polluted or cleaner water, or an improved path. Discuss these questions:

- Which human actions have harmful effects on these ecosystems? Which are beneficial?

- Are these short-term or long-term effects?

- What might we do to keep further damage from occurring?

- Which human actions have a positive effect on the ecosystems?

- What might we do to encourage more of these kinds of actions?

3. It's easier than you think to bring the outdoors inside! Create a class terrarium of a local ecosystem, or have teams of students create terrariums of various ecosystems. See Appendix 8 for complete directions on setting up terrariums that represent different ecosystems.

TEAM CHART

TEAM MEMBERS _____

ECOSYSTEM	SITE 1	SITE 2	SITE 3
SOIL MOISTURE			
SUNLIGHT			
WIND			
TEMPERATURE			
PLANTS			
ANIMALS			

Overview
In this activity, studying tropical rainforests and issues involving the use of rainforests will enable your students to make more informed decisions regarding the future of such regions. While *tropical rainforests* and the *temperate forests* of North America operate on many of the same ecological principles, they differ greatly in their climates, and in the types of soil, plants, and animals that make up the forest ecosystems

LEVELS
Part A: Grades 3-6
Part B: Grades 6-8
Variation: Grades PreK-2

SUBJECTS
Science, Social Studies, Language Arts, Performing Arts, Visual Arts.

CONCEPTS
■ In biological systems, energy flows and materials continually cycle in predictable and measurable patterns. (7.1)

■ Altering the environment affects all life forms—including humans—and the interrelationships that link them. (4.2)

■ Organisms adapt to changes in the environment according to the genetic and behavioral capacity of their species. (4.3)

SKILLS
Reasoning, Discussing, Researching, Interpreting

OBJECTIVES
Students will ① describe the plants and animals that live in different levels of the tropical rainforest, and ② examine and discuss a case study that involves the rights of native inhabitants of a tropical rainforest in a national park, ③ describe the sounds they might encounter when visiting a rainforest.

MATERIALS
(all optional) pictures of rainforests, pictures of rainforest animals, tape recorder, cassette tape of rainforest sounds

TIME CONSIDERATIONS
Preparation: 20 minutes

Activity: Part A—30 minutes
Part B—30 minutes
Variation—20 minutes

Background
What is a tropical rainforest? Tropical rainforests are wet, evergreen forests circling the equator in South and Central America, Africa, Asia, and many of the Pacific Islands. These complex ecosystems have evolved over millions of years. Their environment is distinguished by a warm, humid climate capable of supporting an immense variety of life. (See Project Learning Tree "Forests of the World" map; ordering information is in the Bibliography on page 386.)

Since tropical rainforests are near the equator, each day is roughly the same length. Temperature changes little throughout the year, with an average of 75 degrees F (24 degrees C). Regular rainfall of 60" to 90+" (152 cm to 229+ cm) annually allows plants to grow uninterrupted by seasonal factors. Tropical plants return to the air much of the moisture they receive, helping to maintain the region's high humidity.

Although tropical rainforests cover only 7 percent of Earth's surface, they are believed to shelter almost half of all existing plant and animal species in existence. Literally thousands of species of trees and plants are in rainforests.

Similar to a high-rise apartment building, the vegetation is arranged in distinct levels. Each of these levels—the *emergent, canopy, understory,* and *forest floor*—is characterized by particular varieties of animal life.

The tallest trees may reach heights of 140 feet (43 m) or more. These *emergents* (they "emerge" from the canopy) are exposed to stronger winds and sun than trees in the sheltered levels. Most emergent trees are hardwoods whose leaves are waxy to help them retain moisture. Harpy eagles, monkeys, insect-eating bats, snakes, and flying insects can be found at this level.

The *canopy* level is just beneath the emergent level. Its trees may grow to 100 feet (30 m). The large, leathery leaves of the canopy layer form a dense, nearly continuous layer 20 feet (6 m) thick, which blocks 80 percent of the sunlight from levels below. Those leaves create a warm, humid, and sheltered habitat for many animals, most of whom will rarely step foot on the ground. Inhabitants of the canopy level include margay cats, monkeys, sloths, bats, toucans, parrots, hummingbirds, snakes, lizards, tree frogs, ants, and beetles. Many of these animals feed on the abundant fruits, nuts, and leaves provided by the trees.

The *understory* level consists of small trees and shrubs from 10 to 20 feet (3 m to 6 m) tall. This level receives little light. Many of these plants tolerate shade and will remain at this level; others will grow and replace older trees that fall. Many familiar house plants come from this part of the rainforest. It is also home to animals such as parakeets, snakes, lizards, frogs, toads, ants, termites, beetles, and butterflies.

The *forest floor* is the lowest level. Since only 2 percent of sunlight reaches this far down, there are few flowering plants. Larger animals, like peccaries, tapirs, and giant armadillos, forage for edible roots and tubers. Fungi and plants survive by consuming leaves and other dead materials that fall from the upper levels. This litter is also food for large numbers of termites, millipedes, centipedes, cockroaches, scorpions, slugs, earthworms, and beetles. A leaf that would take one year to decompose in a temperate forest vanishes in a rainforest within six weeks.

The many plants and trees have developed numerous adaptations for survival. Bright and fragrant flowers attract nectar-feeding hummingbirds that carry pollen with them as they hover among blossoms. Flowers that are pollinated by bats are paler by comparison, making the flowers more easily seen at night. The seeds of many fruits develop tough coatings, so they can pass through the digestive tracts of monkeys, hornbills, toucans, and fruit bats without harm.

The straight tree trunks of the rainforest have little branching but are covered with thick climbing vines, or *lianas* (lee-AH-nuhs), and air plants, or *epiphytes* (EP-uh-fights) (whose roots are not in the soil, like orchids). These vines act like thick cables, connecting tree trunks and often spanning different levels of the rainforest. The vines provide a habitat for many rainforest animals. They also support *bromeliads* (bro-MEE-lee-ads), cup-like plants whose fibrous leaves collect and store water, and often serve as miniature ponds for tree frogs and aquatic insects.

Despite what the luxurious growth might suggest, the soil is only moderately fertile. It is not rich in minerals like temperate soils, where bacteria decay matter and return nutrients to the soil. Instead, vast amounts of specialized fungi cycle minerals directly and efficiently into the tree roots themselves. Because most of the organic material is in the living parts of the forest, topsoil may only be a few inches thick.

In contrast to temperate regions, human attempts to farm on deforested areas of tropical rainforest have been largely unsuccessful. Once the trees and fungi are destroyed, the soil rapidly loses its fertility through *leaching* and *erosion.* The rainforest is a fragile ecosystem that cannot tolerate traditional Western agricultural practices.

Many rainforest plants and animals have specialized and limited distribution. Large-scale clearing for agriculture or harvesting for forest products can severely affect habitat and can endanger plant and animal species. The loss of these species, many of which remain to be discovered, upsets the ecological balance of the rainforest, affecting indigenous peoples and their traditions. Further, potentially beneficial resources, such as pharmaceutical materials and crop plants, are lost to people all over the world.

Destruction of vast areas of the rainforest may have global climatic consequences as well and could lead to undesirable changes in weather patterns. It is important for tropical rainforests—and for our future—not only to identify and understand these problems, but also to develop practical solutions to them.

Getting Ready
Activity—Make copies of student pages 165-168.
Variation—(Optional) Buy or borrow an audio tape of rainforest sounds. Record or book stores often sell these tapes as mood or relaxation music, or your library might have some. Bring the tape and a tape recorder to class.

PART A
INSIDE THE RAINFOREST

Doing the Activity
1. Use the "Cross-Section of a Rainforest" sheet on page 165 to discuss the different rainforest levels, types of plants, and their characteristics. Use the "Rainforest Inhabitants" sheet on page 166 to discuss animals' habitat needs and at what level in the rainforest the animals might be found.

2. Hand out a copy of both sheets to each student. Have students cut out the characters on the rainforest inhabitants sheet and place them on the cross-section of the rainforest scene at the appropriate levels. Once the inhabitants are placed in the correct levels, they can be glued on and colored. Explain that the inhabitants on the sheet come from different rainforests around the world and would not be found all together in the same forest.

3. Have students research and prepare a report about a particular person, animal, or plant of the rainforest. (They can choose an inhabitant from the rainforest scene or another that they think of.) They should also describe the particular type of rainforest where the person, animal, or plant lives (including its continent and country).

4. Let students develop a classroom or hall display on the rainforest. Have them make a large mural depicting a cross-section of a rainforest and then draw or tape pictures of animals at appropriate levels.

5. Ask students to develop a cross-section of a forest typical to their own region and compare it with a rainforest. Point out that many birds indigenous to temperate forests, such as the yellow-hooded warbler, spend their winters in tropical rainforests.

PART B
PARKS AND NATIVE PEOPLE

Doing the Activity
1. Read the following excerpt about Public Law 100-571 to your students. You may need to explain difficult terms that appear. The students can also read the actual bill on page 167.

A National Park in American Samoa was established by public law in October 1988. Congress approved this park because it would protect "one of the last remaining undisturbed paleotropical forests," which is "the largest such forest under direct control of the United States," and also "contains the habitat of the last remaining populations of the Pacific flying foxes."

Additionally, the law states that "Tropical forests contain 50 percent of the world's plant and animal species, contribute significantly to the advancement of science, medicine, and agriculture, and produce much of the earth's oxygen. The loss of these forests leads to extinction of species, lessening the world's biological diversity, reduces the potential for new medicines and crops, and increases carbon dioxide levels in the atmosphere contributing to the greenhouse effect that is altering the world's climate."

However, while intending to protect the tropical rainforest environment, the law also allows people from villages within the proposed boundaries to use the park's natural resources in certain ways.

"Agricultural, cultural, and gathering uses shall be permitted in the park for subsistence purposes if such uses are generally prior existing uses conducted in areas used for such purposes as of the date of enactment of this Act, and if such uses are conducted in a traditional manner and by traditional methods. No such uses shall be permitted in the park for other than subsistence purposes."

2. Break the class into small teams and give every student a copy of the case study on page 168. After teams have familiarized themselves with the situation, focus their attention on the part of the bill that states: "Agricultural, cultural, and gathering uses shall be permitted in the park for subsistence purposes if such uses are generally prior existing...." Briefly discuss how this statement might apply to Tuima'a's situation. Then, each team should discuss the following questions and write down students' responses.

■ What would constitute traditional manners and methods of Tuima'a's family's use of the park resources? Are bush knives, chain saws, planting sticks, tractors, weed killers, insecticides, fishing nets, and fish poison appropriate?

■ How does a dictionary define subsistence? How would you define it according to congressional legislation? Which definition applies to Tuima'a's family?

■ How do the farming and fishing activities of Tuima'a's family relate to the legislative purposes of the park? Do you feel that Congress has the right to limit use to traditional methods?

■ If you were the Park Superintendent, how would you address these issues in a written letter to Tuima'a? What would you do if the native people continued to clear more forest than you thought they should?

■ How would you respond to the National Park if you were a member of Tuima'a's family?

1. If you have a tape of rainforest sounds, have students sit very still and play the tape for a few minutes.

2. Tell students that they are going to create a "symphony" of rainforest sounds.

3. With everyone in a circle, instruct students to imitate what you do, until you indicate otherwise. Sit where everyone can see you and perform the following motions and sounds in order.

- Rub palms together back and forth (wind).
- Snap fingers slowly, then quickly (first raindrops).
- Clap hands, not all in the same rhythm (steady, light rain).
- Slap thighs (heavy rain).
- Stamp feet rapidly on ground, while sitting (downpour).
- Slap thighs.
- Clap hands.
- Snap fingers quickly, then slower and slower.
- Rub palms.

4. Divide your class in three sections: rainmakers, birds, and insects (like a symphony's different sections). Tell students that you are the conductor. When you point to a section and raise your hand, that section should get louder; when you lower your hand, it should get softer. If you raise or lower both your hands, everyone should get louder or softer.

5. Have the rainmakers start softly with a light rain (snapping fingers, clapping hands, tapping feet). Next, have the bird section join in softly with tweets, whistles, hoots, screeches, caws, and so forth. Then have the insects join in softly with clicks, buzzes, whirs, hums, rattles, and chirps.

6. Conduct the rainforest orchestra, having the sections get louder and softer at intervals. Eventually, have everyone grow loud and then very soft until the whole group is quiet.

7. Afterward, ask the students what images the rainforest sounds (either the tape or their own symphony) conjured in their minds? How did it make them feel? (Excited? Scared? Sleepy?)

TROPICAL FOREST PRODUCTS

Many common products have their origins in the tropical forests (including dry, moist, and rainforests). The following are examples that may easily be obtained for use in the classroom:

WOODS
balsa, mahogany, rosewood, sandalwood, teak

HOUSEPLANTS
anthurium, croton, dieffenbachia, dracaena, fiddle-leaf fig, palm, parlor ivy, philodendron, rubber tree plant, schefflera, silver vase bromeliad, spathiphyllum, swiss cheese plant, zebra plant

SPICES
allspice, black pepper, cardamom, cayenne, chili, cinnamon, clove, ginger, mace, nutmeg, paprika, sesame seeds, tumeric, vanilla

FRUITS
avocado, banana, breadfruit, coconut, durian, grapefruit, guava, jackfruit, lemon, lime, mango, mangosteen, orange, papaya, passion fruit, pineapple, plantain, rambutan, tangerine

PHARMACEUTICAL
annatto-red dye
curare-muscle relaxant for surgery
diosgenin-birth control pills, steroids, asthma and arthritis treatment
quassia-insecticide
quinine-anti-malarial, pneumonia treatment
reserpine-sedative, tranquilizer
strophanthus-heart medication
strychnine-emetic, stimulant
tuba root-rotenone, flea dip

VEGETABLES & OTHER FOODS
Brazil nuts, cane sugar, cashew nuts, chayote, chocolate, coffee, cucumber, macadamia nuts, manioc/tapioca, okra, peanuts, soft drinks (cola), tea

FIBERS
bamboo-furniture, baskets
raffia-rope, cord, baskets
ramie-cotton-ramie fabric, fishing line
rattan-furniture, wickerwork, baskets, chair seats
jute/kenaf-rope, burlap
kapok-insulation, life jackets, soundproofing

OILS
baby oil-perfume
camphor oil-perfume, soap, disinfectant, detergent
cascarilla oil-confections, beverages
coconut oil-suntan lotion, candles
eucalyptus oil-perfume, cough drops
oil of star anise-scents, confections, beverages
palm oil-shampoo, detergents
patchouli oil-perfume
rosewood oil-perfume, cosmetics, flavoring
sandalwood oil-perfume
tolu balsam oil-confections, soaps, cosmetics
ylang-ylang-perfume

GUMS AND RESINS
chicole latex-chewing gum
copaiba-perfume, fuel
copal-paints and varnishes
gutta pertha-golf ball covers
rubber latex-rubber products
tung oil-wood finishing

Enrichment

1. Visit your local zoo or botanical garden. A major emphasis of these facilities is the preservation and display of endangered animals and plants. Pamphlets and other materials are frequently available through the institution's educational department. Curators, keepers, and educational staff can provide information regarding a particular species.

2. Survey local pet stores to see which animals, including many tropical fish, birds, and reptiles, are natives of rainforests.

NOTE—Because of the endangered species issues, many pet stores will not sell animals caught in the wild, but will work only with breeders who raise their own stock.

3. The study of native, historical, and cultural uses of plants is called ethnobotany. Research what types of plants were used by Native Americans and early settlers in your area.

4. Research the historic and economic importance of a tropical forest product (see the Tropical Forest Products box on page 163). Compare it with a major North American crop, such as corn. Compare agricultural practices (labor intensive or mechanized), derivatives (such as palm or corn oils) and efforts at hybridization to develop more desirable qualities. Investigate the extent to which these practices affect the local environment.

5. Find areas of the school grounds that do not have good vegetative cover, and look for signs of erosion. Check the depth and pH of the remaining topsoil, and compare these findings to areas that still have vegetation. A typical wooded area will have a very rich layer of topsoil, composed largely of humus. Compare this to the rainforest, which has very little topsoil.

6. Many of the birds indigenous to the United States, such as the yellow-hooded warbler, spend their winters in tropical rainforests. Research species of birds that migrate, tracing their flight paths and calculating the distances that they travel.

7. Save information from newspapers and magazines describing research efforts of scientists looking for new medicines or products in the rainforest.

8. Plan an imaginary trip to a particular rainforest. Obtain travel brochures from that country, and discuss problems that might arise in trying to explore the region. Ecologists have found creative ways to explore the canopy level, including using climbing equipment, parachuting from planes, and training monkeys to retrieve desired specimens from treetops. What can your students think of?

9. Have your students read about the lifestyles of indigenous peoples of the rainforests. Compare a day in a rainforest to a student's typical day. See the activity "People of the Forest" on page 54 for more information.

END NOTES...

ASSESSMENT OPPORTUNITY

Public Law 100-571 states that one of the reasons for establishing a national park in American Samoa is "to provide for the enjoyment of the unique resources of the Samoan tropical forest by visitors from around the world." Have students in pairs imagine that they are advertising specialists for the Park Service in American Samoa and that their job is to come up with an advertising campaign to attract visitors to the new park. They can create a series of billboard advertisements, radio or television commercials, or newspaper or magazine stories. They should base their campaign on at least some of the findings that are listed in the selected sections of the actual congressional law on page 167.

RELATED ACTIVITIES

Rain Reasons, People of the Forest, Web of Life, Watch on Wetlands

REFERENCES

Indiana Department of Natural Resources, Division of Forestry, *TROPICAL RAINFORESTS AND THE INDIANA CONNECTION.* Indianapolis:1991.

Lieberman, Grace M. and Lynne C. Hardie. *VANISHING RAINFORESTS: TEACHER'S MANUAL.* Washington, DC.: World Wildlife Fund, 1988.

Mohastersky, Richard. *THE DEFORESTATION DEBATE.* Science News, July 10, 1993, p. 26. [(volume #144)]

National Wildlife Federation. *RAINFORESTS: HELP SAVE THEIR LAYERS OF LIFE.* Washington, DC: 1993.

CROSS-SECTION OF A RAINFOREST

RAINFOREST INHABITANTS

AN ACT TO ESTABLISH THE NATIONAL PARK OF AMERICAN SAMOA

EXCERPTS FROM PUBLIC LAW 100-571-OCTOBER 31,1988

AN ACT TO ESTABLISH THE NATIONAL PARK OF AMERICAN SAMOA

Be it enacted by the Senate and House of Representatives of the United States of America in Congress assembled.

Section 1. Findings and Purposes.

(a) Findings—The Congress finds that:

① Tropical forests are declining worldwide.

② Tropical forests contain 50 percent of the world's plant and animal species, contribute significantly to the advancement of science, medicine, and agriculture and produce much of the earth's oxygen. The loss of these forests leads to the extinction of species, lessening the world's biological diversity, reduces the potential for new medicines and crops and increases carbon dioxide levels in the atmosphere contributing to the greenhouse effect that is altering the global climate.

③ The tropical forest in American Samoa is one of the last remaining undisturbed paleotropical forests.

④ The tropical forest in American Samoa is the largest such forest under direct control of the United States.

⑤ The tropical forest of American Samoa contains the habitat of one of the last remaining populations of Pacific flying foxes.

⑥ The flying foxes of American Samoa are responsible for a large part of the pollination which maintains a significant portion of the species which inhabit the Samoan tropical forest.

⑦ Information presently available indicates the existence of extensive archaeological evidence related to the development of the Samoan culture which needs to be examined and protected.

⑧ The people of American Samoa have expressed a desire to have a portion of the tropical forest protected as a unit of the National Park System.

(b) Purpose—The purpose of this Act is to preserve and protect the tropical forest and archaeological and cultural resources of American Samoa, and of associated reefs, to maintain the habitat of flying foxes, preserve the ecological balance of the Samoan tropical forest, and, consistent with the preservation of these resources, to provide for the enjoyment of the unique resources of the Samoan tropical forest by visitors from around the world.

Section 3. Administration.

(b) Traditional Subsistence
Uses—① Agricultural, cultural, and gathering uses shall be permitted in the park for subsistence purposes if such uses are generally prior existing uses conducted in areas used for such purposes as of the date of enactment of this Act and if such uses are conducted in the traditional manner and by traditional methods. No such uses shall be permitted in the park for other than subsistence purposes.

② Subsistence uses of the marine areas of the park shall also be permitted in accordance with paragraph ①, and no fishing or gathering shall be permitted in such marine areas for other than subsistence purposes.

CASE STUDY

Tuima'a and his extended family have farmed and fished for many years in a rainforest that has now been designated part of a U.S. National Park. His family comprises people from many villages in the different islands that make up American Samoa.

Throughout the years, this family has used both crops and fish harvested from the park area. They used products from the area primarily at traditional family events. They divided any surplus between home use and small sales to obtain money for necessities.

Additionally, Tuima'a practices crop rotation on 10 acres that now lie in the park. He plants only a few acres intensively each five years. Afterwards, he leaves the land uncultivated for several years to restore soil fertility while he clears and plants a new area. More than 15 years have passed since the first area was put to fallow, and it has begun growing back as secondary growth of trees. Soon it will be time to replant.

Farming practices include removing most young trees and controlling weeds by cutting or spraying with weed killer. Tillage operations are used only to grow vegetable crops. Insect problems are managed by a combination of mechanical, biological, and chemical controls.

Fishing practices include hand nets, poles and lines, and traditional tree-derived fish poisons.

Overview
In this activity, students will play the roles of managers of a 400-acre (162-hectare) piece of public forest. Through these roles, students will begin to understand the complex considerations that influence management decisions about forest lands.

Background
Public and private forests cover nearly one-third of our nation's land. Those forests provide both habitats for many species of plants and animals, and vital resources for people. People use forests in many ways such as harvesting timber, camping, hiking, hunting, and fishing. Cattle and sheep graze in forest meadows and grasslands.

The Multiple Use and Sustained Yield Act of 1960 requires that national forests be managed "in a manner to provide the maximum benefit for the general public." Multiple use management of public lands means forest managers must consider values for fish and wildlife, soil, water, timber, and recreation. Private forests are often managed for those same values. (For more about multiple use management, see the background for "A Forest of Many Uses" on page 98.)

In our society, many public policy and legislative decisions are made in terms of costs, benefits, and environmental impacts. Forest managers must consider the economic effects of their decisions about forest lands. But they must also consider the forest's intangible elements such as recreation, water, soil, and wildlife values, even though those items are harder to evaluate. One way to consider the value of a forest for recreational use would be to compare costs and benefits, for example, the cost of developing a camp ground versus the income from fees charged. Another way is to calculate the number and type of visitors a specific attraction or activity will bring to the forest in a year.

One way to determine the value of wildlife is to measure its contribution to the forest's economic value. Calculate this value by finding out the species of wildlife that live in the forest and if those animals consist of game (hunted) species like deer, turkey, or quail. Then determine the income generated from hunters through licenses, guns, equipment, lodging, and travel. Wildlife's economic value might include other uses related to wildlife—photography and bird watching, for instance—that generate income.

Another way to determine the importance of wildlife is to realize that it has intrinsic value, regardless of its economic value. With this approach, managers view the forest as a complex ecosystem in which every part of the system is important to every other part. If managers maintain each component of the ecosystem, the result will be healthy and assorted wildlife and plant communities or biological diversity. To figure out how a specific action or nonaction might affect biological diversity, forest managers look at the effects of an action on several wildlife species with different habitat needs. Sometimes, the decline of a certain species can serve as an early indicator that a whole community or ecosystem is changing.

Getting Ready
Make copies of student pages 172-175 for each person. Then using a light-colored marker, draw a 20" x 20" (50.8 cm x 50.8 cm) grid map of 400-Acre Wood on a piece of butcher paper for each team of four or five students. (Teams can also make their own.) The grid should have 400 1" x 1" (2.5 cm x 2.5 cm) squares, each representing 1 acre (.4047 hectare). On another piece of butcher or poster paper, make an identical, but larger, grid to use in group discussion. If you have an overhead projector, you may want to prepare a transparency of the grid.

LEVELS
Grades 7-8

SUBJECTS
Science, Math, Social Studies

CONCEPTS
■ Resource management and technological systems help societies to meet, within limits, the needs of a growing human population. (8.2)

■ Conservation technology enables humans to maintain and extend the productivity of vital resources. (8.3)

■ Natural beauty, as experienced in forests and other habitats, enhances the quality of human life by providing artistic and spiritual inspiration, as well as recreational and intellectual opportunities. (3.4)

SKILLS
Identifying Main Ideas, Analyzing, Solving Problems

OBJECTIVES
Students will ① create a management plan for a hypothetical piece of public forest land, taking into account factors such as ecosystem stability, monetary income or costs, wildlife, water, and visitors and ② experience the analysis and decision making that goes into managing forest land.

MATERIALS
copies of student pages 172-175; a yellow marker; butcher, newsprint, or poster paper; colored markers; calculators (optional); masking tape; transparencies and overhead projector (optional)

TIME CONSIDERATIONS
Preparation: 60 minutes

Activity: three to five 50-minute periods

Doing the Activity

1. Introduce the activity by explaining that students will look at several complex issues that face forest managers. Help students brainstorm a list of activities that take place on forest land. List their ideas on the chalkboard. Include uses like hiking, fishing, hunting, collecting firewood, camping, rock climbing, skiing, snowmobiling, logging, grazing, or mining. Ask the class to look at the list and decide if any activities would conflict with each other if done on the same piece of land.

2. Discuss these questions:

■ Which activities would cost the most to provide on forest land?

■ Which would bring the most visitors?

■ Which would have the greatest impact on the forest ecosystem? On the wildlife there? Would this effect be permanent or temporary?

■ Which would provide for society's most critical needs?

3. Have students read page 172, "If You Were the Boss." Divide the group into teams of four or five, and explain that each team will decide the best use (or uses) of 400-Acre Wood, which has been donated to the community. Each team will develop a land management plan that will serve the best interests of the entire community. Make sure students understand that their team can use the entire 400 acres (162 ha) for one use or for multiple uses. For example, they may devote 200 acres (81 ha) to wilderness and hiking, 80 acres (32 ha) to a campground, and 120 acres (49 ha) for harvesting timber or hunting.

4. Before students begin, ask these questions:

■ Which forest uses in "If You Were the Boss" are compatible with other uses? (for example, building a campground and hiking trail together)

■ Which might be incompatible with each other? (hunting at a campground)

■ What could you learn by figuring out the costs, revenues, wildlife populations, and number of visitors for each management plan? (how the plan affects different forest values)

- Are owls, wood rats, and salamanders the only wildlife in the forest? (no) What could you learn about the forest ecosystem by analyzing the populations of these three species? (By looking at three animals with different habitat requirements, you get an idea of the general health of the forest ecosystem.)

5. Give each team a map (grid) of 400-Acre Wood. Also give each team a copy of "What's The Score?" on student pages 173–175. (You might need to explain how to use these.) Each team should discuss various strategies for managing the forest. When the team arrives at a consensus on how the land should be managed, direct members to use "What's the Score?" for a cost and benefit analysis of their plan. They should discuss what impact their plan would have in terms of cost, income, timber, wildlife, visitors, and ecological balance.

6. When the teams have completed their management plans, they should use crayons or colored markers to illustrate their plans on the grids. Remind them to include a key showing what different colors and symbols mean.

7. Ask teams to present their plans to the entire group, making clear how they decided on their plans. Have them report the findings of their cost analysis worksheets. Post the maps around the room.

8. Use the large grid map to lead a group discussion of different plans. Ask these questions:

- Which plan enables the most people to enjoy the forest? What is the monetary cost in attracting the most visitors? Are there any other costs besides money?

- Which plan does the most to preserve the forest in its original state? What are the costs of this plan?

- Which plan has the most impact on wildlife?

- Which animals are sensitive to human disturbance? Why should we care if one animal species leaves the forest?

- Which plan seems to provide the best balance of money, trees, wildlife, and visitors?

- How do you think your plan should be paid for? If your plan made a profit, what should happen with the money?

- Which do you think is most important: having the most trees, the most wildlife, or the most visitors? What makes you think so?

- Which do you think is most important—① an activity's cost or income; or ② the activity's effects on trees, wildlife, and visitors? Give an example.

- What will be the long-term effects of each plan? How will costs or income change in the next year? Will the number of trees, wildlife, or visitors change?

Enrichment

1. Repeat the activity by having each team ① extend its management plan into the next year and ② figure out the effect on money, trees, wildlife, and visitors for the second year.

2. Contact the local Forest Service office or forestry agency, and invite a forest manager to talk to your class about how his or her organization makes land-use decisions. Encourage students to ask questions based on what they learned in the activity: For example, how do forest managers weigh the effects of an action on trees, people, and animals in a forested area?

ASSESSMENT OPPORTUNITY

Imagine that 400 acres (162 ha) of forest land has been given to the community to use however people please. Several different groups are competing to have their proposals accepted. Now a Community Council (made up of students) will hear arguments for each proposal and make a decision. Each team (from Step 3 of the activity) should prepare a five-minute argument explaining why their plan should be accepted. Teams can say how much money they would pay for land and what revenues or other benefits (recreation, wildlife, products) their proposal would bring to the community.

When teams have prepared their arguments, select a member from each team to sit on an impartial council (or invite another class to serve as the council). After each team presents its argument, give the council time to make its decision. If the council members cannot reach a consensus, they should choose the proposal with the most support. Use this exercise to assess how well students understand the pros and cons of their proposals.

RELATED ACTIVITIES

Water Wonders, A Forest of Many Uses, Loving It Too Much, Forest Consequences, Forest for the Trees

REFERENCES

STATISTICAL ABSTRACT OF THE UNITED STATES: 1987. Washington, DC: U.S. Department of Commerce, 1986.

IF YOU WERE THE BOSS

Imagine that you and a group of class-mates are given the job of managing a piece of forest land donated to your community. The forest is called "400-Acre Wood" and is located just outside town. As you might have guessed, it contains 400 acres (162 hectares) of forest, mostly pine. *(An acre is 43,560 square feet or 208.7 feet by 208.7 feet. 400 acres is little less than 1 square mile. A hectare is about 2.471 acres. A hectare is 10,000 square meters.)* Approximately 150 pine trees of commercial value are on each acre. Should you decide to build paths or roads through the forest, calculate that one mile (1.6km) of a 4 ft. (1.2m) path or trail will occupy 6 acres (2.4ha). Therefore, an 8' wide path would occupy 12 acres/mi and a 16' wide road would occupy 24 acres/mi.

Because the forest currently has no roads or trails, few people use or visit the land. However, 400-Acre Wood is alive with wildlife such as owls, deer, bear, woodpeckers, wood rats, and woodland salamanders. Wildlife biologists estimate two barred owls per 100 acres (40 ha) of forest, one wood rat per acre, and 25 wood-land salamanders per acre.

Your team's job is to develop a management plan for the forest. You may decide to do more than one thing on the same piece of land. Or you may want to divide the forest and do different things in different areas. Your goal is to find what you think is the best balance between ① money, plant, and animal species; and ② visitor enjoyment.

To balance their management plans, forest managers should analyze the following factors:

- What effect will your plan have in terms of money? Can you pay for it? Would it make money? How much?

- What effect will your plan have on the forest environment? How will it affect the number and types of trees and other plants?

- What effect will your plan have on animal populations in the area? By studying several animals that have different habitat needs, forest managers can predict the effect their actions might have on all wildlife in the forest.

- What effect will your plan have on

visitors? Would certain land-use decisions enable or restrict recre-ational use of the forest?

Below are some different manage-ment strategies you might consider. The chart titled "What's the Score?" summarizes each strategy's effect on money, trees, wildlife, and visitors—and will help you balance your plan.

Action—Create a Wilderness Preserve
This area will have no roads or graded paths and will not attract a large num-ber of visitors. We will set the forest aside for wildlife and plants to exist without human interference. Desig-nating some or all of the woods as a wilderness preserve will cost about $100 per acre per year to manage. However, without trails or campsites, the area will not be easily accessible to many people. Probably five people per acre per year will visit the forest and pay a $2 fee.

Action—Create Hiking and Biking Trails
Paved or graded hiking and biking trails will allow many different types of visitors to enjoy 400-Acre Wood, including walkers, cyclists, families with strollers, and people in wheel-chairs. The trees removed per acre of trail, can be sold for lumber at $10 per tree. A graded wood chip trail will cost about $100 per acre (.4 ha), a paved trail will cost $200 per acre. After the trails are built, management will cost about $150 per acre (.4 ha) each year. The trails should not affect the wood rat population. However, the presence of people could disturb the owls and cause them to leave. And trails will be dangerous for woodland salamanders as they migrate to pools of water dur-ing breeding season. About 50 people per acre per year will use the trails and pay a $2 fee.

Action—Create a Campground
Our campground will have four camp-sites per acre, plus picnic tables, park-ing spaces, fireplaces, and bathrooms. Providing a campground would enable weekend and overnight visitors to enjoy the woods. To build a camp-ground, we will need to build a road so that people can drive to their camp-sites. A 16' wide dirt road will cost $600 per acre, and a 16' wide paved road will cost $1000 per acre. The trees removed to build the road can

be sold for $10 a piece. Management will cost about $200 per acre each year. Building restrooms with plumb-ing and electricity will cost about $1,000 per campsite. We can charge campers a fee of $10 per night to use the campsite. About 50 campers per acre will be able to use the campsites each year. A campground will disturb the owls, wood rats, and salamanders that live in the area.

Action—Allow Hunting and Fishing
Our plan will encourage hunters of deer, turkey, and quail to visit the area. Hunters may need a road into the for-est (use the information in the section above to figure the cost of a road). You can sell the trees you remove to build the road and sell them for $10 a piece. If we decide to allow logging ($10 per tree) in the woods, loggers can use the same road. Management will cost about $150 per acre each year. Hunting licenses will provide $50 per hunter each year. Each acre desig-nated for hunting will bring about 10 hunters each year. Fishing licenses will provide $25 per angler per year. Each acre designated for fishing will attract about 20 anglers per year. Hunters and anglers will patronize local busi-nesses for equipment, food, and lodg-ing. We will regulate hunting and fish-ing to manage fish and wildlife popu-lations, and the presence of hunters and anglers should not have a great impact on other animal populations.

Action—Timber Harvest or Removal
If we log all or part of the forest and sell the wood for lumber, we must choose between cutting all or several of the trees per acre. Cutting all trees (a *clear cut*) will provide the most immediate income ($10 profit per tree). Management will cost $150 per acre per year which includes the cost of planting and caring for new trees. Keep in mind that people may not want to camp or hike in an area that has been clear cut.

Cutting some trees and leaving the rest to grow for later use (a *par-tial or selection cut*) means less imme-diate income, but will have a less noticeable impact.

In either case, loggers will need a road for removing trees. Calculate the cost of the road using the infor-mation in the previous sections.

WHAT'S THE SCORE?

After your team has developed a management plan, count the number of acres you have set aside for each action. Write those numbers in the appropriate spaces on the following chart . Make sure they add up to 400 acres.*

Multiply the number of acres by the estimated factors in each box.

3

Add (or if negative, subtract) the numbers in each column to estimate the costs and benefits in terms of money, trees, wildlife, and visitors of your management plan.

ESTIMATED FACTORS

Money [cost (-) or profit (+)]
-$100 per acre of woodchip trail
-$200 per acre of paved trail
-$600 per acre of dirt road
-$1000 per acre of paved road
-$100 per acre to manage perserve
-$150 per acre to manage timber
-$250 per acre to manage campground
-$150 per acre to manage hunting area.
+$2 per visitor
+$10 per tree
+$10 per camper,
+$25 per angler
+$50 per hunter

Trees (mature pines) (+) or (-)
150 trees per acre

Wildlife (3 species) (+) or (-)
2 owls per 100 acres
1 wood rat per acre
25 salamanders per acre

*To convert acres to hectares multiply by .4047.

WHAT'S THE SCORE?

ACTION	MONEY [cost (–) or Profit (+)] $	TREES (mature pines) + or–	WILDLIFE (3 species) +/–	VISITORS PER YEAR
ACTION **Wilderness Preserve** # of acres _____	_____ x (-)$ 100 (# acres) (mgt.) = (-)$ _____ _____ x (+)$ 2 (# visitors) = (+)$ _____	_____ x (+) 150 (# acres) = (+) _____	_____ x (+)1/50 (per acre) (# acres) = _____ owls _____ x (+)1 (per acre) (# acres) = _____ wood rats _____ x (+)25 (per acre) (# acres) = _____ salamanders	_____ x (+)5 (# acres) = (+)____ visitors
ACTION **Hiking/Biking Trail** # of acres _____	_____ x $ (-)150 (# acres) (mgt.) = $ (-)_____ _____ x $ (-)100/200 (# acres) (trail) = $ (-)_____ _____ x $ (+)10 (# trees) = $ (+)_____ _____ x $ (+)2 (# visitors) = $ (+)_____	_____ x (-) 150(per acre) (# acres of trail) = (-) _____trees	_____ x (+/-)1/50 (per acre) (# acres) = (+/-)_____ owls _____ x (+/-)1 (per acre) (# acres) = (+/-)_____ wood rats = _____ x (+/-)25 (per acre) (# acres) = (+/-)____ salamanders	_____ x (+)50 (# acres) = (+)____ visitors
ACTION **Campground** # of acres _____	_____ x $ (-)200 (# acres) (mgt.) = $ (-)_____ _____ x $ (-)600/1000 (# acres) (road) = $ (-)_____ _____ x $ (+)10 (# trees) = $ (+)_____ _____ x $ (+)10 (# campers) = $ (+)_____	_____ x (-)150 (per acre) (# acres of road) = (-)_____trees	_____ x (+/-)1/50 (per acre) (# acres) = (+/-)_____ owls _____ x (+/-)1 (per acre) (# acres) = (+/-)_____ wood rats _____ x (+/-)25 (per acre) (# acres) = (+/-)____ salamanders	_____ x (+)50 (# acres) = (+)____campers

ACTION	MONEY [cost (–) or Profit (+)] $	TREES (mature pines) + or –	WILDLIFE (3 species) +/–	VISITORS PER YEAR
ACTION Hunting/Fishing # of acres _____	_____ x $ (-)150 (# acres) (mgt.) = $ (-)_____ _____ x $ (-)600/1000 (# acres) (road.) = $ (-)_____ _____ x $ (+)10 (# trees) = $ (+)_____ _____ x $ (+)25/50 (# licenses) = $ (+)_____	_____ x (-)_____ (# acres of road) = (-) _____ trees	_____ x (+/-)1/50 (per acre) (# acres) = (+/-)_____ owls _____ x (+/-)1 (per acre) (# acres) = (+/-)_____ wood rats _____ x (+/-)25 (per acre) (# acres) = (+/-)____ salamanders	_____ x 10 (# acres for hunting) = _____ hunters _____ x 20 (# acres for fishing) = _____ anglers
ACTION Timber Harvest # of acres _____	_____ x $ (-)150 (# acres) (mgt.) = $ (-)_____ _____ x $ (-)600 (# acres) (road) = $ (-)_____ _____ x $ (+)10 (# trees) = $ (+)_____	_____ x (-) _____ (# acres) = (-) _____	_____ x (+/-)1/50 (per acre) (# acres) = (+/-)_____ owls _____ x (+/-)1 (per acre) (# acres) = (+/-)_____ wood rats _____ x (+/-)25 (per acre) (# acres) = (+/-)____ salamanders	_____ x 0-5 (# acres) (visitors) = _____ visitors
add columns TOTAL # OF ACRES= 400	add columns TOTAL $+/– _____	add columns TOTAL _____ trees	add columns TOTAL _____ owls _____ wood rats _____ salamanders	add columns TOTAL _____ visitors

Overview

Paper is one of many products that is manufactured from forest resources. In this activity, students investigate the papermaking process by trying it themselves. While papermaking can be rather messy, it is well worth the effort. Students are usually thrilled to find that they can make paper and that their product is practical as well as beautiful.

LEVELS
Grades 1-8

SUBJECTS
Science, Social Studies, Language Arts, Visual Arts

CONCEPTS
- Conservation technology enables humans to maintain and extend the productivity of vital resources. (8.3)
- By reducing waste and recycling materials, individuals and societies can extend the value and utility of resources and can promote environmental quality. (5.4)

SKILLS
Observing, Organizing Information, Comparing and Contrasting

OBJECTIVES
Students will ① make recycled paper from scrap paper, ② describe the steps of the papermaking process and identify the elements and outputs of the process, and ③ compare making paper by hand to the process used in factories.

MATERIALS
Scrap paper torn into 1" x 1" (2.5 cm x 2.5 cm) pieces (paper towels, construction paper, and toilet paper work well; avoid glossy finishes or paper with ink in it, like newsprint); a large bowl or tub; a wooden frame around 5" x 7" (13 cm x 18 cm) or 8" x 10" (20 cm x 25 cm); nylon or wire screen; staples; a plastic basin at least 2.5 gallons (9.5 liters) in capacity, that is larger than the frame; cloth dishtowels (felt, blotting paper, interfacing, or newspaper may substituted; blender; sponge; household iron; strainer; towels for cleaning up water; colored paper, pieces of colored thread, or dried flowers or herbs (optional) Variation: scraps of construction paper (various colors) and lots of newspaper, water, blender, 9" x 14" (23 cm x 36 cm) cake pan, 8" x 13" (20 cm x 33 cm) piece of window screening, two 16" x 16" (41 cm x 41 cm) pieces of wood (plywood is fine), several large (5-pound or 2-kg) containers to store different colored pulps, measuring cup, old towels

TIME CONSIDERATIONS
Preparation: 30 minutes plus time to gather materials

Activity: two 50-minute periods

Background

Paper is a simple material. It is essentially a mat held together by a fiber's roughness, and can be made from almost any fibrous material such as cotton, hemp, flax, wood or recycled paper. And yet, this simple product has a tremendous effect on our lives. Imagine how different your day would be without paper!

The process for making paper was invented in China in the second century A.D., and all paper was made one sheet at a time until 1798. With the Industrial Revolution and the papermaking machine, papermaking became a major industry that provides countless products, from books and newspapers to packaging and note pads. Some modern machines can make a sheet of paper 26 feet (8.8 m) wide and nearly 40 miles (64 km) long in just one hour! While the technology has changed dramatically over the centuries, the basic steps are simple enough for your students to do in class.

The process begins when trees, grown especially for papermaking, are harvested and transported to a paper mill. At the mill, large machines strip away bark and shred the logs into millions of chips the size of breakfast cereal. The wood chips travel on conveyors to gigantic "pulp cookers," where chemicals and steam are added. The mixture is heated and pressurized, breaking the chips into smaller and smaller pieces and finally forming a dilute water suspension of wood fibers called *pulp.* The pulp then passes through cleaners and screens and sometimes goes through a bleaching process that will give it the whiteness needed for the grade of paper being manufactured. Other chemicals like dyes, pigments, sizings, or resins are sometimes added to provide the paper

or paperboard (thick paper for boxes) with the appropriate finish.

The pulp is then pumped through pipes to a paper machine where it is sprayed onto a wide, moving wire screen. After the water in the pulp drains through the holes, a damp mat of wood fibers remains: the paper. It is picked up from the end of the moving belt and dried over steam-heated rollers.

Commercial papermaking affects the environment in several ways. The energy needed for papermaking comes primarily from fossil fuels, which are nonrenewable. Burning those fuels can put carbon dioxide and other pollutants in the air. However, for public safety, there are state and federal guidelines that control emissions. Most of what you see coming out of the mill's smokestacks is steam, not pollutants. Many mills recycle the waste paper they produce, and use wood waste to generate their own electricity for the process.

The waste water from the papermaking can cause pollution problems. However, in the United States and Canada, the water discharged from mills is tightly monitored and controlled. Additionally, the pulp-cooking process creates strong odors that can be smelled in the vicinity of the mill. Most mills have odor control systems to lessen this problem although these sometimes fail.

Paper comes from trees, which are a renewable resource. Most of the trees used for paper are planted and harvested on plantations for that purpose. More than half of the fiber used for paper comes from residue left when lumber and other wood products are made and from paper which has been collected for recycling.

Paper is easily recycled, which helps reduce the amount of land space needed to store the 200 million tons of solid waste Americans generate each year. However, no matter how much paper we recycle, new trees still will be needed for paper products, because paper cannot be recycled indefinitely. Each time paper goes through the manufacturing process, the fibers deteriorate. After repeated recycling, the fiber is no longer suitable for paper-making. (See Enrichment 2 for a demonstration of this principle.)

Getting Ready

1. Decide how you will conduct the activity. If you are short on materials or adult supervision, you can demonstrate; but, ideally, you should try to find a way for the students to participate. Middle school students might use stations so some students can make paper while others do a different activity. For younger students, you might ask a parent or aide to help at stations, or have an activity for the rest of the class while you help small groups make paper.

2. The papermaking process is a wet one, so plan to use a work space that won't be harmed by moisture. You might want students to wear "wet gear"—an apron or smock, or old clothing.

3. Remove any plastic or staples from the scrap paper, and tear it into small pieces (1-inch or 2.5-cm squares). Soak the paper in hot water in the large container for at least 30 minutes or, if you can, overnight.

4. Buy or build a wooden frame, which you will prepare for paper making. Tightly staple or tack nylon or wire screening to the frame, making a "deckle," which is the surface on which you will layer the fibers.

Doing the Activity

1. Introduce the activity by asking students what they think paper is made of and how it is made.

2. Fill the blender halfway with warm water, then add a handful of the soaked paper. Blend at medium speed until you no longer see pieces of paper, and the pulp has a soupy consistency. You can blend in a piece of construc-

tion paper for color; or stir in short pieces of thread, dried flowers, or herbs for texture.

3. Pour the mixture into the large basin and then fill the basin with warm water, mixing thoroughly until the ingredients are evenly dispersed. Adding a few ounces of liquid starch will help make the paper firm.

4. Slide the deckle into the basin. Put some pulp onto the screen and, still holding the deckle underwater, gently move it back and forth to get an even layer of fibers on the screen.

5. Lift the deckle out of the mixture, keeping it flat. Allow it to drip until most of the water has drained off. You should have a uniform layer of pulp mixture on the deckle. Press the pulp gently with your hand to squeeze out excess moisture (rubber gloves will help). Soak up any excess water from the bottom of the screen with a sponge.

6. Place a clean dishtowel (or newspaper) on a flat surface and turn the screen paper-side-down on the cloth. Lift the screen gently, leaving the paper.

7. Quickly cover the paper with another cloth or piece of felt, and iron it at a medium dry setting. When the paper is dry, pull the cloth gently from both ends, stretching it to loosen the paper from the cloth. Gently peel off the paper.

8. When you're finished making paper, collect the leftover pulp in a strainer and throw it out, or freeze it in a plastic bag for future use. Don't pour the pulp down the drain!

9. Discuss these questions:

- What materials did we use in making paper?

- What forms of energy did you need to make the paper? (electricity and students' own energy)

- What types of wastes resulted from making paper? (dirty water, leftover pulp)

- What did we do with the waste products?

- What were some problems with making paper? (cleaning up the mess)

- What would it would be like in a paper mill, where tons of paper are being made a day? Why do you think recycling paper is important? What about reducing the amount of paper you use?

- How is the new paper different from the old paper that you recycled?

For Older Students:

10. Help students investigate the process used in modern paper factories. Discuss ways it is similar to and different from making paper by hand. (See References.)

VARIATION—PICTURES FROM PULP

1. Collect plenty of construction paper scraps and sort them by color, tearing them into dime-sized pieces.

2. Make different colored pulps. For each color, repeat this process: fill the blender half with paper pieces, and half with water. Blend at medium speed until smooth. Pour each color pulp into a separate container.

3. Fill the cake pan halfway with water and submerge the screen.

4. Choose a background color for your picture, and put one-half cup of that color pulp in the cake pan. Mix it so it is evenly dispersed in the water above the screen.

5. Carefully lift the screen out of the water and allow excess water to run off. Your background layer will remain on the screen.

6. With the background pulp on top, place the screen on several sheets of newspaper on one of the boards.

7. Create your picture by carefully dripping thin layers of the other pulps on top of the background pulp. This can be done by pouring the colored pulps into small paper cups and pinching the cup rims to make pouring spouts. Once pulp is dripped onto the screen, do not try to remove it, or you will tear the background pulp and create holes in your picture.

8. When you finish your design, place a few layers of newspaper on top. Put a board on the newspaper, creating a "sandwich." (See diagram.)

9. Press firmly on the top board to squeeze out moisture.

10. Turn the sandwich upside down. Take off the board, then the newspaper, and then, very carefully peel the screen away from the paper. This is the back of your picture.

11. Leave your picture face down on the newspaper and put it in a warm, safe place to dry. Once it's dry, carefully peel it off to reveal your work.

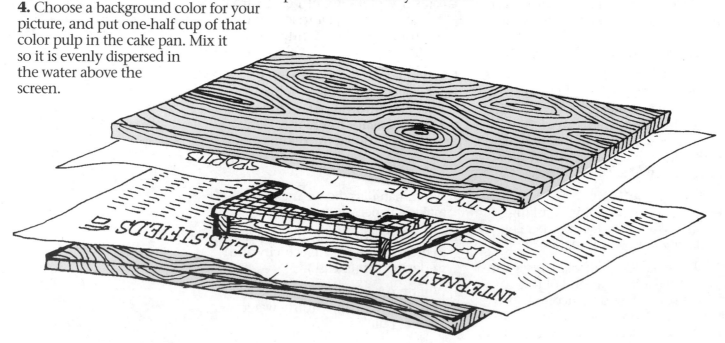

Enrichment

1. Students can use different types of materials to make paper, then compare the papers. Students might try newspaper, paper towels, typing paper, or cotton balls. Which paper is the strongest? Which is water resistant? Which is best for writing? What other comparisons can students make? What kinds of uses can they think of for their new paper? What materials can they use that might otherwise be thrown away?

2. To demonstrate the principle that paper cannot be recycled forever but requires the infusion of new fiber, try recycling the homemade paper once or several times. Using a portion of the paper your students made as the pulp, make a batch of paper, and have students compare the first batch of paper with the second. Which is stronger? Which is more useful? Students can then take a portion of the second batch and use it to make a third, comparing the batches for texture and durability. Does this demonstration tell the students anything about how many times paper can be recycled? (In general, estimates say fiber cannot withstand recycling more than five or six times.)

3. If you live near a paper mill, invite a representative to help your class make paper. Ask him or her to bring samples of wood chips, pulp, and paper, if possible.

END NOTES...

ASSESSMENT OPPORTUNITIES

1. Ask younger students to write the directions for making paper on the piece of recycled paper that they made.

2. Ask older students to guide younger students in a paper-making activity. If possible, the class can make an instructional video on papermaking using a home video camera.

RELATED ACTIVITIES

Paper Civilizations; Resource-Go-Round; Reduce, Reuse, Recycle; Talking Trash, Not! A Forest of Many Uses; Forest for the Trees

REFERENCES

Burdette, Janet, et al. *THE MANUFACTURE OF PULP AND PAPER:* Science and Engineering Concepts. Atlanta, GA: TAPPI Press, 1988.

Grummer, Arnold E. *PAPER BY KIDS.* Minneapolis, MN: Dillon Press, Inc., 1980.

HOW TO MAKE PAPER. New York: American Paper Institute, 1990.

Lee, Helen. *BIBLIOGRAPHY OF PAPERMAKING FOR CHILDREN AND YOUNG ADULTS.* Atlanta, GA: Technical Association for the Pulp and Paper Industry, 1990.

PAPER AND PAPER MANUFACTURE. New York: American Paper Institute, 1981, 1987.

Wright, Helena. *300 YEARS OF AMERICAN PAPERMAKING.* Washington, DC: Smithsonian Institution, 1991.

Overview
This activity will give your students a better appreciation for aluminum, a nonrenewable but recyclable natural resource they use every day. They will learn the steps that go into making aluminum products and will get a better idea of the environmental impact that using this resource has.

LEVELS
Grades 5-8

SUBJECTS
Science, Social Studies

CONCEPTS

■ Resource management and technological systems help societies to meet, within limits, the needs of a growing human population. (8.2)

■ Conservation technology enables humans to maintain and extend the productivity of vital resources. (8.3)

■ All humans consume products and thereby affect the availability of renewable and nonrenewable natural resources. (6.4)

SKILLS
Discussing, Analyzing, Ordering and Arranging, Making Analogies and Metaphors, Restructuring

OBJECTIVES
Students will ① understand how the unique properties of aluminum make it invaluable for many products and technologies on which we depend, ② describe the steps involved in extracting bauxite and processing aluminum from bauxite, and ③ explain the environmental impacts of producing new aluminum and recycling aluminum products.

MATERIALS
Copies of student pages 183 and 184, scissors, aluminum cans (one for every four students), pens and paper, art supplies, containers (optional), Phone Book, Yellow Pages (optional), can crusher (optional), boxes or plastic bags (optional), and magnets (optional)

TIME CONSIDERATIONS
Preparation: 20 minutes

Activity: One or two 50-minute periods with possible extended projects

Background
Without aluminum, airplanes couldn't fly; automobiles and trucks would guzzle a lot more gasoline; and electrical circuits in computers, televisions, and other appliances wouldn't work. Aluminum has many special properties that make it a valuable—indeed, indispensable—material in many products. Although aluminum is an extremely lightweight metal, it is stronger than steel. It reacts instantly with the air, forming a protective coating on its surface that prevents it from corroding. Because it doesn't react with most foods, aluminum is an excellent material for food packaging. It can be rolled, squeezed, and cut into almost any shape. It's a good conductor and it's nonmagnetic, making it invaluable in electronics. It's abundant in the Earth's crust. Finally, aluminum can be recycled over and over again without losing its strength. However, aluminum is not a complete miracle metal. High costs are associated with it. Processing aluminum takes a tremendous amount of energy. In 1990, the world's aluminum smelters used as much electricity as the entire continent of Africa. Because producing aluminum is so energy-consumptive, in some countries production has spurred the development of cheap energy sources such as the massive hydroelectric dams in the Pacific Northwest of the United States, on Brazil's Amazon River, and in Quebec, Canada.

Alumina ore is found most readily in a mineral called bauxite. Bauxite consists of 45 to 60 percent alumina. For every ton of alumina extracted from bauxite, there is an almost equal amount of leftover material. This material, called red mud, is collected in large holding ponds. If the red mud were to leak, it would contaminate water supplies, but it is not currently classified as a hazardous waste substance by the Environmental Protection Agency. Researchers are looking for alternative uses for the red mud such as making it into bricks, kitty litter, or ceramics, but so far none have proved economically feasible.

The world's largest producer of bauxite is Australia, which produces about one-third of the world's total supply. Guinea, Jamaica, and Brazil combine to provide another one-third. The largest processor of aluminum from bauxite is the United States, followed by the former USSR, Canada, and Australia.

Recycled aluminum saves about 95 percent of the energy needed to make new aluminum from ore. In the recycling process, aluminum is melted down to form ingots or rods, which are later remelted and formed into new products. Recycled aluminum can also be melted directly into new products. (See the trivia box for additional information.)

Getting Ready
Make copies of student pages 183 and 184 and assemble the materials for the activities.

PART A
RESOURCE STORY

Doing the Activity
1. Divide the group into teams of four and give each team an aluminum beverage can. Students should examine the can for a few minutes. Which parts of the can are more rigid and which are more flexible? How many separate pieces seem to make up the can? What material is it made of? Is it made of more than one material? How is a can manufactured?

2. Give a copy of student page 183 to each team. The six pictures on the right side show the steps in making an all-aluminum can, but they are not in order. On the left side is a written description of the steps in the proper sequence. Teams should write the letter of the corresponding picture next to each description.

3. Review the correct sequence with the students. Make sure that the students understand the answers to these questions from Step 1: How many separate pieces make up the can? (three) Why are some parts more rigid or flexible? (different type or thickness of aluminum)

4. Ask students if they know where aluminum comes from. Do they know how it is made? Review the information in the Background section.

5. Give a copy of student page 184 to each team. The six pictures on the right side show the process for making aluminum, but not in the right order. On the left side is a written description of the steps in the proper sequence. Teams should write the letter of the corresponding picture next to each description.

6. After the students have figured out the order of the steps used in processing aluminum, have teams create their own visual representation of how an aluminum beverage can is made, from bauxite in the ground to a finished can of soda. They can use the pictures on page 184 to help them draw some of the machinery involved.

7. [Optional] To wrap up, borrow the video "Call Me Can" (see page 386). This funny story explains many benefits of recycling aluminum cans, such as keeping recyclables out of landfills, keeping the environment clean, and making money collecting cans.

CASH CANS

Doing the Activity
One of the most important things students can do to reduce the negative environmental effects of using aluminum is to cut down on the amount of energy needed to process aluminum and manufacture products. One way is to have students create a plan that makes sure aluminum cans get recycled in your area. Even if your area already has a recycling program, many cans are probably not getting recycled. In 1991, Americans used around 91 billion aluminum cans, less than 50 percent of which were recycled. Ask students what actions they should take to launch a recycling program. Here are some suggestions:

1. Create posters that teach people about the need to recycle aluminum cans. Include information from the Background, trivia box, or student page 184. Describe how easy it is to recycle and the environmental effects of not recycling.

2. Set up containers to collect aluminum cans. Put the containers next to soda machines and in other areas where people often discard empty cans.

3. Identify aluminum recycling centers in your area. Check the Yellow Pages under recycling, aluminum, resource recovery, or scrap metals. Or contact an appropriate state or local government agency such as the Department of Environmental Protection, the Department of Natural Resources, or the Department of Public Works.

4. Determine rates, hours of operation, and procedures for cashing in your cans at various centers. Make sure your cans are relatively clean before turning them in.

5. Find out which recycling centers will provide assistance to groups that recycle aluminum cans as a fund-raising project. Ask your local government agencies if they will provide any help. Local businesses—especially

ALUMINUM TRIVIA

Reprocessing (recycling) used aluminum is almost 95% more energy efficient than processing new aluminum from bauxite.

If people in the United States recycled all the aluminum cans they currently throw away each year, they'd save enough energy to power a city the size of Baltimore, Maryland , for one year.

Aluminum is used extensively in the construction of cars, airplanes, boats, and other vehicles, making them lighter and more fuel efficient.

Aluminum is the third most abundant element in the earth's crust.

Aluminum is used in many products, from siding for houses and trays for T.V. dinners to highway signs and airplanes.

Since 1972, the aluminum industry has reduced the amount of aluminum needed to make each aluminum can by almost one third.

Aluminum can be remelted and reformed into new products over and over again without losing its strength.

retailers, soft drink bottlers, beer distributors, and others—may also be willing to help. In many areas, resources such as posters, bumper stickers, fliers, and audiovisual materials can be yours for the asking.

6. Have a group meeting to talk about multiple benefits of aluminum recycling such as fund-raising, solid waste reduction, or energy savings. Ask for volunteers to set goals, plot strategies, produce materials, collect cans, and keep records. Challenge them to attain an overall goal that is defined in terms of the number of cans collected or the amount of money raised.

7. Recruit the aid of local businesses that sell beverages in aluminum cans. Many supermarkets, convenience stores, bars, restaurants, and fraternal halls would welcome the opportunity to pitch in for a worthy cause. They can make your job a lot easier by keeping aluminum cans in separate receptacles.

8. Consider a neighborhood recycling drive. Ask residents to set empty aluminum cans aside until your group can pick them up. Your neighbors will probably be happy to save used beverage cans for six to eight weeks. Civic events such as county and street fairs, major sports events, school dances, and neighborhood block parties can also provide a large bounty of aluminum cans.

9. Use the media. Newspapers, television, and radio stations may help you promote your program. To draw the best coverage, try to develop an interesting angle. You could use recycling proceeds to support a charity, fund a school field trip, buy team uniforms, help a fellow classmate or group member—the list could go on and on. The publicity gained by your initial fund-raising effort could pave the way for even more successful recycling programs in the future. Always help reporters and editors by sharing with them the background information you have accumulated about aluminum recycling.

10. Recycle wisely. Before initiating your collection effort, make sure you have a safe and convenient location in which to store the cans. A garage is ideal. Remember, too, that you can save space by crushing your cans; most recycling centers will accept crushed cans, but always check first. To save time and gas, wait until you have a large quantity of cans before you return them to the center. Load your cans in boxes or large plastic bags that you can use again.

11. Make sure all cans and other products you have collected are made of aluminum. Most aluminum cans are designed with a recycling message and/or the Aluminum Association's recycling symbol. When in doubt, check with a magnet. Unlike steel cans, aluminum cans are not magnetic. Be sure to test the magnet against the side of the cans because steel, or bi-metallic, beverage cans have aluminum tops.

END NOTES...

ASSESSMENT OPPORTUNITY

Students should apply the knowledge they gained in the activity to answer these questions:

■ What are the qualities of aluminum that make it such a good material to use? (abundant in Earth's crust, lightweight, strong, doesn't corrode, increases energy efficiency of planes and cars, recyclable)

■ What are some negative trade-offs of aluminum production? (requires an enormous amount of electricity to produce, results in a large amount of red mud, pollutes air from associated power and processing plants)

■ What are the advantages of recycling aluminum cans instead of creating new cans from bauxite? (It takes 15 times more energy to process new aluminum than to recycle it.)

■ Based on what you've learned about aluminum, what conclusions might you draw about the environmental effects of other products that you use and the materials that went into making them? (Students should realize that manufacturing finished products involves many steps and much energy, and that there can be ways to make or reuse products that have less negative environmental impact than others.)

RELATED ACTIVITIES

A Few of My Favorite Things, Resource-Go-Round, Make Your Own Paper, Talking Trash, Not! Renewable or Not?

REFERENCES

To borrow the 18-minute videotape CALL ME CAN on a free-loan basis, call Modern Talking Picture Service (1-800-243-6877).

ALUMINUM RECYCLING: AMERICA'S ENVIRONMENTAL SUCCESS STORY. Washington, DC: The Aluminum Association.

Trivia adapted from Young, John E. ALUMINUM'S REAL TAB. WorldWatch, March/April 1992, pp. 26-33.

ANSWERS FOR STUDENT PAGES

Proper sequence of pictures on page 183 is b, a, d, f, c, e.
Proper sequence of pictures on page 184 is c, f, e, a, b, d.

HOW ALUMINUM CANS ARE MADE

1 **Cup Forming**—The process starts with an aluminum coiled sheet which is fed through a press that punches out shallow cups.

_____

2 **Redrawing & Ironing**—Cups are fed into an ironing press where successive rings redraw and iron the cup and reduce side-wall thickness to get a full length can. The bottom is domed to obtain strength required to withstand internal pressure.

_____

3 **Trimming**—Cans are spun as a cutting tool trims the rough shell from the inside.

_____

4 **Necking & Flanging**—Cans are necked in at the top to reduce can diameter and flanged to accept the end.

_____

5 **Ends are stamped** out of a pre-coated aluminum coiled sheet. Compound is added to assure a perfect seal between can and end at our customer's plant.

_____

6 **Ends are fed** through a high precision press where rivet making, scoring, and tabbing occur in consecutive operations.

_____

What is the proper sequence for these pictures?

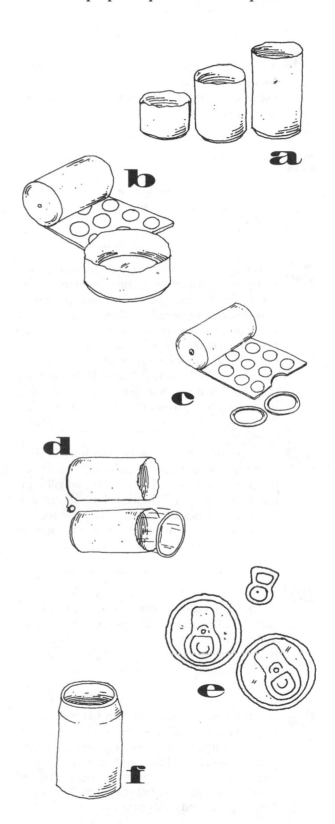

ALUMINUM PRODUCTION

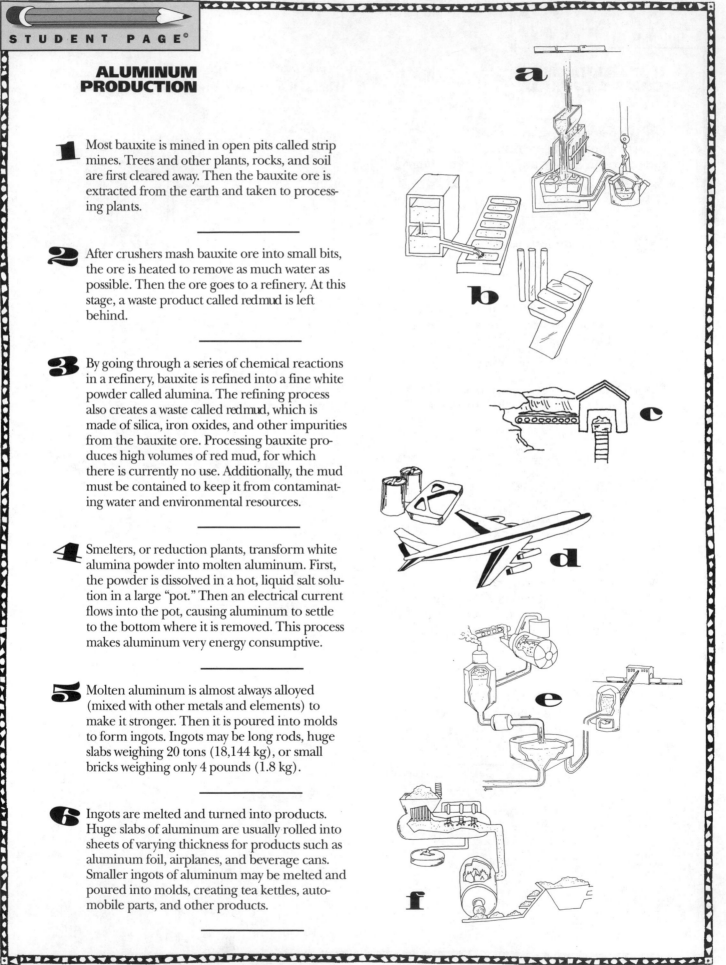

1 Most bauxite is mined in open pits called strip mines. Trees and other plants, rocks, and soil are first cleared away. Then the bauxite ore is extracted from the earth and taken to processing plants.

_____

2 After crushers mash bauxite ore into small bits, the ore is heated to remove as much water as possible. Then the ore goes to a refinery. At this stage, a waste product called redmud is left behind.

_____

3 By going through a series of chemical reactions in a refinery, bauxite is refined into a fine white powder called alumina. The refining process also creates a waste called redmud, which is made of silica, iron oxides, and other impurities from the bauxite ore. Processing bauxite produces high volumes of red mud, for which there is currently no use. Additionally, the mud must be contained to keep it from contaminating water and environmental resources.

_____

4 Smelters, or reduction plants, transform white alumina powder into molten aluminum. First, the powder is dissolved in a hot, liquid salt solution in a large "pot." Then an electrical current flows into the pot, causing aluminum to settle to the bottom where it is removed. This process makes aluminum very energy consumptive.

_____

5 Molten aluminum is almost always alloyed (mixed with other metals and elements) to make it stronger. Then it is poured into molds to form ingots. Ingots may be long rods, huge slabs weighing 20 tons (18,144 kg), or small bricks weighing only 4 pounds (1.8 kg).

_____

6 Ingots are melted and turned into products. Huge slabs of aluminum are usually rolled into sheets of varying thickness for products such as aluminum foil, airplanes, and beverage cans. Smaller ingots of aluminum may be melted and poured into molds, creating tea kettles, automobile parts, and other products.

_____

Overview
In this activity, students will examine transportation systems, which are vital to their community.

Background
In the United States, almost every household has at least one car. It is difficult to imagine life without cars. But until the 1930s, most people used public transportation, walked, or used a horse and buggy to get to their destinations.

Up until the mid-1950s, railways, subways or elevated trains, trolleys, and buses constituted most of the country's public transportation system. In 1945, those transit lines carried 23 billion passengers annually. In 1973, however, those same forms of public transportation carried just over 6 billion people, even though the population had grown from 140 million to over 200 million.

Until 1945, the United States had a transportation network in which the automobile complemented other parts of the system. At the end of World War II, however, mass production of cars, their relative affordability, and improved roadways led to the rise of the automobile and the decline of public transportation systems.

Freight transportation still uses various methods. Container ships and cargo vessels carry goods to destinations accessible by water. Railways and trucks transport freight across land. Airways carry goods that need to be moved quickly. In 1985, approximately 50 percent of all intercity freight traffic in the United States was transported by rail, 30 percent was by motor vehicles, 20 percent was over inland waterways, and 0.3 percent was by airplane.

Getting Ready
Find a map of your community that shows as many different transportation systems as possible: streets, toll roads or freeways, railways, subways, bus routes, bicycle paths, hiking trails, ferry routes, and airports. Each group should have a map. (Local transit authorities can provide maps. Also check with local chambers of commerce, real estate agents, or tourist information agencies.)

If you plan to have students build or draw a transportation system of the future, ask them to start collecting the necessary materials.

PART A
GETTING THERE FROM HERE

Doing the Activity
1. Ask students how they get to school and list the ways on the chalkboard. Ask students what kind of energy each method uses (gasoline, people power, electricity, etc.) and whether it uses roads, railroads, or another type of system.

2. Brainstorm a class list of things, living or nonliving, that are found in or around school such as these:

butterflies	tables	food	hamster
trees	buildings	books	teacher
chairs	chalk	markers	water
pencils	notebook	flowers	electricity

Select a few items, and ask pairs of students to write on scratch paper how each item got to where it is. For example, a pencil may have been carried from the pencil factory by ship to a nearby port, by train to the community, by truck to a local store, and by car to the school. Discuss transportation systems used in getting the items to school and the kinds of energy used. (Students should begin thinking about systems needed to move people and goods.) Add any new transportation systems to the list begun in Step 1.

3. Ask students whether they can think of any other kinds of transportation systems that are not on their list.

LEVELS
Grades 4-8

SUBJECTS
Science, Math, Social Studies, Visual Arts

CONCEPTS
■ The application of scientific knowledge and technological systems can have positive or negative effects on the environment. (8.1)

■ Conservation technology enables humans to maintain and extend the productivity of vital resources. (8.3)

SKILLS
Comparing and Contrasting, Analyzing, Solving Problems, Synthesizing and Creating

OBJECTIVES
Students will ① compare various transportation methods for getting to and from school, ② describe the transportation systems their community uses, and ③ design or propose a practical and efficient transportation system for the future.

MATERIALS
Part A: scratch paper, maps of the community (see Getting Ready), copies of student page 187, colored markers, Post-it notes
Part B: drawing materials, or to make a model transportation system, students can bring a collection of materials such as cardboard, paper cups, egg cartons, meat trays, boxes, toothpicks, popsicle sticks, pipe cleaners, berry baskets, toilet paper tubes, paper towel tubes, margarine tubs, dried grass or twigs, construction paper, glue, wire, tape, paints, brushes, clay, Play-Doh

TIME CONSIDERATIONS
Preparation: 60 minutes

Activity: 50 minutes (Part A) one or two 50-minute periods (Part B)

4. Divide the class into small groups of three to six students. Give each group a map and a copy of student page 187. Challenge groups to find on their maps several types of transportation systems. Have groups use Post-it notes to label each system they find. After thegroups have found all of the transportation systems, ask them to answer the questions on the student page.

5. Lead a discussion about students' findings. In addition to student questions, you might ask these:

■ Which systems carry people? (Automobiles, subways, buses.) Which carry products? (Trucks, trains, boats.) Which carry both?

■ What advantages does each system have?

■ What disadvantages does each have?

■ How would your life be different if there were no cars in your community? No trains? No buses? How would you get food? Clothes? Visit friends?

PART B
MEET GEORGE JETSON

Doing the Activity
1. Ask the class to name one problem they observed in their community's transportation system. Have a brainstorming session to generate ideas for overcoming the problem. Help students by encouraging creative and imaginative ideas.

2. Challenge the student groups formed in Part A to design a transportation system of the future that overcomes a problem in today's transportation or improves it in some way. (Remember "The Jetsons" cartoon!) Groups should brainstorm ideas, then choose one idea to work on. For example, students might design a model car that uses either solar energy or another clean, future energy source to move it. Or they may get rid of the need for streets by designing a com-

pletely new system for transporting people and goods around the community.

3. Have groups work together to create designs. Depending on your time and resources, you can have groups design a physical model using modeling materials, or they can illustrate their designs using drawing materials.

4. Have groups present their designs to the class. Discuss these questions:

■ What problems did you encounter in your design?

■ To solve the transportation problem, did you have to sacrifice efficiency, convenience, or appearance in your design? Are the sacrifices worthwhile? Why?

■ What things do you think people need to consider when designing a transportation system in a community?

Enrichment
1. Have students write a story comparing taking a 50-mile (80 km) trip in your area 100 years ago with the same trip today. Discuss the two trips. What were the major modes of transportation 100 years ago? (Foot, horse and wagon, rail, boat.) In the past how did you travel on your trip? Which trip was harder? Which was more convenient? Which was more fun to write about?

2. Help urban students explore the public transportation system in their community. Plan a trip where students use public transit from school to travel to a destination like a museum or park. After the trip, discuss how many people seem to use the system, how efficient the trip was, and the advantages and disadvantages of using the system.

3. Rural students can survey their school bus system as an example of public transportation. Survey questions might include:

■ How many buses are there? How many routes?

■ Do buses travel more than one route?

■ How many people ride the buses daily?

■ How many miles do the buses travel daily?

■ How much gasoline is used daily by the system?

■ What is the average mileage per gallon (MPG) of the buses?

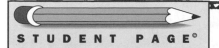
TRANSPORTATION SYSTEMS

Group Members:

....

....

....

....

Look at the map of your community and find all the different transportation systems you can. Then discuss with your group the following questions, and write down your group's answers.

1 What kinds of transportation systems does your community have?

2 What is the most common means of transportation?

3 How many people can each system carry? (Contact your local transit authority.)

4 Which system's routes pass important places in the community, like government buildings, hospitals, schools, restaurants, and shopping centers?

5 Which system seems to be the most convenient? Which is the least convenient?

6 Which type of transportation do you think is the most energy efficient (transports the most people or products per gallon of gas or unit of electricity)? Which is the least energy efficient?

7 What problems does your group find in the transportation systems in your community?

8 What suggestions does your group have for improving the transportation systems in your community?

Overview
In this activity, students will explore the concept that recreation areas are essential elements of a community. By working on a project to improve a local park, they will also learn about the community's system for managing open spaces.

LEVELS
Activity: Grades 4-8
Variation: Grades PreK-3

SUBJECTS
Science, Social Studies, Language Arts, Physical Education, Visual Arts

CONCEPTS
■ Resource management and technological systems help societies to meet, within limits, the needs of a growing human population. (8.2)

■ In democratic societies, individuals and groups, working through governmental channels, can influence the way public and private lands and resources are managed. (9.3)

SKILLS
Observing, Comparing and Contrasting, Defining Problems, Problem Solving

OBJECTIVES
Students will ① describe the characteristics of their favorite recreational area, ② explain the importance of recreational areas to people and other living things, and ③ conduct a project at a local park to improve a habitat or enhance its suitability to people.

MATERIALS
Part A: paper, pencils, crayons, other art materials; 4" x 6" (10 cm x 15 cm) index cards; file box
Part B: collected materials necessary to do park project
Enrichment: An aluminum roasting pan, building materials, paper

TIME CONSIDERATIONS
Preparation:
Part A: 10 minutes
Part B: Several days

Activity:
Part A: One or two 50-minute periods
Part B: Several periods depending on project
Variation: 30 minutes

Background
In today's world, most people live in urban, developed areas. Increasingly, people rely upon areas like parks, urban forests, gardens, and open spaces to provide solitude and opportunities for recreation.

Because recreational areas are so important to people, society has set aside many natural areas for this purpose. To preserve those areas, national, state, county, and city agencies designate them as parks and recreational areas.

A particular park or recreational area is usually set aside because it has important characteristics that people want to preserve. It may be a forested area; contain waterways; be home to wildlife; be particularly beautiful; or have special educational, scientific, or historical significance. An overseeing agency manages parks and recreational areas to preserve those features and to most effectively meet the needs of people who use the area.

In setting aside recreation areas, we also enhance other elements of the ecosystem. For example, wildlife benefits when its habitat is preserved, and water quality remains good when waterways are protected from development.

Because society places great value on recreational and aesthetic experiences, we are becoming increasingly aware of the need to preserve and protect areas that provide those experiences.

To help students learn about managing and protecting such areas, some parks offer special programs that allow classes to work on projects to improve wildlife or enhance the park for human visitors. The programs usually involve working in the park for one or more days as a park employee supervises the project. Projects might include improving a hiking trail, clearing an area for a picnic table, clearing brush to improve wildlife habitats, or planting trees or other native plants.

Getting Ready
For Part A, assemble the file box, cards, and other materials.

For Part B, try to involve students in all phases of the planning. Contact local parks and recreation areas to find a park employee (ranger, naturalist, or groundskeeper) who is willing to work with your class. Collaborate with him or her to determine a project important for the park and that would be appropriate for your class. Then plan a trip to the park. If possible, arrange for parents or other adult volunteers to help supervise. Consider how students will get to the park. You might use public transportation or parent drivers as alternatives to school buses.

PART A
FUN PLACE FILE

Doing the Activity
1. Ask students what they think of when they hear the word *recreation*. If they don't seem to know its meaning, explain that recreation includes activities people do to restore their spirits or to have fun. Introduce the concept of recreation areas: places like parks where people go to participate in recreational pursuits or to enjoy the beauty of nature. Give examples such as zoos, aquariums, national parks, state parks, county parks, wilderness areas, or theme parks.

2. Explain that the class will create a fun place file that students can use and add to throughout the year. Ask each student to think about his or her favorite spot for recreation. It may be a small city park a few blocks from school, a national park, or a wilderness area. Have each student choose a place, write a description, and draw a picture or map.

3. Write the following questions on the chalkboard:

- What is your favorite recreation place?

- Where is it located?

- Why do you like to visit your place?

- What kinds of recreational activities do you enjoy there?

- What is unusual or special about your place?

- What kinds of plants or animals have you seen living there?

- How is your area important for people and other living things?

Encourage students to answer these questions as they draft their descriptions. Then distribute index cards and have students write their final descriptions on the cards. They should include a drawing or map of the area.

4. Gather students into small groups and have members share their descriptions. Ask the groups to list things that are alike about all their favorite recreation areas. Have the groups share these common characteristics.

5. Lead a discussion about why each area is important for recreation, intrinsic aesthetic value, and other living things:

- How would you feel if you could no longer visit your favorite recreation area?

- Why are recreation areas important to us?

- How do they benefit other parts of the ecosystem?

6. Collect the index cards and put them in the file card box. Invite students to add to the box after they visit a place they like, and to look through the box when they want to find new places to go with friends or family.

Doing the Activity

1. Follow the steps under Getting Ready to set up an action project in a local park or recreation area.

2. If possible, invite the park employee who will guide your project to visit your students before their trip and to explain how the park functions and what the project will entail. Help students develop a list of questions in advance about the project and the park. Here are examples:

- What is the history of the park? Why was it established?

- How is this park important for the community?

- How many people visit the park each year? What do they do there?

- What will our class do for the park? How will we do it?

- How will our project help park visitors?

- How will it help plants or animals who live in the park?

- What might happen if we don't do this project?

3. While at the park, allow opportunities for students to explore and enjoy their surroundings.

4. After the project is completed, ask students to reflect on their experience. Discuss these questions:

- How did it feel to work in the park?

- How might our work improve the park for people or other organisms?

- What would happen if people didn't do this work?

5. Ask students to write thank-you letters to the park employee. In the letters, students should state the most important things they learned from the project.

Use the alphabet to make students aware of the many ways we appreciate parks. Starting with an "A" word, students should think of words or phrases that describe parks or recreation areas with which they are familiar. Alternatively, take students for a walk in a local park and have them point out things that begin with A, B, C, and so on. Write down their words and later read the ABC list as a poem about parks.

Enrichment

1. Invite a resource person from a nearby park or recreation area (a park naturalist, park superintendent, city planner, or other employee) to your class. Ask that person to explain how recreation areas are planned and what the agency's or community's goals are for managing the areas. If possible, go to the recreation area to take a first-hand look at its design and features.

2. Help students list recreational activities (baseball, cross-country skiing, or hockey) that use forest products. Ask students to imagine what would happen if forest products were removed from their favorite recreation or sport. For example, in baseball, there would be no wooden bats, wooden benches, paper tickets, or paper cups. Have students draw before (with forest products) and after (without) pictures of a sport or recreational activity.

3. Have students design their own ideal parks. Each student or team will need a large aluminum foil roasting pan and building materials. Each team should sketch a plan for their model. Team members should consider what features their park should have and how to design features such as bodies of water, roads, bridges, foot paths, horse paths, buildings, greenery, a ball field, gates, rocks, playgrounds, and much more.

Students can gather materials (available at garden centers) for their models. They should use a layer of gravel at the bottom for drainage and plenty of soil or sand for a base. The following are suggested materials:

- paths—moss, sawdust, crushed twigs, cloth, gravel

- shelters and fences—twigs, stones, clay, cardboard, toothpicks

- streams—plastic tubing cut in half and placed in soil

- ponds—margarine tubs or jar lids buried in soil

- meadows—pieces of sod, green felt

- people and animals—modeling clay, Play-Doh

- greenery—different sizes of dried or live plants

END NOTES...

ASSESSMENT OPPORTUNITIES

In Part A, use students' descriptions of their favorite areas to help you evaluate their understanding of the importance of recreational and natural areas.

In Part B, use the students' thank-you letters to assess their learning from the project.

RELATED ACTIVITIES

400-Acre Wood, Planning the Ideal Community, Improve Your Place

REFERENCE

Variation and Enrichment 3 are adapted from Finkelstein, Robert J., et al. *CENTRAL PARK WORKBOOK: ACTIVITIES FOR AN URBAN PARK.* New York. 1980.

Overview
In this activity, students will explore the elements that compose a human community. They will survey the area around their school, looking for community systems that help them live there. Then they will plan an ideal community that meets all the needs of its members.

Background
A community includes all the people who live in a place. Different members of a community exchange goods and services so that all people get what they need to live there.

A thriving human community includes residential areas; commercial areas; industrial areas; schools; public services (police, fire department, hospitals); transportation systems; utility systems; food distribution systems; recreation areas; and cultural resources (libraries, churches, theaters, museums).

Getting Ready
For Part A, decide on the size of the area that students will survey. For example, in urban areas, a two-block area around the school is fine. Obtain or draw a simple map of the survey area. Make a copy for each student. (Or have students copy a sketch from the chalkboard). Also make an overhead transparency of the map or an enlargement on chart paper.

PART A
COMMUNITY LIVING

Doing the Activity
1. Ask students what they think a community is. Ask pairs of students to list five places or services they use in their community. Examples might include roads, schools, hospitals, electricity, parks, libraries, police services, or movie theaters. As students share their ideas, list the examples on an overhead transparency or chart paper.

2. Look over the list, and ask students whether anything that people in the community need to live there is missing. Help class members think of services or resources by asking questions such as the following:

■ How do people get the food they need?

■ Where do they live?

■ How do they get around?

Add new ideas to the list, so that the final list includes places to live, work, learn, and play, along with public services, public utilities, and cultural resources.

3. Divide the class into groups of three to six students. Distribute the maps to each student. Explain that groups will survey the area around the school to find the community resources and services they listed in Steps 1 and 2. Divide the list equally among all of the groups. On the back of their map, members of each group should write down the items they will look for. When students find one of the items on their list, they should record on their map the name and location of the item.

4. Take students for a walk around the survey area, allowing time for students to look for and record their findings. Alternatively, you may assign students to survey the area on their way to or from school.

5. Help students compile their findings on the class map. Using that map as a focal point, lead a discussion about students' findings by asking these types of questions:

■ What community services and resources did you find?

■ What seemed to be missing?

■ Does the community have a problem because those things are not present?

LEVELS
Grades 6-8

SUBJECTS
Math, Social Studies, Language Arts, Visual Arts

CONCEPTS
■ Most cultures have beliefs, values, and traditions that shape human interactions with the environment and its resources. (9.1)

SKILLS
Representing, Identifying Attributes and Components, Restructuring, Synthesizing and Creating

OBJECTIVES
Students will ① map the locations of services and resources in their community and ② create a map of an "ideal" community that includes all the services and resources people need to live there.

MATERIALS
Part A: A map of the area around your school (see Getting Ready), chart paper or overhead transparencies, marking pens or overhead pens

Part B: Large pieces of paper, colored construction paper, tape or glue, marking pens

TIME CONSIDERATIONS
Preparation: 60 minutes

Activity: Five 45-minute periods

- Would you have found them if you had surveyed a larger area?

- Were there enough services and resources in the area that you surveyed?

- Does your survey represent what you would find in other communities? What about the area around your home? What might be different?

- What did you learn from your survey? Did anything surprise you?

- What would you like to see changed in the community?

PART B
COMMUNITY PLANNING

Doing the Activity

1. Explain that students will have an opportunity to be community planners and to design an ideal community that meets all the needs of its residents. Ask students to brainstorm a list of the facilities, resources, and services that their ideal community will include.

2. Using the same groups as in Part A, allow students two to four class periods to plan and map their communities.

3. Ask groups to share their maps with the rest of the class and to describe the features of their design.

4. Use these questions to lead a discussion about the maps and the planning process:

- How did your group decide what features to include and where to place them?

- Give an example of how your group resolved a disagreement.

- How are your ideal communities the same as actual communities? In what ways are they different?

- What would it be like to live in each of the ideal communities? What would it be like for a young child? For a store owner? For an animal?

- How are the planned communities the same as the community you live in? How are they different?

- What did you learn from this activity?

Enrichment

1. Invite a representative from an urban planning office or firm to visit your class. Students can ask the planner about the process in which land-use decisions are made, about the community's goals for the future, or about changes the community anticipates making as it grows.

2. Interview residents who have lived in the community for more than 25 years. Ask them how the community has changed and whether they think the changes were for the better.

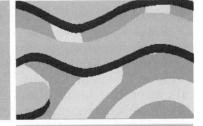

Overview
When certain people decide how to use a particular piece of land, the decision can involve and affect many people in many ways. Therefore, groups must establish processes for planning and resolving conflicts about land use. In this activity, students will develop a plan to address a land-use issue.

Background
Land is a precious commodity in every community. Land-use decisions affect people in many ways, including where they live, what kind of work they do, what kinds of transportation systems they have available, and what kind of environment they live in.

Land-use planning is the process of figuring out how to use a community's land for various purposes. Planning involves relating the resources and characteristics of land to the community's present and future needs. Planners try to predict how to use land to accommodate the community's long-term needs, while considering landowner rights, future development, and population growth.

Most communities have a planning process that includes plan formation, zoning regulations, and city ordinances. A city plan (or general plan) describes the community's goals, objectives, and policies regarding growth and development. Zoning regulations outline the community's decisions about location, intensity, and development of public facilities, and of private land use in other areas. For example, zoning may regulate where parks and businesses can be located or where housing developments can be built. The community might have ordinances that permit or prohibit certain kinds of activities in specific areas of the community. These varied elements of land-use planning work together as a system to help private citizens and public decision makers address development and growth issues in a consistent manner.

However, deciding land-use issues can be a difficult and controversial endeavor. Communities usually set up and follow guidelines for making decisions and resolving conflicts about land use. Three different decision-making models may be used in a community: the consensus model, the legislative model, and the authority model. The models differ in how much citizen involvement is encouraged, who makes the decision, and how the decision is made.

In the consensus model, a group of people becomes aware of a problem and encourages alternative solutions from group members. After comparing alternatives and consequences, the group determines whether there is unanimous agreement on the major points of a solution. The group then makes a group decision about which action to take.

In the legislative model, lawmakers become aware of a problem and encourage citizens and government agencies to become involved and submit solutions. The lawmakers then listen to public testimony about alternatives and consequences. When the decision-making group is ready to vote, the majority vote determines the decision, which then becomes a law or policy.

In the authority model, the authority becomes aware of a problem and, often with little public involvement, considers several solutions. The authority (or that person's staff) gathers information on alternative solutions and consequences. The authority then reaches and implements a decision.

Getting Ready
Make copies of student page 196.

Doing the Activity
1. Ask students, "If you and your friends each want to do something different, how do you decide what to do?" Make a class list of different ways people decide what to do when they have different opinions. Examples might include voting, having one

LEVELS
Grades 5-8

SUBJECTS
Social Studies, Language Arts, Visual Arts

CONCEPTS
- Most cultures have beliefs, values, and traditions that shape human interactions with the environment and its resources. (9.1)
- In democratic societies, citizens have a voice in shaping resource and environmental management policies. They also share in the responsibility of conserving resources and behaving in an environmentally responsible manner. (9.2)
- In democratic societies, individuals and groups, working through governmental channels, can influence the way public and private lands and resources are managed. (9.3)

SKILLS
Discussing, Decision Making, Problem Solving

OBJECTIVES
Students will ① develop solutions to a land-use problem involving urban open space and ② simulate a city council meeting to discuss and decide on a land-use issue.

MATERIALS
copies of student page 196, large sheets of paper, marking pens or other drawing materials, watch or clock with second hand

TIME CONSIDERATIONS
Preparation: 10 minutes

Activity: One or two 50-minute periods

person always decide, taking turns deciding, having everyone decide together, compromising, or having someone else listen and make the decision for them. Explain the consensus, legislative, and authority models from the Background information.

2. Explain that in this activity students will simulate the legislative model for decision making in a community. In the simulation, "citizen groups" of students will present their solutions to a problem and the "city council" will vote to reach a final decision.

3. Distribute copies of student page 196 and read the scenario as a class.

4. Ask the following questions to help students begin thinking about possible solutions as they focus on the areas of conflict.

■ What four parties are involved in this conflict? What do each of them want? (List the parties' goals on the chalkboard.)

Ms. Thomas—used car lot, clean cars, the Heritage Oak cut down, lowest cost, visible advertising, no street trees

Neighbors—no used car lot, no noise, a view, the Heritage Oak preserved

Center City—street trees planted for shade and beauty

Environmental Group—the Heritage Oak preserved, its roots protected, street trees planted

■ What are some points of conflict among the parties? (For example, the neighbors don't want the Heritage Oak cut down, but Ms. Thomas does.)

■ What alternatives can you think of that would satisfy one of these points of conflict? (For example, erect a sound wall or plant screen trees behind the car lot to protect the neighbors from disturbing sights and sounds.)

■ Do you think any of the parties' goals are unreasonable and should be given up?

5. Divide the class into groups of four or five students. Explain that each group represents a city planning group that must come up with a plan to resolve the situation. Provide paper and drawing materials so that groups can draw or list the main elements of their plan. Explain that a city council will be formed to decide on the best plan.

6. Tell students they will have 20 minutes to develop a plan. Explain that they will then make a two-minute presentation to the city council, and that more than one person must help to present the plan.

7. Ten minutes after the groups have started, choose one person from each group to be part of the city council. Have city council members meet together in a separate area of the room. Explain to them that their job is to listen to the plans and to vote on the best proposal. Ask them to decide what criteria they will use to judge the plans. (For example, they can judge the plans as most creative, most environmentally sound, most satisfying to the public, or most legally correct.)

8. Fifteen minutes after the groups have started, remind them that they have only five minutes left.

9. When the time is up, seat the city council members in front of the class. Ask for a volunteer timekeeper to limit each presentation to two minutes.

10. After all of the groups have made their presentations, the city council should meet privately for 5-10 minutes for a final discussion and to vote on the best plan. While the council is meeting, each group can develop a list of the criteria on which it thinks the decision should be based.

11. When the council has reached a decision, ask the members to return, announce their decision, and discuss it.

12. Discuss these questions with the group:

■ Do you agree with the city council? Why or why not?

■ What criteria did the city council use to decide? Do you agree with those criteria?

■ What changes would you have made to the decision process?

■ How is this process similar to what happens in real life? How is it different?

■ Why do you think cities have zoning laws and land-use plans? What would happen if they didn't?

Enrichment

1. Locate two areas near the school for students to compare: one with street trees and one without. What affect do trees have on a street? How do trees affect the temperature, shade, or feel of an area? What benefits do street trees provide? (They cool and clean the air, muffle noise, and provide beauty.) What problems do trees cause? (Their fruits and leaves fall. They block signs and have a potential to damage power lines. Their roots can damage sidewalks. Their falling limbs could cause damage or injury.)

2. Contact your city planners' office to find out what goals, policies, or ordinances involving trees your community has. Help the class discuss whether students agree with those policies, and whether they think the policies are enough.

3. Contact the city zoning office for a map of land-use zoning areas in your community. Learn what the restrictions are for each area. Students might determine if human-built structures near their school or home meet the zoning restrictions. If any structures are inconsistent with the zoning requirements, students might research the terms under which such construction was approved.

ASSESSMENT OPPORTUNITY

Use team plans to evaluate your students' understanding of the decision-making process. How well does each plan resolve the conflict? Does it take into account the needs and rights of all parties? How clear was its position? Was there cooperation and consensus within each group?

RELATED ACTIVITIES

Democracy in Action, Planning the Ideal Community, Are Vacant Lots Vacant?, Improve Your Place

The Sacramento Tree Foundation developed a "Heritage Oak" case study in 1987.

THE HERITAGE OAK DILEMMA

MS. Chris Thomas owns a lot in the fashionable shopping district of downtown Center City. The lot is currently vacant. Ms. Thomas would like to build a luxury car business on the lot and is asking the city for permission to do so. She feels that the lot is perfectly situated to attract customers and to show off her cars. She has been waiting a long time to develop this business; now that she finally has the money, she wants the car dealership to look perfect.

Ms. Thomas plans to build a small sales office on the lot and to pave the entire area for parking. Currently, a huge oak tree is in the middle of the lot. The tree is about 150 years old and is known around town as the Heritage Oak. Ms. Thomas wants to remove the tree because she needs the space to park cars. She also feels that the tree would damage her cars with leaves, twigs, acorns, bird droppings, and large branches.

The city's plan does not prohibit developing a car dealership in that district, but it does state that all lots must have at least one shade tree for every 20 feet (6.1 m) of sidewalk frontage. The regulation exists so shade from trees can reduce glare for drivers and shoppers and can make the area more beautiful.

Ms. Thomas does not want that many trees along the sidewalk because she thinks they would hide her cars. Her lot is about 120 feet (36.6 m) long, which will require six trees. Also, she says those street trees could create a mess that would blow onto her expensive cars and cause damage.

The neighbors who live behind the lot are against development of the car business. They are worried about the ugly sight and loud noises from a car lot. Now they enjoy a view of the Heritage Oak from their windows.

The local environmental group is also against the car business. The group is concerned about the Heritage Oak, which it says is a proud, healthy tree that is a piece of living history. The group wants the city council to protect the Heritage Oak as well as the land immediately around it, because paving around the oak will harm its roots. In addition, the group is working to get the city council to enforce the city's plan of providing street trees, and it wants to be sure that all new and existing lots have street trees.

Overview
Democratic systems depend on the involvement of citizens in policy making and decision making. This activity will help students learn about the roles and responsibilities of citizens' groups in environmental policies and decision making, and about how young people can become involved in the process.

Background
Democratic countries are founded on the principle that all citizens have the right to participate in policy-setting and decision-making processes. Civic participation is especially evident in environmental issues and policies. In the United States, there are currently over 10,000 environmental organizations; and new ones are being formed each year.

Young people are not usually involved in setting policies, yet they are greatly affected by the decisions made by governing bodies. For example, each time the local school board meets, it makes decisions that both affect students and determine what school is like for them. Board members might decide whether to adopt a schedule of year-round classes, which textbooks to use, what the requirements will be for graduation, whether to change the length of the school day, or when vacations will be scheduled. Similarly, local, state, and federal governments constantly decide on issues that touch students in many aspects of their lives. Those issues might include health standards, traffic regulations, rules for recycling, or laws about other environmental choices.

Young people can take part in social decisions and policy making in many ways. They can join a group that represents their interests. They can write letters to lawmakers or other influential parties. They might even ask to sit on local boards or councils as student advisors.

Your local telephone directory is a good resource for locating government agencies, associations, and other groups working on a particular topic. The blue pages usually list government agencies or departments; the yellow pages list businesses, associations, groups, and clubs; and the white pages list both individuals and many organizations also found in the yellow pages. Your local library will have other, specific directories that list organizations nationally and internationally. Addresses of environmental groups and agencies are listed on page 382.

Getting Ready
Draw a large coat-of-arms (see diagram on page 198) on the chalkboard or on a large sheet of paper for the students to see.

Doing the Activity
1. Ask students to jot down a list of five or six things that interest or concern them. Their list might include hobbies they have, animals they care for, sports they like to play or watch, or crime or health issues they care about. Invite volunteers to share their ideas.

2. Explain to students that they will have an opportunity to learn about groups that have interests or concerns similar to theirs. They will try to find out what issues those groups deal with and how the groups try to influence decision-making processes. Have students look over their lists and circle three items they would like to learn more about.

3. Divide the class into teams of two to four students who have similar interests. To do this, ask a student to share his or her first choice; then ask students with a similar interest to join that student's team. (If no one else is interested in the topic, try the student's second or third choice. If the team becomes larger than four students, divide it into smaller teams.) Continue this process until all students are on a team.

4. Ask each team to find two interest groups, organizations, or agencies that are involved in making decisions about that team's topic. Explain that after teams have located two groups, students are to contact each group's offices to get written information and to ask questions. (Give each team two copies of the

LEVELS
Grades 5-8

SUBJECTS
Social Studies, Visual Arts

CONCEPTS
■ In democratic societies, citizens have a voice in shaping resource and environmental management policies. They also share in the responsibility of conserving resources and behaving in an environmentally responsible manner. (9.2)

■ In democratic societies, individuals and groups, working through governmental channels, can influence the way public and private lands and resources are managed. (9.3)

■ Effective citizen involvement in the environmental decision-making process involves a careful study of all sides of the issues, along with the ability to differentiate between honest, factually accurate information and propaganda. (9.4)

SKILLS
Researching, Comparing and Contrasting, Analyzing, Problem Solving

OBJECTIVES
Students will ① compare two citizen groups, special-interest groups, or government agencies involved in the same issues; ② create visual representations of the two groups; and ③ explain ways students can become involved in the civic action process through participation in such groups.

MATERIALS
Scratch paper; copies of telephone directories; list of organizations and agencies; two copies of student page 200 per team; large sheets of colored or white paper; drawing materials, scissors (optional)

TIME CONSIDERATIONS
Preparation: 30 minutes

Activity: Two 50-minute periods over the course of several weeks questions on student page 200.) If a team finds a local citizens' group, they can contact one of its members to answer the questions. (When writing to any group, try to include a self-addressed, stamped envelope, which will greatly increase the chance of a reply. See other guidelines on page 382.)

5. Give students time to brainstorm ideas about starting their search. Have telephone directories available to help students gather ideas and contact sources. If a team can't get started, offer suggestions. For example, if the team is interested in animals, you might suggest that they try the local humane society or the National Wildlife Federation. If they are interested in health issues, you might suggest that they try the local Red Cross chapter or state health agencies. Students might also call the local chamber of commerce or city offices (like the city council or the mayor's office) to ask if there are any committees that address their issues.

6. Allow time for students to contact and question members of their two groups, and to receive necessary printed materials.

7. When all teams have completed the student page, give each team two large sheets of paper. Have them draw the outline of a coat-of-arms on each, similar to the one you drew earlier. Ask students what a coat-of-arms is. (It is an emblem that represents the identity of a group.) Assign teams the task of designing two coats-of-arms, one for each group they researched. The coat-of-arms should have six sections, each with a drawing or symbol that represents the group's answers to the questions on the student page.

8. Have teams share the designs and describe what they represent. Lead a discussion on the value of civic action, using the coats-of-arms as a basis for your discussion:

- What similarities did you find in the two groups you researched? What differences?

- How are both groups you researched the same? In what ways do they differ?

- Why are groups like these important?

- What might happen if either of the groups you researched did not exist?

- In what ways can people take part in policies and decisions in our community? In the state? In the nation?

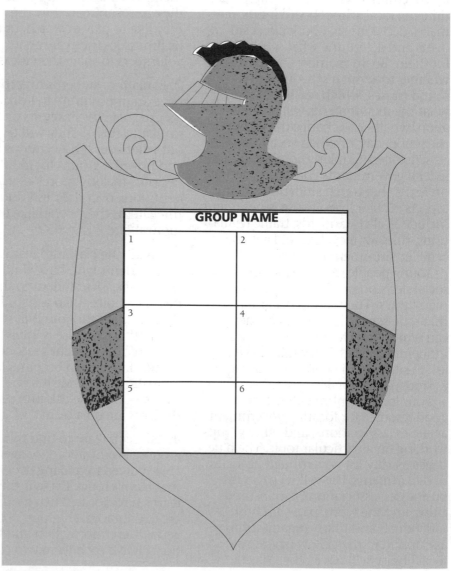

VARIATION—MEET THE EXPERTS

Instead of having teams conduct their own research, invite a local representative from each of several organizations with different perspectives on an environmental issue to speak with your class. The guests might be from groups such as the Audubon Society, Nature Conservancy, Bureau of Land Management, National Association of State Foresters, state forestry associations, an outdoor sports group, or a citizens' group. (See addresses of organizations on page 382.)

Have the class interview the guests by asking questions from student page 200 plus any other questions students think of. (Guests can come on different days or can give a panel presentation.) Afterward, as they answer the questions on the student page, class members should use information and impressions gained from the guests.

Enrichment

Help class members choose an environmental issue or topic about which they would like to learn more. For example, they could choose forests, water, recycling, landfills, endangered species, or a current local topic. Invite representatives of groups with different views to speak to the class about their group's positions on a topic and to answer student questions. Have students prepare questions for each interviewee in advance. After the interviews, use a class discussion to compare the groups' positions on the issue or topic.

END NOTES...

ASSESSMENT OPPORTUNITY

Assess students' comprehension by examining coats-of-arms and student work sheets. For example, how successful were students in getting answers to their questions? How well do the coats-of-arms communicate the identity of the researched organizations? How well does the design identify issues the organization deals with? Does it reflect their position on issues?

RELATED ACTIVITIES

We Can Work It Out, Planning the Ideal Community, There Ought to Be a Law, Improve Your Place

GROUP PROFILE

....
Team's Topic

....
Group's Name

....
Contact Person

....
Name

....
Phone Number

1 What are the overall goals of the group?

2 What does the group do to influence decision making about the topic? (Examples might include lobbying, making recommendations to lawmakers, or encouraging members to write letters to lawmakers.)

3 What important issue is the group working on right now?

4 What is the group's position on that issue?

5 How is this group different from _____ (other group you're researching on same topic)?

6 How can someone become a member of the group? Are any students members?

Overview
In democratic societies, citizens have the power to influence the lawmaking process. In this activity, students will find out how local laws are made and how they can get involved in the process.

Background

In the United States and many other countries, the government is comprised of federal, regional (state or province), and local law-making bodies. Of these three levels, local governments focus on the issues that most affect an immediate geographical area, such as zoning, education, health, public safety, highway improvements, and management and creation of parks.

Only the legislative offices of a local government can actually make laws. But all citizens can initiate and change laws by influencing lawmaking officials to make or revise a law. The process for initiating or changing a law begins when a citizen or group identifies a problem and considers different solutions to it. The next step is to draft a proposal for a new or changed law, and to gather evidence for a case that supports the proposal. After a proposed law is drafted, it must be presented to lawmakers (the mayor, council, commission, or administrator) and then investigated and discussed by the lawmaking body. After considering the proposed law, lawmakers may accept or reject the proposal. For a summary of the lawmaking process, see the chart on page 204.

Most state laws are made by the state's lawmaking body or legislature. New laws are created in response to needs identified by citizens or groups of people. The process involves discussion, investigation, legal review, and voting, similar to the process for local government. Some states share lawmaking power with the people directly through a process called initiative or referendum. This process enables people to create a new law, change an existing law, or challenge a bill passed by the legislature before it becomes law. In this process, concerned citizens

collect a required number of signatures on a petition. After receiving a required number of signatures from the public, the petition can then go to the legislator for consideration, or directly to the people for voting.

Getting Ready
For Part A, list 8-10 groups to which you belong. Make the list as varied as possible. For example, your list might include your family, the school staff, a sports team, people who enjoy singing, people whose birthdays are in January, or people who live in your community. Be prepared to share this list with your students. Make an overhead transparency of page 204.

For Part B, schedule library time for the class to research how a proposed law might be handled by your local government. If possible, arrange for the librarian to suggest some useful reference materials for class research. Make copies of page 204 for each student.

PART A
GROUP RULES

Doing the Activity
1. Introduce the activity by pointing out to students that every person belongs to many groups. Share your list (see Getting Ready) as an example.

2. Invite students to help you brainstorm groups to which different class members belong. List the groups on the chalkboard.

3. Ask students which groups have rules or expectations for group behavior. For example, families have rules about bedtimes, and sports teams have rules for playing games. Circle the groups that have rules.

LEVELS
Part A: Grades 3-8
Part B: Grades 6-8

SUBJECTS
Math, Social Studies, Language Arts, Visual Arts

CONCEPTS
■ Most cultures have beliefs, values, and traditions that shape human interactions with the environment and its resources. (9.1)

■ In democratic societies, citizens have a voice in shaping resource and environmental management policies. They also share in the responsibility of conserving resources and behaving in an environmentally responsible manner. (9.2)

■ Democratic societies, individuals and groups, working through governmental channels, can influence the way public and private lands and resources are managed. (9.3)

SKILLS
Researching, Analyzing, Discussing, Problem Solving

OBJECTIVES
Students will ① describe how a group of students can make and change rules, ② compare rule-making in a group to the lawmaking process in local government, ③ research the steps necessary to make a proposed change in their community, and ④ create a poster that shows the effects of their proposed change and that depicts the lawmaking process.

MATERIALS
Part A: Overhead transparency or large chart showing student page 204
Part B: copies of student page 204, blue pages of the telephone directory, large paper and drawing materials

TIME CONSIDERATIONS
Preparation: 15 minutes

Activity:
Part A: One or two 50-minute periods
Part B: One or two 50-minute periods

4. Discuss these questions with the students:

- Why do groups have rules?

- Why are rules important?

- What would happen if (choose one group) had no rules?

- Can you think of a time when a rule got in the way of a group's working well together?

- What are some ways that people can add to or change a group's rules?

5. As homework, ask students to find out how they could add or change a rule in a group they belong to. Have students write down these questions:

- What rule would you like to change?

- How could you add or change the rule?

- How would it affect the other people in the group if your rule were added or changed?

The next day, ask students to share their responses with a partner. On the chalkboard, make a class list of ways people in groups can add or change rules. Here are examples:

- Propose it to the person in charge, who will decide.

- Have the whole group vote on it.

- Write a letter to the governing body of the group, who will vote on it.

6. Use the overhead transparency of page 204 to show students the steps usually needed to make or change a local law. Help students compare those steps to the lawmaking processes they found out about from their homework. Discuss these questions:

- What is the importance of each step? What might happen if there were no public discussion, for example? What if there were no legal review?

- Why do you need so many steps? (To ensure that many people agree with the change and that the change is for the common good.)

- How is the process similar to or different from the rulemaking process in your group?

PART B
COMMUNITY LAWS

Doing the Activity

1. Tell students that in Salt Lake City, Utah, a city ordinance makes it illegal to steal a parking space from a car that is already waiting for it, or select an example from your own community. Ask students whether they can think of any laws for their community that would make living there better. Help students brainstorm a list of possible laws. Encourage creative and far-fetched ideas. Students might consider laws that would address current environmental concerns in the community. Is there a problem, in general, with having too many laws? (It might be difficult and expensive to enforce them.)

2. Divide students into teams of three to five, and have each team decide on a possible law they would like to see put into action. Explain that each team will research what students would need to do to make their idea become a law. Students might answer questions such as these:

- What is your proposed law?

- Is there already a law related to your concern? Is it adequate?

- What would be the positive effects of your proposed law?

- What negative effects might it have?

- Who would be affected by your law?

- Which people would support your law?

- Which people or groups would oppose it?

- How could your law be enforced? Would enforcement be costly?

- What would be the punishment for breaking your law?

- What government department would most likely be interested in a law like the one you propose?

- Does your proposed law require a change in an existing law or other regulation?

- What kind of local government does your community have? (A city might be managed by a mayor and a council, a council and a manager, a commission, or town meetings.) Who is responsible for signing new laws?

- What steps would you need to go through to change or add your law or regulation? How is this process different from the one on your handout?

- What people would be involved in changing or adding the law or regulation?

- Are there ways other than laws for accomplishing what you propose?

3. Give each student a copy of page 204 to use as a reference. Allow library time and telephone time for students to research their proposed law. If students need help getting started, suggest that they look at the telephone directory's blue pages, which list local government offices. Review with the students "Guidelines for Requesting Information" on page 382.

4. After teams have collected their information, have them make posters summarizing the process for making their idea into law. Each poster should include ① a picture of the community "before" the proposed law, ② a picture showing how the community would be different "after" the proposal became law (including both positive and negative effects), and ③ the people and steps that would be involved with making it a law.

Enrichment

1. Students could work to turn one of their ideas into law. First, the class should gather evidence to support the proposed law. Then they will draft the proposed law. Help students contact a member of the local government about the proposal, and invite that person to your class to see a presentation about the law's importance. Ask that person how students might influence lawmakers to pass this law.

2. The National Environmental Policy Act requires federal agencies to examine the environmental impact of federal projects that may have significant effects on the environment. Possible impacts are described in an "Environmental Impact Statement." Encourage students to examine their proposed laws to determine if their law might have positive or negative impacts on the community's air, water, soil, wildlife, vegetation, sound, economics, or aesthetic qualities.

3. Invite a local lawmaker to visit your group and answer the students' questions on how and why laws are made. Students may have specific concerns relating to local social or environmental issues.

END NOTES...

ASSESSMENT OPPORTUNITY

Use the team team posters from Part B to assess students' understanding of the legal process. Let each team explain its poster to the rest of the group. Does the poster show at least several steps that would be involved in making a law? Does it include people who would be involved in the process (like the mayor, the city council, and citizens)? Does the poster depict some of the negative as well as positive consequences of the proposed law?

RELATED ACTIVITIES

We Can Work It Out, Democracy in Action, Planning the Ideal Community, Improve Your Place

REFERENCES

Student page adapted with permission, from Lewis, Barbara A. THE KID'S GUIDE TO SOCIAL ACTION. Minneapolis: Free Spirit Publishing, 1991.

STEPS FOR MAKING OR CHANGING A LOCAL LAW

Law Signed, Not Signed or Vetoed

The chief executive (mayor, commissioner, or administrator) does one of three things: signs the proposed law, making it a real law; leaves it unsigned; or vetoes (rejects) it. If the law is left unsigned, it may become a real law anyway after a certain number of days, depending on the local government.

Vote by Lawmaking Body

If there is one, the city council (or other lawmaking body) votes on the proposed law. If the body votes "no," the process ends here; if "yes," the proposed law is passed on to the chief executive.

Public Discussion or Hearing

Lawmaking body presents proposed law in a public meeting so other people can hear about it and comment on it.

Draft of Ordinance or Regulation

Proposed law is written in draft form in legal language.

Legal Review

Lawyers review proposed law to see if it conflicts with existing laws.

Investigation

Staff person investigates need for proposed law.

Discussion

Local lawmaking body discusses pros and cons of proposed law and makes changes.

Proposal

Citizen or group presents proposed law to mayor, council, commission, administrator, or staff person.

Overview
Newspapers keep the community informed about current events and trends, provide a forum for discussion of public issues, and are a source of entertainment. In this activity, students will examine articles from different sections of the newspaper by comparing and contrasting the different types of words and styles they employ.

Background
In our society, we rely on television, newspapers, radio, and magazines to provide information to us and to provide a forum for public exploration of different ideas or topics. While these media may sometimes fall short of our expectations for providing objective information, they nonetheless play a vital role in keeping our large and ever-changing communities informed and connected.

The medium of newsprint is one of the oldest forms of communication and is still one of the most popular sources for news and information. A newspaper has many different kinds of things to read besides news: opinion pieces, sports columns, weather forecasts, food articles, television schedules, and advice columns.

Newspapers are organized in such a way that you can learn a lot without actually reading an article. For example, the location of a news story tells you how important it is: The most important stories usually appear on the front page, and the most important of those, called the lead story, is usually at either the top or top right side of the page. Headlines tell what each story is about, and the size of the letters in a headline is another clue to the story's importance. The dateline tells where the story takes place and indicates whether the story is local, regional, or national. Photographs and captions both show and tell about people and places in the news and what happened to them.

Editorial pages (and sometimes op-ed pages for opposite editorial) usually look different from news pages. The print may be more solid, and you will not find photographs or advertisements. Again, headlines or titles usually indicate the content and point of view of each article. Either on or opposite the editorial page is a section where readers can express their opinions. These letters are usually printed under the heading "Letters to the Editor" and may include headlines that inform you of the letters' content.

A well-written news story provides objective information about events that have happened. Most news articles tell all the important facts in the first few sentences. These sentences are called the lead and should include who, what, where, and when. Why and how appear next.

News articles usually present details either by listing them in the order of importance or by listing events in the order they happened. Reporters use an inverted pyramid in writing so the most important points are first and the least important are last. Responsible journalists carefully select their words so they do not present a biased picture of the event.

In contrast, editorials and opinion pieces are written to express a particular viewpoint. The writers often include emotional words to affect and persuade readers.

Getting Ready
For Part A, if possible, gather enough copies of the local newspaper so that students in each team can examine an entire copy. The newspaper company might donate old copies to the class, or you might ask students to bring in yesterday's paper from home.

From different sections of the newspaper, gather short articles that all focus on the same environmental issue, and make copies of them. For example, you might find a news article, an editorial, an editorial cartoon, and a letter to the editor all dealing with a local landfill initiative or a proposed recycling program. You will probably need to look in several newspapers on different days for related

LEVELS
Activity: Grades 6-8
Variation: Grades 3-6 or older students with limited English

SUBJECTS
Social Studies, Language Arts, Visual Art, Performing Arts

CONCEPTS
- Effective citizen involvement in the environmental decision–making process involves a careful study of all sides of the issues, along with the ability to differentiate between honest, factually accurate information and propaganda. (9.4)
- Increased public knowledge of the environment and the need for conservation of natural resources have resulted in lifestyle changes in many cultures. (15.5)

SKILLS
Comparing and Contrasting, Analyzing, Synthesizing and Creating, Composing

OBJECTIVES
Students will ① compare different sections of a daily newspaper, ② analyze some of the ways that ideas and opinions are expressed through word choice, ③ research opposing sides of a local environmental issue, and ④ write articles on environmental issues using both objective and subjective points of view.

MATERIALS
copies of the local newspaper; two or three news items from different sections of the newspaper (possibly from different papers or editions) that all focus on the same environmental issue—news items may be a news article, an editorial, an editorial cartoon, or a letter to the editor; staples or binder

TIME CONSIDERATIONS
Preparation: 30 minutes

Activity: 30 minutes (Part A)
one or two 50-minute periods (Part B)

items. (Your students might help you with this.)

For Part B, arrange library time for students to research the issue they decided to investigate.

PART A
HEADLINES

Doing the Activity

1. Ask students how often they look at the local newspaper. Ask them to name the parts they have read: the news, comics, sports section, television guide, or advice column. Discuss these questions:

- Why do you think newspapers have different sections?

- Why do you think a newspaper is important to our community?

2. (Optional) Distribute copies of the newspaper. Point out the main sections of your local paper. (For example, the first section might focus on national and world news, and the second section might include local news and editorials.) Point out the political cartoons and any other features that would be helpful to students.

3. Divide students into teams of two to four students. On the chalkboard write the headlines or captions from each of the articles you collected on the same topic (see Getting Ready). Ask a volunteer to read one article (without the headline), and have students guess what they think the article is about and whether they think it is a news story, opinion piece, or another kind of article. Repeat using other articles.

4. Give each team a set of articles. Have each team read each piece aloud. Ask these questions:

- What is the purpose of this newspaper piece?

- Is it supposed to inform people about the whole issue or to persuade people to take one side?

- Can you tell on which side of the issue each author (or cartoonist) stands?

- What clues did you have about the author's (or cartoonist's) views?

- What kind of article do you now think it is: a news article, a letter to the editor, or an opinion piece?

5. Ask students what mental picture they have if you say you *broke* your sunglasses yesterday. Then ask what mental picture they have if you say you *smashed* your sunglasses. Were the images of your sunglasses different? If so, how? Why did they picture different images?

Point out that even though broke and smashed have similar meanings and can often be used to describe the same situation, the words suggest different images to the listener (that is, they have different connotations). Ask students for their ideas of words that have similar meanings, but different connotations.

6. Ask groups to read through each newspaper article again and circle any words or phrases that bring to mind graphic images or strong emotions (strong connotations).

7. List those graphic and emotional words on the chalkboard. Discuss the effect of those words in the newspaper pieces. Then ask questions such as these:

- Which piece used more emotional words?

- Which piece is more factual?

- Which is more persuasive?

- When might you want to use emotional kinds of words? When might you want to avoid them?

For each word listed on the chalkboard, ask students whether they can think of a different word that means the same thing, but is less graphic or less emotional. Discuss how the newspaper articles would be different if those words were substituted.

Doing the Activity

1. Ask students whether there are community issues or local environmental issues they would like to learn more about. Students might include issues from Part A or other issues such as wearing school uniforms, widening a nearby highway, or developing a local wetland. Write their ideas on the chalkboard. Then, have each team select an issue on which to focus.

2. Explain that students will first learn as much as they can about this issue, and then put together a newsletter to inform others about it. Help students research the facts about the issue by either interviewing people or requesting information from groups on both sides of the issue, or by finding information in the library.

3. After the teams have gathered as much information as possible, explain that each team should produce factual and opinion pieces on the issue. Each team member will write one article that is either fact or opinion. The factual piece will be a straight news story, written in an objective style. The opinion piece (an editorial or letter to the editor) should be written in a subjective tone and try to persuade the reader to accept one viewpoint. Before students begin writing, the team should list all the facts they want to include in their news stories and the ideas they want to emphasize in their opinion articles.

4. When the students have finished, have them read their pieces aloud within their teams. Then have the entire group discuss these questions:

- In which type of article are there more emotional words?

- Which style is more effective in persuading the reader?

- Do you think readers like being told what to think about an issue?

- Were you tempted to change the truth to persuade your readers?

- If the purpose of an article is to persuade the reader, does it matter if it is accurate? Why or why not?

- Why do you think it is important for newspapers to include factual pieces as well as opinion pieces?

5. Collect all of the articles, arrange them according to the issues, and bind them together to form a newspaper. Make copies to distribute to other audiences such as peers, parents, and teachers.

VARIATION

For Younger Students or Students with Limited English Proficiency
1. Collect a variety of automobile advertisements from magazines and newspapers.

2. Divide students into small teams and give each team several different advertisements to examine. Ask team members to answer these questions:

- Which advertisement tries the hardest to appeal to a person's emotions?

- Which uses the most facts to persuade?

- What values does each advertisement convey? (safety, freedom, speed, family togetherness)

- Which advertisement seems most effective? Explain your answer.

3. Ask students to pretend they were hired by a forest. The forest wants to attract plants and animals to live in it and needs the students to help advertise. As a group, list things that forests have to offer plants and animals. Alternatively, have students pretend they were hired by a local park to attract visitors. Help students list features they might include in their advertisements.

4. Individually or in small teams, have students create an advertisement directed at a particular plant or animal to attract it to live in the forest (or at a particular group of people to attract them to the park). Ask students to create posters or commercials involving drawings, writing, drama, music, and dance.

5. Have students present their advertisements to the rest of the group. Discuss these questions:

- What techniques did you use to persuade your potential customers?

- Did you exaggerate, or did you use only facts?

- Did you leave out any information? If so, why?

- Did you include any "minuses" in addition to positive information? If not, why not?

Enrichment

1. Have students find out the effectiveness of the newspaper they made in Part B. Students might ask parents, schoolmates, or teachers their opinions on the issues before those people read the articles. Students should poll the readers again about their position on the issue after they have read the newspaper.

2. Have students listen to National Public Radio or watch the national television news to compare those news sources to the newspaper. As they listen or watch, ask students to consider these questions:

- Which medium used more emotional kinds of words?

- Which is more factual and complete?

- Which seems more balanced or unbiased?

- Which is more persuasive?

2. Bring in a variety of editorial cartoons for students to examine. Invite the students to draw humorous cartoons about forest-related environmental issues such as depletion of rainforests, problems of acid rain, preservation of endangered species, or recycling.

3. Locate billboards in your community and help students photograph or draw pictures of them. For each billboard, have students decide what the billboard's purpose, who its intended audience is, if it is effective, and if it is compatible with its surroundings. Find out whether your community has billboard regulations. If so, discuss whether they are adequate; if not, discuss whether you need such regulations.

4. Play popular recordings from any era that have environmental messages. Examples are Joni Mitchell's "Paradise Paved," the Talking Heads' "(Nothing But) Flowers," Nanci Griffith's "From a Distance," or any others you or your students can think of. In small groups, have the students discuss these questions:

- Why do you think the song was written? What could be the artist's intention?

- How do these songs make you feel? Does the artist want you to feel a certain way? Do you agree? Encourage students to compose their own songs or raps expressing their concerns about the environment or celebrating any aspects they value. Students might start with a popular song or rap and revise the lyrics to express their ideas about the environment.

END NOTES...

ASSESSMENT OPPORTUNITY
Use each team's written articles to assess students' understanding of the differences between straight news and opinion articles.

RELATED ACTIVITIES
There Ought to Be a Law, Publicize It!, Democracy in Action

REFERENCES
Statistical Abstract of the United States: 1987 (107th edition). Washington, DC: U.S. Department of Commerce, 1986.

Overview
The news media, including television, newspapers, and radio, provide community members with a system for getting and spreading information about environmental issues. This activity can be done in conjunction with any of the action projects in this activity guide. Students will conduct an environmental action project and use various media to inform others in the community about the project.

Background
Television, radio, and newspaper reporters like stories about students involved in community action. To get their attention, students should write news releases describing their project. Besides the local newspaper, don't forget smaller community newspapers or bulletins.

Members of a community use communications media extensively to influence public opinion and raise awareness of events or issues. To increase public awareness of a problem or project, news releases and letters to the editor publicize the views of individuals or groups. Television and radio stations also accept public service announcements written by groups. Unlike news releases and letters to the editor, which may be controversial, public service announcements are issued on an informational level. They often publicize events that might interest the community. Students can also create posters for the same purpose.

Your school district may have a public information specialist who can suggest media contacts and other ideas about how to maximize coverage. If so, use this person! To get advance coverage of a project, you need to plan ahead. You will need to send your students' news releases, public service announcements, or letters well ahead of the time you want the information to be published or broadcast: two weeks to one month ahead.

Getting Ready
Decide if you want students to develop and plan their own environmental action project or if you want to present two or more project ideas from which they can choose. If you are the one presenting project ideas, look through the activities in this guide for ideas. You may need additional adult or parental support to complete the action project.

Doing the Activity
1. Ask students for their ideas on how radio, television, and newspaper reporters get information about things to include in news stories. Write their ideas on the chalkboard. If it has not been mentioned, explain that reporters often rely on news tips from the public. Explain to students that groups or individuals planning an event or project often tell the media about it because they want other people to know. Explain that students will have a chance to learn more about how people can get media coverage as they conduct their community action project.

2. If you have chosen two or more possible projects for students to decide among, explain each project to the class. Answer any questions students have about the projects, and let them vote to select one.

3. If you decide to let students develop their own action project, help them think of a problem they would like to work on. (You may want to lead them in a brainstorming session.) To get them thinking about how they can take action, pass out copies of student page 212, and have them read "Reclaiming a State Park," which is about a successful student project. You can use these questions to discuss how these students succeeded:

■ What kind of local resources did the students use to complete their project? (A state grant to reclaim the park; help from the shop teacher to build picnic tables.)

LEVELS
Grades 5-8

SUBJECTS
Science, Social Studies, Language Arts, Visual Arts, Performing Arts

CONCEPTS
■ Effective citizen involvement in the environmental decision-making process involves a careful study of all sides of the issues, along with the ability to differentiate between honest, factually accurate information and propaganda. (9.4)
■ Increased public knowledge of the environment and the need for conservation of natural resources have resulted in lifestyle changes in many cultures. (15.5)

SKILLS
Decision Making , Identifying Main Ideas, Problems Solving, Evaluating

OBJECTIVES
Students will ① plan and carry out a community action project and ② use the media to create public awareness about the event.

MATERIALS
Copies of student pages 212-214, telephone directory, school or institutional letterhead, envelopes and stamps, camera and film (optional), typewriter (optional), and poster-making materials (optional)

TIME CONSIDERATIONS
Preparation: 30 minutes

Activity: Variable amounts of time over several weeks

- What was the goal of the FFA chapter's project? (to help reclaim Sugarite State Park by reducing stream erosion) Did students accomplish more than their original goal? (Yes. They also helped to improve trails, set up tables, operate a wildlife rehabilitation center, and start a tree farm.)

- How do you think the FFA students benefited from taking part in the Sugarite project? (They developed personal skills and relationships with other people, gained personal satisfaction by reclaiming the park, and were paid for their work.)

- Would you take part in a project like this? Why or why not?

4. As a group, brainstorm about problems affecting your local environment, school, or neighborhood. You may find areas that look neglected or need improvement. For example, are there corners of the school that have no plants, places that smell bad, or streets that have dangerous crossings? Help students choose one problem on which to focus, and encourage them to brainstorm possible solutions. Have the class select one solution, and develop an action plan to carry it out.

5. Distribute copies of student pages 212-214 to each person. As a class, read aloud "Tips for Getting Media Coverage." Ask students in what other ways they could tell people about their project. (They could write an announcement for the school or make posters to put in store windows.)

6. Have students think about the best way to tell others in the community about their project. Here are examples:

- What kind of audience do you want to tell about the project? (students in the school; other kids, parents, or other adults who could help)

- What might be the best way to reach this audience?

- Do you want to tell people about the project beforehand? What might be the best way to do this?

- Do you want to ask people in the community for help? How should you do this?

- Do you want to let people know about the project after it is completed? Why would you want to tell them about the project? (maybe to encourage them to do the same) How could you let them know what you have done?

7. Help students use the yellow and blue pages of the telephone directory to make a list of names, addresses, and phone numbers of media resources and other people the class will contact. Students might begin by listing the radio stations they listen to or the newspapers they read. For each resource, help the class decide what would be the best way for targeting that resource. (news release, public service announcement, or another format)

8. Divide the class into small groups of two to four students. Divide the list of resources so that all groups have an equal number of resources to target. Have the class use student pages 213-214 to draft the necessary public service announcements, news releases, or letters to publicize the project. If students have decided to make posters or flyers, have materials available.

9. After they have written drafts of their publicity materials, encourage students in each group to read their drafts to each other. They should be sure the writing is accurate, clear, and informational. After students revise their own drafts, they may type or copy their writing onto school stationery.

10. (Optional) Before or during the project, students may take photographs to accompany their letters or news releases.

11. After conducting the action project, discuss these questions:

- How did it feel to do something for the community or environment (or school)?

- What effect did the media have on your project? What makes the news media important? How might your community be different if there were no television? No radio? No newspaper?

- Do you need different kinds of news media? Do you need televisions, radios, magazines, and newspapers?

- How do you think people use the media to influence people's thinking about community issues?

Enrichment

Watch for media coverage of your class' project. If possible, clip out newspaper articles and letters to the editor, and record any television and radio stories or announcements. Compare the actual media stories to students' publicity materials. How close did the media keep to what students wrote? Were the changes an improvement?

If the project received no coverage, what went wrong? How might students do things differently next time to improve media coverage? How was this a learning experience for the students?

END NOTES...

ASSESSMENT OPPORTUNITY

Look at the students' written pieces, list of media contacts, and overall publicity efforts to assess their understanding of how the media can publicize messages. How well do their written pieces communicate the importance of the students' project?

RELATED ACTIVITIES

Power of Print, Plant a Tree, Adopt a Tree, I'd Like to Visit a Place Where..., There Ought to Be a Law, Improve Your Place

REFERENCES

Student pages adapted, with permission, from Lewis, Barbara. KID'S GUIDE TO SOCIAL ACTION. Minneapolis, MN: Free Spirit Publishing, 1991.

RECLAIMING A STATE PARK

Sugarite State Park is located in the rough, mountainous area of Raton, New Mexico. In the 1900s, the Sugarite area was mined for coal. Miners dumped the waste, or tailings, from the mines in the park area. Over the years, the tailings eroded and created acidic waste that ran into nearby streams. The waste affected water quality and endangered wildlife in the park.

Students of the local chapter of Future Farmers of America (FFA) learned about the problem in the park and decided to take action. With the help of their chapter leader, they applied for and received a contract from the state to help reclaim the park. To reduce stream erosion, the 80 teenagers dug more than 1,000 seed basins, constructed more than 50 rock dams, terraced 780 feet (238 m) of steep slopes, and built a diversion channel to change the flow of a small stream.

The determined group also cleaned up a 4.5-mile (7.2-km) trail in the park and made 150 trail markers. They used their shop classes to weld 65 metal frame picnic tables, which they set up throughout the park. Finally, the FFA students planted an experimental tree farm, complete with a special water-saving irrigation system, and they operated a center to care for injured wild animals.

Bob Salter, of New Mexico's natural resources department, marveled at the FFA group's accomplishments. "The work they did was better than we often get from professional contractors."

As part of the contract with the state, all participants in the project were paid for their efforts. But they agreed that they got more than money from the project. Remy Martinez felt comradeship. "It was hard work and we got really dirty. But everybody helped everybody else out, and we got it done."

And the reclamation project provided a chance for Elizabeth Morgan to grow personally while she helped her community. "I gained leadership skills I was lacking…. In [a project like Sugarite], students build themselves as well as their communities."

TIPS FOR GETTING MEDIA COVERAGE

Getting media coverage is not always easy. Here are some suggestions to increase your chances of success:

- Use your imagination to create an interesting story angle that will catch the media's interest.

- Write your news release or public service announcement for a general audience. Consider that the more people it affects, the greater your chance of coverage.

- Write clearly and simply.

- If possible, include a black-and-white photograph for newspapers or a slide or videotape for television. Pictures add visual interest to a story.

- Send out lots of news releases. Coverage may not happen each time you send out a release.

Tips for Writing a News Release
One goal of a news release is to alert the media and the public to an important problem in your community or school, and to tell what you are doing to resolve it. Use action words and short sentences. List the most important information in the first paragraph by including who, what, when, where, why, and how.

Give less important information and explanatory details in later paragraphs. If possible, use direct quotations from people in your group or class, or from people who know details about the problem or the solution. Be accurate and honest. Do not exaggerate or alter facts to support your views.

Tips for Writing a Public Service Announcement
The goal of a public service announcement (PSA) is to inform the public about a meeting or other event they may want to attend or know about. Write the PSA in the words you want read on the radio or television.

Use "high impact" words that create images people will remember. Briefly state who, what, when, where, why, and how. Read your words aloud as you check the length, which should be no more than 20 seconds. Write the time in seconds on the PSA.

Tips for Writing a Letter to the Editor
The goal of a letter to the editor is to express your position on a problem or issue, and to explain how your group or class is resolving it. Keep your letter short. It is okay to give your opinion, but be sure that you do not say anything unfair about someone else. You must sign your letter or it may not be printed.

LETTER TO
THE EDITOR

....
Name of the Editor

....
Name of the Newspaper

....
Address of the Newspaper

Dear ——————————
      Name of the Editor

First paragraph: State that you are a member of the group or class, and express your position on the problem or issue.

....

....

Second paragraph: Give a very brief history of the problem and description of the current situation.

....

....

Third paragraph: State your opinion about how the problem should be resolved and why (give reasons).

....

....

Fourth paragraph: Urge attendance at a meeting or other action related to the problem in question.

....

....

Fifth paragraph: Thank the editor.

....

....

                                  Sincerely,

                        ....
                             Your Signature

                        ....
                             Your Address

FOR IMMEDIATE RELEASE:

....

Name of Your Group or Class

....

Address

....

City, State, Zip Code

....

Contact Person, Phone Number

....

Title of Release

Who ....

....

What ....

....

Where ....

....

When ....

....

Why ....

....

How (Details) ....

Structure & Scale

Overview

All students, no matter how young, have an idea of what a tree looks like. But many are unfamiliar with either the actual structure of a tree or the function of its principle parts. In this activity, your students will take a closer look at trees and their parts.

Background

There's a lot of variety in the more than 50,000 kinds of trees in the world. For example, some trees tower more than 360 feet (110 m) high, like coastal redwoods, and some reach only 15 feet (5 m), like bluejack oaks. Tree leaves may be needle-shaped, broad and flat, or made of little scales. Tree bark may be smooth, rough, shaggy, or deeply furrowed. Branches may spread out to form a huge, broad crown or may rise narrowly like a column.

Getting Ready

In your community, locate several different kinds of trees that your students can observe closely. If there are no trees in your area, try to find one or more cut trees (like old Christmas trees) or a live potted tree to bring inside the classroom. If this is not possible, collect pictures of trees that students can use to make their observations in Step 3. (Try books, calendars, and magazines for good color pictures of trees. Tree posters are usually available from district offices of the U.S. Forest Service, see addresses on page 383.)

Doing the Activity

1. Pass out drawing paper and crayons or markers to the students. Have them draw a picture of a tree from memory. Tell them to save their pictures for later.

2. Explain to the students that they are going to take a closer look at trees and later they will use their observations to draw a new picture of a tree. Ask them to list different features they might look for when they make their observations. You can use the questions below to guide their observation. Depending on the level of your group, you may want to use these questions to create a worksheet for your students to use. Students can take notes or make sketches as they make their observations.

■ What shape is the trunk? Is it tall and straight, or bent and gnarled? Is there only one trunk or do several trunks come out of the ground near the same spot?

■ What color is the tree's bark? How does it feel? How does it look?

■ What shape are the tree's branches? Are there any thorns or other things on the branches or twigs?

■ What shapes are the tree's leaves? What color are they? Where are the leaves on the tree's branches? (only at the tips? all along the branches?) Do leaves grow in groups or singly? How do they feel?

■ Are there any seeds, flowers, fruits, nuts, or cones on the tree?

■ What shape is the tree's crown as a whole? (round, pointy, shapeless, oval?)

■ What other plants or animals live on or in the tree?

3. Take the students outside and have them examine the trees you located in "Getting Ready," or have them examine the tree pictures you collected. (Encourage students to pick a tree that is similar to the one they drew in Step 1.)

NOTE—If you're working with very young children, lead them to one or more trees and examine the trees together. You might also have the children use their bodies to bend and twist like the branches, flutter around like the leaves, stand straight and tall like the trunk, or mimic other characteristics of the trees you examine.

LEVELS
Grades PreK-6

SUBJECTS
Science, Visual Arts, Language Arts

CONCEPT

■ Populations of organisms exhibit variations in size and structure as a result of their adaptation to their habitats. (10.1)

SKILLS
Observing, Comparing and Contrasting, Identifying Attributes and Components, Interpreting

OBJECTIVES
Students will ① describe the overall structure of a tree, and ② describe the structure and function of a tree's principle parts.

MATERIALS
drawing paper, crayons or markers

TIME CONSIDERATIONS
Preparation: 30 minutes

Activity: 50 minutes

4. When the students have finished their observations, have them draw a second tree. Encourage them to include as much detail as they can.

5. Hang each student's pair of drawings (from steps 1 and 4) around the room. Let students walk around as they compare and contrast each pair of drawings. What new details, for example, appeared in the second drawing? Was anyone's second picture radically different from the first? Have students compare and contrast drawings done by different students. What characteristics were similar?

Enrichment

1. Have students make bark or leaf rubbings of the trees they examined. Students can create a new picture of their tree (or add to the one made in Step 4) using rubbings of the tree's parts; attaching actual flowers, nuts, or seeds from their trees; or using parts of the tree such as bark, fruit, or flowers to color their picture by rubbing the parts against the paper so that their natural color comes off.

NOTE—Whenever possible, have students use leaves, seeds, or other tree parts that they find on the ground to make their rubbings, rather than picking those items off the tree. (See Appendix 6 on page 379.)

2. Follow up this activity with related activities that expand your students' knowledge of the structure of trees and will help them make connections between structure and function in trees and other plants.

ASSESSMENT OPPORTUNITY
Use the pictures the students created in Steps 1-4 to assess their conceptual understanding of a tree's structure. Look for the accuracy of how they represented the tree's principle parts. You can also try the "Assessment Opportunity" for "Tree Factory" on page 226.

RELATED ACTIVITIES
Tree Factory, Name That Tree, Looking at Leaves, Bursting Buds, Trees as Habitats, Tree Lifecycle.

Overview
By making a tree costume, your students will gain an awareness of a tree's structure and functions.

Background
See Background for "Tree Factory" on page 223.

Getting Ready
Before you begin, read through the activity and make a sample costume (see diagram on page 220). Cut green tissue paper into two 5-inch (13-cm) squares per student. Cut enough yarn or string into 5-inch (13-cm) lengths so each student will have six.

Doing the Activity
1. Have students make leaf rubbings using white paper and different colored crayons. To do so, they should place four or five leaves (several types) on a flat surface and put white paper over them. They should use the sides of different crayons to rub across each leaf.

2. Have students cut out each leaf rubbing along its outline and punch a hole in it using a pencil or hole puncher. With your help, they should thread a piece of yarn through all the paper leaves and tie the yarn around their heads to make a crown of leaves. Their heads now represent the leafy crowns of trees. Discuss with students how the leaves in the tree's crown soak up sunshine and make food (sugar) for the tree.

3. Give a pre-cut paper bag vest to each student. (Older students may be able to cut their own—see diagram on page 220.) Have each student put on a vest; everyone's body now represents a tree trunk. Discuss how the trunk supports the tree and holds the crown up where the sun can reach it.

4. Tell students to take off their vests and glue bits of bark or crushed cinnamon sticks to the outside of the vest. This represents the bark on the tree's trunk. If actual bark is not available, students can make rubbings of tree bark and glue these to the outside of their vests. After the glue dries, students may put the vests back on. Discuss how bark protects the tree from rain, cold, insects, disease, and sometimes even fire.

5. Give each student two pieces of pre-cut green tissue paper. Tell students that this paper represents the thin layer of growing skin (cambium) that is under the bark. Have them remove their vests again and glue or tape the tissue paper to the inside. Discuss how this tissue layer produces new bark and wood for the tree. Use a fresh twig to demonstrate where the cambium is. Scratching the twig with your thumbnail will reveal the living, often green layer just underneath the bark.

6. Give each student four drinking straws (or pieces of straws) to represent the vessels in the sapwood or xylem (ZEYE-luhm) layer of the tree. Students should tape the straws to the inside of their vests. Explain that the straws represent the tiny vessels (like blood vessels) through which sap travels in the tree.

7. (Optional) Have students look at a cross section of a tree (tree cookie) with magnifying glasses. Have them look for tiny holes in the sapwood. These are the vessels by which sap and water travel. (See "Tree Cross Section" diagram on page 290.)

8. (Optional) Discuss how sap is a blend of sugar and water absorbed by tree roots. Tree sap can be boiled down and thickened to make sweet, sticky syrup. You might want to give students a little maple syrup to taste.

9. Show students a cross-section diagram of a tree's heartwood. (See "Tree Factory" on page 223.) The heartwood is the darker circle of woody layers in

LEVELS
Grades PreK-4

SUBJECTS
Science, Visual Arts, Performing Arts

CONCEPTS
■ Populations of organisms exhibit variations in size and structure as a result of their adaptation to their habitats. (10.1)
■ The structure and scale of an ecosystem are influenced by factors such as soil type, climate, availability of water, and human activities. (10.2)

SKILLS
Ordering and Arranging, Representing, Identifying Attributes and Components

OBJECTIVE
Students will create a tree costume and learn the structure and function of tree parts.

MATERIALS
A variety of (fallen) leaves; small pieces of bark from a fallen or dead tree, or pieces of crushed cinnamon sticks, sawdust, pine shavings, cedar chips (pet stores will have these), or bark mulch from a garden shop; supply of white paper; old crayon pieces; yarn or string; a large, brown paper grocery bag per student; glue; straws; tape; green tissue paper; sawdust, wood chips, or pine shavings; Optional: maple syrup; cross section of tree trunk or branch; twig from live tree; magnifying glasses; white paper towel; glass of water and food coloring

TIME CONSIDERATIONS
Preparation: 30-45 minutes,
Activity: Two 50-minute periods

the center of the trunk. Explain that the function of the heartwood is to support the tree. Point out how darker and lighter rings on the cross section represent new years of growth. People can tell a lot about the tree's history by examining these rings. (See "Tree Cookies" on page 289 for more on reading tree rings.)

10. Pass out sawdust, pine shavings, or cedar chips to the students. Students can smell the wood pieces. Have them glue these pieces to the inside of their vests to represent the sapwood and heartwood.

11. Give each student six 5-inch (13-cm) lengths of yarn or string to represent roots. Ask students to tuck the roots into their socks so their roots dangle onto the ground. Discuss how roots absorb water and nutrients from soil. You might try demonstrating absorption by twisting a piece of white paper towel and dipping its end into a glass of water colored with dye. (You will see colored water travel up the paper towel the way water travels up tree roots.)

12. (Optional) Finally, while the children are dressed in their costumes, ask them to stand together to form a forest. Teach them the "Oh, Learning Tree" song on page 221.

Enrichment
1. While the students are standing together, forming their forest, ask them what they might see as trees in the forest (i.e. plants, animals, people). Ask what kind of relationship they (as trees) have with the things they see. (For example, they provide nuts for squirrels, wood for people, and branches for birds to build their nests on.)

2. Read THE GIVING TREE by Shel Silverstein and discuss what life is from a tree's perspective. You might also read APPLE TREE by Peter Parnell.

END NOTES...

ASSESSMENT OPPORTUNITY
Try the Assessment Opportunity for "Tree Factory" on page 226.

RELATED ACTIVITIES
Tree Factory, The Closer You Look, Bursting Buds, Looking at Leaves, Poet-Tree, Get in Touch with Trees

REFERENCES
Parnell, Peter. APPLE TREE. New York, New York: McMillan, 1987.

Silverstein, Shel. THE GIVING TREE. New York, New York: Harper and Row, 1964.

OH, LEARNING TREE. Song, words and music by Kent Grizzard.

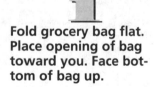

Fold grocery bag flat. Place opening of bag toward you. Face bottom of bag up.

Place a crease in the middle of the bag's bottom. Lift bottom of flap up and fold at crease so that points ✖ meet.

Cut along dashed lines.

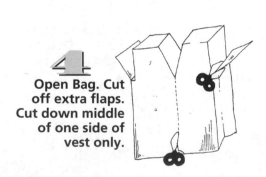

Open Bag. Cut off extra flaps. Cut down middle of one side of vest only.

Now you are ready to decorate and wear your vest.

"OH, LEARNING TREE"

Words and Music by Kent Grizzard

© KENT GRIZZARD, 1989

From the sow-ing of your seed to the fall-ing of your leaves, there's so much that you can teach to me; you are my Learn-ing Tree. Your grace-ful limbs brush the sky, your shade cools the air. thous-and les-sons I can learn from you and with oth-ers I will share.

Oh, Learn-ing Tree, please share with me the se-crets that you know, so I can go and teach the world of how you live and grow. Oh, Learn-ing Tree, I prom-ise you that I will do my best to save the soil and air and the wa-ter which we share. I'll prove to you that

"OH, LEARNING TREE"

Overview
By acting out the parts of a tree, your students will see how a tree works like a factory. Afterward, they can create their own "tree factories."

Background
From a tree's tiny *root* hairs buried in the ground to the highest leaves in its *crown,* each part of a tree plays a role in helping it to function. Here's a rundown of the various parts of a tree and what each one does:

Leaves
Leaves are the food factories of a tree. Using energy from the sun, which they capture with a pigment called *"chlorophyll,"* leaves convert carbon dioxide and water into oxygen and sugar (food!) through the process of *photosynthesis.* The gases needed for and generated by photosynthesis enter and exit through tiny holes called *"stomata,"* on the under surface of the leaves. Water vapor also exits through the stomata in the process of transpiration.

Trunk and Branches
The trunk provides support for branches, which in turn support the tree's leaves. The trunk and branches contain the tree's "pipes"—the tubes that transport water and nutrients to the leaves, and sugar from the leaves to the rest of the tree. They also contain the growing layer of the tree that makes the trunk, branches, and roots of the tree thicker each year. Here's a look at a tree trunk from the inside to the outside and a description of what each layer does: (see diagram below)

a *Heartwood* forms the central core of the tree, is made up of dense dead wood, and provides strength for the tree.

b *Sapwood,* also called the xylem (ZEYE-luhm), brings water and nutrients up from the roots to the leaves; older xylem cells become part of the heartwood.

c *Cambium* (KAM-bee-uhm), a very thin layer of growing tissue, makes cells that become new xylem, phloem, or cambium.

d *Phloem* (FLOW-uhm), also called the inner bark, carries sap (sugar and nutrients dissolved in water) from the leaves to the rest of the tree; at certain times of the year, phloem may also transport stored sugars from the roots up to the rest of the tree (for example, in the springtime, the sap of sugar maples rises from the roots and is tapped by people to make maple syrup).

e *Bark* protects the tree from injury caused by insects and other animals, by other plants, by disease, and by fire; bark characteristics vary from species to species (for example, it may be thin, thick, spongy, rough, smooth, covered with spines, and so on, depending on the type of tree).

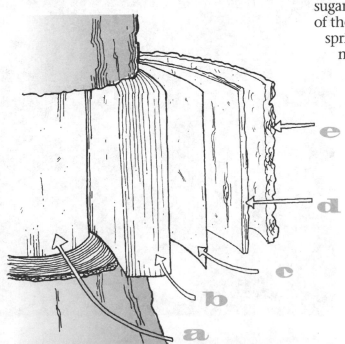

LEVELS
Activity: Grades 3-6
Variation: Grades PreK-2

SUBJECTS
Science, Physical Education, Performing Arts

CONCEPTS
■ Populations of organisms exhibit variations in size and structure as a result of their adaptation to their habitats. (10.1)
■ The structure and scale of an ecosystem are influenced by factors such as soil type, climate, availability of water, and human activities. (10.2)

SKILLS
Ordering and Arranging, Representing, Identifying Attributes and Components, Comprehending

OBJECTIVES
Students will ① describe the general structure of a tree and ② explain how different parts of a tree help the tree function.

MATERIALS
Slips of paper, paper sack, tape (optional), yarn or string, art supplies (see "Assessment Opportunity"), copies of student page 227

TIME CONSIDERATIONS
Preparation: 20 minutes
Activity: 50 minutes

Roots

A tree's roots help anchor the tree in the ground. They also absorb water and nutrients from the soil. Trees have *lateral roots* that spread out from the tree and cover a broad area. Many trees also have a *taproot* that grows straight into the ground. As a tree's taproot and lateral roots grow away from the tree, they branch into finer and finer roots called *rootlets.* The rootlets themselves are, in turn, covered by even finer *root hairs.* These root hairs absorb approximately 95 percent of the water and nutrients absorbed by the tree.

Getting Ready

Activity—Write the following parts of a tree on separate slips of paper and put them in a sack. (We've included enough parts for a group of 30 students. However, you may need to adjust the numbers depending on the size of your group.)

Heartwood	(1)	
Sapwood	(3)	
Taproot	(1)	
Lateral roots	(2)	
Cambium	(5)	
Phloem	(6)	
Bark	(8)	
Leaves	(4)	
Total	=	30 slips of paper

Afterward, make four branches for your tree by cutting yarn or string into four 6-foot (1.8-m) lengths. Then find a large, open area where the students can build the tree. Also make copies of student page 227.

Variation—Find an outside area that has a tree and enough space to allow the students in your group to spread out and sit on the ground.

Doing the Activity

1. Ask the class to think about trees and what they need to survive. (food, water, air, and so on) List the ideas on the chalkboard. When students have completed the list, ask them how the tree gets these things, especially since trees can't move around the way most animals can. For example, ask students how a tree gets the water it needs.

- Where does the water come from?

- How does it get into the tree?

- How does it get around to all parts of the tree?

- How do trees get the food they need?

- How do they keep from blowing over in the wind?

Don't worry about answering all these questions completely at this stage. During the rest of the activity, students will learn the answers to these questions.

2. Use the Background information to answer the questions raised in Step 1.

3. Tell students that they're going to create a tree by acting out the tree parts they just discussed. Have each student pick one slip of paper from the sack (prepared earlier) to find out what role to play in the tree. Take students to an area with lots of space to build the tree.

4. Ask students what makes up the center of the tree and gives the tree strength? (heartwood) The students portraying heartwood should stand in the center of an open area, tighten their muscles, and chant, "I support; I support."

5. Ask students what tree part transports water to all parts of the tree. (sapwood) Have the sapwood students join hands to form a small circle around the heartwood. Have these students chant,

"Gurgle, slurp. Gurgle, slurp. Transport water," as they raise their joined hands up and down.

6. Ask students where the water in the sapwood comes from (it's absorbed by the roots). Then have the taproot sit down with his or her back against the sapwood, and have the lateral roots lie down on the ground with their feet toward the sapwood and their arms and fingers spread out to represent root hairs. Have the roots make sucking noises.

NOTE—Be sure to warn other students not to step on the roots!

7. Ask students where the water in the sapwood travels (to the leaves). Then have the heartwood hold the ends of the four pieces of yarn or string that you cut earlier. Give the other end of each piece to a different student who represents leaves. Ask the leaves what they do all day (make food through photosynthesis). Have the leaves flutter their hands and chant, "We make food; we make food."

8. Ask the leaves what happens to all the food they make using sunlight, air, and water. (It gets transported to the rest of the tree.) Ask everyone what part of the tree transports the food from the leaves to the rest of the tree. (phloem) Have the phloem students join hands and form a large circle around the tree. Then have them simulate the role of the phloem by reaching above their heads and grabbing (for food), and then squatting and opening their hands (releasing the food) while chanting, "Food to the tree!"

9. Ask students if they've left out an important part of the tree. What layer produces new sapwood and phloem to keep the tree growing and healthy. (cambium) Have the cambium students form a circle between the phloem and the sapwood. Tell them to sway from side to side and chant, "New phloem, sapwood, and cambium. New phloem, sapwood, and cambium."

10. Ask students what final component of their tree is missing—it's something that protects the tree. (bark) Have the bark students lock arms and form a circle that faces out from the center of the tree. Ask them to look tough. Have them march in place chanting, "We are bark. Please keep out."

11. When the tree is completely assembled, have all students act out and chant their parts simultaneously. If you want, you can end the session by telling the students their tree is old and falls over. Let everyone carefully fall down.

VARIATION—FOR YOUNGER STUDENTS

1. Ask students to name things that living things need to survive (sun, air, water, food, space, and so on). List their ideas on a chalkboard. They will now go outside and find out how members of one group of living things (trees) get the things they need to survive.

2. Take students outside and have them sit down around a tree. Ask how trees get the water they need.

■ Where does the water come from? (rain, snowmelt, groundwater)

■ How does it get into the tree? (It's absorbed by the roots.)

■ How does it get around to all parts of the tree? (Tiny "pipes" in the sapwood carry water to the trunk, branches, and leaves.)

As the students discuss each question, have them act out the answers. For example, they can simulate rain falling by patting their hands on their legs or the ground, they can simulate roots by lying on their backs with their arms and legs spread out as they make slurping sounds, and they can simulate sapwood chanting, "Gurgle, gurgle, gurgle. Water to the tree."

3. Next, ask students where trees get the food they need to survive. Do they chase after animals? Grab things with their branches? (No! They make their own food in their leaves by using energy from the sun.) Then have the students imitate how the leaves make food. Have them hold their arms up and alternately curl and straighten their fingers ("leaves") while chanting, "Making food, making food." Afterward, explain that the leaves also "breathe" by taking in gases from the air and releasing other gases through tiny holes in their under-sides (stomata). You might pass around some leaves and magnifying glasses so students can look for these holes.

4. Have students stand up and wrap their arms around the trunk of the tree. What does the trunk do for the tree? (It provides strength, supports the branches and leaves, and contains all the "pipes" that transport water and food around the tree.) Then have the students act out the trunk of the tree by standing straight and tall and by looking strong.

5. Have students feel the bark of a tree and describe what it feels and looks like. Then ask them how bark might be useful to a tree. (protects it from pests and disease) Have students act out the role of bark by holding hands and forming a circle with all students facing out from the center. While they still hold hands, have them chant, "We're the bark. Insects, keep out!"

6. Have students look for seeds, fruits, nuts, or cones on the tree. Ask them what these parts of the trees do. (produce new trees) Then have them act out a seed growing into a tree by scrunching down into a ball (the seed) and then slowly straightening up until their arms are raised over their heads.

7. Ask students what keeps the tree from blowing over. (roots) Then divide the group into two parts. Have all students lie down with their arms and legs spread out, and have one group make slurping sounds (to simulate the roots absorbing water) while the other group chants: "Stay in place. Stay in place" (to express how roots anchor the tree).

8. Finally, call students together to build a model tree. Divide the students into three groups. One group, the roots, should stand close together with their arms entwined and chant, "Gurgle, gurgle, gurgle. Water to the tree." The next group, the bark, should make a circle around the roots, join hands, and chant, "We're the bark! Insects, keep out." Members of the last group, the leaves, should stand at various distances around the bark and chant, "Making food, making food" while flexing their fingers.

Enrichment

1. Have the students take a look at cross sections of a tree (tree cookie) and identify the heartwood, sapwood, phloem, and bark. You may also want to do the activity "Tree Cookies" on page 289.

2. Ask students how a tree is similar to a factory. (It takes sunlight, air, and water; and manufactures leaves, fruits, nuts, and flowers.) What different departments are in a "tree factory," and what jobs are done by each? (In the "roots department" the tree gets anchored to the ground and water is absorbed from the soil, and so on.) Have students draw a cut-away diagram of a tree factory in which you can see the jobs that get done by each department.

3. After exploring how a tree works, have your students consider how they benefit from trees. Give each student a blank piece of paper; have each draw a small tree in the center. Have students draw eight lines radiating from the tree like the spokes of a wheel. On each line, have them write the name of something the tree gives to them (beauty, shade, protection from wind, furniture, pencils, paper, apples, something to play on).

END NOTES...

ASSESSMENT OPPORTUNITY

1. Pass out art supplies, such as drawing paper, scissors, construction paper, toilet paper rolls, straws, aluminum foil, scissors, and tissue paper. Tell students to create a model of a tree. Explain that they should include and label all tree parts they've learned about and be able to explain what each part does. They may explain orally, or create labels that give these explanations. Encourage them to be as creative as possible while still being accurate.

2. For younger students, pass out copies of "Living Labels" student page 227 to pairs of students. Explain that the sheet is like a talking book, but without electronics. Instead, each student will do the talking when one of the buttons on the bottom is pressed. Depending on the level of your group, you may want to go over each of the words on the buttons below the drawing. Explain that each partner should take turns pressing the buttons on the bottom. Each time a student presses a button, the partner must point to the corresponding part of the tree and explain how it helps the tree survive.

RELATED ACTIVITIES

The Closer You Look, Bursting Buds, Looking at Leaves, How Plants Grow, Soil Stories, Trees in Trouble, To Be a Tree

REFERENCES

Adapted in part from: Cornell, Joseph. *SHARING THE JOY OF NATURE*. Nevada City, CA: Dawn Publications.

LIVING LABELS

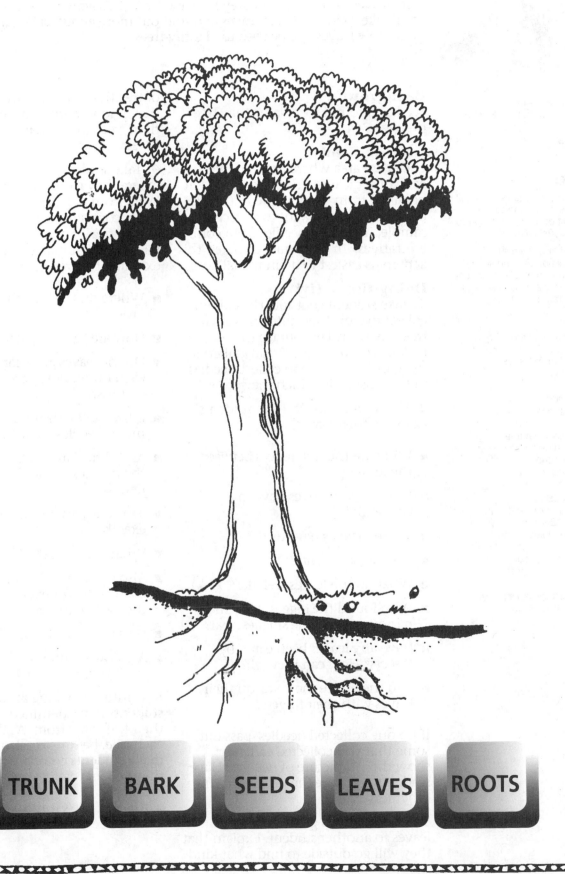

TRUNK   BARK   SEEDS   LEAVES   ROOTS

Overview
Are leaves ever hairy? Do they have teeth? In this activity, your students will take a closer look at leaves and find out more about leaf characteristics and how leaves can be used to identify trees.

LEVELS
Activity: Grades K–4
Enrichment: Grades PreK–8

SUBJECTS
Science, Visual Arts

CONCEPTS
■ Populations of organisms exhibit variations in size and structure as a result of their adaptation to their habitats. (10.1)
■ Biological diversity results from the interaction of living and non-living environmental components such as air, water, climate, and geologic features. (1.1)

SKILLS
Comparing and Contrasting, Classifying and Categorizing, Identifying Attributes and Components

OBJECTIVES
Students will ① describe how leaf shapes, sizes, and other characteristics vary from tree to tree and ② explain how particular types of trees can be identified by their leaves.

MATERIALS
Tree leaves, pencils, leaf print supplies for "Enrichment" (Types will vary depending on print method used; see various "Enrichment" activities.), copies of student page 231 (for assessment),

TIME CONSIDERATIONS
Preparation: 20 minutes
Activity: 50 minutes

Background
See Background for "Name that Tree" on page 244.

Getting Ready
Locate an area where the students can collect leaves (from the ground, if possible) from several different kinds of trees. You may want to collect a sample, including needles from coniferous trees. In temperate climates, this activity is easiest to do in the fall.

Doing the Activity
1. Take students outside. Have them collect two or three different kinds of tree leaves, and encourage them to pick leaves that have already fallen to the ground. Be sure to collect needles in the clusters in which they grow.

2. When back inside, have students examine their leaves.

■ What are the differences between the leaves?

■ What do the leaves have in common?

■ Do any leaves have teeth?

■ Do any have hairs?

■ What do the leaves feel like?

■ Who found the biggest leaf? the narrowest leaf? the smallest leaf?

■ Have any leaves been eaten by insects? How can they tell?

■ Can they trace the veins on their leaves with their fingers?

If no one collected needles, pass out some that you collected earlier or show them a picture of needles. Have students compare the needles to the other leaves.

3. Have students give one of their leaves to another student. Explain that they will go outside to find what kind of tree that leaf came from. How will they know when they've found the right tree? (It will have the same kind of leaves.)

4. Take students back to the same trees where they gathered leaves in Step 1. Walk from tree to tree, and have students compare their leaves with leaves on the tree. If one or more students has a leaf that matches a tree, stop and examine the tree more closely.

■ Where on the branch do leaves grow?

■ How are they attached?

■ Do the leaves grow far apart from each other, close together, or in clumps?

■ If the leaves are needle-like, how many needles are in each cluster?

■ Are all the clusters the same? Are all the needles in the cluster the same length?

■ Do all leaves on the tree match exactly?

■ What color are the leaves?

■ Also examine other characteristics of the tree. For example, what is the bark of the tree like?

■ What color is the bark?

■ Are flowers, nuts, or fruit on the tree? What do they look like?

5. Continue looking at trees until all students have identified the tree that their leaf came from. As they examine each tree, be sure to ask questions to make students compare trees that they've looked at. For example, ask:

■ Are this tree's leaves larger or smaller than the last tree's leaves?

- This tree's leaves grow in a clump. Have we looked at any other trees that have leaves which grow in a clump?

- What's similar or different about these two trees?

Enrichment—Leaf Art

Have students use the leaves they collected in Step 1 of "Doing the Activity" to create their own prints. Here are four "leafy" ideas for you to try, depending on the age of your students and the amount of time available.

Leaf Crayon Rubbings

Materials

Dark-colored crayons, plain drawing paper

Directions

Set the leaf on a smooth surface, preferably vein-side up; then cover it with a plain piece of paper. Rub a crayon sideways back and forth across the paper above the leaf. The margin of the leaf as well as its veins should begin to show on the paper as you rub gently.

Spatter Prints

Materials

9" x 12" (23 cm - 30 cm) wire, plastic, or nylon net screen; toothbrush; straight pins; tempera paint; paper

Directions

Place a leaf on a sheet of paper and secure it with pins. Then place the screen over the leaf and paint across the screen using a toothbrush. Afterward, lift off the screen, unpin the leaf, and carefully lift the leaf away.

Pressed Leaves

Materials

Iron, towel, wax paper

Directions

Place a leaf between two layers of wax paper and then cover with a towel. Press the towel with a warm iron, being sure to iron over the entire area of wax paper. (This will seal the leaf between the two layers of wax paper.) Afterward, you can cut out each leaf, leaving a narrow margin of wax paper around the entire edge of the leaf. Then you can punch holes through the wax paper at the top margin of the leaf and hang the pressed leaf. Use several leaves to make a hanging leaf mobile.

Leaf Print T-Shirts

Materials

Clean, poly-cotton-blend T-shirt; acrylic paints; paintbrush; piece of cardboard; wax paper; paper towels

Directions

Place the shirt on a clean, flat surface; then slide the cardboard between the front and back of the shirt to keep paint from soaking through. Place a leaf on a sheet of wax paper and coat it with a thin layer of paint. Make sure your fingers are clean; then carefully lift the painted leaf up and place it (painted side down) on the shirt. Cover the leaf with a paper towel and press it down. Lift the leaf straight off the shirt. Make as many more leaf prints on the shirt as you would like; then hang the shirt to dry.

NOTE—Do not use fabric softeners to clean or dry your shirt before you start printing. Also, to help make the prints last longer, rinse the finished shirt in a mild water and vinegar solution before washing it for the first time.

Cherokee Leaf Printing

Materials

A medium-sized, flat-headed hammer (a flat rock will also work); masking tape; a large, flat board; a supply of newspapers; wax paper; pieces of white cloth or clothing to print on (100% cotton or unbleached muslin works best); leaves from marigolds, tulip poplars, red or white oaks; carrot tops; strawberries.

Directions

The idea is to transfer the natural dyes from a leaf to a fabric, while retaining the design of the original leaf. Do this by beating the leaf's chlorophyll directly into the cloth, which will set the dye through natural chemical action. Use this technique to decorate any natural cloth surface such as table cloths, curtains, wall hangings, T-shirts, handkerchiefs, and headbands. Lay several thicknesses of newspaper on a flat board. Spread your cloth, right side up, on top of the newspaper. Put leaves on the cloth in a pattern of your choice. Place wax paper over the leaves and tape it around the edges. Use a hammer to pound the leaf until the color transfers to the cloth. Pound evenly for a good print. If the leaf does not print evenly, crumple up another leaf, dip it water, and use it to "paint" the unstained spots. The dyes from the leaves must be set into the fabric to resist fading. This process also affects the color. For bright colors, soak the fabric in a solution of 3 tablespoons (44 ml) of ferrous sulfate per gallon (3.8 liter) of water for 1-2 minutes (or use the same solution of alum for a less-brilliant color set). For rich, reddish-brown hues, use a solution of 1 cup (240 ml) wood ashes to 3 gallons (11.3 l) of cold water for 5 minutes. Rinse the fabric in clean water, and air dry it away from direct sunlight. To help retain the natural colors, you can soak the finished piece in 1/2 cup (120 ml) of salt to 2 gallons (7.5 l) of water for 10 minutes [or in a solution of 3 tablespoons (44 ml) of baking soda to 1 gallon (3.8 l) of water]. Rinse and dry as directed above.

Leaf Batik
Materials:
100% cotton cloth squares, pencils or pens, yellow and/or orange fabric dye, red and/or brown dye, household paraffin, hot plate, heavy saucepan, metal spoons, natural bristle paintbrushes, large glass or metal bowls, clothesline and clothespin, leaves for tracing patterns, newspaper, glass cups or dishes for melted paraffin, iron, rubber gloves for students and adults.

Directions
Trace a leaf pattern onto a cloth square with pencil or pen. Using yellow and/or orange dyes only, dip each square in dye. Hang squares on the clothesline to dry. After they have dried, "paint" the leaf shape on the cloth with melted paraffin, filling in the outline of the leaf you have traced. Constantly reheat the paraffin; if it is not sufficiently heated, it will turn white (cool) immediately after being painted onto the fabric and will not protect the fibers from receiving the final dye color. Ask students what they think will happen when they dip the cloth into the next colors of dye. (The dye will affect only those areas not covered by the paraffin.) Crumple the prepared cloth, then dip it into the red and/or brown dye(s). Hang the cloth on the clothesline to dry. When it is dry, iron the cloth between layers of newspaper. Change the paper when it becomes saturated with paraffin. When no more paraffin melts onto the paper, the batik is finished. You might display the finished squares of cloth as a quilt.

END NOTES...

ASSESSMENT OPPORTUNITY
Pass out a copy of page 231 to all students, and tell them that they have to identify which tree each leaf on the right side of the page came from. Explain that they should use the tree drawings on the left side of the page to make identifications. As they identify the leaves, have students draw a line from leaf to tree and then copy the tree name onto the line next to the leaf. Afterward, have students explain how they identified each leaf.

RELATED ACTIVITIES
Name That Tree, The Closer You Look, Bursting Buds, The Shape of Things, Adopt a Tree

A LOOK AT LEAVES

SASSAFRAS

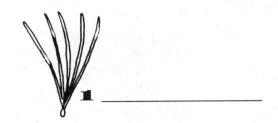

1 _____

SWEET GUM

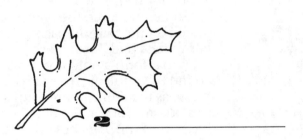

2 _____

PIN OAK

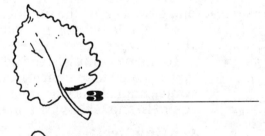

3 _____

WHITE PINE

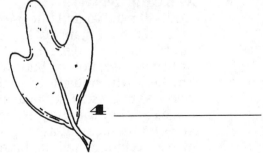

4 _____

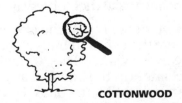

COTTONWOOD

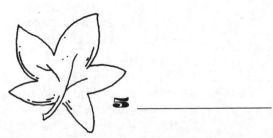

5 _____

Overview
In early spring, the tiny, bright green leaves of many trees burst forth. Where do the leaves come from? How do they form? In this activity, your students will find the answers to these questions on their own by observing tree buds throughout the year.

LEVELS
Grades K-6

SUBJECTS
Science, Visual Arts

CONCEPTS
■ Populations of organisms exhibit variations in size and structure as a result of their adaptation to their habitats. (10.1)

■ While every organism goes through a life cycle of growth, maturity, decline, and death, its role in the ecosystem also changes. (13.3)

SKILLS
Observing, Ordering and Arranging, Identifying Attributes and Components, Concluding

OBJECTIVES
Students will ① explain the purpose of a tree's buds and their relationship to the leaves and ② describe the stages that buds go through as the leaves develop throughout the year.

MATERIALS
Trees (preferably deciduous) with branches low enough for the students to be able to look closely at them, paper and pencils

TIME CONSIDERATIONS
Preparation: 20 minutes

Activity: Three to four 30-minute periods spread out over the school year, particularly in the fall and spring.

NOTE—This activity includes observing a tree or shrub every few months throughout the year. In temperate climates, this observation begins in the fall.

Background
By the time a tree's leaves drop in the fall, its leaves for the next spring are already formed. Tiny leaves, stems, and sometimes even the flowers are located on the twigs in packages called ***buds.*** These buds are made of tough scales that form a waterproof case around the miniature tree parts. In spring, as the temperature warms and days become longer, sap rises from the roots to the branches; the scales fall off the buds; and the tree's leaves, stems, and flowers begin to unfurl and grow. During the summer, the tree begins to develop new buds for the following year.

For many animals, tree buds are a concentrated food source. During the winter, animals such as grouse, deer, squirrels, and rabbits feast on buds.

Getting Ready
You will need to find one or more trees that have branches low enough for the students to see them. Shrubs will work also, but the buds will be smaller. If the students have already adopted trees (see "Adopt a Tree" on page 65), they can use their adopted trees for this activity, as long as the tree is deciduous and has branches low enough for the students to study. Copy the diagram on page 233 on to a large sheet of paper.

Doing the Activity
1. In late fall, after trees have lost their leaves, ask the students whether the trees will be leafless forever. (Students should realize that the trees will sprout new leaves in the spring.) Ask them where the new leaves will come from? (buds) When are buds formed? (Usually the previous summer.)

Are there buds on the tree? (Yes, if it's the fall.) Encourage students to share their ideas.

2. Take the students outside to look closely at tree branches. Hold a branch down so that the students can examine the tree's buds. Have the students point out different features they notice on the branch. (bark pattern, leaf scars, buds, thorns, etc.) Then use your fingernail or pocketknife to split a bud in half lengthwise to reveal the tiny leaves tucked inside. Ask the students to describe what they see.

3. Show students the twig diagram you made in Getting Ready. Go over the diagram, identifying the different parts of the twig.

4. Explain that they are going to observe buds over a long period of time. Have each student choose a live twig to examine. (If students have already adopted trees, you may want to have them use their adopted trees for this activity.) Tell students to take notes about what their twig and its buds look like. Older students should try to identify the different parts of the twig: buds, terminal bud (not every tree has one), leaf scars, and ring of terminal bud scars (bud scale scars). All students should draw a picture of the twig and a close-up of one or more of its buds. You may also have the students mark the twigs with flagging tape or some other marker so that they can return to the same twig each time they make their observations.

5. Have students visit the tree and observe the twig and buds at least once in the winter. They should look for changes in the bud and any signs of animals eating the buds. Have them make notes and draw pictures of what they see.

6. Have students visit their trees again several times in the spring and record their observations during each visit.

Enrichment

1. In early spring, have the students bring in small twigs. Make cross sections (both length and width) of a few buds on each twig and have students compare the buds of different trees. (use magnifying glasses if possible.)

2. In early spring, before the buds have opened, bring in some branches of one or more flowering trees, such as apple, dogwood, maple, oak, etc. Place the branches in water and observe them for several days. What happens? Ask students why the buds on these branches open before the buds on the same kinds of trees outside. (You may want to have older students collect small twigs from a tree and design a simple experiment to test their theories.)

3. Students can cut one bud off their "observation" tree every one or two months between fall and spring. These buds should be quickly frozen or dried to stop their growth. Buds can be arranged chronologically and mounted on poster board as an exhibit.

NOTE—For the sake of the tree's health, each student should use a different tree and take buds off different twigs.

END NOTES...

ASSESSMENT OPPORTUNITY
Have students assemble their collection of drawings and observations into a notebook. Then, at the end of their notebooks, have them create a pictorial representation or write a description of how buds change into leaves.

RELATED ACTIVITIES
Adopt a Tree, Name That Tree, Looking at Leaves, Tree Lifecycles

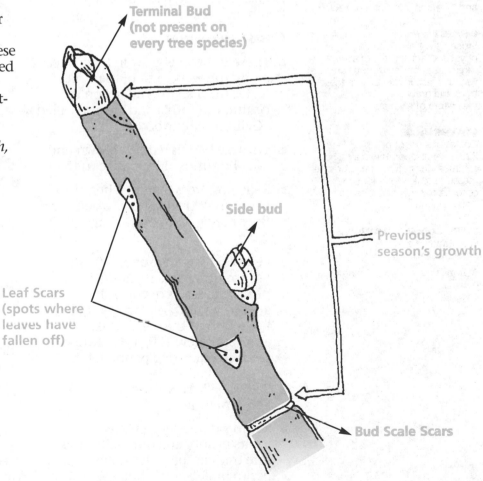

Terminal Bud
(not present on
every tree species)

Side bud

Previous
season's growth

Leaf Scars
(spots where
leaves have
fallen off)

Bud Scale Scars

Overview
In this activity, students can sharpen their math skills by comparing their local trees to the world's tallest tree, the coast redwood, and to the tree with the largest seeds, the coconut palm.

LEVELS
Grades 4-6

SUBJECTS
Science, Math

CONCEPTS
■ Populations of organisms exhibit variations in size and structure as a result of their adaptation to their habitats. (10.1)

■ While every organism goes through a life cycle of growth, maturity, decline, and death, its role in the ecosystem also changes. (13.3)

SKILLS
Comparing and Contrasting, Concluding, Identifying Attributes and Components, Solving Problems

OBJECTIVES
Students will ① measure certain physical characteristics of at least three different trees and ② compare various measurements from these trees and draw conclusions about the nature of each tree.

MATERIALS
Copies of student pages 237 and 238, several laboratory scales, pencils, measuring sticks, string or tape measures, calculators (optional), a coconut or other edible seeds or nuts (optional).

TIME CONSIDERATIONS
Preparation: Several days to gather different seeds

Activity: One or two 50-minute periods

Background
A seed is simply a fertilized plant egg. In scientific terms, it is a mature ovule (egg) that contains an embryo (baby plant) and nutritive tissue (plant food), which is enclosed in layers of protective tissue or a seed coat (egg covering). Under suitable conditions, the seed is capable of sprouting and developing into a plant. In many plants, seeds are enclosed in fleshy tissue known as fruits. (For more background on fruits and seeds, see "Have Seeds, Will Travel" on page 139 and "Pass the Plants, Please" on page 50.) This activity focuses on two tree species:

Coast Redwood

■ These redwoods grow in foggy areas along the west coast of the United States from southern Oregon to central California and are also called "California redwoods."

■ The tree bark is reddish brown and may be almost 1 foot (30 cm) thick.

■ Redwood trees mature when they're between 400 and 500 years old, and they may live for more than 2,000 years.

■ Redwood seeds are about .08 inch (2 mm) long and are packed underneath the scales of cones. Ripe seeds are brown and have wings equal to the width of the seed. It takes approximately 100,000 redwood seeds to equal one pound (.45 kg).

■ Redwood leaves are less than 1 inch (2.5 cm) long.

■ Redwood lumber is highly valued for its beauty and durability, and one tree can provide enough lumber to build several houses.

■ Virgin stands of these trees are protected in California's Redwood National Park, along the Redwood Highway, and in several state parks.

Coconut Palm

■ These trees grow in tropical and subtropical regions throughout the world.

■ They have long, compound (pinnate) leaves and no branches; their leaves grow directly out of the top of the trunk.

■ Coconut palm seeds, or coconuts, are round. On the inside, coconuts have white "meat" (nutritive tissue) and on the outside, they are covered by a brown shell (seed coat). These seeds are about 6 inches (15 cm) in diameter and are covered by a thick, fibrous, green husk.

■ Coconuts, the tree's fruit, can float in the ocean for months without being damaged.

■ One coconut palm can produce as many as 100 coconuts each year.

■ Many products are made from coconut palms. For example, palm fronds (leaves) are woven into baskets, mats, and other products and coconuts are pressed for oil or dried and shredded for use in cooking.

Getting Ready
In this activity, students can use their trees from "Adopt a Tree" on page 65. If they have not adopted trees, you should find trees they can use for this activity. Most measurements the students will make are simple. However, you should see "How Big Is Your Tree?" on page 239 for instructions on how to measure a tree's height. And you may want to try "Name That Tree" on page 244 so that the students can learn how to identify trees before beginning this activity. For younger students, you might skip measuring

the height of their tree. You may also need to help them with math problems.

Doing the Activity

1. On a chalkboard, draw a simple picture of a coast redwood (see diagram on page 237). Point to the drawing and tell students that the tallest tree in the world is a coast redwood that stands 367 feet (112 m) tall, as tall as a 33-story building. It has a 42.5 ft (13 m) circumference. Ask the students to draw or show with their hands how big a seed they think this giant grew from. Ask them to share why they think the tree's seeds are that size. (Some students may think a big tree must come from a big seed.) Next to your drawing of the redwood, draw a simple picture of a coconut palm. The tree should be drawn to the same scale as the redwood (less than 1/3 the redwood's height—see diagram on page 237.) Explain that coconut trees grow to a maximum height of about 100 feet (30 m), or 9 stories and a maximum circumference of 6 feet (1.8 m).

2. On a chalkboard, draw a life-sized picture of a redwood seed (about .08 inch or 2 mm long). Tell students that the seeds of coast redwood trees are so small that you it would take about 100,000 of them to weigh just 1 pound (.45 kg)! Next, draw a picture of a coconut (see diagram on page 237) and tell students that each of these fruits contains a single seed that may be more than 6 inches (15 cm) long and weigh over 2 pounds (0.9 kg)!

3. Ask students what's inside a coconut. If possible, bring in a coconut and pass it around. Some students will know that it contains white "meat" and "milk" that are used as food. You can break the coconut into pieces or give each student a little bit of shredded coconut to taste. Tell them it's high-energy food. Ask if there are other seeds that people or animals like to eat. (sunflower, sesame, acorn, cashew) Why are these seeds such a high energy food? (See the definition of seed in Background; explain that the plant embryo needs a food source

until it grows big enough to make its own.) Why might a coconut need a large food supply? (To improve its chances for survival) Ask students to compare the reproduction strategy of the redwood to that of the coconut palm. (The coconut palm produces relatively few seeds but each has a large food supply to ensure survival, while the redwood produces many seeds but each has less food and less of a chance of surviving.)

4. Give a copy of page 238 to each student. Have each student use a local tree to complete the top half of the sheet. Students will use the data they collect to do the problems at the bottom of the page. If students have adopted trees (see "Adopt a Tree" on page 65), they should use their adopted trees to fill out the top part of their sheets.

NOTE—You may want to have the students work in small groups.

5. Give the students a few minutes to plan their data-collecting strategy. Then, take them outside and let them begin.

6. Invite the students back inside and give them time to do the calculations at the bottom of the page. Have students share their results. Afterward, through discussion, have them consider how the seeds of their trees, like the redwood and the coconut palm, might be specially structured for their own reproductive needs.

Enrichment

1. A good follow-up to this activity is "Have Seeds, Will Travel" on page 139.

2. You can also have students solve additional math problems by using the data they collected. For example, they can ① calculate the diameters of all three trees (redwood, coconut palm, and their own tree), because they know the circumferences (circumference = π(3.14) diameter); ② figure how many palm fronds it would take to equal the height of the coast redwood or their own tree; ③ estimate how many coast redwood needles it would take to equal the length of one palm frond; etc.

3. Students can plant and sprout some of the seeds they brought in during the assessment activity. They can graph how long it would take the different seeds to sprout from the time each was planted. They can also graph the growth of new plants from week to week. They should soak seeds overnight before planting. Seeds that have been cooked or roasted will not sprout.

END NOTES...

ASSESSMENT OPPORTUNITY

Gallery of Seedy Characters

Here's a creative way to assess your students' understanding of seed structure and function. Have students bring in seeds of various sizes, shapes, and functions. For example, a walnut (large, fleshy seed with a hard shell) or a maple samara (small seed with a stiff seed coat shaped like a wing for fluttering in the wind). With the students' help, make a list on the chalkboard of other types of seeds. Have each student select and study one or more seeds, and then create fictional character profiles such as this:

Name: Wally Walnut

Nickname: "The Nut"

Height: 2" (5 cm) diameter

Weight: .5 oz (14 g)

Features: large, oily seed wearing a hard, tan shell, and a green husk

Mission: Jump from a walnut tree, bounce to a suitable growing place, and begin growing into a plant before being eaten by an animal

Last Seen: Supermarket shelf

RELATED ACTIVITIES

Adopt a Tree; Have Seeds, Will Travel; Pass the Plants, Please; How Big Is Your Tree? Looking at Leaves

REFERENCES

TEACHERS GUIDE TO THE NORTH GROVE. Arnold, CA: Calaveras Big Trees Association, 1990

ANSWERS TO GIANT COMPARISONS

ANSWERS TO THE PROBLEMS WILL VARY DEPENDING ON THE DATA THE STUDENTS COLLECTED. HERE'S HOW THE PROBLEMS SHOULD BE SET UP:

1. $\dfrac{\text{weight of tree's seed}}{\text{weight of redwood seed}} = \dfrac{\text{weight of tree's seed}}{.00001 \text{ lb } (.0000045 \text{ kg})} = \text{answer}$

2. $\dfrac{\text{weight of coconut seed}}{\text{weight of tree's seed}} = \dfrac{2 \text{ lbs } (0.9 \text{ kg})}{\text{weight of tree's seed}} = \text{answer}$

3. $\dfrac{\text{length of longer leaf}}{\text{length of shorter leaf}} = \text{answer}$

4. $\dfrac{\text{length of longer leaf}}{\text{length of shorter leaf}} = \text{answer}$

5. $\dfrac{\text{height of redwood}}{\text{height of tree}} = \dfrac{367 \text{ feet } (112 \text{ m})}{\text{height of tree}} = \text{answer}$

6. $\dfrac{\text{circumference of redwood}}{\text{length of armspan}} = \dfrac{42 \text{ feet } 6 \text{ inches } (13 \text{ m})}{\text{length of armspan}} = \text{answer}$

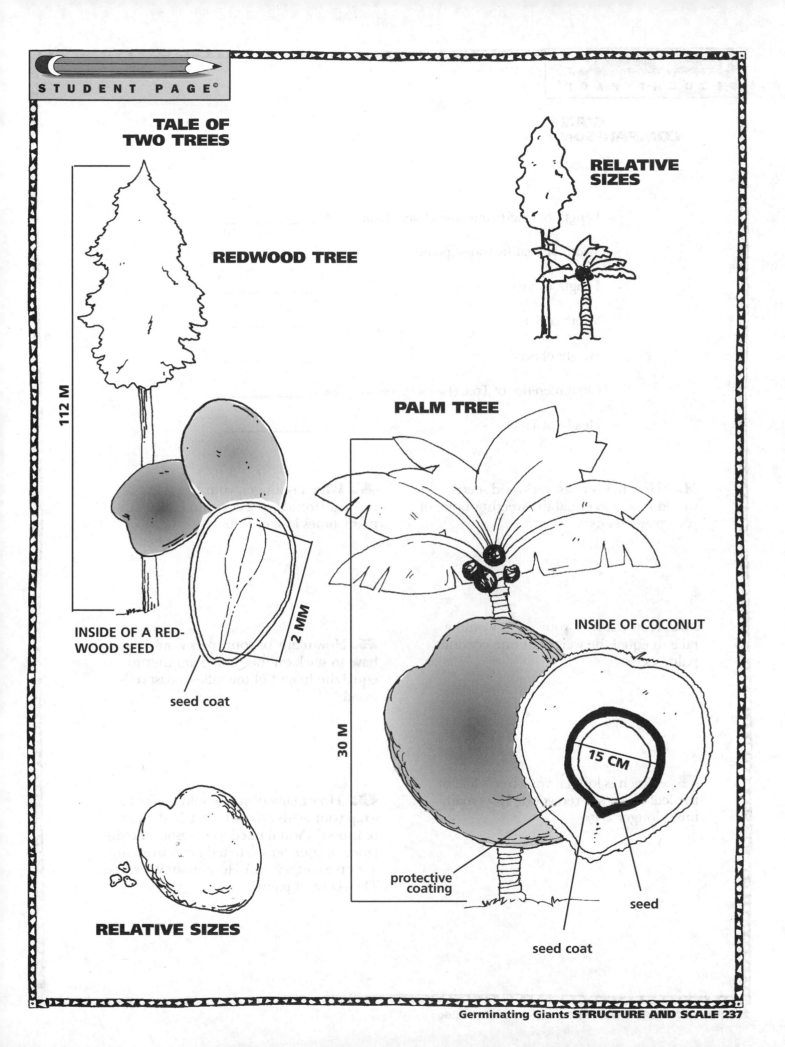

TALE OF
TWO TREES

RELATIVE
SIZES

REDWOOD TREE

112 M

PALM TREE

INSIDE OF A RED-
WOOD SEED

2 MM

seed coat

INSIDE OF COCONUT

30 M

15 CM

protective
coating

seed

seed coat

RELATIVE SIZES

GIANT COMPARISONS

Length of Leaf (from base of stem to tip) _____

Width of Leaf (at widest point) _____

Length of Seed _____

Width of Seed _____

Weight of Seed _____

Circumference of Tree (4 feet or 1.2 m from the ground) _____

Height of Tree _____

1. How many coast redwood seeds would it take to equal the weight of one of your tree's seeds?

2. How many of your seeds would it take to equal the weight of one coconut palm seed?

3. Which is longer, your tree's leaf or the leaf of a coast redwood? How many times longer is it?

4. Which is longer, your tree's leaf or the leaf (frond) of a coconut palm? How many times longer is it?

5. How many of your trees would you have to stack on top of one another to equal the height of the tallest coast redwood?

6. How many of you would it take to wrap your arms around the tallest coast redwood? (You'll need to measure the distance of your outstretched arms from finger tip to finger tip.) How about your tree? The coconut palm?

Overview
Trees come in various shapes and sizes. In this activity, students will measure trees in different ways and become familiar with the tree's structure. They will also learn the importance of standard units of measure and measuring techniques.

Background

Take a walk through your neighborhood to look closely at the trees. You may notice an assortment of sizes, shapes, colors, and textures. Some tree species such as firs tend to be tall and straight with relatively short branches. Other species such as Japanese maples tend to be shorter with long and broad branches.

An experienced *forester* or *arborist* may be able to judge the age of a tree simply by looking at its diameter and location. The growth rate of trees depends on the species and environmental conditions.

The world's most massive (not necessarily tallest) tree is the giant Sequoia (Sequoiadendron giganteum), which lives in scattered groves in central California. This species can grow more than 250 feet (76 m) tall and more than 20 feet (6 m) in diameter. It is also among the world's oldest trees: some Sequoias are more than 3,000 years old!

Foresters measure trees to plan harvesting and to make other forest management decisions. To determine the approximate timber yield of a stand of trees, foresters do a "timber cruise" in which they calculate the volume of lumber in a given area, examine the health of the forest, and survey the species found there. This information is used to determine how the forest should be cared for and what the economic feasibility of a harvest should be. Volume of wood can be measured in board feet [a piece of lumber 12 inches square (77 sq cm) and 1 inch (2.5 cm) thick], cords (a stack of logs 4 ft x 4 ft x 8 ft or 1.2 m x 1.2 m x 2.4 m), cubic feet or cubic meters. One giant Sequoia could yield more than 500,000 board feet, enough to make 33 houses!

Getting Ready
Before doing this activity, select a tree or trees for students to measure. For older students, the tree ideally should be in an open area so that students can measure its shadow. If students have already adopted a tree, have them use their adopted tree for this activity. Make copies of student page 243.

Doing the Activity
1. Briefly tell the students about a time you measured an object to find out something (for example, measuring a window to learn how much curtain fabric you needed to buy, or measuring your waist for a pair of pants). Ask them to think of a time when they measured something. Have them think about what they measured, how they measured it, why they measured it, and what they learned from measuring it. Have the students share their thoughts with a partner. Ask the class to come up with some general statements about why people measure things. In what ways do they measure?

2. Explain to the students that people in early times used their own bodies (hand spans, for instance) to measure things. Divide the students into pairs or small groups, and ask them to measure identical objects in the classroom (like desks) using different parts of their bodies: foot, hand span, arm span, length of a finger, or walking paces. Have them record their findings on scratch paper.

3. Talk with the students about the accuracy of each type of measurement. For example, "When Eric measured the desk, he found it to be 10 hand spans, but when Maria measured it, she found it to be 9 hand spans. Why did Eric and Maria get different measurements?"

If students do not make the connection between hand size and the number of hand spans needed, have those who came up with very different measurements compare the size of their hands. Compare the number of spans counted by students with large hands to the number counted by students with smaller hands. Ask students how they can be sure the measurement of their desks is consistent. (Use the same person or use a standard measure like a ruler.)

4. If necessary, have pairs or small groups of students practice using rulers.

5. Ask students why a person might want to measure a tree. After students have suggested their ideas, you may share how and why foresters measure trees. (See Background.)

6. Take students outside to measure their adopted tree or another tree you have chosen. Take large sheets of paper and marking pens for recording the class's measurements.

7. Ask students to estimate the circumference of the tree's trunk (in inches or centimeters) and then measure it in arm spans (wrapping arms around the trunk) or hand spans (for small trunks). Record the class' estimates on the butcher paper. Then have students measure the circumference using a piece of string and a metric ruler or yardstick, or a tape measure. Record their measurements on the chart. Have students compare their actual measurement to their estimate, and the standard measurement to their personal measurement (arm or hand spans).

8. Foresters always measure the diameter of a tree at 4.5 feet (1.4 m) above the ground. This measurement is called "Diameter at Breast Height" (DBH). To see why this is an important measurement standard, have students measure the circumference of the tree at 1 foot (.3 m), 2 feet (.6 m), and 4.5 feet (1.4 m) to see how sizes differ (trees usually get wider toward the base). Ask students what would happen if everyone measured the circumference of a tree at a different height (everyone would get different results). Could you easily compare the size of two trees if one was measured to be 5 feet (1.5 m) at 1 foot (0.3 m), and the other was 3 feet (0.9 m) at 6 feet (1.8 m)? (no) Explain that foresters created DBH as their measurement standard, or "ruler."

9. Show students what is meant by the tree's crown spread (the distance the tree's branches spread away from its trunk). Ask students to estimate the tree's crown spread in hand spans, paces, feet, or meters. Help students measure and calculate the average crown spread by having one student stand under the branch tip farthest from the trunk (Person A) and another under a branch tip opposite that one (Person B) (see Illustration 4 on student page 243). Measure the distance from Person A to Person B. Then, have one student stand under the branch tip closest to the trunk (Person C) and another under the branch tip opposite that one (Person D). Measure the distance from Person C to Person D. Calculate the average of the two measurements. Why would the measurement of a tree's crown be important? (The bigger the crown, the more leaves it has, the more food it can make, and the bigger it can grow.)

10. Ask students whether they think that all of a tree's leaves or needles are the same size. Divide students into pairs, and ask each pair to measure the length and width of a tree leaf or needle using finger widths and then a ruler. (Use a low-hanging branch or fallen leaves.) Record findings on the class chart. Ask students to compare their measurements.

11. On a sunny day, have students determine the height of the tree by measuring the length of its shadow (see Illustration 2 on student page 243). Students must first measure their own height and the length of their shadow at the same time of day. Show students how to use a ratio comparison to determine the height of the tree:

$$\frac{\text{Tree's Height}}{\text{Tree's Shadow}} = \frac{\text{Student's Height}}{\text{Student's Shadow}}$$

OR

$$\text{Tree's Height} = \text{Student's Height} \times \frac{\text{Tree's Shadow}}{\text{Student's Shadow}}$$

Ask students to compare their calculations. What might explain any differences?

12. If shadows are not apparent at the place or time you're doing the activity, you might try the proportional method of estimating a tree's height. (See Illustration 1 on student page 243). Have one student stand at the base of the tree to be measured. Have another student hold a ruler at arm's length and walk backward, keeping arm stiff, until the top and bottom of the ruler line up with the top and bottom of the tree. Note where the top of the partner's head appears on the ruler (for example, at 2" or 5 cm). Divide the length of the ruler (12" or 30 cm) by this figure. For example, 12" ÷ 2" = 6" or 30 cm ÷ 5 cm = 6 cm. Measure the partner's actual height and multiply it by the previous result (i.e., 6). For example, if the student's height was 55" or 1.4 m, then the height of the tree would be 55" x 6 = 330" (27.5 feet) or 1.4 m x 6 = 8.4 m. Ask students to compare their calculations. What might explain any differences?

13. Back in the classroom, review the chart of the class' findings. Older students might work in pairs or groups to make graphs or diagrams that will create a visual summary of the results.

VARIATION—FOR YOUNGER STUDENTS

On your school grounds or on a trip to a park, challenge the students to find the tree with the largest trunk. Have students measure various trees by joining arms around a large tree or by using hand spans around a small one. For each tree, help students mea-sure the trunk by wrapping string around it and cutting the string to fit each tree's circumference. Staple or tape the strings to your classroom wall. Help students to compare the strings and measure them using a ruler or different body parts: foot, hand span, arm span, length of finger, or paces.

Challenge the students to find a very small tree (if none is present, you could bring a potted tree to class). If the tree is small enough for students to reach its top, ask them whether they think the tree's height is greater than or less than the spread of its crown. Have the students measure the height of the tree in hand spans and in standard measure. Record findings on the chart, and ask the students to compare their measurements to their estimate.

Enrichment
1. "Champion Trees" are the largest known trees of their species. *American Forests* records them in the NATIONAL REGISTER OF BIG TREES. Each state also has a record of its state champions. Help your class to find the champions in your local community or neighborhood and compare these with the national or state champions. (Contact—American Forests, PO Box 2000, Washington, DC 20013, for information on national and state champions.)

Champions are determined by using a tree's dimensions to calculate a total number of points. To find out a tree's total points, add together— the tree's circumference at 4.5 feet (1.4 m) above the ground (in inches) + its height (in feet) + one-fourth of its average crown spread (in feet). If you have an adopted tree, calculate its points. (To nominate a tree to become a champion, contact AMERICAN FORESTS.)

2. The giant Sequoia is the largest living thing (organism) on Earth. To help students picture how large one of these trees is, help them make a life-size drawing on the playground using tape, string, or chalk for the outline (see Background).

3. Ask students to collect samples of various tree leaves, needles, or flowers. Mount each sample on a piece of paper, in a small plastic bag, or between contact paper. Have students measure and compare the samples. Use field guides and other references to help students identify and label samples for a class collection.

4. Determine the total leaf area of a deciduous tree by measuring the width or diameter of the crown (the widest part of the branch and leaf area). You can do this by pacing off the distance underneath the tree. Then, to determine the square inches of a tree's leaf area, use this formula: $5 \times 144 \times 3.14 \times (\text{diameter}/2)^2 = $ Total leaf area per tree (sq. in). In the formula, 144 is the square inches in a

square foot; $3.14 = \pi$; the diameter of the crown divided by 2 is the radius which is squared (multiplied by itself); and 5 assumes 5 layers of leaves on the ground which is typical for an average hardwood tree. As an example, a tree with a typical globe-shape crown that is 20 feet across would have total leaf area of about 226,080 square inches (1,458,577.7 sq cm), using this formula.

Now, to find the number of leaves on your tree, divide the average leaf size of your particular type of tree into the total area, which allows for spacing branches. An average Norway maple has a leaf of 19 square inches (124.3 sq cm); an average elm has leaves of 8-9 square inches (51.6-58 sq cm); and an average white ash has 2-square-inch (12.9-sq cm) leaflets.

So, using this formula, you can estimate how many leaves you'll rake in your yard this autumn.

END NOTES...

ASSESSMENT OPPORTUNITY

Evaluate the students' understanding by having them write a paragraph or draw a diagram describing the steps that they would take to measure a particular tree. Have them explain how this information might be used. Students should create a mathematics word problem that relates to measuring a tree. They can exchange math problems and try to solve them. You can evaluate the problems and the attempted solutions.

RELATED ACTIVITIES

Adopt a Tree, Tree Cookies, To Be a Tree, Looking at Leaves, Germinating Giants

REFERENCES

Enrichment Step 4 is adapted from *COUNTRY MAGAZINE*, August/September, 1992.

HOW BIG IS THAT TREE?

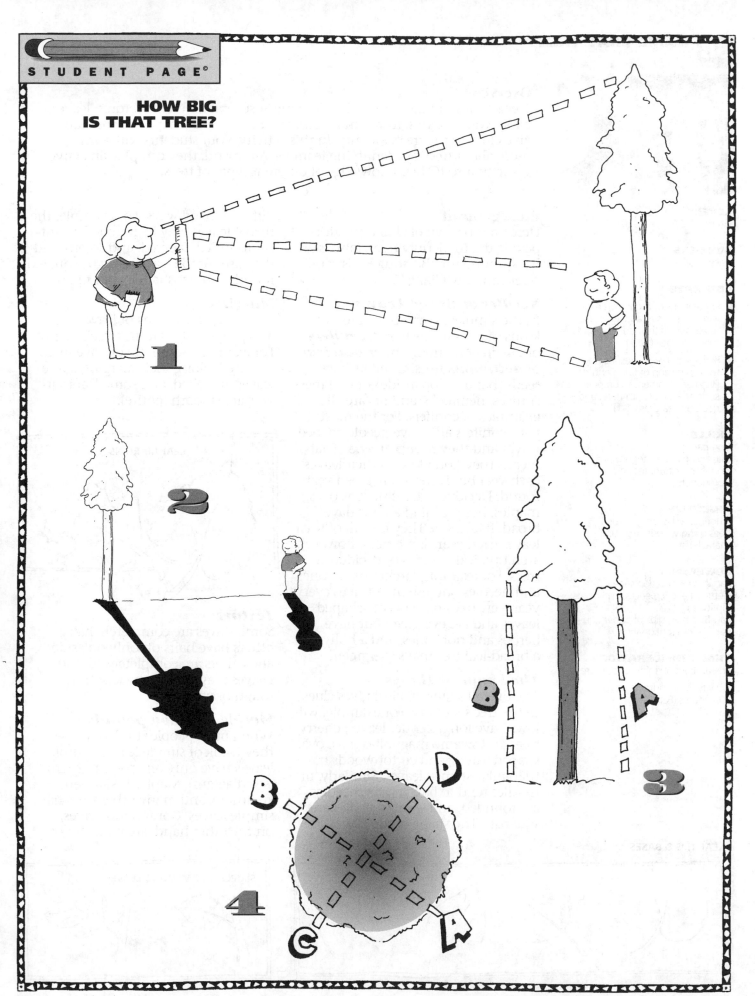

Overview
Tree species can be identified by looking at several different features: leaves, bark, twigs, flowers, fruits, and seeds. Even the overall shape of a tree can give clues to the tree's identity. In this activity, your students will learn more about trees by identifying features. Afterward, they can play an active game that tests their knowledge of different types of trees.

LEVELS
Grades 2-8

SUBJECTS
Science, Physical Education

CONCEPTS
- Populations of organisms exhibit variations in size and structure as a result of their adaptation to their habitats. (10.1)
- Biological diversity results from the interaction of living and non-living environmental components such as air, water, climate, and geologic features. (1.1)

SKILLS
Comparing and Contrasting, Classifying and Categorizing, Identifying Attributes and Components

OBJECTIVE
Students will identify several trees using various structural characteristics.

MATERIALS
Part A: identification sheets (see Getting Ready), pencils, clipboards (optional)
Part B: leaves, slips of paper and paper sacks (optional)

TIME CONSIDERATIONS
Preparation: 60 minutes or more

Activity: 50 minutes (Part A)
30 minutes (Part B)

Background
Here's a rundown of characteristics people use to identify trees: (also, see Background for "Bursting Buds" and "Germinating Giants")

Needles or Broad Leaves
In the simplest sense, there are two kinds of trees in the world: *conifers,* or *coniferous* trees, and *broad-leaf* or *deciduous* trees. Conifers have seeds that develop inside cones. Pines, spruces, hemlocks, and firs are all examples of conifers. For the most part, conifers also have needle-shaped leaves and they're *evergreens*. That means they don't lose all their leaves each year but instead stay green year-round. Deciduous trees such as oaks, maples, beeches, and aspens have broad, flat leaves. They lose all of their leaves each year. Some trees, however, aren't typical conifers or deciduous trees. For example, larches have cones and needles but lose their leaves every year, yew trees have needle-shaped leaves and are evergreen but have berries and not cones, and a holly is a broad-leaf tree that's evergreen.

The Shape of Things
The overall shape of a leaf gives clues to the tree's identity. For example, willows have long, slender leaves; cherry trees and swamp magnolias have oval-shaped leaves; and cottonwoods have triangular-shaped leaves. Similarly, fir needles tend to be flat, pine needles are rounded, and spruce needles are squarish. The shape of the leaves

differ in many ways. For example, the tips of leaves may be notched, pointed, rounded, tapered, and so on. And the bases of the leaves may be squared, rounded, heart-shaped, and so on.

Margins
The edges or margins of leaves can also provide clues to the tree's identity. For example, some leaves have teeth (serrated) along their margins, some leaves are lobed, and some leaf margins are smooth (entire).

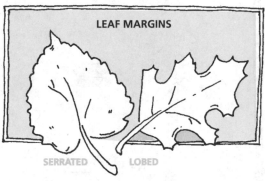

LEAF MARGINS

SERRATED   LOBED

Textures
Some leaves are completely hairy, others have hairs on only one side, and others are completely smooth. Leaves may also be thick or thin, rough or waxy.

Simple and Compound
When most people think of leaves, they think of simple leaves. Simple leaves have only one piece to them (see diagram). Maple, oak, aspen, sycamore, and many other trees have simple leaves. Compound leaves, on the other hand, are made up of

LEAF TIPS & BASES

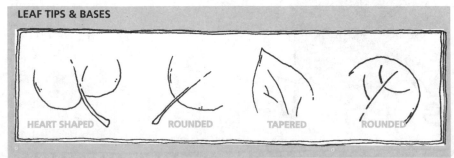

HEART SHAPED   ROUNDED   TAPERED   ROUNDED

SIMPLE & COMPOUND LEAVES

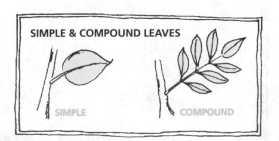

SIMPLE   COMPOUND

several leaflets (see diagram). Ash, walnut, and sumac trees all have compound leaves.

Leaf Arrangements

Another characteristic to identify a tree is the way its leaves are arranged on the twigs. Many trees have alternate leaves that are staggered along the twig (see diagram). Other trees have opposite leaves that grow in pairs along the twig (see diagram). And some leaves grow in **whorls,** or are whorled (see diagram). The leaves on pines, spruces, firs, and other needle-leaved trees also grow in patterns. For example, leaves on pines may grow in **clusters** of two, three, or more.

Twiggy Clues

If you know what to look for, even leafless twigs on a tree can tell you the tree's identity (this is especially helpful when identifying deciduous trees in the winter). By looking at where the leaf scars or **buds** are on the twig, people can tell if the leaves grow in an alternate, opposite, or whorled pattern. (Leaf scars are the places on the twigs where leaves used to be attached.) The size, color, and shape of buds can also be used to identify trees. Spines and thorns on twigs can also help identify a tree.

Fruit and Flowers

Different trees produce different kinds of fruit, such as berries, winged seeds, nuts, pods, or some other type of fruit. Different conifers produce different kinds of cones. Different trees also have different flowers. The shape, color, texture, size, and other characteristics of both the fruit, cones, and flowers can be used to identify trees.

Bark Basics

Many people can identify trees just by looking at the color and texture of tree bark. For instance, bark may be shaggy, smooth, or rough; it may have deep furrows or markings. Paper birch is an example of a tree easily identified by its white, paper-like bark. However, when using bark to identify a tree, it's best to look at bark growing on the trunk rather than on branches and twigs (because the bark on a

branch is thinner and newer, it may look quite different from the trunk). Bark also looks different as a tree gets older.

Shaping Up

Many trees have characteristic shapes that can be used to identify them. In fact, just by glancing at the shape of a distant tree (and the color of its leaves), some people can tell what kind of tree it is. See diagram.

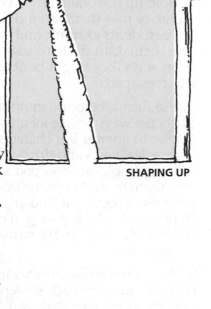

SHAPING UP

Getting Ready

Before doing this activity, you should identify 7-10 trees in your vicinity. If you don't have trees where you are, you can use shrubs instead. To identify the trees, you may use field guides; ask a groundskeeper or fellow educator to help; or enlist the help of a **forester, naturalist, arborist,** or other tree specialist. After identifying the trees, you will need to create tree identification sheets for the students to use. On one sheet, copy drawings of the leaves from the different trees you identified. Under each leaf, write the tree's name.

On the second sheet, create clue "blocks" about each tree. The clues might describe the tree's bark and the shape of the tree. These clues should not, however, include phrases that tell the students where to look for the tree. For example, you should not include clues such as, "It grows near the gym." Under each set of clues, draw a line for students to fill in the name of the tree after they've identified it.

LEAF ARRANGEMENTS

OPPOSITE

ALTERNATE

WHORLS

Finally, collect twigs or small branches from two to four different trees. The twigs should be long enough to show several leaves. If possible, use twigs that have already fallen to the ground or have been pruned. Try to collect twigs from both needle and broad-leaf trees.

PART A
MYSTERY TREES

Doing the Activity

1. Ask students what characteristics they might use to identify trees. As they give their ideas, ask how they could use these characteristics to identify trees. List their ideas on a chalkboard.

2. Hold up the branches you collected earlier, or pass them around the room. Have students examine and compare them. Can students suggest any other ways they might be able to tell trees apart?

3. Use the background information to discuss ways people identify trees. Be sure to go over leaf characteristics such as leaf bases and tips, leaf margins (edges), simple and compound leaves, and alternate and opposite branching patterns, especially if students in Steps 1 and 2 did not suggest characteristics like these to differentiate between trees.

4. Divide the group into teams of two or three, and give each student a copy of both sheets you made earlier (see Getting Ready). Tell teams that they will use trees on the school property to match the drawings and names on Sheet 1 with the tree descriptions on Sheet 2. Explain that first the students must find a tree whose leaves match the leaves on Sheet 1. Then, by examining the tree closely and comparing their observations with the clues on Sheet 2, they should be able to find a match. As they match tree characteristics with tree leaves and names, they should write the tree's name on the line below the clues.

5. Invite students outside and let them get to work. Don't forget to set parameters for how far students may wander and how much time they have to work.

6. When back inside, go over the sheets as a group. Which team made the most correct identifications?

PART B
LEAF HUNT RELAY

Doing the Activity

1. Divide the group into teams and have each team collect three leaves from each of the trees identified in Part A.

NOTE—Encourage students to collect leaves that have fallen to the ground beneath the trees rather than taking live leaves off the trees. They could also cut the proper leaf shapes out of paper and laminate them between two pieces of clear contact paper.

2. Take the students to an open area and explain that they will have a relay race. Line them up in their teams, and place each team's leaf pile a set distance in front of each team. Tell the students that you're going to call out the name of a tree and then say, "Go."

3. At the signal to go, the first student in each team should run to the pile of leaves, find the leaf that comes from the tree you named, and hold it up. Each team gets one point for each leaf correctly identified. The team with the most points wins.

NOTE—Depending on the level of the group, you might want to hold up a leaf shape rather than call out the tree's name.

4. After each round, put the leaves back in the piles, and ask players to go to the end of their team's line.

VARIATION—SPEEDY RELAY

1. Prepare a bag for each team which contains slips of paper with names of the leaves they collected and sorted in steps 1 and 2 above.

2. Have students line up in their teams with their leaf piles a set distance away (Step 2 above), but this time put their bag of names at the front of each line.

3. When you give the signal, the first member of each team will reach in the bag and pull out a name. Then he or she should run to the pile of leaves, grab the leaf that matches the name, and run back to tag the next person in line. Each player does the same.

4. The team that finishes the race first and has correctly matched the names with the leaves, is the winner.

REFERENCES
Elias, Thomas S. *THE COMPLETE TREES OF NORTH AMERICA.* Van Nostrand, Reinhold Co., 1980.

Symonds, George W.D. *THE TREE IDENTIFICATION BOOK.* Quill, 1958.

Petrides, George A. *Peterson FIELD GUIDE TO TREES AND SHRUBS.* Boston, MA: Houghton Mifflin, 1972

Randall, W.R., R.F. Keniston, and D.N. Bever. *MANUAL OF OREGON TREES AND SHRUBS.* Corvalis, OR: OSU Bookstores, Inc., 1978.

* Most state Natural Resource Departments have booklets and posters, that identify trees native to each state. Encourage students to send away for information about local trees.

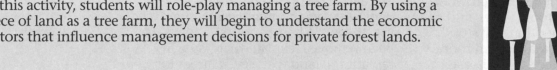

Overview
In this activity, students will role-play managing a tree farm. By using a piece of land as a tree farm, they will begin to understand the economic factors that influence management decisions for private forest lands.

Background

The United States has 731 million acres (296 million ha) of forestland that make up about one-third of the total land base. Canada has 1,118.5 million acres or 453 million ha of forestland. To be classified as forestland, an area must be at least 1 acre (.4 ha) and contain about 10 percent tree cover. About 483 million acres (195.6 million ha), or two-thirds, of U.S. forestlands are also classified as commercial *timberland* (forests capable of growing merchantable crops of trees). Canada has 244 million acres (99 million ha) classified as commercial. U.S. commercial timberlands are owned by three sectors of society: private individuals own 57 percent; public agencies (federal, state, county) own 28 percent; and forest industries own 15 percent. Timberlands that are owned and managed by private individuals are often referred to as tree farms.

Tree farms are forests that are managed to grow trees for wood products such as paper and lumber. Like other forests, tree farms not only produce timber and other forest commodities, but also provide homes for wildlife, produce oxygen, reduce soil erosion, help protect water quality, and offer recreation areas. Although tree farmers often have different goals for managing their lands, most have one thing in common: they want to manage their forests in an aesthetically pleasing and ecologically sound way, while growing trees for forest products.

Silviculture is the practice of establishing and managing a forest to best meet the objectives of the owner. Tree farmers apply silvicultural techniques to maintain and enhance their forest-land. In doing so, they can control forest composition, structure, and growth. Through *harvesting* (tree removal), cutting, *thinning*,

prescribed burning, and various other methods, a tree farmer can manipulate the variety and age of tree species within a forest, the density of trees, the arrangement of different layers or stories of vegetation, and lighting and shading. Even before a forest matures, tree farmers must consider how the next forest will be regenerated and managed. The management techniques a tree farmer applies to his or her land not only affect the present forest but also influence its future characteristics.

For more specific information on silvicultural systems of management, refer to student page 250.

Getting Ready

Find a comfortable seating area indoors or outdoors where you can arrange students in rows. You'll divide your group into about five rows of roughly equal numbers. Prepare three signs that read FIREWOOD, PULP, and LUMBER which will go around students' necks. For the Enrichment, make copies of student page 250 for each team; for the Assessment, make copies of student page 251.

Doing the Activity

1. Ask students for the definition of a tree farm. Using the background information, explain that a tree farm is a forest ecosystem that provides many valuable products.

2. Place students in rows. After each is in place, tell students that they are now tree seedlings. You have planted them on a barren piece of land that you own. You want this land to be a productive tree farm, so you call the State Forest Service for advice. They recommend planting pine trees. They also help you develop a long-range management plan for your land.

3. Tell the "trees" that they have now been growing for 15 years, and they

LEVELS
Activity: Grades 4-8
Enrichment: Grades 6-8

SUBJECTS
Science, Math, Social Studies

CONCEPT
■ Conservation and management technologies, when appropriately applied to the use or preservation of natural resources, can enhance and extend the usefulness of the resources as well as the quality of the environment. (11.2)

SKILLS
Identifying Main Ideas, Analyzing, Solving Problems, Synthesizing and Creating

OBJECTIVES
Students will ① participate in a simulation designed to teach how forest resources are managed and ② simulate managing a piece of land for various products.

MATERIALS
Activity: Three pieces of cardboard and string to make three signs to go around students' necks
Enrichment: copies of student page 250
Assessment: copies of student page 251

TIME CONSIDERATIONS
Preparation: 30 minutes

Activity: 50 minutes

Enrichment: Two 50-minute periods

need to be thinned so they can continue to grow quickly. If they are not thinned, they will become crowded and compete for food, water, and sunlight. Such competition will stunt their growth and make them more susceptible to insects and disease.

4. For this thinning, you will remove native hardwood "trees" such as oak, hickory, or maple that have occurred naturally in your pine plantation. These "trees" will be used for firewood. Place a FIREWOOD sign around one student's neck and have him or her stand to one side where the others can see. You will also need to cut some pine "trees" during this thinning. They will be grouped behind another student standing to the side wearing a PAPER sign (because pine trees will be turned into pulp for making paper). You should remove approximately every other "tree" during this initial thinning operation. You can designate these "trees" as firewood or paper and then have them stand behind the respective students.

5. Tell the remaining students that they have now grown for another 10 years and need to be thinned again. This time you will harvest every other pine "tree" for paper. This thinning will enable the remaining "trees" to continue growing at the maximum rate. All "trees" that are cut down will join the others already behind the PAPER sign. Explain that pulp from the trees will be used to make books, boxes, tissues, and other paper products.

6. After growing another 15 years, the remaining "trees" will be as big as they will probably get. If left as they are, they may be attacked by insects, infected by disease, or destroyed by wildfire. If any of these things happen, the "trees" will lose most, if not all, of their value as timber.

Therefore, you have decided to harvest all remaining "trees" for lumber. Place the LUMBER sign on one student and begin to remove all remaining "trees." When all "trees" have been removed, explain that you will replant the land with several trees for every one that you removed in the final harvest. You may also opt to leave some mature seed trees standing for natural regeneration (see student page 250).

7. Line up all the "trees" in the same rows as the beginning and ask them what natural events could drastically change the forest. (Wildfire, insect infestation, or plant disease could kill many trees and plants and could greatly affect the ecosystem.) Discuss students' answers. Pretend you are a wildfire roaring through the forest and destroying the "trees" (all students sit down). Discuss the results: Wildlife is homeless; soil is charred; streams are choked with sediment and ash; valuable timber is lost. Explain that although you, the landowner, are very upset, fire is a natural, and sometimes vital part of the forest lifecycle. The forest will return through natural regeneration and planting.

8. Replant the forest so that all "trees" are back in their places. Tell the students that you have decided to retire and move away. Before you leave, you must sell the land. You sell to someone who isn't interested in forest management. This person has decided to develop the property for housing without consulting forest managers.

9. First, the new landowner puts in a road so prospective homebuyers can see the lots. Remove one row of "trees" and put them aside to be burned. (This is often what happens.) Next, remove some "trees" from the rows next to the road so homes can be built. (Again, put them in a brushpile to be burned.) Continue cutting down "trees" to make room for the construction of businesses, schools, and roads until all "trees" are gone. Ask the students, "Would you like to live in this community?" Point out the many benefits that trees provide for a development like this. (beauty, shade, recreation, clean air, and homes for animals) Discuss how the landowner could have developed this housing community with the assistance of foresters so that many of these benefits could have remained.

Enrichment

1. Divide students into forest management teams of three or four. Give each team a copy of student page 250.

2. Review this information with students to make sure they understand the forestry terms (also use the Glossary on page 371).

3. Tell each team they will lead the group through the same type of simulation they did in the activity, only they will make all management decisions.

4. Give teams about 20 minutes to plan a strategy for managing a forest in which students are the trees (the number of students in the group minus themselves). They can choose one of the silvicultural systems described on the student page, can use a combination of systems, or can make up their own system. Whatever they choose to do, they must explain each action they take.

5. Allow time for each team to lead the entire group through a simulation.

END NOTES...

ASSESSMENT OPPORTUNITY

Pass out copies of the Forest Stand puzzle on student page 251. Tell students to number Boxes A to F in a logical sequence. On the back of the page, have them describe the sequence of events and say what actions were taken in each box. (See possible Answers below).

RELATED ACTIVITIES

400-Acre Wood, A Forest of Many Uses, Forest Consequences, Tree Lifecycle, Nothing Succeeds Like Succession, Who Works in This Forest?

REFERENCES

Smith, D.M. *THE PRACTICE OF SILVICULTURE, 8TH ED.* New York: John Wiley & Sons, 1986.

SOCIETY OF AMERICAN FORESTERS WITH COOPERATION OF THE WILDLIFE SOCIETY. CHOICES IN SILVICULTURE FOR AMERICAN FORESTS. Washington, DC.: Society of American Foresters, 1981.

POSSIBLE ANSWERS TO ASSESSMENT

1. (c) A young pine forest is planted on barren land.

2. (a) Several trees are removed for firewood.

3. (e) With initial thinning after 15 years, removed trees are used for firewood or paper.

4. (d) With pulpwood thinning after 20 years, removed trees are used for paper.

5. (b) With harvesting of mature trees for lumber after 40 years, a few mature seed trees are left for regeneration.

6. (f) When seed trees are harvested for lumber, young seedlings are growing.

FOREST SILVICULTURAL SYSTEMS

Silviculture is the practice of growing and managing forests to control their composition, structure, and growth. Forests are frequently managed in smaller units called stands. A stand is a group of trees similar enough in species composition, condition, and age distribution to be considered a unit. Stands may be even-aged (trees are of relatively the same age) or uneven-aged.

A forest manager can choose among several systems of silviculture to harvest and grow new trees within a forest stand. These include the clearcutting, seed-tree, shelterwood, and single tree and group selection systems.

In the *clear-cutting system,* all trees in a stand are harvested at once, with the expectation that a new, even-aged stand becomes established. The clear-cut system works well for establishing trees that grow best in full sunlight. The new stand may develop by seeds from nearby stands, from seeds stored in the forest floor, or from stump or root sprouts of cut trees. In other cases, a clear-cut area is regenerated by scattering seeds or by planting seedlings.

The *seed-tree system* requires leaving a few good seed-producing trees on each stand when the mature stand is harvested. These trees provide the seeds needed to regenerate a new, even-aged stand. The seed trees are sometimes harvested after a crop of new, young trees has become established.

The *shelterwood system* involves a series of partial cuttings over a period of years in the mature stand. Early cuttings improve the vigor and seed production of remaining trees and prepare the site for new seedlings. The remaining trees produce seeds and shelter young seedlings. Later, cuttings will harvest shelterwood trees and allow regeneration to develop as an even-aged stand.

The *single-tree selection* system differs from the other systems by creating and maintaining an uneven-aged stand. Foresters examine a stand and judge each tree on its individual merit. Trees are harvested as they mature. Seedlings or sprouts grow in the spaces created. Periodic thinning and harvesting results in a stand that contains trees of many ages and sizes. Because relatively few trees are harvested at any one time, and because the forest floor is generally shaded, this system favors species that thrive in low light.

The *group selection* system requires harvest of small groups rather than individual trees. The openings created resemble miniature clear-cuts, with the major difference being that the resulting regeneration occupies too small an area to be considered an even-aged stand. As in the single-tree system, both thinning and harvest cuttings are done at the same time. The new trees that grow in these small openings are regarded as parts of a larger stand containing trees of many ages. In either single-tree or group selection systems, frequent harvests are needed to maintain a balance of tree ages, classes, and sizes.

FOREST STAND
PUZZLE

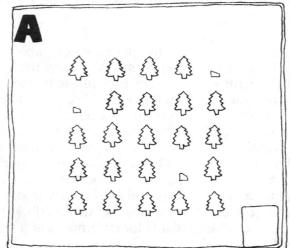

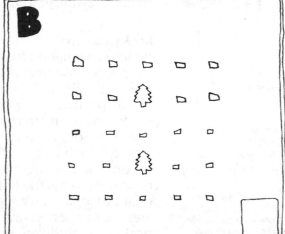

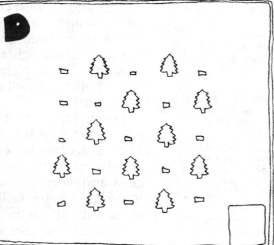

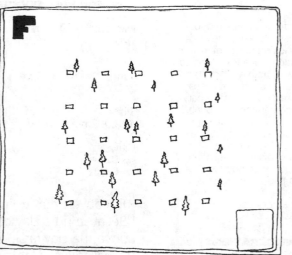

LEVELS
Grades 5-8

SUBJECTS
Science, Math, Social Studies

CONCEPTS
■ The structure and scale of an ecosystem are influenced by factors such as a soil type, climate, availability of water, and human activities. (10.2)
■ Conservation and management technologies, when appropriately applied to the use or preservation of natural resources, can enhance and extend the usefulness of the resource as well as the quality of the environment. (11.2)

SKILLS
Observing, Identifying Attributes and Components, Concluding

OBJECTIVES
Students will ① identify components of soil and how these components determine its function, ② explain how different soil types determine the characteristics of ecosystems, and ③ predict the influence of soils on water filtration and on human use of an area.

MATERIALS
Part A: for each student-copies of student page 256, hand lens (could be shared within group) for each team-small plastic bag, trowel or shovel, beaker or jar, stirring rod or jar lid, 100-ml graduated beaker for the entire group, scientific balance scale, water
Part B: for each group-set of instructions on student page 257, food can (soup size) with both ends removed, measuring cup, watch that keeps time to the second, 20-penny nail, flat board and hammer (optional), ruler, paper and pencil, water-carrying container, water
Enrichment: soil survey book; radish seeds; growing containers and flower pots with holes in bottoms; graph paper; various soils including gravel, loam, sterile sand, powdered clay, or peat moss; paper towels

TIME CONSIDERATIONS
Preparation: 60 minutes
Activity: Two 50-minute periods

Overview
Students often wonder why certain plants grow in some places and not in others. Climatic factors such as temperature, moisture, and sunlight keep palm trees in Florida and fir trees in Oregon, but subtle differences in soil allow an oak to compete more successfully in one area and a maple in another. In this activity, students will explore differences in soil types and what they mean to us.

Background
Soil, the foundation for life on Earth, is a mixture of **mineral** ingredients (rock, clay, silt, and sand); **organic** ingredients (living organisms, decomposing organic matter); moisture; and air spaces. Soils are often classified by texture, which is determined by the amounts of clay, silt, and sand they contain. **Loam** is the term for a fairly equal mix of all three. Other soil textures are heavier on one element than another, i.e. silt loam, sandy loam, clay loam, sandy clay, and so forth.

The ratio of these components in relationship to other environmental factors helps determine ① how well soil can sustain plants and withstand erosion, ② which plants will grow well, or ③ whether the soil can support development.

Another important component of soil is the spaces between soil particles. These spaces are critical to plant growth, since they are where roots grow and where moisture and air are trapped. Moisture facilitates the transfer of nutrients to the roots.

Although soil may appear to be static, constant changes are actually taking place. For example, glacial deposits may change the amount of sand or rock in the surface soils; a fallen log will add organic matter as it decomposes; a stream can wash away fine silt, clay, and organic matter; or construction projects may move subsoil with less organic material to the surface. Various types of soils probably exist right on your school grounds. The table below describes the standards for common soil textures.

Getting Ready
This activity is most effective when students are able to collect and compare several different soil samples (try for five). Ideally, students can choose sites and collect the soil. Possible collection sites include low or wet spots, baseball fields, garden areas, overgrown fields, lawns, forested areas, or under trees. You may wish to scout around the school to find appropriate areas for digging and removing about 2 cups (470 ml) of soil.

NOTE—Remember to get permission from the property owners and to always wash your hands thoroughly after handling soil because it might contain contaminants.

COMMON SOIL TEXTURES

PARTICLE SIZE[a]	FEEL	FERTILITY	AIR SPACE	H₂O AVAILABILITY
Sand 2.0-.05mm	gritty	low	many large	low
Silt .05-.002mm	smooth	medium	many fair/small	good
Clay <.002mm	sticky	high	few tiny	slow movement of water[b]

[a]To convert mm to inches, multiply by .04.
[b]Because pure clay compacts tightly into a solid mass, water may be suspended above the clay (as in a swamp or pond) or trapped below the clay, making it unavailable to plants. When clay is one component of the soil mixture, it reduces water movement so the soil feels moist.

If five different soils are not available near the school, consider these options:

- Ask students to bring in a plastic bag of soil from different sites around their homes.

- Use only two or three different sites, but obtain different soil types by digging deeper: surface soil, 6" (15 cm) deep, or 12" (30.5 cm) deep.

- Buy sterile sand (for sandboxes or concrete), peat moss (for gardening), and powdered clay (for pottery or sculpture) so you can make your own soil types. Use five different formulas to create variety (equal parts, three times more of one ingredient than the others, and so forth).

PART A
RECIPE FOR SOIL

Doing the Activity

1. What do plants get from soil? (air, water, nutrients, structural support) Do different plants have different soil requirements? (Yes. Some require dry soil, others need wet; some require acidic, others need basic.) How does this characteristic of having different requirements benefit plants? (Reduces competition for requirements.)

2. Tell students that you will divide them into teams, and that each team will analyze a different soil sample. Later, they will predict how well plants might grow in each sample and test their predictions (Enrichment for Part A).

3. Distribute student page 256, bags, and digging tools to each team.

4. Divide the class into five groups (or whatever number of different soils they will compare). Ask each group to collect a sample of soil (about 2 cups or 470 ml) from a different location. You can either assign locations or let them choose their own.

5. Back in the room, designate a study station for each team. Ask teams to examine their soil by answering questions on student page 256, and to compare their answers to other teams' answers. Distribute hand lenses to help students with their observations and comparisons.

6. Ask students about the importance of air spaces in soil (space for the air and water that plants need). Tell them they will measure the air space in their sample.

7. Give each team a beaker or jar. Have students measure 100 ml (6 cu in.) of dry soil (clumps should be broken up) in a graduated cylinder (or measure 1/2 cup = 118 ml), put the soil in their jar, and record the weight of the jar with the soil. Next, have students pour water into the jar very slowly until water reaches the top edge of soil. By weighing the container again, they can determine the weight of the water that filled up the air spaces in the soil (weight of jar with soil and water minus weight of jar with just soil). Because 1 gram of water displaces 1 milliliter of air, they can estimate the volume of air (ml) in each soil sample.

8. Discuss each team's results. What might have caused the difference? Invite students to hypothesize about the ratio of sand or silt to clay in each sample. (The silt and sand particles result in more air space.) The next step will test their hypothesis.

9. Have students continue to add water until the soil is covered with 2 inches (5 cm) of water. Cover the jar and shake it for several minutes, or vigorously stir the soil in a beaker. Allow the soil to settle for at least two hours; then observe the layers in each jar. Since larger components settle out first, soil particles will fall out of suspension in layers: Pebbles will fall first; then sand, silt, clay will fall; and some organic matter might float. Clay may make the water cloudy for a long time. Compare the layers in each sample. How do the results compare with their hypothesis?

10. Each group should prepare a verbal summary of its findings or create a poster that explains the components of the soil. After examining variations in these soils, discuss why vegetation might grow differently on those sites. Lead a discussion comparing the soil samples each team studied.

- Why did some have more organic matter? (perhaps the area has more vegetation)

- Which soil will drain water better: sandy loam or clay loam? (sandy loam because it has larger particles and air spaces)

- In which soil would a plant that needs a lot of water (willow or black spruce) grow best? (silt loam, which has small air spaces to retain water but will still drain fairly)

Enrichment for Part A

1. Before the shake test, distribute graph paper and ask students to estimate the portion of each component in their soil sample (how much sand, gravel, clay, or organic matter it contains). Then have them graph the result of the shake test to show a soil profile and to compare it with their original estimate. Compare soil profiles of different samples, and compare each soil profile to the amount of air space calculated for that sample.

- Set up an experiment to determine the "best" soil for young plants. Try sprouting seeds (radishes grow quickly) under several different soil conditions while maintaining equal amounts of sun and water. To grow the seeds, use the following:

- Different soil samples collected in Part A

- Moist paper towels (no soil)

- Sterile sand

- Peat moss

Measure growth until noticeable differences can be detected.

PART B
A SOIL MYSTERY

Doing the Activity

1. Read the following mystery (in the side bar) to your students and have them discuss it in teams.

2. Lead a class discussion about the mystery. Help students identify the key questions: What is a perk test? How would it prevent someone from building a house? To find the answer to these questions, each team will perform a percolation (perk) test on soil from different areas.

3. Divide the class into teams of five. Distribute "Soil Percolation Test" on student page 257 and let your students get started. Circulate among the teams to help answer questions. If this process is too difficult for your students, you may conduct the perk test yourself as a demonstration.

4. When the groups finish summarizing their data, lead a class discussion about their results. Guide students toward understanding that dense or compacted soil has fewer air passages so that water percolates (drains) through it more slowly, while porous soils drain water very quickly.

5. Collect all the students' suggestions about the need for soil to drain near houses. Students should understand the need for soils to drain wastewater (discharged from sinks, showers, washing machines) for houses not connected to a waste water system and the need to prevent flooding from rains. On the other hand, soils that drain too fast may not properly filter impurities out of the water, which may result in contamination of groundwater (for drinking).

6. To solve the mystery, your students might suggest that the soil on Sam and Laticia's new property did not properly drain the wastewater and their house would not be hooked into a waste water system. This problem is not uncommon in more rural areas where the soil has large amounts of clay. What possible solutions might Sam and Laticia pursue to build their

SOIL MYSTERY

Two weeks ago, Laticia and Sam received a phone call from a lawyer who told them that Sam's grandfather, who had recently passed away, had willed a piece of land to them. They now owned the property and could do with it whatever they wished.

It didn't take long for Sam and Laticia to decide what to do with the land. They had often dreamed of building their own small house. They were both good carpenters and were sure that with some boards and bricks and a lot of work, they could make a fine house for themselves.

When Sam and Laticia went to visit their new property, their dream seemed as if it would come true. They started right away by filing the proper building permits and having the site tested for a well by having a percolation (perk) test done.

When they received the test results, their hearts sank. The soil on the property had failed the perk test, and they would not be able to build their dream house. Why not? What was wrong with the soil?

dream house? (Some of these are expensive solutions.)

- Conserve water to produce less wastewater and reduce the burden on the house's septic system.

- Build a cesspool to hold wastewater.

- Dig a large, deep pit and fill it with gravel, sand, and soil to increase the drainage ability.

Students may also have suggested that the soil drained too quickly and might allow contamination of well water. How could this problem be solved? (by installing equipment that filters wastewater before allowing it to enter the groundwater)

Enrichment for Part B

1. Ask your state Natural Resources Conservation Service for a copy of your county's soil survey. The book will contain aerial photographs of your county, marked with the different kinds of soil. Soils will be rated by texture (such as sandy loam) and qualified for appropriate uses (such as agriculture, highways, housing, and so forth).

By matching their knowledge of local areas with the soil survey, students can see how land-use patterns correlate to soil classifications. If a new development is proposed for your county, students can check the soil survey to see if the soil type is suitable for that development.

2. Here are additional soil mysteries for your students to investigate:

- A mudslide destroys homes. What soil conditions caused this to happen? (Soils of different textures overlapped, for example, a coarse-textured soil over a fine-textured soil caused moisture to build up at the point of contact, which in turn caused the coarse soil to slide over the fine soil on a slope).

- A building's foundation cracks as soil subsides. What soil type would cause this to happen? (Soil with a high organic content tends to subside as organic matter is broken down.)

- A flood in a city is blamed on increased runoff. What caused the runoff? (Soil has been paved over for streets, sidewalks, or parking lots.)

3. To demonstrate the drainage properties of different soil textures, use a flower pot with drainage holes in the bottom. Place different soils in the pot. As a student pours water into the pot, have the class count aloud until water leaks from the bottom. Use gravel, sand, loam, and, finally, clay.

Explain that some trees need soils that hold a lot of water, while others need drier soils. Here are examples of trees and their preferred soils:

- Poorly drained soils—cedars, red and silver maples

- Moderately drained soils— hemlocks, red spruces, balsam firs, aspens

- Well-drained soils—white pines, white birches

It is possible to predict the type of soil under your feet by recognizing the kinds of trees growing there. Likewise, you can tell what trees will grow best on a piece of land if you know the soil type.

END NOTES...

ASSESSMENT OPPORTUNITY
Have students imagine they are inspectors for your county's Soil Conservation Service. They must write a letter to Sam and Laticia explaining what the results of the perk test indicate. They should explain the reasons Sam and Laticia cannot build a house on their property because of its present soil conditions. They can also explain what steps could be taken to prepare the land for building a house or what alternate uses the land could be prepared for.

RELATED ACTIVITIES
The Fallen Log; Nature's Recyclers; How Plants Grow; Field, Forest, and Stream

SOIL
INVESTIGATION

FOR PART A

SOIL INVESTIGATION

Team Members

_____

_____

Describe where the soil is from.

- Where was your soil site? Use words or draw a picture.
- What was growing on this site?
- Was it level or on a slope?
- What other things did you notice?

Describe the soil.

- What color is it?
- How does it smell?
- How does it feel? Roll some in your fingers.
- What do the largest soil particles look like? The smallest?
- How does your sample compare to the other soil samples?

Describe the air space.

- How much does the container with 100 ml of soil in it weigh?
- How much does the container with water to the top of the soil weigh?
- What is the weight of the water added to the container?
- What is the volume of air in this soil sample?
  NOTE—1 gram of water displaces 1 milliliter of air.
- Which soil sample has the greatest amount of air space?

Describe what is in the soil.

- What are the components of your soil sample after they have settled in the jar?
  Draw what the layers look like.
- How do they compare to the other samples?

SOIL PERCOLATION TEST

FOR PART B

SOIL PERCOLATION TEST

Getting Ready

1. Within your team, choose a person for each role:

■ Equipment Monitor—collects equipment, keeps track of it, and returns it in good condition.

■ Time Keeper—uses a watch that tells time to the second.

■ Recorder—makes a data chart and records the time for each experiment.

■ Facilitator—reads directions and helps everything get done.

■ Checker—reads directions and makes sure everything is done correctly.

2. Have the Equipment Monitor collect the necessary equipment from the instructor. Have the Facilitator read the instructions out loud to the team and make sure everyone understands.

Team Instructions

1. Choose five different locations outdoors where there is a small patch of ground. Open soil, grass, leaves, or bushes are fine; asphalt, sidewalks, or concrete will not work.

2. At each location, record what is on the ground, and push one end of the can (which has both ends removed) 1" (2.5cm) into the ground. (It may be easier to rest a board on top of the can and firmly tap on the board with a hammer to push in the can.) Pour 1 cup (240 ml) of water into the can. Record how long it takes for the water to completely disappear. In some cases, the water will not disappear entirely during the class period. If this occurs, ask students to consider why all of the water does not percolate into the soil (The soil may already be saturated; the soil may be compacted at the ground surface; or there may be a hardpan layer near the soil surface.)

3. At each site, ask one person in your team to use his or her thumb to push a nail into the soil as far as it will go using moderate force. Then the student should measure the nail's height. Record this number.

NOTE—Try to use the same amount of force to push in the nail at each site. Do not use excessive force.

4. Rank your sites by how long it took for water to percolate; then present the data chart from your group. You may have students graph the results and present that data. Is there a relationship between nail heights and the time it took for the water to disappear?

5. What does the data tell you about the soil's ability to filter water, or to percolate? What assumptions can you make about the differences in soil you tested?

6. Why would a percolation test be important before someone builds a house? Why can't Sam and Laticia build their dream house?

Overview

If a duck can paddle in it, it's a wetland. If a duck can waddle on it, it's not. If only wetlands could be defined as simply as this, wetlands issues and legislation would be less muddy. In this activity, students will learn more about wetlands and about how land-use decisions and legislation affect these areas.

LEVELS
Grades 7-8

SUBJECTS
Science, Social Studies, Language Arts, Performing Arts

CONCEPTS
■ Populations of organisms exhibit variations in size and structure as a result of their adaptation to their habitats. (10.1)

■ The structure and scale of an ecosystem are influenced by factors such as soil type, climate, availability of water, and human activities. (10.2)

■ When the Earth is studied as an interacting ecological system, every action, regardless of its scale, affects the biosphere in some way. (10.3)

SKILLS
Analyzing, Making Decisions, Identifying Attributes and Components, Interpreting

OBJECTIVES
Students will ① study a wetland ecosystem and ② analyze the issues and opinions relating to the management and protection of wetlands.

MATERIALS
copies of student pages 263 and 264, materials listed in team assignments for Part A

TIME CONSIDERATIONS
Preparation: 20 minutes

Activity: Two or three 50-minute periods (Part A)
50 minutes (Part B)
50 minutes (Part C)
50 minutes (Part D)

Background

There are many types of *wetlands* including *bogs*, freshwater and salt water *marshes*, and *swamps*. Many of these areas are forested. They differ from lakes, rivers, and oceans because they are defined as areas having, at least periodically, waterlogged soils or standing water.

Wetlands stay wet for any of several reasons: They are in low areas that stay saturated by rain, they are fed from below by groundwater that is at or near the surface, they are near rivers or other bodies of water that flood them periodically, or they are saturated along the coasts by the tide. Beavers can make wetlands by damming a stream. People also create wetlands unintentionally by blocking normal water flow with construction, or intentionally by flooding areas for uses such as waterfowl breeding grounds.

For years, many people considered wetlands to be unproductive wastelands that should be filled in, channeled, or drained. However, in recent years, most people have come to appreciate the importance of maintaining this resource. Wetlands are valuable and productive in critical ways. They control floods by slowing down rushing water, thereby letting it spread out over a broader area and eddy around trees or other vegetation.

Wetlands also help purify water by trapping silt. As flood waters slow down in wetland areas, *sediments* and their impurities are deposited around roots of plants or trees. These sediments and impurities might otherwise affect aquatic life or cover the eggs of aquatic animals.

Wetlands along coasts or large lakes take the brunt of storms, reducing damage to adjacent land and reducing *erosion.* Finally, wetlands provide one of the most richly populated wildlife habitats in our nation.

According to the U.S. Fish and Wildlife Service's *Wetlands: Losses in the United States, 1780s to 1980s,* the area we now call the United States had about 450 million acres (159 million hectares) of wetlands during the Colonial American era. Broken down, the lower 48 states contributed approximately 221 million acres (89.5 million ha), Alaska another 170 million acres (70 million ha), and Hawaii about 59,000 acres (23,895 ha) to the total acreage of wetlands.

Today, we estimate that about 103.3 million acres remain. The change in numbers after 200 years is dramatic.

Although Alaska has lost less than 1 percent and Hawaii about 12 percent of their original wetland areas, the continental United States has lost about 53 percent of its total wetlands, which amounts to about 60 acres (24 ha) of wetlands lost every hour from the 1780s to the 1980s! California leads as the state with the largest percentage of wetlands lost (91 percent) with Florida losing the most acres of wetlands (9.3 million acres or 3.8 million ha). Much of the wetlands were developed to meet the demands of a growing population: converted into farms, towns, highways, and suburbs.

Of the 103.3 million acres (41.8 million ha) of wetlands in the U.S., 97.8 million acres or 39.6 million ha are freshwater wetlands and 5.5 million acres or 2.2 million ha are *estuarine,* or coastal wetlands. Most wetlands are found in the southern states of Alabama, Florida, Georgia, North Carolina, South Carolina, Louisiana, Mississippi, and Texas. Wetlands also cover large stretches of the Great Lake states of Michigan, Minnesota, and Wisconsin. Canada has about 127.2

million acres (0.75 million ha) of wetlands, 274.8 million acres (111.3 million ha) of which are classified as *peatlands.*

You might be surprised to learn that of the U.S. wetlands remaining today, roughly half are covered by forests. Good forestry practices have been recognized by both the environmental community and the federal government as compatible with wetlands conservation. Wetland forests provide clean water, flood control, fish and wildlife habitat, and recreation, in addition to a renewable timber supply.

A good example of a forested wetland is a *bottomland* hardwood forest, like those in Louisiana. An extension of the Mississippi River, these wet forests provide refuges for many animals. Multitudes of birds winter over in them and others breed there. Fishing industries downstream depend on the forests to slow fast-flowing water, to let the silt settle, and to keep nutrients necessary to the aquatic chain from being flushed downstream too rapidly. Although everyone agrees that wetlands must be protected, the problem is how to balance wetland values with conflicting human activities. Controversies revolve around land-use and private property rights, and over federal regulations that define wetlands.

Getting Ready
Part A: You will need permission and access to study a local wetland. Teams should gather the materials listed under their team assignments. Obtain a large map of your county.

PART A
ADOPT A WETLAND

Doing the Activity
1. Using the background information, discuss with students the characteristics of a wetland. Describe various types of wetlands: marshes, bogs, swamps, peatland, bottomland, and other places that are wet part of the year. (See the Glossary on page 371 for definitions of these terms.)

2. Have students describe wetlands they are familiar with in the area.

Display a large county map and try to locate several wetlands.

3. Have students choose several wetland areas that they might be able to study several times during the school year. (Local parks might offer the best opportunities.) Assign individuals or pairs the responsibility of contacting the owners or managers of these wetlands to find out if they can study the area, and if so, what guidelines they must observe. From among the possibilities, have students vote for the wetland they would like to adopt. Make sure that your class can get to the area and that administrators and parents support the project. You will probably need additional adult supervision when visiting the wetland.

4. Before they visit their adopted wetland, have students gather preliminary information about it from owners or managers or from local biologists or naturalists. Assign several students to be contacts for gathering this information. They should share with the rest of the class all information they receive. The class should determine the boundaries of the area they will study.

5. Prepare for the trip to their "adopted" wetland by dividing class members into several study teams: ① Photo Survey Team, ② Map Survey Team, ③ Plants Survey Team, ④ Animals Survey Team, and ⑤ Water Quality Survey Team. Explain the following instructions to each team and allot time for students to prepare before visiting the wetland. (You can also photocopy these instructions and mount each team's instructions on an index card.)

Photo Survey Team
This team will need at least one camera and film (preferably color), a clipboard, and flagging material. They should have a pre-trip conference to discuss what features of the wetland they should capture on film (for example, photos of wetland vegetation). When visiting the wetland, they should walk slowly around the perimeter of the designated area. Several students should tie pieces of

flagging to items they want to identify in the photos (such as a particular plant, boulder, or log). One or more students will take pictures of the flagged item plus general pictures of the area. One student will keep notes about every picture taken. Remind students to remove the flagging before they leave the area.

Map Survey Team

This group will need graph paper, clipboards, magnetic compasses, and flagging material. Students should have a pre-trip conference to decide how to design their map of the area and what features they should highlight on the map. When they arrive at the site, pairs of students will use clipboards and graph paper to make rough maps of the area from different vantage points. Students should estimate the distances as best they can or use a long tape measure. They should use a compass to indicate directions on the map. Afterward, with colored markers and symbols, the team should use the pairs' rough maps to create a large, detailed map of the wetland on a piece of poster paper.

Plant Survey Team

This team will need a clipboard and some basic field guides for trees, shrubs, flowers, and grasses that might occur in the wetland they've adopted (see Bibliography on page 385). They should have a pre-trip conference to decide how they will categorize and record the plants they observe (tall trees, small trees, shrubs, tall grasses, short grass, flowers, water plants). For their plant survey, they will set up a chart that has columns for describing each plant, its immediate environment, and its location. (Students can leave space for sketches.)

Animal Survey Team

This team will need several jars, a long-handled dipnet, a sieve, a magnifying glass, a clipboard, a white enamel tray (if possible), and field guides about animals likely to be in the area (see Bibliography on page 385). They should have a pre-trip conference to decide how they will locate and record animals. Remind them to

look for insects and other invertebrates in addition to birds, mammals, amphibians, and reptiles. For recording animals, they should make up a chart that has columns for descriptions, immediate environment, and location. At the site, have students use binoculars and magnifying glasses to look for animals. They can isolate aquatic creatures by dragging a dipnet through the water or by gently straining wet mud. They can observe organisms in a white enamel tray or white plate partially filled with water. (Try to involve a local naturalist or a college professor in the aquatic study project.) Students should describe or sketch these creatures as best they can and should use field guides to identify them. Tell students that some animals (regardless of size) can have a painful bite or sting. They should not handle animals unless they are told it is all right.

Water Quality Team

This team will need a pH testing kit or litmus paper, a test kit for dissolved oxygen (if possible), thermometer, meter stick, and a clipboard. Before going out, this team should practice using the testing equipment (pH, dissolved oxygen); the thermometers; and their touch to test soil moisture. (See "Soil Stories" on page 252 for the soil moisture test.) In their pre-trip conference, the team should assign pairs to perform tests at different locations (in the water, at the water's edge, at five meters from water). Tests should include measuring the depth of standing water in various spots, along with describing the water's color, smell, and movement, or the soil's moisture. When at the site, the pairs should gather information about water quality at various locations. Back in class, they should transfer their data to a chart that has columns for various water quality factors and for the location where factors were tested. Remember that sight and smell are not reliable indicators of water quality; low pH and low dissolved oxygen are more significant but also need to be analyzed by an expert.

6. After teams make one or more data-collecting trips to their adopted wetland, have them prepare data charts, reports, or maps. Each team should take 20 minutes to brief the group on their team's findings, lead a class discussion on the general features of each wetland, and give an impression of the area's ecological health.

7. Ask students to use the data presented so they can discuss whether some environmental warning signs in this wetland need further attention (such as low oxygen content in water, oil in the water, trash in the area, lack of wildlife). They should document why there might be problems and then should contact the owners or managers of the area to discuss ideas on how they might help improve the situation. Often, students can get permission to clean up a site or can take on more complicated projects under the supervision of those who manage the area.

PART B
WET DILEMMA

Doing the Activity
1. Describe the following scenario to the students:

Dr. Aliza Garcia wants to build a dental office on property she owns in Slidell, Louisiana. Although dry most of the time, her property and the surrounding area have been designated a wetland by the parish (county) government. She has heard that she must get a permit to build on her land.

2. Have students put themselves in Dr. Garcia's position. They should make a list of questions they want answered:

■ What classifies land as wetland?

■ What are the threats to the environment from building on wetlands?

■ What are the threats to the construction project?

■ What are Dr. Garcia's rights as a landowner?

Through brainstorming and looking through phone books, students should identify government agencies or private organizations that might provide information on how Dr. Garcia can get a permit. Display their brainstorming list on the chalkboard.

3. Ask students to contact agencies or organizations to get additional information and answers to their questions. Review with them the tips for gathering information in the Appendix 10 on page 382. Students may also invite members of various groups knowledgeable on wetlands regulations to make a class presentation. See addresses on page 382 for national agencies (such as the Army Corps of Engineers) whom they can contact for information on wetlands and permits.

4. When each team has gathered information from several sources, have students draft a letter to Dr. Garcia advising her whom to contact and what course to follow. Teams should then read their letters to the rest of the class and present findings that support their advice. Other teams can ask questions.

5. Have the entire class use these reports as students work together on a large piece of paper or chalkboard to create a flow chart that advises Dr. Garcia of the process she should follow to build (if possible) her office. A flow chart should indicate applications, costs, and responsibilities involved throughout the process.

PART C
MARSH OR MALL?

Doing the Activity
1. Have students read the letter to the editor on page 263.

2. Discuss with students the key issues presented in the letter. Who are the players and what are their positions? (property owner, local county official, federal government representative, land developer, interest groups)

3. Divide students into groups that research and write a short description of the positions of key players. What does each player stand to gain or lose by a decision concerning the property?

4. Set up a class debate between two teams with different interests: the property owner and land developer on one side and the government environmental officials on the other.

5. After the debate, discuss and summarize the issues presented. Try to reach a consensus about how to address the property owner's concerns.

6. Have each team write a letter to the property owner stating the result of the debate and their reaction to it.

PART D
HOME ON THE LAGOON

Doing the Activity
1. Have students read the Pala Lagoon case study on page 264.

2. Present to the students the following scenario in which a family wants to build a house on a piece of forestland on Coconut Point.

Fiaaipa'a wants to build a new home on a piece of wetland next to the Pala Lagoon. He will have to cut down some mangrove (togo) trees and fill the area with soil to have enough land to build. The village has requested that the government protect the area because it provides a large amount of food to the village. The government has a permit system to review project proposals and to make sure people build properly without hurting the community or the environment. A local environmental group is concerned because there is a rare tree, puzzlenut, on the proposed site.

3. Divide the students into teams, with each team taking the role of family, villagers, environmental group members, government officials, and others who are involved in the issue.

The following are possible role-playing assignments:

- Fiaaipa'a
- Home builder
- Village of Coconut Point
- Local environmental group representative
- Coastal Management Program Manager for American Samoa
- Parks and Recreation archeologist
- Environmental Protection Agency official for American Samoa
- Building engineer for Public Works
- Sewer and Water Division engineer
- Representative of the Government Office of Samoan Affairs
- Fiaaipa'a's lawyer
- Panel of judges at public hearing

4. Have students meet at a public hearing to decide if the building can be built and if so, how. After each group has presented its argument, have the panel of judges make a final decision. (It can be a compromise decision.)

REFERENCES
Dahl, Thomas E. *WETLANDS: LOSSES IN THE UNITED STATES, 1780s TO 1980s.* Washington, DC.: US. Fish and Wildlife Service, 1990.

Dahl, Thomas E. *WETLANDS: STATUS AND TRENDS IN THE CONTERMINOUS UNITED STATES, MID-1970s TO MID-1980s.* Washington, DC.: US. Fish and Wildlife Service, 1991.

Yamasaki, G., D. Itano, & R. Davis. *A STUDY OF AND RECOMMENDATIONS FOR THE MANAGEMENT OF THE MANGROVE AND LAGOON AREAS OF NU'UULI AND TAFUNA,* American Samoai. NOAA, 1985.

Land Grant Program, American Samoa Community College, Pago Pago, American Samoa.

LETTER TO THE EDITOR

Dear Editor:

A very important debate is currently raging in the country. Right now "wetlands" is a catch-all term that is used to describe a variety of ecosystems ranging from prairie potholes to tidal salt marshes. As a result, my rights on my own land have been sharply limited.

Nearly 25 years ago, I bought 30 acres (12 hectares) of land as a retirement investment. The property was then farmland but was later zoned as commercial. For the past five years, my property has been under contract by several developers who have spent many thousands of dollars trying to get a government permit to develop the land for a shopping mall. The plan has been refused because under new government regulations my property is considered a "wetland."

Now the county wants to put a high tax on my property because it is zoned commercial even though its best use right now is as a mosquito breeding area and a dumping ground for anyone who needs a trash disposal site. Radical environmentalists see my property as some kind of monument to plant life at my expense. I am not alone. Many people all over the United States are in the same predicament.

I want the government off my back. I have rights to my own property.

Signed,
Dissatisfied Landowner

THE PALA LAGOON CASE STUDY

The following information is adapted from a study of Pala Lagoon conducted in 1985:

Pala Lagoon is the only large, well-protected lagoon on the island of Tutuila (TOO-too-EE-luh) in American Samoa. Tutuila is mountainous and roughly circular, approximately 1 mile (1.6 km) across, and has a surface area of about 0.75 square miles (1.9 sq. km). Depths within the lagoon vary from 1-5 feet (0.3-1.5 m), depending on the tide. The lagoon entrance is approximately 1,200 feet (366 m) wide with most of it a shallow reef top—1-3 feet (0.3-0.9 m) deep. Water flows in and out through the channel with about 40 percent of the lagoon changing on each tidal cycle.

Along the eastern and northern shores of the lagoon, extensive stands of red mangle (Rhizophora) and oriental mangroves (Bruguiera gymnorhiza) cover an approximate area of 90 acres (36.5 hectares). Because the flat part of the island is the mangrove area, residents like to build homes there. The northern shore has several streams that carry freshwater into the lagoon. In addition to the larger Papa and Vaitele streams, there are a number of small streams. Except for the Papa, the streams flow only during rainy periods, which are frequent; the average yearly rainfall is nearly 200 inches (508 cm).

On the western edge of the lagoon is a public recreation and picnic area that is regularly used by large numbers of residents. Many of them use the lagoon on a daily basis for fishing, crabbing, and other food-gathering activities.

Mangrove ecosystems have been proven valuable in many ways. They help prevent shoreline erosion, settle sediment that is washed down from uphill, and break down organic material to be used in the food chain. One of the most valuable functions of the mangrove ecosystem is as a nursery and spawning area for many of the fish and invertebrates found on the reef outside the lagoon.

The residents need to realize the health risk and cost of an unhealthy lagoon. An example of the cost of an unhealthy lagoon was the 1984 outbreak of cholera in Truk (another island in American Samoa): Many lives were lost; tourism and fishing industries declined.

Another reason for special concern about Pala Lagoon is the flora found there. The mangrove forests on Tutuila are being threatened. Mangrove areas that existed in Pago, Fagatogo, Faga'alu, and Utulei have been completely eliminated. The only major mangrove forest still existing is found in Nu'uuli (Pala Lagoon), with smaller patches in Aua, Vatia Alofau, Masefau, and Leone. These areas, however, are slowly being reduced. The mangrove and lagoon areas are presently being affected by numerous activities, including cutting and filling.

Most of the cutting and filling was to build home sites. At several sites, trash had been commonly used as the initial fill material over which layers of cinders were packed. In one particular area, behind a village called South Pacific Traders, an extensive portion of the mangrove forest and lagoon had been cut and filled by this method. Along Coconut Point, many families use the edge of the lagoon as a dump site.

The largest mangrove forest— along the main road near the intersection to Coconut Point—is slowly being cut and filled as the demand for new land and home sites increases. A large area near the end of Coconut Point has a new stand of mangroves that, if left undisturbed, should be comparable in size to the older forests in the next 20 to 30 years.

The area around the lagoon also contains two and possibly three species of plants that are considered endangered or threatened. These rare species, along with all other plants and animals in the lagoon ecosystem, maintain a balance and have a purpose, or niche. If this balance is not maintained, all plants and animals will be affected. With cooperation among and proper management by the surrounding villages and government agencies, future generations of Samoans and visitors may be able to see the natural wildlife and vegetation as it exists today in a "natural" balance.

One of these rare species is Xylocarpus moluccensis, known as "le'ile'i," or the puzzlenut tree. Originally recorded only along the western end of the lagoon, it was also found along the lagoon edge of Coconut Point during this study. More than a dozen trees were counted in this one area. Attempts to locate the tree along the western edge of the lagoon (Lions Park) were unsuccessful. Those trees may have been cut during one or more of the fill projects along the lagoon in the past five years. It is likely that the puzzlenut also exists along the northern shore of the lagoon.

Indiscriminate landfill and clearing for homes or plantations could be detrimental, not only to the mangroves and water quality of the lagoon, but also to the unusual and rare trees and shrubs on the island. These threatened species and the areas where they are found should be identified, and the village council and landowners should be told of their special values so they can be protected in the future.

Overview
Did you know that sometimes the air in our homes, schools, and offices can be worse for our health than the air outside? In this activity, students will learn more about indoor air quality, and what can be done about it.

Background
This activity deals with indoor air quality. For a long time, when people talked of air quality, they meant the quality of the air outside and pollutants like acid rain, automobile exhaust, smokestack emissions, and smog. More recently, issues of indoor air quality have begun to attract attention as various human ailments have reportedly been linked to the quality of indoor air, and terms like "sick buildings" or "secondhand smoke" are often used. Health experts are calling for routine testing of indoor air and for further study of indoor air hazards.

On the average, people in North America spend about 80 percent of their time indoors—working, cooking, eating, sleeping, watching television, shopping, and so on. The trend toward tightly sealed buildings and homes for energy conservation complicates problems of indoor air quality by preventing fresh outside air from replacing polluted indoor air.

Indoor air pollutants come from a variety of sources that can lead to health problems. Small leaks from gas appliances can build up to dangerous levels. Potentially dangerous vapors are emitted from certain types of building materials such as carpets, drapes, ceiling panels, and plywood. Paints, pesticides, aerosols, air conditioners, household cleaners, and dust put pollutants in indoor air. Stoves, heaters, and fireplaces give off smoke, soot, and gases that can be harmful to human health.

Unfortunately, most pollutants are made of particles that are too small to see, and smell is not a reliable indicator. Many pollutants actually have a pleasing smell such as ingredients found in some perfumes and air fresheners, pipe smoke, and new leather that has been chemically treated.

Some indoor air pollutants are actually microscopic organisms such as mold, mildew, bacteria, viruses, and dust mites that can cause sickness or allergic reactions.

Of all indoor air pollutants, radon is probably one of the most insidious. Radon is an odorless, colorless gas that occurs naturally in varying concentrations in all types of rock and soil. It is produced naturally from the radioactive decay of Radium-226. Radon breaks down into several radioactive particles that become attached to larger particles in the air. When inhaled, these particles get lodged in lungs and can increase the risk of lung cancer.

Radon differs from other indoor air pollutants in that it occurs naturally and enters buildings on its own. Radon gas constantly emerges from the earth and goes into the atmosphere. But when it seeps into the basement of a poorly ventilated home or building, it can accumulate in unhealthy amounts. Most radon that enters buildings comes through holes or cracks in the building's foundation. Radon also gets into buildings through well water and through building materials made from rock, brick, or concrete.

Getting Ready
Make copies of student pages 269–273.

PART A
PARTICLE PURSUIT

Doing the Activity
1. Ask students if they've ever seen indoor air pollution. Chances are they haven't seen much, because, for the most part, it's invisible.

2. Tell them they will learn about many types of indoor air pollution. Most of these pollutants are made of particles that are too small to be seen

LEVELS
Grades 6-8

SUBJECTS
Science, Language Arts

CONCEPTS
- Pollutants are harmful by-products of human and natural systems which can enter ecosystems in various ways. (7.3)
- The structure and scale of an ecosystem are influenced by factors such as soil type, climate, availability of water, and human activities. (10.2)
- When the Earth is studied as an interacting ecological system, every action, regardless of its scale, affects the biosphere in some way. (10.3)

SKILLS
Defining Problems, Observing, Comparing and Contrasting, Determining Causes and Effects, Identifying Attributes and Components, Analyzing, Interpreting, Solving Problems

OBJECTIVES
Students will ① identify various types of indoor air pollutants and their sources, ② understand how various pollutants can be harmful to people's health, ③ trace how radon can get into buildings and eventually into our bodies, and ④ take action to improve indoor air quality.

MATERIALS
Part A: microscope slides or blank overhead transparencies, petroleum jelly, white paper, masking tape, magnifying glasses, wax paper, a boiled potato, microscope (optional)
Part B: copies of student pages 269, 270 and 271, balloon, felt-tip marker, handful of soil, large glass jar, water, blue food coloring, transparencies and overhead projector (optional)
Part C: copies of student page 272
Enrichment: copies of student page 273

TIME CONSIDERATIONS
Preparation: 40 minutes
Activity: Four 50-minute periods over a month (Part A) One or two 50-minute periods
(Part B) One or two 50-minute periods, possibly over several weeks
(Part C) Enrichment: 30 minutes plus homework

with the naked eye; however, some pollutant particles are large enough to see.

3. Divide your group into teams. Each team should have a flashlight, notebook, and pencil. (If you only have one flashlight, perform the activity as a demonstration.) Tell students that they will do this activity in the dark, so they should be careful and stay calm.

4. Close the blinds and turn off the lights. Show the students how particles in the air show up in the flashlight beam.

5. Tell each team to go to a different location in the room and use the flashlight to see what's in the air. As one person holds the flashlight steady, the others should look at the projected beam and try to describe the particles they see and the relative abundance of different types of particles. Have students hold the flashlight very high and very low to see if there's a difference in the particles they see.

6. After about 10 minutes, turn the lights back on and have each team describe what they saw in their beams. Do not have them draw any conclusions at this point.

7. Tell students that they will now look for smaller particles. Give each team a microscope slide. (If slides are not available, cut an overhead transparency into strips approximately the size of microscope slides.)

8. Tell each team to smear a thin layer of petroleum jelly on the slide and to place it in a different location in the room or building. Make sure teams select a wide variety of locations such as on shelves or in closets. Two teams should put their slides outdoors (either on the window sill or taped to the window) for comparison with the indoor samples. Leave the slides in place for 24 hours.

9. The next day, each team should put their slide on a white piece of paper and study the particles that stuck to it. Students should use a magnifying glass and, if possible, a microscope to examine their slides. They should take notes of what they see, draw sketches if they want, and try to categorize the particles they find. Do their findings differ from what they saw in the light beam?

10. Each team should report its findings but students should not draw any conclusions at this time.

11. Finally, give each team a thin slice of boiled potato on a piece of wax paper. Take one slice, wrap it completely in wax paper, and put it in the refrigerator—this is the control slice. Tell students to put their slice in the same place they put their slides. The potato slice will collect particles the same way the slide did. The difference is that when biological pollutants such as bacteria, mold, and mildew land on the potato, they will grow into visible colonies.

12. Leave the potato slices in place for a week or two. Students should examine the slices every day with a magnifying glass, then make notes on different shapes, colors, and smells that they notice.

13. After this period, have each team report on what they saw on their slice. Besides other particles, do they notice growths, or any living colonies? Do they have an idea what these organisms are?

14. Have each team review its findings in each phase of the experiment: flashlight, slide, and potato. Students should draw conclusions as to what particles are present in the indoor air (soot, fibers, bacteria, mold, chalk dust).

■ Are certain people more sensitive than others to these pollutants? (Yes, people with allergies.)

■ Do students think these pollutants are in dangerously high concentrations? (They will probably have to ask an air quality expert.)

■ How could the concentration of the pollutants be lowered? (Better ventilation or air-filtering devices could be installed.)

PART B
INVISIBLE GAS ATTACK

Doing the Activity

1. Ask students if they've heard of radon, and if so, what are their perceptions? Using the background information, discuss a few facts about radon and its potential harm. Students should read "Invisible Gas Attack" on page 269.

2. Ask students what we mean when we say radon is a gas. Discuss how the characteristics of gases influence radon and its movement. Explain that gases will expand or move to fill up a space. Demonstrate movement by blowing up a balloon. As the gas (air) expands, the balloon gets larger.

3. Explain that gases such as air and radon move through soil slowly. When minerals decay or organic matter decomposes, the gases generated in these processes are released through the soil into the atmosphere. With the following experiment, demonstrate how air moves through soil:

Put a large, clear glass jar of water in a place where it is easily visible and will not be disturbed. The water represents the soil. Put a large drop of blue food coloring, which represents air, into the water. Have students check the jar several times during the class to see how much the "air" has spread. Does it spread quickly or slowly? In any particular direction?

4. Radon can seep through all kinds of rock fractures. These fractures occur when different rock types (*igneous, sedimentary, or metamorphic*) are side by side. Sedimentary rocks (such as limestone or shale) also have many internal fractures and cracks.

5. Distribute "Where will the Radon Go" on page 270. Allow students 5 to 10 minutes to trace radon's route from the ground into the atmosphere or into people's homes.

6. Make a transparency of student page 271 and put it on an overhead projector. Ask several students to come forward one at a time to trace different radon routes, until all possible routes have been traced.

7. Distribute copies of "Trace the Radon Routes" on page 271 and repeat the same exercise as in Step 5 to see how radon might travel within a building. Discuss these questions with students:

- How many different ways can radon enter a home?

- What do you think happens to radon once it is in your home?

- Can you get rid of radon once it is in your home? How?

- How do you find out if your home is contaminated with radon?

- What can you do to prevent radon from continuing to enter your home?

PART C
AIR PATROL

Doing the Activity

1. Have the students read about "Primary Pollutants" on student page 272. Discuss with students the harmful effect each pollutant can have if it enters our indoor air supply in significant proportions.

2. Using this information, have students design a checklist to look for indoor air quality hazards in their own homes. (old garbage, excessive dust, chemical smells, mildew odors, tobacco smoke, gas leaks, crack in the foundation—possible radon)

3. Have students take their checklist home to inspect for potential air quality hazards. They should put a checkmark next to the ones they find and a star next to the ones they feel might be severe enough to warrant action.

4. After a few days, review the checklists with your students. Spend time discussing the starred items. Does the whole class think that these problems are severe enough to warrant action? Are there items on the list that weren't starred but should have been?

5. Have students suggest ideas on how they might remedy some of the problems they identified in their home survey of indoor air (test for radon; restrict indoor smoking;

improve ventilation; clean or change filters in air conditioners, heaters, humidifiers, and purifiers; cultivate house plants; seal cracks in foundations; hang dry-cleaned clothes outside for a few minutes before bringing them in).

6. Have students choose a few actions they can take to improve the air quality in their homes, and give them several days or weeks to implement these improvements. At a set date, have each student give a progress report to discuss any changes or difficulties in making improvements.

Enrichment
Give students the "Home Radon Exposure Survey" on student page 273 to fill out at home. You can suggest that students ask a parent to help them answer the survey questions. Have students report their findings.

END NOTES...

ASSESSMENT OPPORTUNITY
Have students list ways radon could potentially contaminate their homes. The students can make a cut-away drawing similar to the handout on page 271, to help them identify possible radon routes in their own homes.

RELATED ACTIVITIES
Air Plants, Pollution Search, Waste Watchers, Air to Drive, Plant a Tree

REFERENCES
A CITIZEN'S GUIDE TO RADON: WHAT IT IS AND WHAT TO DO ABOUT IT. Washington, DC.: US. Environmental Protection Agency, Office of Air and Radiation, August 1992.

DEADLY DANGER IN US. HOMES. Weekly Reader 46(6). (October 12, 1990.)

ENVIRONMENTAL RESOURCE GUIDE: AIR QUALITY FOR GRADES 6-8. Pittsburgh, Pennsylvania: Air and Waste Management Association, 1991.

EPA ACTIVITIES UPDATE. Washington, DC.: US. Environmental Protection Agency, Office of Communications and Public Affairs, October 15, 1991.

Swiss, Martha B. *AIR POLLUTION.* Pittsburgh, Pennsylvania: Air and Waste Management Association's Public Education Division, 1991.

INVISIBLE GAS ATTACK

What Are Sources of Radon?

Radon is released as a gas when small amounts of uranium break down in the ground. Usually, the gas rises through the soil and escapes into the air outside where radon has low concentration and little effect on people inside buildings. However, when the rising gas releases into a house or other building, the radon seeps in and builds up to dangerously high levels.

Radon enters buildings through cracks and holes in the foundation such as cracks in a concrete floor or wall, drains in the floor, or holes around pipes that go through the floor or wall. Sometimes even well water can carry radon and release the gas into a house. Several things help radon to enter a building. Fans in kitchen ranges, bathrooms, and clothes dryers force air out of the house, creating a small suction that can draw radon into the house from the ground. Also, as warm air rises in a building, a draft forms, which can draw radon up through foundation cracks or holes.

How Does Radon Affect Health?

Radon gas forms tiny radioactive particles. Breathing carries the particles deep into the lungs. These particles then release small bursts of energy that can damage the lung tissue. This damage can lead to lung cancer later in life.

Breathing air with high radon levels is like smoking cigarettes. The more you breathe smoke or radon, the more risk you have of getting lung cancer.

People who smoke and are exposed to radon have higher health risks than do nonsmokers exposed to radon, says the Environmental Protection Agency (EPA).

While scientists do not agree on exactly how great the health risk from radon is, there is little debate that the risk is serious. The longer the time and the higher the radon level a person is exposed to, the greater the risk of developing lung cancer. According to the EPA, testing your home is the only way to know if your health is threatened by radon.

How Widespread Is the Radon Risk?

The EPA estimates that millions of homes have high radon levels. Studies have also shown that radon is a problem in many school classrooms.

Since radon is found almost everywhere in our country, the EPA urges all homeowners and schools to test for radon. Although a house may have a low radon reading, each neighboring house should still be tested, because levels may vary widely from house to house even in the same neighborhood.

How Can You Deal with Radon?

Radon is a serious problem in many homes, but high levels of radon can be easily lowered. Experts are available who specialize in reducing high radon levels. The cost is usually comparable to the cost of many other home repairs.

The important first step is to test your home for radon to find out if there is a problem. For more information about how to test, call 1-800-SOS-RADON.

How Is Radon Detected?

Since you cannot see or smell radon, you need special equipment to detect it.

- Radon can be detected using small devices that measure radon in the air. These devices are called "radon detectors" and are sold in hardware or retail stores and by mail.

- The detector is left in a room for several days and is then sent to a laboratory to be analyzed. If the laboratory tests show a level of radon above 4 pCi/L, remedial action is called for.

- The two most popular, commercially available radon detectors are the charcoal canister and the alpha track detector. Both devices are exposed to the air in your home for a specified period of time and sent to a laboratory for analysis. Charcoal canisters have a test period of three to seven days and one canister costs approximately $10 to $25; alpha track detectors have a minimum test period of two to four weeks and one detector costs approximately $20 to $50.

- Other techniques used to measure radon levels may require operation by trained personnel, and such techniques may be more expensive than the devices shown above.

WHERE WILL THE RADON GO?

DIRECTIONS—Use a colored marker to trace radon's route from the ground into the atmosphere or into people's homes.

TRACE THE
RADON ROUTES

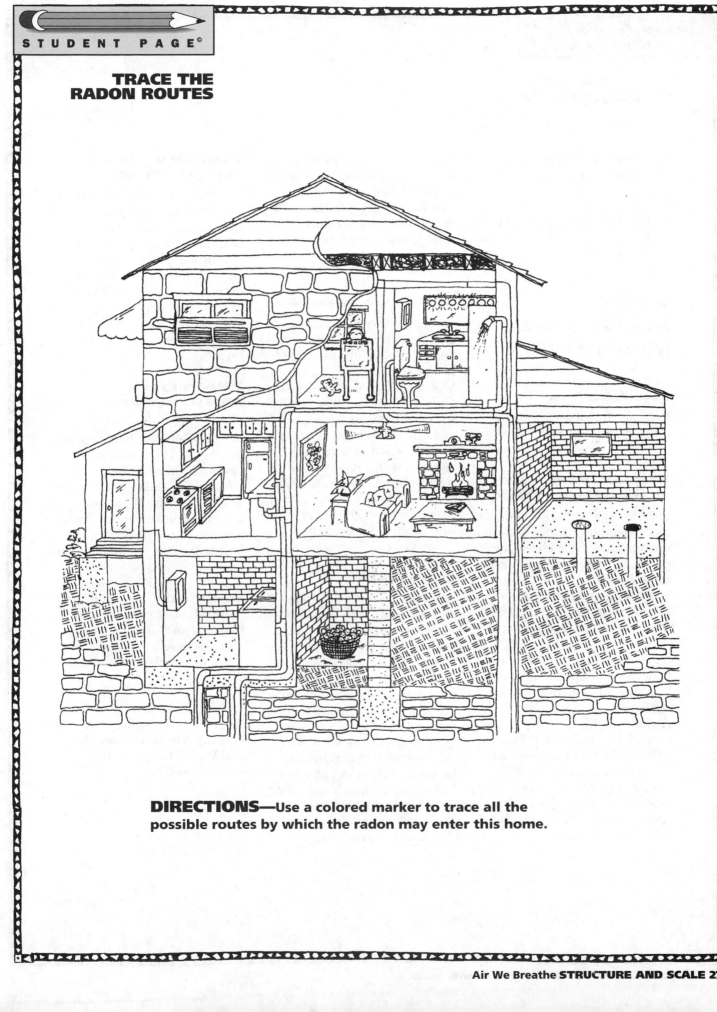

DIRECTIONS—Use a colored marker to trace all the possible routes by which the radon may enter this home.

PRIMARY POLLUTANTS

These indoor air pollutants pose health risks:

1 Radon

2 Formaldehyde (for-MAHL-duh-hide) and Other Volatile Organic Compounds (*VOCs*)

3 Tobacco Smoke

4 Asbestos

5 Combustion By-products

6 Biological Pollutants

Radon

Refer to "Invisible Gas Attack" on student page 269.

Formaldehyde and Other VOCs

Volatile organic compounds are made of atoms that are found in various products such as glues, paints, and solvents. Although these compounds are "naturally" derived, they may pose serious environmental and health threats when in high enough concentrations or in poorly ventilated enclosures. Formaldehyde, for example, is a common VOC found in furniture, foam insulation, plywood, carpets, drapes, particleboard, glues, and other building supplies. It irritates the eyes and nose, may cause respiratory ailments, and has been linked to cancer in laboratory studies. Other sources of VOCs are household cleaners and paints, wood finishes, pesticides, air fresheners; chemicals in carpeting and fabric; and even dry-cleaned clothes. (Perchlorethyene, a VOC, is among the solvents used in the dry-cleaning process.)

Tobacco Smoke

Smoke from cigarettes, pipes, and cigars contains many pollutants including inorganic gases, heavy metals, particulates, VOCs, and aromatic hydrocarbons. Unfortunately, people who don't smoke are still faced with the bad effects of breathing these VOCs: The latest EPA report says that secondhand tobacco smoke may cause 6,000 deaths and cases of cancer and heart disease each year in otherwise healthy nonsmokers.

Asbestos

Asbestos was once a commonly used building and insulation material (until the 1970s in the United States). It was often mixed with a cement-like substance and could be conveniently sprayed or plastered on ceilings or other surfaces. With time, asbestos starts to disintegrate and it releases tiny fibers that float in the air. They can be inhaled and can lodge deep in lung tissue, which may cause lung cancer and asbestosis, a chronic scarring of the lungs that hinders breathing.

Combustion By-products

The fuels we use in our homes for heat, hot water, and cooking can release pollutants into our homes. Kerosene, natural gas, and oil can give off nitrogen and sulfur dioxides, carbon monoxide, and formaldehyde. Even wood burned in fireplaces gives off very fine particulates, which can be unhealthy to breathe.

Biological Pollutants

Fungi and bacteria will grow in humidifiers and heating, ventilating, and air conditioning systems if they are not properly cleaned and maintained. These systems can also bring biological contaminants indoors and circulate them throughout a building. The contaminants can cause people to have allergic reactions to pollen, fungi, and animal dander (dandruff from animal hair, feathers or skin); bacterial and viral infections; and reactions to chemical toxins that are released by fungi.

(Adapted from ENVIRONMENTAL RESOURCE GUIDE—AIR QUALITY FOR GRADES 6-8 by permission of Air and Waste Management Association.)

HOME RADON EXPOSURE SURVEY

1 Check geologic and soil maps of your area. Determine the type of bedrock and soil underneath your home.

- What is the main type of bedrock in your area?

- What types of soil are in your area?

2 What types of building materials are in your home?

3 Describe the foundation of your home.

4 Do you have a basement?

- Does the basement floor have cracks?

- Do your basement walls have cracks?

- Is your basement sealed to keep moisture out?

- Is your basement completely below ground?

- Does the basement have ventilation?

5 Is your home drafty or tightly sealed with insulation?

6 Is there a place for air to circulate beneath your home?

7 Does your home have an exhaust fan? Where is it located? How often do you use it?

8 Do you use fans other than exhaust fans? What kind? Where are they located?

9 Do you air out your house for several hours or days from time to time?

10 About how many hours do you spend in your home every day?

11 In which room(s) do you spend most of your time at home?

12 What is the water source for your home? If you use well water, does the water flow through limestone or shale?

(Adapted from ENVIRONMENTAL RESOURCE GUIDE–AIR QUALITY FOR GRADES 6-8 by permission of Air and Waste Management Association.)

Overview

Every year some 41 percent of all the energy we use in the United States is wasted needlessly. By cutting energy waste, we can reduce our demand for sources of new energy and reduce the amount of pollution we create. In this activity, your students can take a look at how they use energy in their own homes and how they can reduce the amount of energy they waste.

LEVELS
Grades 5-8

SUBJECT
Science, Math, Social Studies

CONCEPTS
■ Conservation and management technologies, when appropriately applied to the use or preservation of natural resources, can enhance and extend the usefulness of the resource as well as the quality of the environment. (11.2)

■ If planned, constructed, and landscaped to be compatible with the environment in which they will be located, human-built environments can conserve resources, enhance environmental quality, and promote the comfort and well-being of those who will live within them. (11.3)

SKILLS
Observing, Solving Problems, Evaluating

OBJECTIVES
Students will ① identify ways to save energy in their daily lives and ② explain how saving energy can reduce air pollution.

MATERIALS
copies of student pages 278 and 279, thermometers, art supplies, calculators (optional)

TIME CONSIDERATIONS
Preparation: 15 minutes

Activity: Several 50-minute periods over a week

Background

When you drive to the store, take a shower, turn on the air conditioner or a lamp, you're using energy. Much of the energy we use comes from burning fossil fuels such as coal, natural gas, oil, and gasoline. When fossil fuels are burned, large amounts of carbon dioxide (CO_2) are emitted into the atmosphere.

Carbon dioxide, water vapor, and methane are sometimes referred to as *greenhouse gases*. They are a natural part of Earth's atmosphere. Like the walls of a greenhouse, they let sunlight in, but trap the heat that radiates from Earth (see diagram on opposite page). This heat-trapping mechanism is called the *greenhouse effect* and is critical to life on Earth. Without it, the planet would be much colder—too cold to support life as we know it. However, concentrations of many greenhouse gases in the atmosphere have been increasing for the past 130 years or so, and this increase could lead to changes in Earth's climate.

Since 1860, average CO_2 levels have increased more than 25 percent. A lot of this excess CO_2 has come from burning fossil fuels (in automobiles, power plants, factories, and so on). Although most of these fuels are being burned in more developed countries, less-developed countries are expected to put greater levels of CO_2 into the atmosphere as they acquire more automobiles and other fossil-fuel burning technologies. Levels of *chlorofluorocarbons* or CFCs (used in air conditioners, solvents, the manufacture of plastic foams, and other products); methane (from sources as diverse as rice paddies, landfills, cows, and termites); and nitrous oxide (from fertilizers, livestock wastes, and other sources) in the atmosphere have also increased. Concentrations of all these

gases in Earth's atmosphere continue to rise: CO_2 at about 0.4 percent per year, methane at about 1 percent per year, CFCs at about 5 percent per year, and nitrous oxide at 0.2 percent per year.

The United States is an urban industrial society, and most of our machines run on carbon-based fuels. Each person in the United States is responsible for producing 2.3 tons of atmospheric carbon a year. About half of that comes from our cars. Close behind us are citizens of other industrialized countries: Canada (1.8 tons per capita); Western Europe (0.9 tons); Japan (0.9 tons); China (0.2 tons); and India (0.1 tons). At current rates of growth, atmospheric concentrations of CO_2 will have doubled from pre-industrial levels by approximately 2025. Some scientists agree that this doubling of atmospheric CO_2 levels will raise average temperatures on Earth by a few degrees Celsius.

While these scientists agree that the increase in atmospheric CO_2 concentration will raise average world temperatures, they do not agree on the effects of such *global warming*. Some scientists believe global warming could disrupt weather patterns worldwide; could flood coasts; could extend the ranges of some disease-causing organisms; and could alter natural habitats, causing some plants and animals to become extinct. Others believe that the changes could be beneficial—increasing food production by lengthening growing seasons for crops and decreasing the need for heating in many areas. Some scientists don't believe global warming will happen at all. Because no one can predict with any certainty what effects increased levels of CO_2 will have on the planet, people disagree about what should be done. For instance, the many people who believe that global warming will occur with severe negative effects on the planet argue for immediately reducing CO_2 emissions, more stringently banning CFCs, planting trees, slowing population growth, raising the cost of fossil fuels, and other actions. Many others believe that we don't know enough yet; they advocate a more cautious approach. They believe that greatly curtailing CO_2 emissions, for example, could have devastating economic consequences and that we should be more sure of the problem before designing solutions (see Background for "Our Changing World" on page 328).

Many countries, organizations, and individuals around the world are concerned enough about the threat of global warming that they've already taken steps to reduce their CO_2 emissions.

At the United Nations Conference on Environment and Development (UNCED, or the Earth Summit) in Rio de Janeiro, Brazil, in 1992, all participating countries signed an agreement to stabilize or reduce their CO_2 emissions (no target dates or reductions were set).

Getting Ready

Make a copy of student pages 278 and 279 for each student. You might also call your local electric company and find out how your electricity is generated.

Doing the Activity

1. Ask the students to brainstorm a list of ways they use energy in a day.

2. Create a master list of all these activities and put it where everyone can see it.

3. Using the background information, discuss with your students the connection between energy use and pollution. Be sure to point out that burning fossil fuels is a major source of air pollution, including CO_2 emissions that contribute to the greenhouse effect.

4. Have students identify which of the energy-using activities that are listed in Step 2 rely on fossil fuels. (See Background for "Energy Sleuths" on page 126 for more about fossil fuels.) Have them name some ways they could cut down on this energy use. List their ideas where everyone can see them.

5. Pass out copies of "Home Audit" on page 278 to the students and explain that they're going to do an energy audit of their homes or apartments. Explain that the first thing they need to do is read their electric meter. Use the diagram on page 276 to explain how students can read their electric meter. You may also need to create other examples to be sure that everyone understands how to read a meter.

1 The sun's energy warms the Earth's surface.

2 Some of the sun's energy is radiated from the Earth's surface, through the atmosphere, and back into space.

3 When green house gases and water vapor accumulate in the atmosphere, they tend to absorb heat radiated from the Earth's surface and direct it back toward the Earth. As a result, the temperature of the earth's surface may increase.

Reading an Electric Meter

An electric meter consists of four round dials. Read the dials from left to right. If the dial points directly to a number, record that number. If it lies between two numbers, record the smaller number. For example, the number of kilowatts shown below are 4,130 (in "A") and 2,045 (in "B").

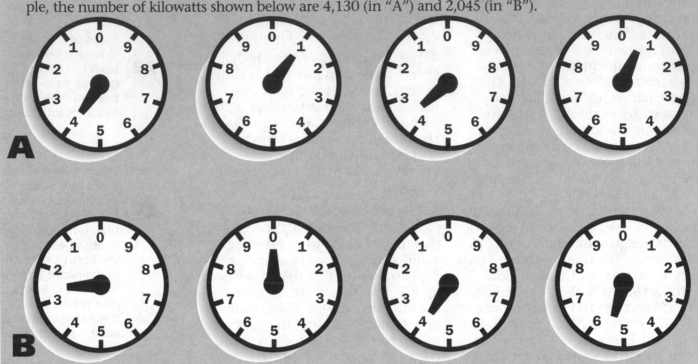

For students who live in apartment buildings, suggest that they talk to the building superintendent to see if they can have access to the meters.

6. Exactly one week after their first reading, students will read the meter again to determine the number of kilowatt hours of electricity their family used during the week (a kilowatt hour is the amount of energy expended by 1 kilowatt in 1 hour). During the time between their two readings, they should go all around their home, filling in the other items on the sheet.

NOTE—Depending on the level of your students, you might want to recommend that they do their energy audits with help from their parents.

7. When the students have filled out their sheets, have them share the information they collected. Keep a running total on the chalkboard of everyone's kilowatt usage, and post the class total where everyone can see it.

8. Have students calculate the amount of CO_2 their family generates each week and the amount the class generates each week using the fact that, on average, power plants (of all types) in the United States generate 1.5 pounds (.68 kg) of CO_2 per kilowatt hour. Then have students calculate how much CO_2 they generate in a year.

NOTE—Utilities usually get their electricity from a variety of sources, including coal-burning, natural gas, hydro-electric or nuclear power plants. These different types of plants generate different amounts of CO_2 per kilowatt hour. For example, hydropower and nuclear power plants generate little CO_2 per kilowatt hour. High-sulfur, coal-fired steam plants, however, generate 2 pounds (.90 kg) per kilowatt hour. Just how much CO_2 your students generate per kilowatt hour at any given time depends on the types of plants your local utility uses to generate electricity at that time. The simplest way to estimate the amount of CO_2 you generate per kilowatt hour is to use the national average for all power plants which is: 1.5 pounds (.68 kg).

9. Have students look back at the list of energy-using activities they generated earlier. Which ones do they think use the most energy? Can they think of anything they could do to reduce the energy they use? For example, they could turn off lights when they leave a room, carpool, ride their bike, or take public transportation, think about what they want before they open the refrigerator door, encourage their parents to buy energy-efficient appliances when they need new ones, and so on.

10. Now pass out copies of "Saving a Ton of CO_2" on page 279 and go over it with the students. You might, for instance, ask them which action on the page will result in the single greatest savings of CO_2 production. [For example, turning down the thermostat 10 degrees at night on an electric heating system saves 2,070 pounds (937.7 kg) a year.] Or how many pounds of CO_2 could you save in a year by replacing a single 100-watt light bulb with a lower-energy fluorescent bulb. [160 pounds (72.5 kg) a year.] What actions on the page look like things they could do in their own homes?

11. Have the students take the pages home to go over with their families. They should identify things they will do to reduce the amount of CO_2 they produce. Have students record those things in the blanks on the right side of the page and then add the total CO_2 they would save in a year.

Enrichment

1. Have students read their electric meter or look at their electric bill so they can keep track of the number of kilowatt hours of electricity they use over a longer period. (Electric bills specify the number of kilowatt hours used each month.) Is the monthly usage fairly constant through the year or does it rise and fall? (Students can analyze their usage by making a graph.) What might account for increases or decreases in energy use during the year?

2. Do an energy audit at your school, or contact your local electric utility company, and ask if they will do a professional energy audit (with students watching). Then design and carry out an energy-savings plan. As part of the plan, for example, students could educate other people or younger students about turning off lights when they leave a classroom. Or they could caulk windows in their classroom or throughout the school.

3. Ask a landscape architect to visit and recommend ways to save energy by planting trees, shrubs, and ground cover on the school grounds. For example, the landscaper might recommend planting trees or shrubs to block winter winds, provide shade, or channel cooling breezes to the building. Then develop and carry out a plan to implement some of the recommendations. Besides saving energy, trees and other plants will absorb CO_2 out of the atmosphere. (See "Plant a Tree" on page 95.)

4. Have students take copies of the brochures made in the Assessment Opportunity and distribute them in their neighborhoods. They could also make copies of the "Saving a Ton of CO_2" page and distribute them along with their brochures. If people decide to reduce their CO_2 production, they can let your group know and they can keep a tally in your room of how many tons of CO_2 people have saved because of their campaign.

5. Have students research energy-efficient home designs such as active or passive solar and earth-sheltered homes, or examine other energy-saving technologies and report on them to the rest of the group.

END NOTES...

ASSESSMENT OPPORTUNITY
Have students write a brochure that outlines energy-saving actions people can take and explain why saving energy is important. Their brochure should include an explanation of the link between energy use and air pollution.

RELATED ACTIVITIES
Energy Sleuths, Pollution Search, Air to Drive, Every Drop Counts

REFERENCES
SAVING A TON OF CO2 adapted from Beat the Heat: The CO2 Challenge. Scholastic and the Children's Earth Fund.

Brown, Lester, et al. *STATE OF THE WORLD*. 1992. New York: W.W. Norton. 1992.

Hammond, Allen L., ed. *WORLD RESOURCES 1992-1993:* A Report by the World Resources Institute in Collaboration With the UNDP. New York: Oxford University Press. 1992.

Miller, G.T. *LIVING IN THE ENVIRONMENT*. Belmont, California: Wadsworth Publishing Co., 1992.

HOME AUDIT

Kilowatcher
What is the reading on your electric meter? _____
What is the reading on your electric meter one week later? _____
How many kilowatts did you and your family use during the week? _____

Staying Warm and Keeping Cool
What is the temperature setting of your thermostat? _____
Is your thermostat on a timer that automatically controls it at night or during the day
when no one is home? _____

Lights!
How many light fixtures are in your home? _____
How many have compact fluorescent bulbs? _____
How many lights are on even though no one is in the room? _____
How many radios or televisions are on with no one listening to or watching them? _____

Out the Window
How many windows are in your home? _____
How many windows have storm windows? _____
Check for drafts around the frames of your windows. Move a piece of ribbon all around the frame
and check to see if the ribbon flutters. Hold a lit candle around the frame and see if the flame flick-
ers. How many windows have drafts? _____
Check for drafts around door frames by using the same procedure used for your windows. How
many doors have drafts? _____

Down the Drain
What temperature is your hot water heater set on? _____

*NOTE—If your hot water heater doesn't have a temperature setting, measure the temperature of the water.
Just run the water until it's hot; then use a thermometer to record its temperature.*

Does your hot water heater have an insulated cover? _____
Does your shower have a low-flow shower head? _____
Do your sink faucets have low-flow aerators on them? _____
Do any faucets or pipes in your house leak? _____
Do you usually wash your clothes in hot, warm, or cold water? _____
Do you run the drying cycle on your dishwasher or let the dishes air dry? _____
Do you clean the lint trap on your clothes dryer before drying a load of clothes? _____

New Life
How many of the following materials do you recycle on a regular basis:
    _____ aluminum
    _____ newspaper
    _____ plastic
    _____ mixed metal cans
    _____ cardboard
    _____ paper (other than newspaper)

SAVING A TON OF CO$_2$

Keeping a ton of CO$_2$ from getting into the atmosphere each year will also mean saving at least $100 on your utility bill! Decide which of the following energy-saving measures you can take. (To convert pounds to kilograms, multiply by .453.)

Electricity Simplicity

Replace a 100-watt incandescent bulb with a 27-watt compact fluorescent bulb. We save 160 pounds per year for each bulb. _____

Replace a 75-watt incandescent bulb with an 18-watt compact fluorescent bulb. We save 120 pounds per year for each bulb. _____

Turn lights out when we leave the room. We save 120 pounds every year for each room. _____

TOTAL CO$_2$ Saved Here _____

Getting Into Hot Water

Give our water heater a warm-up jacket of insulation to make it more efficient. If we use

electric, we save 600 pounds _____
oil, we save 360 pounds _____
gas, we save 260 pounds _____

Cool the hot-water heater down by 10 degrees (but not below 120° Fahrenheit). If we use

electric, we save 660 pounds _____
oil, we save 400 pounds _____
gas, we save 290 pounds _____

Make our hot water go further with low-flow shower heads. If we use

electric, we save 920 pounds _____
oil, we save 560 pounds _____
gas, we save 400 pounds _____

Chill out our washing machine by doing four out of five laundry loads in cold water. If we use

electric, we save 460 pounds _____
oil, we save 280 pounds _____
gas, we save 200 pounds _____

TOTAL CO$_2$ Saved Here _____

Turning Over a New Leaf

Plant a tree on the south or west side of our home to provide cooling shade. We save 150 pounds _____

Home Is Where the Heat Is

Nudge our thermostat down one degree this winter. If we use

electric, we save 410 pounds _____
oil, we save 250 pounds _____
gas, we save 180 pounds _____

Give that overworked heating system a 10 degree rest when we're in bed at night. If we use

electric, we save 2,070 pounds _____
oil, we save 1,260 pounds _____
gas, we save 900 pounds _____

Turn our air conditioner's thermostat up a single degree this summer.

We save 220 pounds _____

Get annual tune ups.

For our air conditioner,
we save 220 pounds _____
For our furnace, if we use electric,
we save 1,030 pounds _____
For our furnace, if we use oil,
we save 640 pounds _____
For our furnace, if we use gas,
we save 450 pounds _____

Plug leaks around windows and doors with weather stripping—and close the curtains and shades at night. If we use
electric, we save 1,600 pounds _____
oil, we save 1,000 pounds _____
gas, we save 700 pounds _____

TOTAL CO$_2$ Saved Here _____

GRAND TOTAL OF CO$_2$ WE WILL
SAVE THIS YEAR _____

Overview
By taking a closer look at their community, students can gain an appreciation for its structure and complexity. In this activity, students will develop a deeper understanding of the many people, places, and things on which they depend every day.

LEVELS
Grades K-3

SUBJECT
Social Studies

CONCEPT
■ If planned, constructed, and landscaped to be compatible with the environment in which they will be located, human-built environments can conserve resources, enhance environmental quality, and promote the comfort and well-being of those who will live within them. (11.3)

SKILLS
Observing, Discussing, Classifying and Categorizing, Summarizing, Representing

OBJECTIVES
Students will ① explain how human communities are made up of different types of people, places, and things, and how they all fit together and ② investigate some of the people, places, and things that make up their own community.

MATERIALS
drawing paper, crayons or markers

TIME CONSIDERATIONS
Preparation: 20 minutes
Activity: Two 50-minute periods

Background
Communities are structured in order to provide people with the goods, services, and space that they need. Communities usually provide places to live, work, study, shop, pray, and play. They also provide services such as fire protection, police, and health care.

Maintaining these important places and services depends on the work of many different people: architects, bus drivers, construction workers, hospital workers, librarians, sanitation workers, police, and teachers, just to name a few.

Since we spend most of our time in built environments (houses, buildings, parks, and malls), the design of these environments is important to our well-being. Our built environment should be designed in a way that meets our needs, and raises, rather than lowers, our spirits.

Getting Ready
Make arrangements to take your students on a walking tour through a local neighborhood. Get parental permissions and extra adult supervision.

PART A
IMPORTANT SPACES

Doing the Activity
1. Ask the students what kind of places they think are in the neighborhood. Record their answers on the chalkboard.

2. Take the students outside for a walk around the block or through the neighborhood. Along the way, have them point out places around your school where people live, work, and play. Note houses, apartment buildings, stores, recreation centers, libraries, playing fields, parks, and so forth.

3. When back inside, compare their earlier ideas with what they saw outside. Then, write the words "Living Places," "Working Places," and "Playing Places" where everyone can see them. Then have students recall the places they spotted on their walk and put each place in one of the three categories.

NOTE—You might also want to create additional categories such as "Learning Places," "Meeting Places," or "Praying Places."

4. Have the students think about other places in their community that could fit into one of these categories and add those places to the lists. Then have students look on their way home and in their own neighborhoods for more examples of working, living, and playing places. When the students return, add these examples to the lists.

PART B
FRIENDLY FACES

Doing the Activity
1. Tell the students that besides places, our communities also have people on whom we rely. Pass out drawing paper and crayons or markers. Have the students think about, and then draw a picture of someone in their community on whom they depend.

2. Have the students share their pictures, describing the person they drew. As you discuss the pictures, talk about people whom students depend on but who they might not have thought about—the people who collect garbage, police the streets, fight fires, run the grocery store, and so on. If possible, have some of these people visit your group and talk about what they do.

PART C
THINGS IN PLACES

Doing the Activity

1. Have the students describe things in their community they've already learned about. Then ask them to describe how they got to school that day. Ask what kinds of things made the journey easier and safer. What if the traffic lights broke down? What if there were no sidewalks?

2. Brainstorm a list of things in the community on which everyone depends. (The list might include streets, sidewalks, street lights, traffic lights, trash bins, recycling bins, trees, telephone and electric poles, fire hydrants, and public phones. It should not include "things" they've already listed as "places," such as houses or stores.) Post this list where it can be seen by all students.

3. Have the students look at the list and think about the purposes of these things. Then have them group the things into two or more categories. For example, which of the things on the list are "safety" things? (fire hy-

drants, sidewalks, streetlights, traffic lights) Which are "convenience" things (public phones, trash bins, recycling bins) Which things beautify the community?

Enrichment

1. If you're working with older students, have them make maps of their neighborhood. Maps should include people; places (including living, playing, and working places); and things. They may also include a map key and a scale indicator.

2. Have students write an imaginary story about what would happen if something important disappeared, such as "The Day the Sidewalks Disappeared," "When all the Lights Went Out," or "The Town Without Trees."

3. Ask students to think about what would make their community better. What kinds of places, people, or things would they like to see in it? Then, have them work in small groups to draw a picture of their idea of an ideal community.

END NOTES...

ASSESSMENT OPPORTUNITY

Have teams of students put together creative presentations that show the different people, places, and things that make up their community. Possible presentations could be a poster, a collage (from clippings), a mobile, a photo essay, a song or rap, a model or sculpture, or a video. A more simple option is for groups of students to make maps of neighborhoods they visited. On the map, have them label the important people, places, and things that they saw.

RELATED ACTIVITIES

A Look at Lifestyles, Web of Life, Then and Now, Three Cheers for Trees!, Improve Your Place, Planning the Ideal Community, I'd Like to Visit a Place Where…

REFERENCES

Adapted in part from *LIVING LIGHTLY IN THE CITY:* An Urban Environmental Education Curriculum. Milwaukee, Wisconsin: Schlitz Audubon Center, 1983.

Overview
Whether it's a 100-room palace or a small hut made of branches, all human shelters serve the same basic purposes: they provide privacy, shelter from inclement weather, and protection from danger. In this activity, your students will take a close-up look at one kind of dwelling—the tipi used by Native Americans on the Plains—and will discover how homes can give clues about the lives of people who live in them.

LEVELS
Grades 4-8

SUBJECTS
Science, Social Studies, Visual Arts

CONCEPTS
■ Conservation and management technologies, when appropriately applied to the use or preservation of natural resources, can enhance and extend the usefulness of the resource as well as the quality of the environment. (11.2)

■ If planned, constructed, and landscaped to be compatible with the environment in which they will be located, human-built environments can conserve resources, enhance environmental quality, and promote the comfort and well-being of those who will live within them. (11.3)

SKILLS
Observing, Identifying Attributes and Components, Inferring, Synthesizing and Creating

OBJECTIVE
Students will describe several different types of Native American shelters and the materials that were used to make them.

MATERIALS
copies of student pages 285 and 286, pens or pencils, paper

TIME CONSIDERATIONS
Preparation: 20 minutes

Activity: 50 minutes

Background

Life on the Plains
The Plains, in this activity, refers to the large center of North America—from the Gulf of Mexico in the south, to Saskatchewan and Alberta in the north, from the Mississippi River in the east, to the Rocky Mountains in the west. This large area was home to many different Native American groups including the Crow, Sioux, Kiowa, Arapaho, and Blackfoot. Though there were many differences among these groups, there were also many important similarities.

Although the following information on Plains Indian society focuses on similarities, it is not meant to imply that Plains Indian culture was homogenous or static. (You should point out that this activity describes the traditional Plains Indian lifestyle that existed when European settlers first arrived. Today, Native Americans live in the same type of houses as other Americans.)

■ Trees grew mostly in the western end of the region and along river valleys. Much of the rest of the land was dry and covered mostly with grasses and shrubs.

■ Weather on the Plains was extremely variable: Summers were very hot; winters were bitterly cold; and blizzards, tornadoes, hail storms, and flash floods were common.

■ Bison were an extremely important resource for Plains Indians. The Indians ate them, made tipis and robes from their hides, made water buckets from their stomachs, burned their dung for fuel, and used their bones for tools. In fact, they used the bison in more than 200 different ways.

■ Bison formed large herds in the summer and scattered over a wide area during the rest of the year. Plains Indians moved around, following the bison. In summer, entire tribes camped together for several weeks, then broke into smaller bands to follow the dispersing bison.

Place to Call Home:
Here are some reasons why tipis made such good shelters:

■ Tipis were large, spacious structures.

■ Tipis were not perfect cones. Instead, they were tilted slightly, which made it more difficult for the wind to blow them over. An anchor rope (made from leather) helped increase stability.

■ Most tribes faced their tipis toward the east, so the doors opened away from the direction in which the wind was usually blowing. This helped prevent drafts.

■ In cold weather, the tipi's base weighted down with rocks. In hot weather, the tipi's sides could be rolled up 3-4 feet (91-122 cm) to let breezes in.

■ Smoke flaps at the top of the tipi could be adjusted by long poles to keep both wind and rain out of the internal fire. The smoke hole could even be closed completely in heavy rains or very cold weather. By opening the flaps, people could clear the tipi of smoke in just a few minutes.

■ Inside, a lining hung all around the tipi from about 6 feet (1.8 m) high down to the ground. The lining kept drafts and rain from coming into the tipi, kept dew from forming on the inside wall, and provided extra insulation by creating an air space between it and the tipi. The air space also helped ventilate the tipi: Warm air inside the tipi would rise through this space, helping to draw the fire and to keep the tipi free of smoke without lowering the temperature where people were sitting.

■ Plains Indians did not accumulate a lot of possessions—they needed to be able to pack and move quickly. But they did furnish the tipis with bison hide beds, willow-rod backrests, fur floor coverings, and personal belongings.

■ Everything had its place in the tipi. Every family member had a place to store his or her personal belongings including clothes. Large rawhide envelopes held some objects while other pouches hung from tipi poles. Sacred objects were stored near the back of the tipi. Men often kept their weapons on a tripod near the doorway, where they could grab weapons quickly in case of an enemy attack.

■ Men killed the bison whose hides were used to make the tipi, but women did all the work to turn the skins into a tent. Women also put up and took down the tipi, unpacked and set up the furnishings after a move, and packed the furnishings when it came time to move again. Women usually owned the tipis.

■ Men hunted bison and other game, and protected the group from danger. Women prepared food; cared for the children; gathered wild fruits and vegetables; and made and decorated clothing, containers, and other household items.

■ There were rules of proper behavior inside a tipi. For example, the man of the tipi usually sat opposite the door, other men sat on the north side of the tipi, and women sat on the south side. If you needed to pass people who were already sitting, you walked behind them. (That way, you wouldn't come between anyone and the fire.)

■ There were no separate rooms for people of different status (e.g., no "master bedrooms") and no locks. People were expected to discipline themselves to respect the status and possessions of others. Theft within tribes was very rare.

■ When they were camped in the summer, the Plains Indians often set their tipis up in a circle, around an inner circle of special tipis such as the chief's tipi and the tipi where the tribal council met.

■ The people believed that the sacred spirit was in physical objects—even the tipi itself. The doorway faced east, not only to keep the prevailing winds out, but also to face the rising sun, the source of life. The floor, walls, and poles of the tipi defined a certain physical space, but at the same time the people experienced the floor as the earth, the walls as the sky, and the poles as the paths that lead from the earth to the spirit world. The tipi also included a small altar—a square of bare earth behind the firepit.

After doing this activity, students should realize that tipis were well suited to the life of the Plains Indians. They were easy to transport, and they could be set up and taken down quickly. They also were excellent shelters from the weather in the region.

Getting Ready
Make copies of page 285 and 286.

Doing the Activity
1. Begin by asking students what houses are for (privacy, comfort, protection from bad weather). Then ask if all people build or live in the same types of houses. (no) Have students name as many different kinds of dwellings as they can, and list their responses where everyone can see them. (row house, mobile home, log cabin, apartment, houseboat, tipi, wigwam, adobe, yurt, and so forth)

2. Have students look over the list of dwellings they created in Step 1. Then have them list similarities and differences among dwellings. Also have them compare these dwellings to the types of homes where they live. (For example, do they have the same number of doors and windows? What materials are they made from? How many stories tall are they? What kinds of comforts do they have?) Then ask why there are so many different kinds of dwellings. (Environments and climate differ from place to place; available materials and technologies vary; people's lifestyles and values vary.)

3. Now tell the students that they're going to learn more about a particular cultural group (Plains Indians) by studying their dwellings (tipis). Pass out copies of pages 285 and 286 and explain that students should use the pictures and information on page 286 to fill in the first two columns of the chart on page 285. Tell them that they won't be able to answer all of the questions—there isn't enough information on page 286 to do so. However, they should make guesses (inferences) based on the information that is provided. They should list the evidence they used to reach each answer in the second column.

4. Have students work on their own to fill out page 285. Give them plenty of time to do so. Afterward, have them share their answers and the evidence they used. (Don't give them any correct answers at this point—they'll find out more information later.)

5. Have the entire group discuss possible answers to the questions in the third column. On the basis of evidence presented on student page 285, what conclusions might students draw about the lifestyle of the Plains Indians? (The Plains Indians hunted bison, they moved around a lot, they had free time to decorate things, women played an important role in the society, tipis didn't provide a lot of privacy, and so on.)

NOTE—The students may draw some incorrect conclusions as well. For example, they may conclude that trees (for tipi poles) were plentiful when, in fact, many parts of the plains were treeless and the people had to travel long distances to find the wood they needed.

6. Using the information in the Background, tell students more about the life of Plains Indians. Afterward, give them a chance to modify their answers.

Enrichment

1. Have students research other types of homes. They can choose other traditional Native American dwellings (wigwam, long house, pit house, sweat lodge, adobe, igloo) from more than a century ago. Have students research and make models of these structures. Afterward, they should assess the pros and cons of those structures and determine how the homes are adapted to the conditions and functions they serve.

2. Have students design their own homes for a real or imaginary environment. They should imagine the environment— What is the weather like? What building materials are available? Then they should design the home including its floor plan, furnishings, and outside appearance.

TIPI WORKSHEET

Question	Answer	Source for answer	What does this help you infer about the Plains Indians' way of life?
How big were tipis?			
What were tipis made of?			
How long would it have taken to put up a tipi?			
Who built tipis?			
How many rooms did a tipi have?			
What kinds of furniture might a tipi have?			
How did tipis protect people from bad weather?			
How did people store things inside the tipi?			
Who owned a tipi?			
Who would live together in one tipi?			
Did tipis provide privacy? If yes, how?			
How did tipis reflect people's spiritual beliefs?			
Which direction did a tipi face?			
How were the tipis arranged in a community?			

BASIC TIPI FACTS

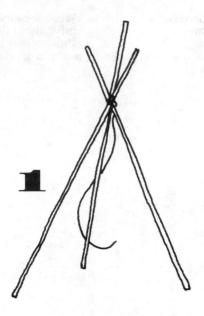

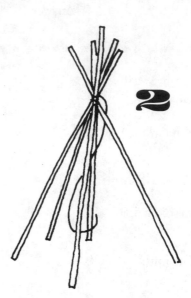

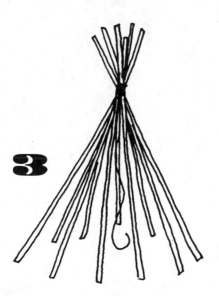

Tipis are about 10 feet high and 5 feet in diameter. They are made of wooden poles. An average sized tipi cover was made of about 14 buffalo hides and weighed about 100 pounds. It took expert women as little as 10 minutes to complete this process.

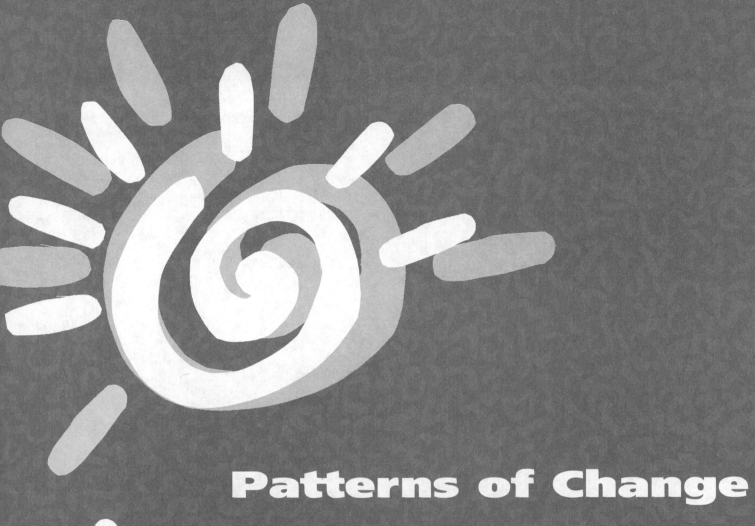

Patterns of Change

Overview
One of the best ways to learn about a tree is to look at its annual rings. Tree rings show patterns of change in the tree's life as well as changes in the area where it grows. In this activity, students will trace environmental and historical changes using a cross section of a tree trunk, or "tree cookie."

Background
By counting a tree's growth rings, you can tell its age. Every growth season, a tree adds a new layer of wood to its trunk. Each ring has two parts: a wide, light part (early wood) and a narrow, dark part (late wood). The early wood grows during the wet, spring growing season. During the transition from the drier summer to fall and winter, growth slows and the late wood forms. The rings provide clues about the climate, or weather, of the area over time and evidence of disturbance to and around the tree, such as fires and floods.

The shape and width of the annual rings often differ from year to year because of varying annual growth conditions. During a moist growing season, a tree in a temperate region may produce a particularly wide ring. During a drought, a colder-than-average winter, or an unseasonable frost, a tree will produce a particularly narrow ring. In a science called dendrochronology (which literally means "the study of tree time"), scientists have found that they can learn about past climates by studying the ring patterns of very old trees.

Many factors besides weather can affect a tree's growth. Accordingly, tree rings reflect a tree's response to such stressors as root damage, disease, and competition from other plants. Sometimes a disturbance will occur after the growth season, producing a narrow or misshapen ring in the following year. (See diagram, page 291.) To study a tree's growth rings without harming the trees, scientists use a technique called coring. By drilling into the center of a tree trunk with a hollow instrument called an *increment borer*, they can remove a long, narrow cylinder of wood (called a core sample). The growth rings of the tree appear as lines on the core sample.

Getting Ready
From the trunk or limb of a fallen tree, saw cross sections 1½"-2" (3.8 cm-5 cm) thick. (Cross sections, or "tree cookies," can usually be obtained from a local tree-trimming service, county or state forester, forest products company, firewood company, or utility company.) If the wood is not dry, you will need to dry it to keep it from splitting. The wood can be dried by placing the tree cookies on small wooden slats and microwaving them for 20 minutes. After that, let the cookies dry for a couple of days. If you cannot obtain tree cookies, make photocopies of page 292. Also, try to obtain an overhead projector and make an overhead transparency of page 292.

PART A
COOKIE COUNTING

Doing the Activity
1. On the blackboard make a copy of the diagram on page 290 for class review. Have students help identify these parts of a tree: ***bark, phloem*** (FLOW-uhm), ***cambium*** (KAM-bee-uhm), ***xylem*** (ZEYE-lem), ***heartwood*** (see "Tree Factory," page 223, for a discussion of the function of each of these tree parts). Explain how to count the rings to find the age of the tree (count only the light OR only the dark rings). As a class, count the number of growth rings. Try to find indications of past disturbance or events in the life of the tree, such as fire, insect damage, drought, or the loss of a branch.

2. Pass out the tree cookies, if available, or photocopies of page 292 to individuals or small groups.

3. Have students estimate how old the tree was when the tree cookie was cut. Ask the students how they counted and if they think they are accurate.

LEVELS:
Activity: Grades 3-8
Variation: Grades 1-3

SUBJECTS
Science, Social Studies, Visual Arts, Language Arts

CONCEPTS
- Organisms change throughout their lifetimes. Species of organisms change over long periods of time. (13.1)
- While every organism goes through a lifecycle of growth, maturity, decline, and death, its role in the ecosystem also changes. (13.3)

SKILLS
Researching, Observing, Identifying Relationships and Patterns, Interpreting Information

OBJECTIVES
Students will ① identify heartwood, sapwood, and a tree's annual rings, ② infer from a tree's rings what damage or stress might have occurred in its life, and ③ make a timeline of human history that coincides with a tree's rings.

MATERIALS
tree cookies (cross-sectional slices of tree trunks or limbs) or photocopies of the tree cookie on page 292, string, pins, small paper labels, paper plates, optional hand lenses

TIME CONSIDERATIONS
Preparation: 15 minutes

Activity: 50 minutes

4. When students have discovered how old the tree is, ask if there is anything else they can guess about the tree's life.

5. (optional) Hand out hand lenses to the students. Have them look for small holes in the sapwood and heartwood of the tree cookie. These tiny channels are the xylem, through which water travels up and down the trunk and branches of the tree.

PART B
TREE STORIES

Doing the Activity
1. Divide the group into teams. On a very large piece of paper, have students draw a life-size cross section of a redwood tree. It should be about 6 feet (1.8 m) in diameter to be of average mature size. Draw an appropriate number of growth rings for its size: about 150-200 rings. As a group, decide on the year the tree began growing and the year it was cut. Remember, there should be some variety in the growth rings to reflect changing environmental conditions.

2. Have teams research different information that relates to the redwood tree cookie. Categories for research should include ① possible significant events in the tree's lifetime, such as years of drought, flood, or fire; ② significant world events during the life of the tree; ③ significant events in U.S. or Canadian history during the life of the tree; and ④ significant events of people in your classroom, school, or community during the life of the tree. Teams should each identify at least five dates for events in their category.

3. Have each group select a color for its event labels. Labels can be placed around the outside margin of the cross section and connected with string to a map tack and inserted at the appropriate year.

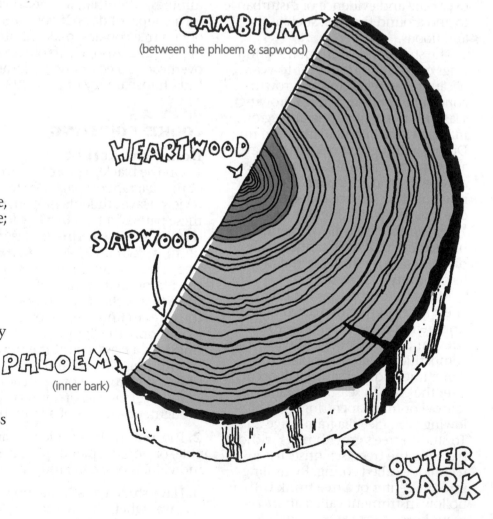

CAMBIUM
(between the phloem & sapwood)

HEARTWOOD

SAPWOOD

PHLOEM
(inner bark)

OUTER BARK

VARIATION—MY LIFE AS A TREE

1. Show students a tree cookie and explain how it was obtained from a tree. Let students feel and examine the tree cookie.

2. Explain what the rings on the cookie are and what they tell us about the tree. (age of tree, years of rapid or slow growth) Show students how to count the rings to determine the tree's age and let them practice.

3. Using white paper plates with ridges, demonstrate for students how to create a "tree cookie" using the bumpy perimeter as the bark, the smooth inside edge as the cambium, and center circle as the heartwood.

4. Have students each use a paper plate and crayons to create a tree cookie the same age as themselves. They can then use sticky labels to identify when important events in their lives took place such as when they were born, when they started school, and so on.

Enrichment

Invite a forester to talk with your group about how he or she uses core sampling to learn about trees and the forest environment. If possible, have the forester bring an increment borer and demonstrate its use on a tree in your school yard or neighborhood (if necessary, get permission to use the tree).

END NOTES...

ASSESSMENT OPPORTUNITY

Slowly read the following story to your students and ask them to take notes. (Have them pay particular attention to the years mentioned.)

Once upon a time, a tree grew in the forest. In its first 10 years it grew slowly because the large trees overhead blocked the sunlight. In its 11th year, the large tree next to it blew down in a storm. This allowed sunlight to reach the little tree, and for the next 10 years it grew rapidly. In its 21st and 22nd years there was a severe drought, and the tree could not get enough water. This stress caused the tree to grow very slowly for three years. In its 25th year, favorable conditions returned and the tree grew normally for 15 years. In its 40th year, wildfire raged through the forest. The tree's thick bark enabled it to survive, but it was deeply scarred. It grew slowly for several years after that. Year 45 was particularly bad. Bark beetles got under its skin, fungus entered its body through woodpecker holes, and caterpillars ate most of its leaves. For five years the tree hardly grew at all and became very weak. In its 50th year, it blew down in a storm. A science teacher found the fallen tree and used a chain saw to make a big tree cookie from the trunk.

After telling the story, allow students to ask questions so that their notes are complete. Then, ask each student to draw a picture of what the tree cookie of this tree might look like. Assess each drawing to make sure students have indicated the events in the tree's life at points that match the time frame given in the story.

RELATED ACTIVITIES

Tree Factory, Trees in Trouble, Nothing Succeeds Like Succession, Every Tree for Itself, Forest Consequences, Tree Lifecycle

DEAD BRANCH

DROUGHT OR INSECT ATTACK

FIRE ATTACK

TREE RINGS

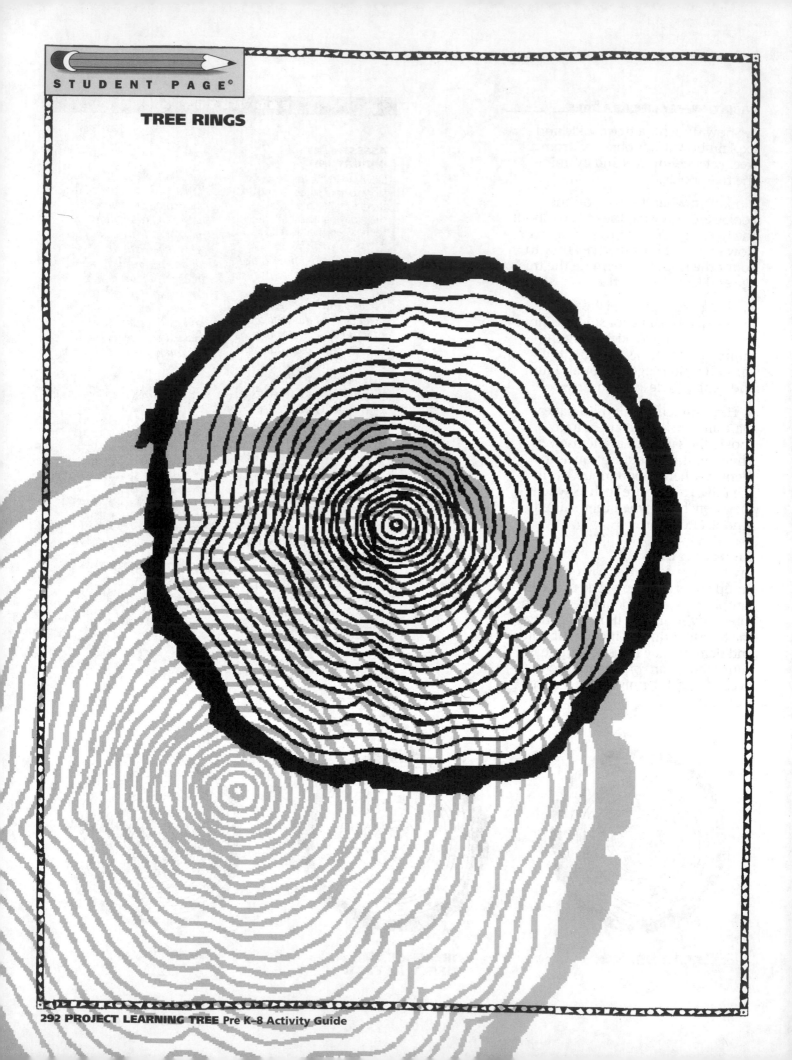

Overview
Like humans, trees can become weak and unhealthy, suffer injury, and die. People have learned to read the symptoms of unhealthy trees to help them. In this activity, students will examine trees for signs of damage or poor health.

Background
Trees require some of the same things people and other animals need to grow and thrive. For example, they need plenty of water, food, and room to grow. If these requirements are not met, a tree may grow slowly or die. The growth rings on a cross section of a tree reveal whether the tree's requirements have been met over the years, and they provide a record of a tree's health over its lifetime. (See Background for "Tree Factory," "Tree Cookies," and "Every Tree for Itself.")

Getting Ready
Plan a trip on the school grounds, in a park, in the woods, or along a tree-lined street. Make copies of student pages 296-298. For younger students, play "This Bark on Me" by Billy B, and discuss the meaning of the song (see References).

PART A
NEIGHBORHOOD CHECKUP

Doing the Activity
1. As a group, discuss what causes a person to get sick or become unhealthy. Responses might include poor nutrition; unclean water; a lack of food or water; toxic substances like smoke or drugs, disease, and physical injury. Students should also think of ways to prevent or combat these things, like proper diet, regular exercise, and safe behavior. With older students, ask them to name several human diseases or illnesses and their causes, symptoms, and cures.

2. Compare elements that keep humans healthy with those that keep trees healthy.

3. Tell students that they will become "tree-tectives" (tree detectives) and search their neighborhood for healthy and unhealthy trees.

4. Students should use the "Tree-tective Trouble Guide" and "Reading Leaf Symptoms" student pages to identify symptoms of unhealthy trees. They should take additional notes and make sketches of their findings such as broken branches; unusual leaf colors or shapes; holes; trunks damaged from scratches, carvings, or graffiti; or uprooted, fallen trees that still appear to be alive. Take measuring tapes or rulers to record the size of wounds and diameters of trees that have been affected. As an option, students can use a camera to photograph damaged trees.

5. Have students hypothesize about what caused the damage. Note that some problems may be more common in certain regions than in others. Older students can read and discuss the article "Trees May Tell Each Other of Attacks," on page 298. This article describes research that seems to indicate that trees can send alarm signals to each other about certain unhealthy factors in the environment.

6. After your field trip, combine all the information the class collected and make a "Tree Damage Report." Then find the people or agency in your area that cares for unhealthy trees (many city, county, or state forestry and park agencies have urban foresters). Send a copy of your report to the agency (or person) in charge of trees in your area. Follow up a couple of weeks later to find out if the agency is going to take action. Ask if you can be informed of any planned tree work so that your class can be at the location to observe. You can also visit a garden center, nursery, or tree-trimming company in your area to find out what they do to keep trees healthy.

LEVELS
Part A: Grades 1-8
Part B: Grades 4-8

SUBJECTS
Science, Math, Social Studies, Language Arts, Performing Arts

CONCEPTS
- Organisms change throughout their lifetimes. Species of organisms change over long periods of time. (13.1)
- While every organism goes through a lifecycle of growth, maturity, decline, and death, its role in the ecosystem also changes. (13.3)
- Ecosystems change over time through patterns of growth and succession. They are also affected by other phenomena such as disease, insects, fire, weather, and human intervention. (13.4)

SKILLS
Observing, Analyzing, Researching, Comparing and Contrasting, Solving Problems

OBJECTIVES
Students will ① cite factors that can cause trees to become unhealthy, ② describe symptoms of unhealthy trees, ③ compare environmental conditions that affect both human health and plant health, and ④ identify people or agencies that care for trees and forests.

MATERIALS
Part A: copies of student pages 296-298, measuring tape or rulers, optional camera
Part B: half-gallon milk cartons, rigid paper plates, potting soil, white vinegar, pH test strips or litmus paper, fertilizer (liquid or granular), radish seeds, rulers or measuring tapes, graph paper, knife, paper bags, bleach, lemon juice, ammonia. Optional: cross section of a tree; Billy B Sings About Trees (see References) and cassette player.

TIME CONSIDERATIONS
Preparation: Part A: 15 minutes
Part B: 45 minutes

Activity: Part A: One to two 50-minute periods

Part B: Two 50-minute periods over several weeks and 10 minutes daily to record observations

PART B
PLANTS UNDER STRESS

Doing the Activity
Divide students into investigation teams and tell them they will conduct a series of experiments to determine conditions that cause plants to become unhealthy.

NOTE—*To plan your time allotment for this activity, check the estimated sprouting time for the seeds you are using.*

Experiments
Explore the effects of the following on plant growth: Crowding, Acidic Precipitation, Fertilizer.

Crowding
Trees need space to grow so they can spread their branches to collect sunlight and their roots to collect water. Discover what happens when plants are grown too close together.

1. Have students form a hypothesis about what will happen to plants that grow under crowded conditions. The hypothesis can be stated in an "if-then" form: "If plants are grown too close together, then_____."

2. Each team should cut milk cartons in half to make planting pots.

3. Punch a few holes in the bottom of each pot and set it on a rigid or coated paper plate that will catch water as it drains.

4. Fill the pot with potting soil.

5. Half of the teams should plant only one or two radish seeds in their pots. The other teams should plant a dozen or so seeds in a single hole. All the pots should have the same light and water conditions. The only variable is the amount of seeds per pot.

6. See how long it takes for the seeds to sprout. Measure the height of the plants above the soil level and record at daily intervals for several weeks. After a specified time, students can dig up the plants and observe differences in the size of the radish bulbs. Cut the radishes in half; measure and record the diameters. Discuss the findings. Which radishes appear to be healthier?

Acidic Precipitation
Many scientists believe that acid precipitation, or acid rain, causes negative health effects on vegetation. To test this, set up a series of plants similar to those in the previous demonstration. You will use white vinegar in water to simulate acid rain.

1. Have students form a hypothesis about what will happen to plants that grow under the influence of acidic water conditions. This hypothesis can be stated in an "if-then" form: "If plants receive more acidic water, then _____."

2. Before proceeding with the experiment, discuss the phenomenon of acid rain with your students. Ask them to research acid rain in a library or media center. Discuss the differences between acidic and basic solutions. Use litmus paper and test for acid or base color reactions for substances such as tap water, lemon juice, vinegar, household bleach, and household ammonia. (Be sure to take proper precautions when handling these substances.)

Only small amounts are needed for litmus testing. For more advanced students, the concept of pH can be demonstrated using pH indicator strips, which give more precise readings of the pH value of substances.

3. Prepare solutions of varying acidic strengths. Sample solutions could include ranges from tap water to quarter, half, and three-quarter strength water-vinegar solutions to full strength vinegar.

4. Determine what happens when plants are "watered" with water-vinegar solutions of varying concentrations. Keep the light conditions and the watering schedule the same for all plants, varying only the strength of the water-vinegar solutions.

5. Keep a daily log of observations and discuss changes in the health and growth of the plants.

Fertilizer

Like people, plants need vitamins, minerals, and other nutrients in their diet to maintain good health. Most of these are supplied by the soil and water in which the plants grow.

1. With a set-up similar to past experiments, hypothesize about the effects of fertilizer, or "plant food," on the growth of plants.

2. Keep all variables constant, except the amount of fertilizer (i.e., Miracle-Gro) added to the soil on a periodic basis. Follow directions on the package or bottle of fertilizer. Make certain that one group of plants receives no fertilizer at all.

3. Check and record observations and discuss results.

4. As in all the experiments, you can show observations and results by plotting the data on a graph.

(Additional tests for light, water, and soil conditions can be found in "How Plants Grow" on page 135.)

Enrichment 1
Adopt a Sick Tree

Perhaps on your field trip you found a "tree in trouble" that could use some help. Maybe it had been damaged; or, maybe it appeared to be healthy and you want to help it stay that way. Have the class adopt the tree. If you choose a tree close to the school, you can report on the progress of its health. Contact the appropriate municipal agencies (see Step 6 in Part A, Doing the Activity) to find out ways to help a sick tree.

Enrichment 2
Dead Tree of Life

Trees, like humans, eventually become sick and die. If you found a dead or partially dead tree on your field trip, you may want to return to see what activity is taking place. Is there evidence of insects at work to decompose the tree and return its remains to nature? Are there signs of woodpeckers living in the dead tree? Are any animals living in holes in the tree? Are fungi growing on the tree? Did the city remove or trim the tree for safety reasons?

Enrichment 3
Useful to Be Useless

Consider the following story attributed to the ancient Chinese philosopher, Chuang Tzu:

A sage, in rambling about the Heights of Shang, saw a large and extraordinary tree. The teams of a thousand chariots might be sheltered under it, and its shade would cover them all! He said, "What a tree this is! It must contain an extraordinary amount of timber!" When he looked up, however, at its smaller branches, they were so twisted and crooked that they could not be made into rafters and beams; when he looked down to its root, its stem was divided into so many rounded portions that neither coffin nor shell could be made from them. He licked one of its leaves, and his mouth felt torn and wounded. The smell of it would make a person frantic, as if intoxicated, for more than three whole days together. "This indeed," said he, "is a tree good for nothing, and it is thus that it has reached so great an age." … The cinnamon tree can be eaten, and therefore it is cut down. The varnish tree is useful, and therefore incisions are made in it. Everyone knows the advantage of being useful, but no one knows the advantage of being useless.

Have each student write his or her own story about the many values of trees, both healthy and unhealthy.

Enrichment 4
Look Inside a Tree

If a cross section of a tree or a stump is available, "read" the annual rings—they can tell some interesting stories about the health, life, and history of the tree. Tightly spaced annual rings may mean that the tree underwent a period of stress, such as a drought, and did not grow very much in that period. Look for evidence of drought and damage from lightning, fire, or insects. (See "Tree Cookies" on page 135.)

TREE-TECTIVE TROUBLE GUIDE

BROKEN BRANCHES ATTACHED

BROKEN BRANCHES HANGING

BROKEN BRANCHES ON GROUND

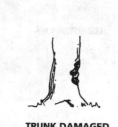

TRUNK DAMAGED
HIT BY CAR OR LAWN MOWER

BRANCH STUBS
SHOULD BE TRIMMED
SO TREE CAN HEAL

CRACKED TRUNK
FROM LIGHTNING OR FROST

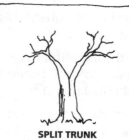

SPLIT TRUNK

TREE LEANING

VANDALIZED
CARVED INTO OR
BRANCHES TWISTED

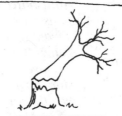

BROKEN OFF TREES

PROBLEMS WITH STAKED TREES
STAKES BENT, WIRES LOOSE,
TREE NOT SECURED

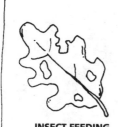

INSECT FEEDING
MANY LEAVES MISSING
OR FULL OF HOLES

LEAF DEFORMITIES
ROLLED, CRINKLED
OR FUNNY SHAPED

ROTTEN SPOTS

DEAD TREES

READING LEAF SYMPTOMS

Trees can't tell us when they are sick. Instead, we must interpret the signals trees send out to determine what and how serious their health problems are.

The leaves usually communicate the first symptoms of disease, insect or physical damage, so by learning leaf-reading, you can diagnose your tree's condition. Here are some common leaf symptoms and their probable cause.

1 Ragged leaves with holes in them.
Suspect insect feeding, especially if it's summer and the leaves were not showing damage earlier. But if it's springtime, and the leaves never developed properly, chances are the damage is due to low temperatures during the bud stage.

2 Leaves suddenly turn brown or black.
If a frost occurred a day or two earlier, that's probably the cause. Sudden high temperatures in springtime also cause problems. If no temperature extremes are noted, suspect either a leaf or a stem disease. If the symptoms show up on a branch or two at a time, trunk or branch invasion or injury is probably the cause.

3 Spots or bumps on the leaves.
Insects and mites cause most leaf swellings. Leaf spots are usually the result of disease or insect activity. Chemicals, such as sulfur dioxide from nearby coal-burning plants, or improperly applied fertilizer or pesticides, can cause leaf blotches, too.

4 Margins of leaves turn brown.
Moisture deficiencies or high temperature stresses are usually to blame. Sometimes root or trunk damage, including injury from road salt, can be involved.

5 Sudden leaf drop.
This may or may not be serious. If inner leaves are dropping during a dry spell, or if a few leaves fall from throughout the tree, it shouldn't be serious. Drought or squirrels may be to blame. But if leaves are dropping heavily from one branch and then another, there is a problem somewhere with the water-conducting system of the tree—probably disease, possibly insect borers.

6 Light green or yellow leaves.
Probably a "micronutrient" disorder, such as iron or manganese deficiency. Curiously, trees rarely show deficiencies of the major plant nutrients such as nitrogen and potassium.

7 Leaves twisted or malformed.
The most common cause for this is stray herbicide drift, but insects, occasionally a disease, and sometimes low temperature injury can all produce similar-appearing symptoms.

8 Leaves turn fall–colored prematurely.
A serious symptom suggesting trunk or root damage of some kind.

Trees can withstand a certain amount of abuse to the leaves, but leaf injury becomes serious when: heavy losses occur two or more years in a row, early season loss causes a new flush of leaves, the tree is marginally hardy to the area, or the tree is under some form of stress, such as recent transplanting. Your county extension agent has a number of publications to help in diagnosis and treatment of tree problems, or you may need to call an arborist who is competent in tree health diagnosis.

Gayle Worf, UW-Extension plant pathologist
Reprinted by permission of UW-Extension

TREE MAY TELL EACH OTHER OF ATTACKS

Trees may warn each other of attacks by insects or disease by emitting a special chemical from their pest-ravaged leaves, according to preliminary evidence gathered by two researchers.

The two University of Washington researchers say their findings, if confirmed, could significantly change the understanding of trees' behavior, particularly in light of recent discoveries about how trees combat insects and disease.

Changes in the chemical composition of leaves by trees to ward off insects or diseases was discovered in sugar maples and oaks by a group of New Hampshire researchers last year.

The nutritional content of Sitka willow leaves also changed in trees that had suffered damage by western tent caterpillars and fall webworms, according to a report by the two Washington researchers, David F. Rhoades and Gordon H. Orians. To their surprise, leaf quality also declined in undamaged trees up to 200 feet away, they said.

"This effect may be due to a defensive response in unattacked trees stimulated by volatile compounds emitted from attacked trees," the researchers said in a report to the National Science Foundation.

Orians said similar reactions have been seen in red alder trees as well, "but not as strong as with the willow."

"Presumably, this is not a reaction unique to one or a few species, but we have not yet had the opportunity to examine others," he said.

With a new science foundation research grant, the two scientists will place Sitka willows in closed chambers in an attempt to isolate any chemicals that influence the trees' behavior.

From The Associated Press, Washington

Overview
In temperate regions, people can observe the annual change of seasons. In autumn, leaves of many trees turn color and fall to the ground, many animals migrate or go into hibernation, the days get shorter, and the air gets colder. This pattern repeats itself every year.

Background

Seasonal changes result from the angle of the Earth's axis and the Earth's movement around the sun. Angled toward the sun at 23.5 degrees, the Northern Hemisphere experiences its summer from June 21 to September 23. June 21 signals the summer solstice when the sun's rays strike the earth farthest north of the equator. With the sun hitting more directly (more or less perpendicularly), the Northern Hemisphere has longer and warmer days. At the same time, the Southern Hemisphere—angled away from the sun—experiences shorter and colder days, marking its winter. As the Earth revolves half-way around the sun, December 22, the winter solstice, beckons winter to the Northern Hemisphere and summer to the Southern Hemisphere.

As winter approaches in temperate regions, animals begin to prepare for the cold. Some animals migrate to warmer areas where there is more shelter and food, while others gather food or add an extra layer of fat or fur to keep warm.

The colder temperatures and shorter days also trigger responses in plants. Deciduous trees begin to undergo changes. The cells at the base of each leaf stem begin to die, forming a barrier that keeps water and nutrients from traveling to the leaf. Chlorophyll, the green pigment in the leaves, starts to break down, and other leaf pigments begin to show through. These pigments produce the various and brilliant shades of red, orange,and yellow that we see in autumn leaves.

NOTE—Red pigments were not present from the start; they form as a result of chemical reactions as weather turns cold and photosynthesis slows.

As the cells die, they also weaken the leaf's attachment to the twig.

When the attachment breaks, the leaf falls to the ground. With the leaves gone, the tree is less likely to suffer damage from freezing. However, without leaves the tree cannot photosynthesize; therefore, deciduous trees remain dormant in the winter until the longer days and warmer weather of spring trigger their new cells, and leaves, to grow.

Getting Ready
Identify a wooded site in or near your area. Make copies of the "Signs of Fall" on student page 301. While outside for Part A, be sure and collect the green leaves needed for Part B. Also for Part B, cut three 2" x 6" (5 cm x 15 cm) strips from coffee filters. Since leaf collecting is also part of the activities in "Looking at Leaves" and "Name that Tree," you may want to combine these activities.

PART A
VISIBLE CHANGES

Doing the Activity
1. In the fall, take your students on a walk through a wooded area with both deciduous and evergreen trees. Ask them to find as many signs as possible that indicate winter is approaching and to describe their observations. Colorful falling leaves are easy to see, but encourage them to look for animal signs as well (birds migrating, squirrels storing nuts). Puddles, ice, frost, and mud are also indicators of the cooler or wetter fall climate. If you cannot get to a wooded area, have students explore their school grounds, local parks or gardens, or neighborhood sidewalks for signs of fall.

2. Before going out, pass out copies of page 301 and review the questions. Hold a discussion outdoors in which the students share their observations and answers to the questions.

LEVELS
Part A: Grades K-5
Part B: Grades 3-6

SUBJECTS
Science, Language Arts, Visual Arts

CONCEPTS
■ Organisms change throughout their lifetimes. Species of organisms change over long periods of time. (13.1)
■ While every organisms goes through a lifecycle of growth, maturity, decline, and death, its role in the ecosystem also changes. (13.3)

SKILLS
Observing, Identifying Relationships and Patterns, Comparing and Contrasting, Inferring

OBJECTIVES
Students will ① describe some of the differences between deciduous and evergreen trees, ② identify patterns in the changing of seasons, and ③ understand why leaves of deciduous trees change color in the fall.

MATERIALS
copies of "Signs of Fall" student page 301, coffee filters, tape, scissors, metric ruler, rubbing alcohol, at least six green leaves, three pencils and three glass jars not taller than 6 inches

TIME CONSIDERATIONS
Preparation: 20 minutes

Activity: Part A: 30 minutes
Part B: 30 minutes

3. When you return back indoors, have students draw or write answers to the questions.

PART B
INVISIBLE CHANGES

Doing the Activity

1. Tear up two of the green leaves collected on the outing into tiny pieces. Place the fragments in a glass jar not taller than 6 inches (15.2 cm). Do exactly the same thing for two additional jars. Add enough rubbing alcohol to cover the leaf pieces in each jar. (You can also divide your group in teams and have each team use two green leaves and one jar to do this demonstration.)

2. Tape each filter strip you prepared to a pencil. Lay the pencil across the top of the jar. Adjust the strip so that the end just touches the rubbing alcohol. The strip should begin to absorb the liquid (See illustration below).

3. When the alcohol has moved about halfway up the strips, (at least an hour) remove them and lay them on clean paper towels to dry. Observe the green bands (chlorophyll) and the yellow or orange bands (other leaf pigments).

4. Discuss the fact that the yellow and orange pigments are always in the leaves, but are usually masked by the green chlorophyll. In the fall, when the leaves no longer produce chlorophyll, the other pigments show through.

Enrichment

1. Try the experiment in Part B with leaves that have already turned color. What differences do you find? (Leaves show very little, if any, green pigment.) How might this be explained? (Chlorophyll has broken down.)

2. Tell your students the following is a Native American legend about why leaves change color in the fall:

Celestial hunters killed the Great Bear (a constellation) in the fall, causing his blood to drip on the forest and turn many of the trees red. Other trees turned yellow from the fat that dripped out of the kettle as the celestial hunter cooked the bear meat.

■ Discuss with students how this explanation differs from the scientific one they just learned. Have them consider how this legend might reflect important elements of Native American culture. (Constellations were important indicators of seasons; the bear was an important food source; fall was an important time for hunting and preparing meat for the winter.)

■ Invite the students to create their own imaginative legends explaining why leaves change color in the fall.

END NOTES...

ASSESSMENT OPPORTUNITY
Have students draw a sequence of pictures of a local forest as it might change through the seasons. In each picture, ask them to include at least three signs of the season, including one human sign (e.g., clothing); one animal sign (e.g., nut gathering); and one plant sign (e.g., leaf colors). Assess the pictures by checking for three seasonal signs in each.

RELATED ACTIVITIES
Name that Tree, Looking at Leaves, Trees as Habitats, The Fallen Log, Rain Reasons, Tree Lifecycle, Sunlight and Shades of Green

REFERENCE
Missouri's Season of Splendor. US. Forest Service and Missouri Conservation Commission, 1992. (includes a full color wall poster)

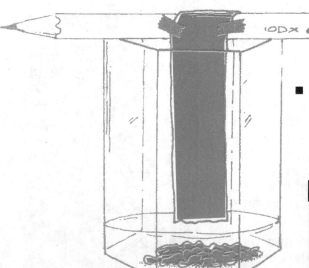

ANSWERS TO QUESTION 4 ON THE STUDENT PAGE

4a—Decomposition by water, insects, worms, bacteria, and so forth

4b—Return nutrients to the soil, which will help the tree to grow

SIGNS OF FALL

1 How many different leaf colors can you find?

2 Make a leaf rubbing. Take three different colored leaves. Put each leaf on a flat surface and place a sheet of white paper over it. Rub the side of a crayon back and forth across the paper above the leaf. Use the color crayon that most closely resembles the leaf color.

3 Find the following trees. If you or your instructor knows the name of the tree, write it down.

a The tree with the brightest yellow leaves?

b The tree with the deepest red leaves?

c The tree with the darkest green leaves?

4a What causes the leaves to break down into little bits?

b What might these leaf bits do for the soil?

5 Do all trees lose their leaves at the same time?

6 Do you see any animal signs that indicate it is fall?

7 Do you notice any changes in the weather?

Overview
In this activity, students will discover that trees have a lifecycle that is similar to that of other living things. They will investigate a tree's role in the ecosystem at each stage of its life.

LEVELS
Activity: Grades 3-6
Variation: Grades PreK-2

SUBJECTS
Science, Language Arts, Visual Arts, Performing Arts

CONCEPTS
- Organisms change throughout their lifetimes. Species of organisms change over long periods of time.(13.1)
- While every organism goes through a lifecycle of growth, maturity, decline, and death, its role in the ecosystem also changes. (13.3)
- Ecosystems change over time through patterns of growth and succession. They are also affected by other phenomena such as disease, insects, fire, weather, and human intervention. (13.4)

SKILLS
Ordering and Arranging, Representing, Identifying Relationships and Patterns

OBJECTIVES
Students will ① diagram the lifecycle of a tree, ② compare a tree lifecycle to a human lifecycle, and ③ explain the role each stage of a tree's life plays in the forest (or other) ecosystem.

MATERIALS
art materials, copy of student page 305.

TIME CONSIDERATIONS
Preparation: 15 minutes
Activity: 50 minutes

Background
One of the best ways to learn about trees is to look at their life history. Trees, like all living things, have a lifecycle that includes birth, growth, injury and disease, aging, and death. As trees go from birth to death, their physical form changes, as well as their role in the forest ecosystem. You can learn about past changes in environmental conditions by looking at the growth rings in a cross section of a tree. (See "Tree Cookies" on page 291.) Even more can be learned about the tree's lifecycle by observing the tree from birth as it grows and develops throughout its life.

Most trees begin as seeds. Generally, trees are put into flowering and non-flowering categories. The angiosperms are flowering plants, including wildflowers, shrubs, and many trees. Angiosperms are pollinated by insects, bats, birds, and the wind. Plants that have flowers also protect their seeds inside a fruit. Maple, oak, and all other broad-leaved trees are angiosperms. Gymnosperms (from Latin "gymno-," meaning "naked") have seeds that are not enclosed in fruit or flowers. Rather, most gymnosperms produce their seeds in cones and are pollinated by the wind. The most common type of gymnosperms is the cone-bearers, or conifers, like redwoods, firs, pines, and other trees with needle-like leaves.

If a seed lands in an area with favorable soil, climate, and nutrient conditions, it will germinate (some remain dormant for long periods before sprouting). Usually, many more seeds will be produced than can possibly survive. Most seeds will be destroyed by fungi or other decomposers, or eaten by birds or mammals, leaving only a few sprouts to survive and become mature members of the forest community.

As part of the understory, young saplings must compete with other trees and plants for sunlight, nutrients, water, and space. In dense forests, many young trees must wait for years for older trees to fall and leave openings in the canopy for them to grow into.

The length of time it takes a tree to reach maturity depends on the species of tree.

Trees have many different roles in the forest community depending on their age and size. Their leaves, bark, seeds, flowers, fruit, and roots provide food for many kinds of animals. Trees also provide roosts, shade, and shelter to many living things. For example, holes in older trees and around their roots provide shelters for nests and dens.

Like all living things, trees are subject to disease and injury. Physical damage may not kill the tree, but may provide holes and openings in which animals and insects can live and feed. Eventually, trees weakened by injury and disease will die, fall down, and be decomposed. When they die, trees return their nutrients and other elements back into the soil to be recycled through the forest ecosystem.

Getting Ready
Select a few books on trees from the school library including field guides and stories. (See Bibliography on page 385 for suggested titles). Start a "Tree-Source" center, so the students have easy access to materials for researching trees. Make a copy of page 305 for each student.

Doing the Activity
1. Discuss the idea of lifecycles by asking students to describe the lifecycle, or history of a person. Make sure students include childhood, teenage years, young adulthood, and so forth,

in the discussion. Write these stages on the chalkboard. Ask students to identify the different jobs, roles, or things that a person might do in each stage of the lifecycle. Next, ask them to describe the lifecycle of a tree in similar terms (see diagram below).

2. Distribute art materials and ask students to create the lifecycle of a tree, from birth through death and decomposition. Students should include at least three stages or events in their lifecycles (e.g., a forest fire or insect invasion). Encourage them to research a particular species of tree for accuracy in life characteristics, climate, and environment. Remind students that one event that affects the tree (e.g., insect damage) is likely to clear the way for another event (e.g., a hole for nesting birds). The lifecycle could be represented by a circle on the page, with illustrations and a label for each stage or event, or could be shown in a line on a long, narrow piece of paper taped together at the ends.

3. Students should fill in the details for at least three stages or events on the "Tree Lifecycle" student page. Some items may stay the same throughout the tree's life.

4. Give students the opportunity to share their lifecycles in small groups or with the entire group. Create a "History of the Forest" exhibit by mounting all the lifecycles around the classroom.

VARIATION—PLANT PERSONIFICATION

1. Ask students if trees are alive. How do they know? (They grow.) How are trees born? (from a seed) Do they die? (Yes, but they can live a long time.)

2. Ask students to imitate your movements as you enact the life of a tree.

- Curl up in a tight ball—you're a seed.

- Uncurl and kneel—you've sprouted.

- Stick up one arm (fist clenched)—you've grown a branch.

- Stick up the other arm—you've grown another branch.

- Wiggle your fingers—you grow lots of leaves.

- Stand up (feet together)—you grow tall.

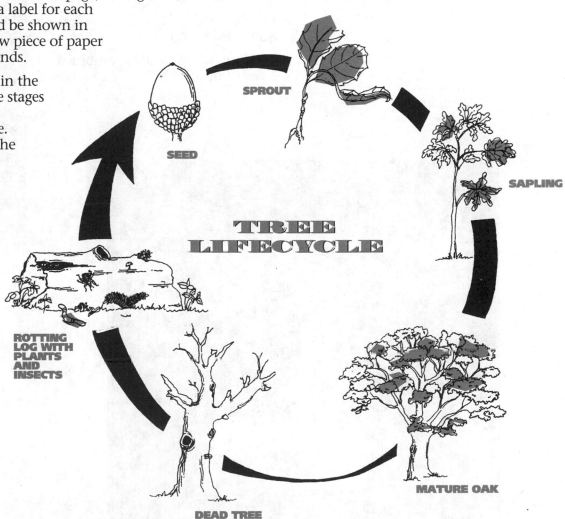

TREE LIFECYCLE

SEED · SPROUT · SAPLING · MATURE OAK · DEAD TREE · ROTTING LOG WITH PLANTS AND INSECTS

- Spread feet apart—you spread out lots of roots.

- Wiggle your toes—you grow lots of little roots (rootlets).

- Start scratching all over—you're attacked by insects and fungi.

- Make a loud noise (kchhhhh!)— you get hit by lightning and lose a limb.

- Smile and sigh (ahhhhhh!)—you become a home for wildlife in your old age.

- Make a hammering noise (knock, knock, knock) and vibrate—wood-peckers peck into your dead wood.

- Make a creaking sound and fall down—you blow down in a storm.

- Stick up one arm—a new seed sprouts from your rotting wood.

Enrichment

Take students on a walk through a neighborhood, local park, or forest site that has plants and trees of various ages. Ask the students to look for trees at various stages in their lives. Have them try to identify at least one tree in each of the following categories:

- Young sapling (stem or trunk < 1/2 inch [1.3 cm])

- "Juvenile" (stem or trunk 1/2 inch to 2 inches [1.3 cm to 5 cm])

- "Young adult" (stem or trunk > 2 inches [5 cm], but tree still under canopy)

- "Adult" (trunk > 2 inches [5 cm], tree in upper canopy)

- Injured or unhealthy trees (showing signs of injury, disease or stress—Is the tree likely to survive?)

- Elderly tree (What factors are weakening the tree?)

- Dead tree (What factors combined to cause death?)

END NOTES...

ASSESSMENT OPPORTUNITY

Have students write an imaginative story about the lifecycle of the particular tree they created. The story can be written as a fable in which the trees, plants, and animals can talk.

In the story, students should include at least three stages or events of the tree's life, such as sprouting from a seed, or dying and decomposing into the soil. Ideally, the life events should show a cause-effect connection (e.g., a drought one year might lead to a fire that enables the cones of a particular tree to sprout).

RELATED ACTIVITIES

Nothing Succeeds Like Succession, Tree Cookies, The Fallen Log, Every Tree for Itself, Trees in Trouble, Bursting Buds, Signs of Fall, Have Seeds Will Travel, Living with Fire

REFERENCES

Brennan, Bill. *Billy B. Sings About Trees* (audio cassette).

Buscaglia, Leo. *The Fall of Freddie the Leaf*. Slack Inc., 1982.

Gile, Joan. *The First Forest*. J. Gile Communications, 1989.

Tressalt, Alvin. *The Gift of the Tree*. Lothrop, 1992.

TREE LIFECYCLE WORK SHEET

Fill in the information for various stages or events your tree's life-cycle. Describe at least three stages or events.

TYPE OF TREE (COMMON NAME)

SCIENTIFIC NAME

CHARACTERISTICS OF TREE

LIFECYCLE STAGE OR EVENT

TREE AGE

ROLE IN FOREST ECOSYSTEM

LIST OF THINGS TREE DEPENDS ON TO SURVIVE

LIST OF THINGS THAT DEPEND ON THE TREE TO SURVIVE

PROCESSES THAT MIGHT MOVE TREE INTO THE NEXT STAGE

LIFECYCLE STAGE OR EVENT

TREE AGE

ROLE IN FOREST ECOSYSTEM

LIST OF THINGS TREE DEPENDS ON TO SURVIVE

LIST OF THINGS THAT DEPEND ON THE TREE TO SURVIVE

PROCESSES THAT MIGHT MOVE TREE INTO THE NEXT STAGE

LIFECYCLE STAGE OR EVENT

TREE AGE

ROLE IN FOREST ECOSYSTEM

LIST OF THINGS TREE DEPENDS ON TO SURVIVE

LIST OF THINGS THAT DEPEND ON THE TREE TO SURVIVE

PROCESSES THAT MIGHT MOVE TREE INTO THE NEXT STAGE

LIFECYCLE STAGE OR EVENT

TREE AGE

ROLE IN FOREST ECOSYSTEM

LIST OF THINGS TREE DEPENDS ON TO SURVIVE

LIST OF THINGS THAT DEPEND ON THE TREE TO SURVIVE

PROCESSES THAT MIGHT MOVE TREE INTO THE NEXT STAGE

Overview
Succession is a natural pattern of change that takes place over time in a forest or ecosystem. In this activity, students will study the connection between plants, animals, and successional stages in local ecosystems.

LEVELS
Part A: Grades 3-6
Parts B and C: Grades 4-8
Enrichment: Grades 3-6

SUBJECTS
Science, Math, Language Arts, Visual Arts

CONCEPTS
■ While every organism goes through a lifecycle of growth, maturity, decline, and death, its role in the ecosystem also changes. (13.3)

■ Ecosystems change over time through patterns of growth and succession. They are also affected by other phenomena such as disease, insects, fire, weather, and human intervention. (13.4)

SKILLS
Observing, Classifying and Categorizing, Identifying Attributes and Components, Identifying Relationships and Patterns, Analyzing, Interpreting, Evaluating

OBJECTIVES
Students will ① explore basic relationships between species diversity and ecosystem stability, ② identify successional stages in ecosystems based on plant and animal species, and ③ draw conclusions about the process of succession based on study test plots in different stages of succession.

MATERIALS
chart paper, crayons, pencils, fencing (or rope), grass clippers, stakes, hammers, string, colored felt, felt board, supply of clear plastic transparencies, permanent or erasable ink markers, copies of student pages 309 and 310, optional camera

TIME CONSIDERATIONS
Preparation: 30 minutes

Activity: Part A: 50 minutes
Part B: One or two 50-minute periods
Part C: Small intervals of time over the course of the year

Background
Succession is the orderly replacement of plant and animal species through time in a given location, leading to a relatively stable biotic community. In a landscape that lacks both vegetation and soil (such as a sand dune or a recently cooled lava flow), primary succession may begin. In primary succession on land, living organisms slowly, often over hundreds or thousands of years, build soil. The first plants to arrive, sometimes called pioneer species, are usually fungi, lichens or mosses, and ferns, which are the oldest types of land plants. Over time, rock is weathered to soil; mosses and ferns cover the landscape; and small seeds, carried by animals or blown by wind, take root. Small shrubs and plants become established. Eventually, if conditions are right, a healthy plant community with mature trees and plants will grow. Secondary succession occurs on landscapes previously occupied by vegetation and can be considered an extension of primary succession (the soil building phase). Grass may begin to grow, followed by herbaceous and small woody plants, followed by shrubs and trees.

Each successional stage is accompanied by its characteristic animal species. Early-successional animal species find food and shelter among the weedy pioneer plants that invade areas cleared by natural or human causes. Mid-successional species are found in partially open areas. Openings in the forest canopy promote the growth of plants that are favored as food by many mammals and birds.

These openings provide edge habitat where field and forest meet, allowing animals to feed on the vegetation in the opening and to escape quickly into the forest. Late-successional animal species require mature forest habitats to provide the food and cover they need. Many species thrive in other types of mature plant communities such as grasslands, tundra, or deserts.

In some cases, whole regions are undergoing succession. For example, in the eastern United States, most of the trees were once cut down for timber and cleared for agriculture. When the fields were left to fallow, native plants slowly began to recolonize the old fields. Today, whole new forests stand where the original ones used to be. A mature forest isn't always the stable climax to succession. For example, because the redwoods of California live to be hundreds of years old, ecologists traditionally believed that they were a climax species. However, ecologists now believe that redwood forests that do not undergo periodic disturbances, such as fire or windstorm, will eventually give way to a forest of hemlocks, which thrive in the shade of the redwoods. However, if the hemlock forest burns, it will grow back as a redwood forest, since redwoods have thick bark and are fairly fire resistant.

Sometimes, people purposely hold back succession to allow one stage to dominate, as when a farmer continually harvests and plows a field. Abandoned lots and neglected lawns, as well as parks, all show signs of secondary succession. When human-caused "setbacks" such as mowing or plowing are discontinued, new species of vegetation appear or begin to dominate the landscape. What we call weeds, are the first stage of secondary succession.

Getting Ready
Identify a nearby area that exhibits several stages of succession or plan this activity to correspond with a field

trip to a natural area. If a field trip or walk is not possible, use the pictures of various stages of succession provided on page 310, or cut additional pictures from magazines, or obtain pictures from land-use agencies (e.g., forestry, soil conservation, parks). Make copies of student pages 309 and 310.

PART A
IN THE CLASSROOM

Doing the Activity

1. Hand out the story on page 309 to each student. After reading it, discuss the changes that took place during the course of the story. (Forest burned and slowly grew back; people grew up, got old, died, had children and grand-children.…)

2. Hand out copies of the succession sequence on page 310 to let students see how succession typically proceeds in a forested area. Point out how each successional stage has its characteristic plants and animals.

3. Divide your group into teams. Using transparent overlays and colored markers, each team will create a sequence of pictures to show succession.

- The base drawing on a piece of 8½" x 11" (21.6 cm x 28 cm) white paper should show a disturbed area (e.g., burned by fire or bulldozed).

- Overlay drawings on 8" x 11" (20.3 cm x 28 cm) transparencies should show successive phases of growth.

- For example, the base picture could show blackened ground with stumps of trees (perhaps with an animal passing through).

- Transparency 1 could display grass, flowers (seeds borne by wind or animal), and small animals returning.

- Transparency 2 could add small bushes, shrubs, and more animals.

- Transparency 3 could add young, small trees with characteristic animals.

- Transparency 4 could add full-grown, mature trees with characteristic animals. Have each team

tape or staple the overlays to the base picture.

4. When finished, the teams can demonstrate their work to the group and describe what is happening in each successive scene.

PART B
IN THE FIELD

Doing the Activity

1. Take your students on a field trip through an area that has several types of vegetative communities (e.g., an urban park with wooded areas). Have them try to find plant communities in different stages of succession. Tell them not to worry about plant or tree names, only types (i.e., grasses, non-woody herbaceous plants, woody shrubs, trees). Have them look for animals and signs or sounds of animals. They should also look for evidence of disturbance (such as erosion, tire tracks, fire, construction) that might have altered the natural succession. They can look for the following stages of succession:

- Grasses and nonwoody plants only

- Grasses, and woody and nonwoody plants

- Grasses and shrubs, with young tree saplings (stem < ½" [1.3 cm])

- Ground vegetation and young trees (stem ½" to 2" [1.3 cm to 5 cm])

- Mature trees (stem > 2" [5 cm] can still be under canopy)

2. Call the group together and define the stages of succession evident at your site. Discuss what factors might alter succession at your site, including disease, insects, fire, wind, lightning, pollution, and drought.

3. Divide the class into teams with three members each. Have students draw a general map of the study area, including major landmarks (such as major trees, trail junctions, parking lots, benches, creeks, etc.), and then identify and draw areas on the map that fall into the different categories of succession identified in the preceding step.

PART C
IN YOUR BACKYARD

Doing the Activity

1. For your study, get permission to designate three areas that are 10.75 sq ft (1 sq m) on the school grounds or at a site nearby. The first area should be a non-black-topped area that has been trampled. The second area should be a patch of lawn that is untrampled and is regularly mowed and watered. The third area should also be a lawn or grassy area that you will fence off and leave untouched (no mowing, watering, or fertilizing).

NOTE—You will need to coordinate with your school's maintenance staff to designate this plot so it is not disturbed.

2. For an extended period of time (e.g., the school year), ask students to make written journal observations, drawings, or photographs of these three areas on a regular basis, about once a week. The camera position should be marked on the ground, so the same position can be used for each photo. This pictorial record should be displayed in the classroom. Photos can show the following:

- Types of plants (record changes)
- Plant growth rate (measure in centimeters and graph each week)

- Changes in plant density (number of stems per square meter)
- Changes in species composition (Do some plants gradually become more abundant and others less abundant?)
- New plant species
- Evidence of animal or human life

3. After each observation period, ask the students to make a general statement about apparent succession and differences in species diversity in all three sites. Create a wall chart to graph observations and measurements.

Enrichment—Say It on Felt

Assign teams for each of the stages of succession that were studied in the activity. Have teams use different colors of felt to cut out the shapes of plants and animals that are characteristic of their assigned stage of succession. Have each team write a brief story describing it. Create a large felt board, in which the bottom third is brown (for soil) and the top two-thirds are blue (for sky). Have groups come up, in order, and place their plants and animals in appropriate places on the felt board and tell their stories (felt naturally sticks to felt). Your class can re-create the story of succession, stage by stage.

END NOTES...

ASSESSMENT OPPORTUNITY
At the end of the designated observation time in Part C, ask students to write a summary report of what happened at all three sites and what stages of succession they observed. Look for descriptions of the lifecycles and stages of plant growth, disturbance factors, and evidence of animal life.

RELATED ACTIVITIES
Environmental Exchange Box, The Forest of S.T. Shrew, Planet of Plenty, The Fallen Log, Adopt a Tree, Every Tree for Itself, Trees in Trouble, Have Seeds-Will Travel, Living with Fire

REFERENCES
Story on page 309 adapted with permission from Butts, Patricia. *TREE TOPS VALLEY.* ForesTree Explorations. Surrey, British Columbia, Canada: British Columbia Forestry Association.

Owen, Oliver S. Natural Resources Conservation: *AN ECOLOGICAL APPROACH.* Macmillan Publishing.

Young, Raymond A. *INTRODUCTION TO FOREST SCIENCE.* John Wiley and Sons.

TREE TOPS VALLEY

Once upon a time, a boy and a girl lived with their parents at the edge of a beautiful green valley in the Pacific Northwest. Their names were Sara and John.

The valley was filled with a vast evergreen forest. Its trees towered over the log cabin where John and Sara lived. Sara and John loved the forest. Every day they went exploring. They paddled in the forest's cool streams and made trails under the giant conifers.

They also liked to have picnics at the top of a hill near their home. Up there, they could look down on the tops of the valley's huge trees.

One day when they were up on the hill, they decided to give the valley a name. They called it Tree Tops Valley.

Then, in the middle of a hot summer day, everything changed. A lightning storm started a fire in the forest. Luckily, the wind blew the flames away from Sara and John's home. But when the fire went out, they saw it had burned their Tree Tops Valley. All the tall trees were burned. The tender little seedlings that had grown on the forest floor were gone. All that was left was the burned remains of trees.

They both wanted to cry. Sara said, "I just can't look at it. Our beautiful forest is gone forever. I never want to sit on our hill again." After the fire, the family moved away to a settlement where other families lived. There were children there, and Sara and John made new friends.

Then, five years after the fire, their father said, "Why don't we visit the valley? It would be good to see it again."

Sara and John didn't want to go. They remembered how the valley had looked after the fire. But they agreed, and one day, the family saddled their horses and rode up to the valley.

What a surprise! Things had happened since the fire. Winds had blown seeds into the valley. Birds had dropped them from the air. The seeds had sprouted. Now, instead of bare, burned ground, there were mosses, weeds, grasses, and ferns growing everywhere. The children rode back home feeling much better about Tree Tops Valley.

The years went by. Before they knew it, Sara and John had grown up. The settlement where they lived was much bigger now. John became a teacher and taught at the one room school that the settlers had built.

Sara decided to be a prospector. She had heard stories about people who were finding gold farther north. So Sara bought supplies and one day was ready to leave. She promised John she would write him.

John didn't hear from Sara for many months. Then, finally, a letter arrived. In the letter, Sara wrote, "On my way north, I passed through Tree Tops Valley. You would be amazed at how the valley looks now! Our old cabin is still there, but everything else has changed. The whole valley is full of berry bushes. I had a feast!"

The letter gave John an idea. He thought, "When I have children of my own, I'll take them berry picking in the valley. That would be fun!"

Soon after that, John got married. When his oldest son was 10 years old, he remembered his idea. He took his family to the valley to pick berries. His children loved the valley. But there were no berries to pick. Most of the bushes were gone.

Instead, the valley was filling with deciduous trees. John wrote to Sara about them. He wrote, "There are lots of leafy green trees in the valley. And I saw some conifer seedlings. The leafy trees have shaded the berry bushes and choked them out. I don't know what the trees are called, but they have made the valley all green again."

Many years passed. John's children grew up and had families of their own. One summer, when John was 75 years old, he received a letter from Sara. It read:

> Dear John,
> Remember how we loved Tree Tops Valley when we were young? Last month I decided to visit it again, before I got too old to make the trip. It was a long ride, but I made it! You would be happy to see our valley now. It's beautiful!
> Remember those leafy green trees you saw on your last trip there? Well, most of them are gone. Now the valley is full of young coniferous trees. Who knows? Maybe our grandchildren will see the valley looking the way we once saw it.
> Love,
> Sara

The years went by. It was now 100 years since the fire had swept through Tree Tops Valley.

One day, John's granddaughter, Jennifer, was looking at some old family letters. She found the letter Sara had written to John after her last visit to Tree Tops Valley.

"Look at this," Jennifer said to her husband. "It's a letter that belonged to my grandfather John. His sister wrote it to him. It's all about a place called Tree Tops Valley. I wonder if we could find the valley. Why don't we try?"

And that's what they did. Jennifer and her husband found the valley. They even found the hill where Sara and John had taken their picnics.

From the hill, they could see tall conifers filling the whole valley. They climbed down and explored. Jennifer and her husband didn't know it, but Tree Tops Valley was well into the long journey of rebuilding the same kind of forest that Sara and John had enjoyed so many years before.

PICTURE OF
SUCCESSION

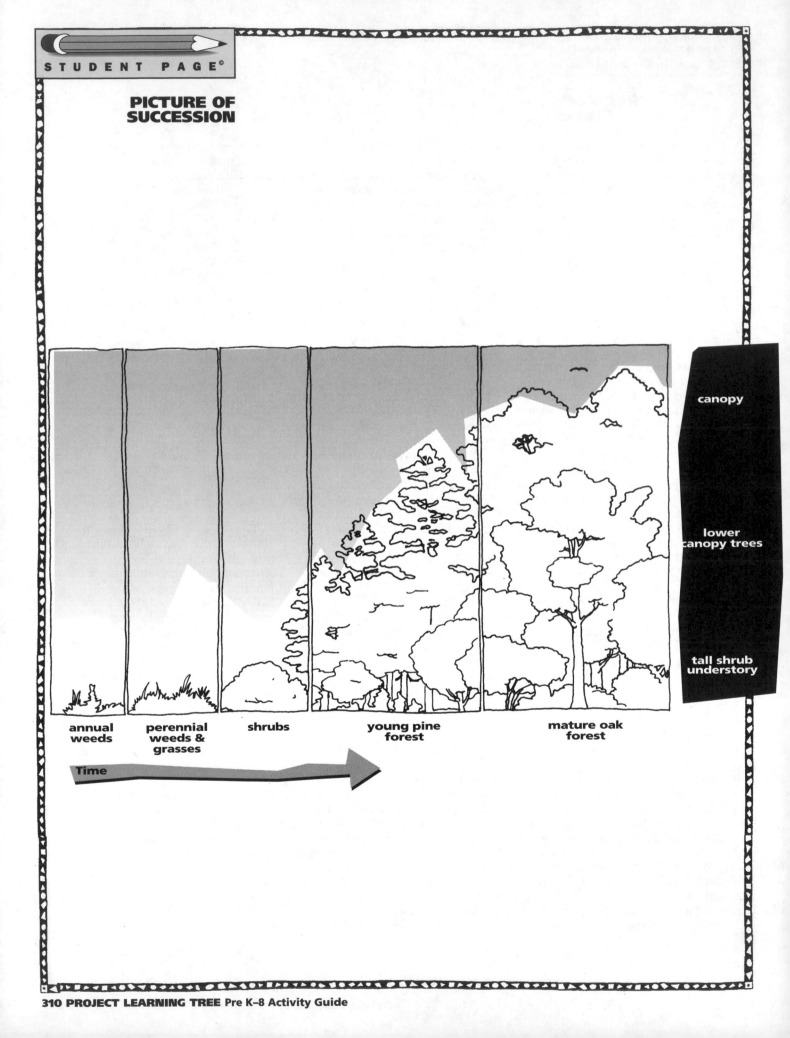

annual
weeds

perennial
weeds &
grasses

shrubs

young pine
forest

mature oak
forest

canopy

lower
canopy trees

tall shrub
understory

Time

Overview

The term "forest fire" may conjure up images of fear and devastation. Preventing fires is still important, but times have changed. In this activity, students will learn how fire is a natural event in forests and other ecosystems and how it helps keep plants and other parts of the ecosystems healthy.

Background

Fire is a natural event in most forest ecosystems. Some forests depend on fire to recycle nutrients back into the soil. From an ecological standpoint, fire is neither "good" nor "bad." Fire occurs naturally through lightning strikes in the presence of dry fuel. Fires also occur when humans start them intentionally or accidentally.

Fires need heat, fuel, and oxygen to burn—these three elements are known as the "fire triangle." Remove any one of these three elements and the fire will not burn. Initially, the heat is provided by the source of ignition. Fuels include dry trees, dead trees and limbs, leaf litter, and dry grass.

Oxygen is, of course, available in the air. Weather conditions have a great influence on when fires occur and how they spread. Hot temperatures and dry winds can dry out trees and grasses in a forest, making them available as fuel for a fire to consume. The stronger the winds, the more quickly moisture evaporates from the vegetation, and the faster the fire can spread.

Even in the largest fires, such as the Yellowstone fire in 1988, not everything burns. Patterns of burned areas across the landscape can help keep ecosystems healthy. Areas that have recently burned do not have much fuel or dry dead litter, and they are less likely to burn again soon. Having trees of mixed ages is healthy for the forest ecosystem in many ways, one of which is preventing the entire forest from burning down.

In the southeastern United States, the months of March, April, and May are called "fire season," when 75 percent of forest fires occur. Fire season in the West usually runs from June through October, during the very dry months of the year. In the Northeast, it is March through May, and then again in the fall, corresponding to the leaf drop. Wildfires do not generally occur when the fuels (trees, shrubs, and grasses) are wet and cold.

Fire was an important tool in Native American culture and is in other cultures around the world. Some Native American peoples set fires to prairies knowing that new growth would attract game. Fire has traditionally been used to drive game, reduce populations of unwanted animals, enhance crop growth, and clear forests.

Fire can be an effective management tool for state and federal agencies to manage their wildlands, which include forests, grasslands, and other ecosystems. Over the years, fire management policies and techniques have changed. A prescribed burn (one that is lighted by trained fire personnel within prescribed fuel and weather conditions) can prepare a logged area for reforestation, enhance wildlife habitat, protect a native tree species, control insect populations or disease, or reduce future fire hazard by reducing burnable fuels.

Fire is an essential component in the lifecycle of several tree species. Some depend on the heat of fire to open their cones and release the seeds, while others simply need fire to open the forest canopy to provide light. In general, fires return nutrients to the soil in the form of ash.

Preventing, controlling, and suppressing wildfires is becoming more vital as more urban people seek woodland settings for their homes. More and more homes, property and lives are endangered by fire along the wildland-urban interface. Once again, balancing the needs of humans against the needs of the forest system has no easy answers.

LEVELS
Activity: Grades 4-8
Variation: Grades PreK-2

SUBJECTS:
Science, Social Studies

CONCEPTS
■ Ecosystems change over time through patterns of growth and succession. They are also affected by other phenomena such as disease, insects, fire, weather, and human intervention. (13.4)

■ Our increasing knowledge of the Earth's ecosystems influences strategies used for forest management and environmental stewardship. (14.1)

SKILLS
Observing, Classifying and Categorizing, Analyzing, Summarizing

OBJECTIVES
Students will ① describe a forest fire: how it starts, spreads, and burns out and ② explain several approaches to forest fire management.

MATERIALS
Activity: copies of "Fire Triangle" work sheet on student page 315, art materials, glass jar with metal lid, wooden kitchen matches, small birthday candle, paper match, corn or potato chip
Variation: 20 strands of yarn and pieces of blue poster board or construction paper to make necklaces, pieces of red and green construction paper to make headbands
Enrichment: five metal buckets (or large coffee cans); five 1-gallon containers (such as milk jugs) filled with water; assortment of different-sized fuels (pine needles, leaves, cones, etc., some dry and some green); matches

TIME CONSIDERATIONS
Preparation: 50 minutes

Activity: 50 minutes
Variation: 30 minutes
Enrichment: 50 minutes

Getting Ready

Activity: Make copies of page 315 and gather materials for the demonstration. You may want to invite a local firefighter or forester who is involved with fire management to visit your class.

Variation: You will need an outdoor area or large room for the game. Make four green headbands out of construction paper for the "rangers." Make one red headband for "fire." Make 20 "fire protection necklaces." These can be made by cutting squares out of blue poster board and tying string through them.

Enrichment: You will need extra adults to supervise the fire demonstration buckets. Make sure proper precautions have been taken and that water and/or fire extinguishers are available. If you cannot do the fire demonstration, try to borrow one of the forest fire videos described on page 314. This will help your students understand the dynamics of wildfire.

PART A
FIRE TRIANGLE

Doing the Activity

1. Pass out the "Fire Triangle" work sheet on student page 315. Have students read and work through it on their own. When everyone is finished, ask the class what three things are needed for fire to burn. Draw the fire triangle on the board. Ask them under what conditions they think it would be easy to start a fire, and when they think it would be hard.

2. Demonstrate how a candle burns in a glass (from a science lab) when each of the three different elements are limited:

■ Place a small, lighted birthday candle in a jar (you may want to mount it in a dab of modeling clay). Then seal the jar with the lid to cut off the supply of oxygen. As the flame consumes the oxygen in the jar's air, the flame will go out. Explain that cutting off oxygen is one way of managing a fire.

■ Open the jar, relight the candle, and put the lid back on. Only this time, when the flame starts to go out reopen the lid to let more oxygen in; the candle will reignite. Explain that this illustrates what happens when the wind picks up during a fire; the fire may reignite or burn out of control.

■ Take the lid completely off and allow the candle to burn until all the fuel (paraffin) is consumed and the fire extinguishes itself—give the students time see how long it takes. Set up a wooden match and a paper match (similar size) in bases of clay. Light them both and see which burns longer. How do these two tree products—wood and paper—burn differently? Place a corn or potato chip on a piece of tin foil and light it. See how long it takes to burn up. What fuel in the chip made it burn? (vegetable oil, found in all plants)

Explain that the primary way fire managers prevent fires is by reducing fuels so that fires will not start as easily, and won't burn as intensely or for as long.

3. Finally, extinguish the flame by adding water, which removes the heat and smothers the flame. With all of today's "high-tech" firefighting equipment, water is still the primary "tool" used to fight fires.

4. Try to have a local firefighter visit your group to talk about the equipment and techniques that are used to suppress fires. Prepare students to ask questions about how fire can be prevented and how they can protect themselves should a fire occur. You can also have a forester visit your group to talk about wildfires. Prepare students to ask questions about how forest fires are managed in their region, and how they can best be prevented.

Note: For grades 6–8, the demonstration can be done by groups of students rather than the teacher.

PART B
CAUSE AND EFFECT

Doing the Activity

1. Students should contact their state forestry agency (usually within the state department of natural resources or department of agriculture) or a state office for the U.S.D.A. Forest Service. They can ask for information concerning the causes of all large forest or range fires in the state over the past several years, including data on both prescribed burns and uncontrolled wildfires.

2. Using this information, have the students develop tables and pie charts showing the actual numbers and percentages of fires from different causes for the years studied (see sample table).

3. Have students compare the data for at least three different years and determine: which cause was responsible for the most large fires in each year; and the fewest? The number of fires caused by each category in each year, noting increases or decreases. Reasons why increases or decreases might have occurred. The average yearly number of fires from each cause for all the years studied.

4. Have students research the effects of fire on the economy and the environment, both detrimental and beneficial. They could find out about: financial costs involved in the loss of natural resources and in fire management; ecological costs involved in the loss of natural resources and in fire management; ecological costs or benefits from forest fires; and how various agencies or forest industries manage fire and handle fire prevention.

VARIATION—FIRE TAG (PREK-2)

This game will simulate how trees can be destroyed by fire, how they can be protected from fire, and how they grow back.

1. Choose one child to become the Wildfire that burns the trees. She or he wears a red head band.

2. Choose four children to be Smokey Bear rangers. They wear green head bands. Give each ranger five "fire protection" necklaces to hold (see Getting Ready).

3. The remaining children should pretend to be trees. They should scatter to different parts of the room and stand still.

4. The Smokey Bear rangers should gather around the Wildfire in the middle of the room

5. The game starts when someone yells, "Fire!" Then the Wildfire runs to grab the hand of a tree. When this happens, the tree becomes part of the Wildfire, and the two of them run to grab another tree. Thus, the fire builds and spreads.

The Cause of Fires
(FOR THE YEAR OF 1990 IN NJ)

CAUSE	NO. OF FIRES	% OF TOTAL
1. Arson	717	49.3%
2. Children	234	16.1%
3. Miscellaneous	204	14.0%
4. Smoker	84	5.8%
5. Debris Burning	68	4.7%
6. Equipment Use	51	3.5%
7. Campfires	37	2.5%
8. Railroad	11	0.8%
9. Lightning	4	0.3%
10. False Alarms	45	3.1%

6. At the same time, the Smokey Bear rangers run to protect the trees by putting fire protection necklaces around their necks. They can protect only trees that have not yet caught on fire.

7. When a tree receives a necklace, it must join hands with the other protected trees to make a "fire break" (a line of protection that the fire cannot penetrate). In reality, this could be a strip of wet or bare earth.

8. When the fire runs out of fuel, it burns out (Wildfire students should drop their hands and stand still to show that new trees have grown in the enriched soil). Once again, there is a forest.

9. Before dismissing the group, discuss the meaning of Smokey Bear's slogan: "Only you can prevent forest fires!"

ENRICHMENT
FIRE AND FUELS
DEMONSTRATION

1. Divide the students into five numbered teams. Give each team a metal bucket (or large metal coffee can) to fill, no more than half-way, with the following fuels: (or you can fill the buckets yourself beforehand)

Team #1: Use an assortment of different-sized branches, leaves and needles, ALL GREEN.

Team #2: Use an assortment of different-sized dead and dry branches, leaves, and needles.

Team #3: Use an assortment of different-sized dead and dry branches, leaves, and needles that have been sprayed lightly with water before being placed in the bucket.

Bucket #4: Use an assortment of fuels (branches, pieces of wood) all of large diameter (small surface area to volume ratio, i.e., no small kindling).

Bucket #5: Use an assortment of fuels, all partially burned (from a fireplace or campfire, but not completely consumed).

2. Explain to students that in five groups (supervised by adults) they will try to start small fires—it may not be easy! (You may decide to have only the adults light the fires.) Explain that each group will have a bucket with a certain type of fuel, and must carefully plan a strategy to try to get as much of their fuel as possible to burn in the allotted time. Remind them that forests will not burn unless all three parts of the fire triangle exist. (See Background.)

3. Review the following rules before going outside:

a. Each group must work with and listen to their adult supervisor.

b. All fires must be built within the metal bucket on the designated surface area (i.e., an open asphalt playground or parking lot away from cars, buildings, and dry vegetation).

c. No fuels may be used or added other than those assigned to each group.

d. Only seven matches will be given to each group.

e. A two-minute group-planning session is mandatory before lighting matches.

4. Explain that all the groups will start at once and have 15 minutes maximum to use their seven matches to burn as much fuel as they can.

5. Afterward, hold a class discussion. Which groups were successful? Why or why not?

■ Visit each fire bucket and examine differences in fuel types and success of burning.

■ Do these differences in fuel type occur naturally?

■ Where and under what conditions can each be found?

■ What other factors besides fuel type came into play?

■ Point out strategies observed, such as blowing on or fanning the fire.

■ Ask students to identify which part of the fire triangle suppressed their fire from burning, or allowed it to burn.

END NOTES...

ASSESSMENT OPPORTUNITY

Have students create a picture-board story of wildfire—it's like a comic book but without any dialogue. The picture board should have at least 10 frames showing ① how the forest looked before the fire (the fuel-dead trees, leaf litter-should be labeled); ② how the fire was ignited (natural or human source); ③ the pattern the fire burned (burning near a cabin because there are dry trees around it); and ④ how the fire was put out-which parts of the fire triangle were removed to stop the fire?

RELATED ACTIVITIES

Nothing Succeeds Like Succession, Tree Lifecycle, Who Works in this Forest?, Tree Cookies

REFERENCES

De Golia, Jack. *Fire: The Story Behind a Force of Nature.* Las Vegas: KC Publications, 1989.

Despain, Don, Douglas Houston, Mary Meagher, and Paul Schullery. *Wildlife in Transition: Man and Nature on Yellowstone's Northern Range.* Boulder, CO: Roberts Rinehart Publishers, 1986.

Pyne, Stephen J. *Fire in America: A Cultural History of Wildland and Rural Fire.* Princeton, NJ: Princeton University Press, 1982.

Pyne, Stephen J. *Introduction to Wildland Fire: Fire Management in the United States.* Princeton, NJ: Princeton University Press, 1984.

Stewart, George R. *Fire.* University of Nebraska Press, 1984.

Wright, Henry A., and Arthur W. Bailey. *Fire Ecology: The United States and Southern Canada.* New York: John Wiley and Sons, 1982.

Wuerthner, George. *Yellowstone and the Fires of Change.* Salt Lake City: Haggis House Publications, 1988.

VIDEOS

Yellowstone Forest 1988, produced by Video Visions, P.O. Box 6721, Bozeman, MT 59715. 1 hour.

Yellowstone in the Summer '88, produced for Travel Montana and Wyoming Travel Commission by Sage Advertising, P.O. Box 1142, Helena, MT 59624. Phone (406) 442-9500. 17 minutes.

A FIRE TRIANGLE WORKSHEET

1. Fires need heat, fuel, and oxygen to burn—this is known as the "fire triangle." Draw a triangle below and label each of the three sides with the word and a picture for each of the three parts.

2. Initially, the heat is provided by an ignition source, which can be human or natural. Name two natural and two human-caused sources of heat for fire ignition.

Natural: 1._____   Human-caused: 1._____

2._____   2._____

3. Fires need fuel to burn. In a forest, what sort of fuels might you expect to find? Name three potential fuels:

1._____

2._____

3._____

4. Oxygen is available in the air. Weather has a great influence on when fires occur and on how they spread. Hot temperatures and dry winds can create severe fire conditions by affecting fuel, moisture, and oxygen. What can dry winds do to fuels to make them more likely to burn?

5. If you cut off any one of these three elements, a fire will not burn. What are some ways that firefighters might cut off each of the three parts of the fire triangle?

Overview

This activity gives students the opportunity to explore a variety of natural resources and products that people depend on every day. In addition, students will gain insight into the processes by which these natural resources are turned into products and, when possible, recycled into new products.

LEVELS
Grades 4-8

SUBJECTS
Science, Social Studies

CONCEPTS
■ Technologies that are developed to meet the needs of an increasing world population should also be environmentally sound. (14.2)

■ Consumers "drive" the marketplace with their demands for goods and services. Such demands shift with time and may have positive or negative effects on the availability of natural resources and environmental quality. (15.2)

■ Industries usually respond to consumer demand for recyclable, recycled, or otherwise environmentally friendly products. (15.3)

SKILLS
Observing, Researching, Organizing Information, Analyzing

OBJECTIVES
Students will ① identify the natural resources from which products are derived; ② trace the lifecycle of a product from natural resources, to the raw materials, to the finished product; and ③ describe how energy is consumed in the manufacturing and transportation of products and how it might be conserved.

MATERIALS
pencils, colored markers, poster or butcher paper for "Cycle of Life" diagrams, large world map, copies of student pages

TIME CONSIDERATIONS
Preparation: 20 minutes

Activity: Part A: 30 minutes
Part B: 30 minutes

Background

In our decisions as consumers and citizens, we should be aware of the cycle of natural resources and the flow of energy throughout the environment. From pencils to airplanes, from school lunch bags to television sets, every material and every form of energy used to make a product comes from a renewable resource or a nonrenewable source. Renewable resources—like trees for shelter, animals for food and clothing, and plants for medicines—can all be replenished through natural processes. On the other hand, nonrenewable resources—like graphite for pencils, gold for jewelry, aluminum for automobiles—are finite and cannot be replenished naturally. Once these materials are mined or taken from their points of origin, they cannot grow again naturally or replace themselves.

The energy needed to make the products we use—or to light, heat and cool our homes, to pump water to the tap, operate our cd players, and power our cars—also begins in the form of renewable or nonrenewable resources. Fossil fuels, like coal and oil used to generate electricity or burn as gasoline in engines, are nonrenewable resources. Likewise, selenium and cadmium used in batteries are nonrenewable resources. There are limited supplies of these minerals and elements in the Earth's crust. On the other hand, the sun, wind and geothermal sources (super hot steam from deep underground) are perpetual, renewable resources, and can supply us with a nearly endless supply of energy.

Energy is required to produce the materials that go into a product. The engine powering a steam shovel used to mine a metal consumes energy in the form of gasoline. The equipment used to fell a tree, whether powered by hand or by engine, consumes energy.

The process of transporting the metal-bearing ore to a refining plant or milling the tree requires energy to power the machinery. Combining the processed metal and wood with other raw material to make a finished product—like the pencil in this activity—draws on even more energy. Producing packaging for the product, shipping the product, even selling the product and using the product requires energy every step of the way. Finally, disposing of the used product, or recycling it if possible, completes the resource and energy cycle, but it will never return 100% of either the resource consumed or the energy consumed back to nature. Nothing can be created or used without expending energy in the process.

Producing some materials requires more energy than others, but the return in efficiency in the use of those materials, and their ability to be recycled, can offset the cost of production. For example, transforming bauxite ore into an aluminum ingot requires high levels of electricity—much more energy than is needed to produce the same amount of steel from iron ore and carbon. Yet the ease with which aluminum can be tooled, when compared to steel tooling, saves energy in manufacturing products made with aluminum; its reduced weight in the construction of vehicles provides cost savings in transportation by reducing the amount of energy needed to propel cars, trucks, and airplanes made with aluminum, and the efficiency of recycling aluminum; once it has been used may offset the initial cost of production and expenditure of energy when compared to other metals that do not share these qualities.

Whether we use wood for pencils, aluminum for airplanes, electricity to light a city, or water to quench our thirst, the choices billions of people make everyday to use renewable and nonrenewable resources to meet their needs as consumers have an impact on the global environment. When we choose to use nonrenewable materials and energy sources, we must realize that at some point in time they will cease to be available. Decisions to recycle whenever possible and to develop new recycling technologies can extend the available pool of nonrenewable resources. When we use products that are derived from mostly renewable resources—both material and energy—we must also make a decision to manage those resources wisely in order to assure their availability for future generations.

Many products we use every day are actually composed of a variety of materials. Many of these materials can only be found on distant continents. No matter where the materials are found, they all contribute to the Earth's resources and energy cycles. How wisely we choose the products we use, and how wisely we use the products we choose, determines the outcomes of those cycles.

Getting Ready
Set up a chalkboard or poster paper on which to draw a large diagram. Display a large world map. Copy pages 318 and 319.

PART A
MAKING THE GLOBAL PENCIL

Doing the Activity
1. Begin the activity by having each student handle and observe a pencil. Challenge students to identify all the materials that make up the pencil, along with the natural resources from which they are derived. Ask where these natural resources might have come from. Using the Background information, discuss possible origins of these resources and locate these areas on a world map.

2. A cycle is defined as a course of events or operations that recur regularly and that usually lead back to a starting point. Have students describe a cycle that occurs in their own lives (i.e., the school year may consist of

buying supplies, attending classes, taking tests, going on vacation, attending classes, taking tests, receiving report cards, having summer break, and starting again).

3. Have the students consider the lifecycle of a pencil. With students' help, draw and label a large diagram of "Life and Times of a Pencil" on the chalkboard. Refer to the diagram on student page 318. (You may want to make a transparency of the diagram and use an overhead projector to present it.)

4. Discuss the pathways of natural resources and materials that go into the finished pencil. By what means were they transported? Identify the energy required to extract, process, manufacture, and distribute the resource. What could be done to make those steps more energy efficient? What could be done to lessen the environmental impact of each step?

5. You can also trace the lifecycle of one or more of the pencil's raw materials. This can be shown as a smaller concentric circle or as a separate circle.

PART B
RESEARCHING OTHER CYCLES

Doing the Activity
1. Ask each student to think of (or bring to class) an item that is in some way a product of a forest ecosystem. You may instead provide a box of various items and have the students choose one.

2. For the item they choose, each student should identify the steps necessary to produce the finished product from its natural resources, and the steps necessary to recycle it back to nature or into a new product. The steps can be drawn and labeled in a "Cycle of Life" diagram similar to the pencil diagram. Students should also trace the lifecycle of the item's raw materials and show this as smaller concentric circles or separate circles.

3. Upon completion, have students explain the steps where energy was used to manufacture or transport the product or its raw materials, and where pollution might result. Discuss the consumer's dependence on energy to produce and to transport raw materials and finished products.

END NOTES...

ASSESSMENT OPPORTUNITY
Have students research the product they identified on student page 318, and fill in the map on page 319, which traces product's components from their various sources. Connect all the regions with lines, and label each connection with the type of transportation most likely used to move the product from one location to another.

RELATED ACTIVITIES
Renewable or Not?; We All Need Trees; Tree Treasures; A Forest of Many Uses; A Peek at Packaging; Reduce, Reuse, Recycle

A PENCIL'S LIFE CYCLE

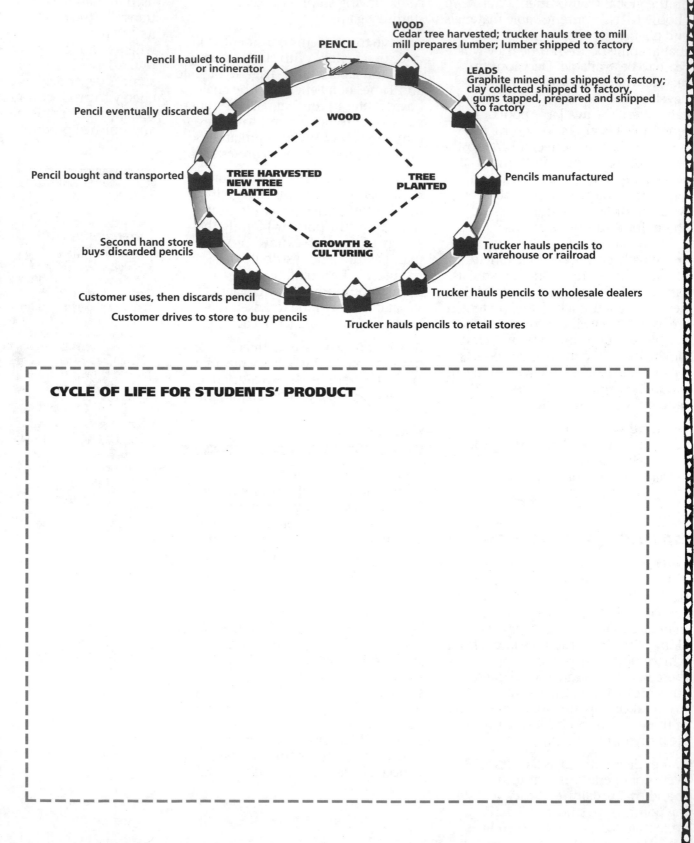

WOOD
Cedar tree harvested; trucker hauls tree to mill
mill prepares lumber; lumber shipped to factory

PENCIL

Pencil hauled to landfill
or incinerator

LEADS
Graphite mined and shipped to factory;
clay collected shipped to factory,
gums tapped, prepared and shipped
to factory

Pencil eventually discarded

WOOD

**TREE HARVESTED
NEW TREE
PLANTED**

**TREE
PLANTED**

Pencil bought and transported

Pencils manufactured

Second hand store
buys discarded pencils

**GROWTH &
CULTURING**

Trucker hauls pencils to
warehouse or railroad

Customer uses, then discards pencil

Trucker hauls pencils to wholesale dealers

Customer drives to store to buy pencils

Trucker hauls pencils to retail stores

CYCLE OF LIFE FOR STUDENTS' PRODUCT

MAPS

SAMPLE—MATERIALS THAT GO INTO A PENCIL

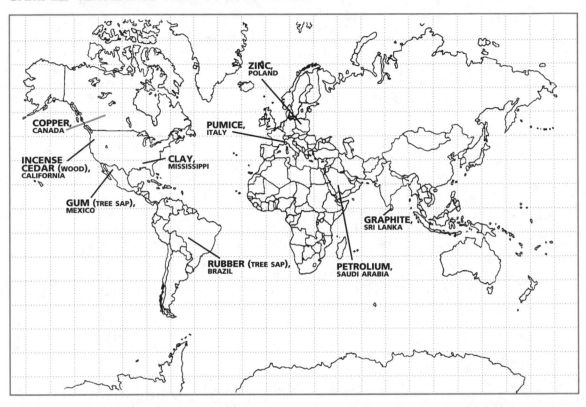

ZINC, POLAND

COPPER, CANADA

PUMICE, ITALY

INCENSE CEDAR (WOOD), CALIFORNIA

CLAY, MISSISSIPPI

GUM (TREE SAP), MEXICO

GRAPHITE, SRI LANKA

RUBBER (TREE SAP), BRAZIL

PETROLIUM, SAUDI ARABIA

MATERIALS FOR YOUR PRODUCT

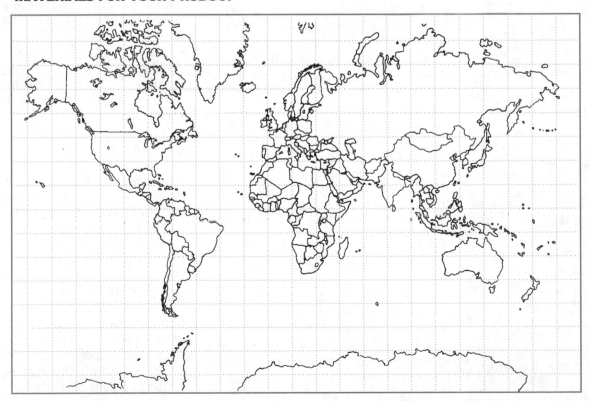

Overview
Patterns for reducing solid waste can be seen in community efforts to reduce consumption and recycle resources. In this activity, students will set up a program for reusing, recycling, and reducing consumption of resources at school.

LEVELS
Projects 1 & 2: Grades 4-8
Project 3: Grades 6-8

SUBJECTS:
Science, Math, Social Studies, Language Arts

CONCEPTS

■ Technologies that are developed to meet the needs of an increasing world population should also be environmentally sound. (14.2)

■ Consumers "drive" the marketplace with their demand for goods and services. Such demands shift with time and may have positive or negative effects on the availability of natural resources and environmental quality. (15.2)

■ Industries usually respond to consumer demand for recyclable, recycled, or otherwise environmentally friendly products. (15.3)

■ Increased public knowledge of the environment and the need for conservation of natural resources have resulted in lifestyle changes in many cultures. (15.5)

SKILLS
Reasoning, Classifying and Categorizing, Evaluating, Making Decisions

OBJECTIVES:
Students will ① learn about ways to reduce solid waste in their community by reducing consumption, reusing products, recycling materials, and composting and ② communicate to others the importance of recycling in their community.

MATERIALS
labeled recycling bins (purchased or made from boxes or bags)

TIME CONSIDERATIONS
Preparation: 60 minutes

Activity: Each project requires multiple periods

Background
Humans have always produced waste, and societies have always had to deal with waste management. With populations growing rapidly, some communities are running out of places to put their garbage. We know that some of our resources are limited and that irresponsible methods of waste disposal can put the environment at risk.

Everyone throws things away. But did you ever stop to consider where "away" is? The landfill? The ocean? An incinerator? Decomposed into the soil? When you stop to think about it, there really is no such place as "away." Everything, no matter how small, goes somewhere. Where it goes is very important.

The average American generates about 1,300 pounds (590 kg) of solid waste each year! Most of it ends up in a landfill, and in many communities the landfills are full. In fact, 14,000 of America's 20,000 landfills closed between 1978 and 1988. It is often difficult to site a new landfill, because most people do not want one sited near them. One reason for this is that some older landfills can leak harmful pollutants into groundwater supplies. However, newer landfills are lined in a way that prevents leaking. A common alternative to landfills is to burn the waste in an incinerator; however, incinerators still produce large amounts of ash, which end up in landfills.

There are many actions people can take as part of an integrated solid waste management and material recovery plan. Many of these are described by the three R's: reduce, reuse, and recycle. Reduce consumption of products when possible. Reuse items more than once—repair them and make them last. Recycle as many resources as you can.

Technology has made it possible to recover many materials before they become part of the waste stream, to be used in recycling, composting, or energy conversion facilities.

Some communities pay a high price for solid waste disposal. Recycling can save money by reducing waste disposal, and it can make money if there's a market for the recyclable materials. Recycling can also save energy needed in production.

Organic wastes such as food scraps, leaves, grass clippings, and paper can be composted and kept out of the waste stream.

Getting Ready
Gather several large containers to use as recycling bins.

Doing the Activity
1. Divide the group into two or three teams to work on different projects, or have the entire group work on one project.

Project 1
Set up a classroom program for separating items that can be reused from those that can be recycled. Separate recyclables by paper, glass, aluminum cans, and so on. Once the program is in place, the team should create a pamphlet showing how to set up a classroom recycling program. Students can then present their plan to other classes to help them set one up in their own classrooms.

Reusable products can be collected and reused by the students. For example, they could make writing tablets out of paper that has been printed on only one side. The program might include collection days for old lunch bags, writing paper, and pencils that could be reused, and a booth set up at recess or lunch on certain weekdays to redistribute the reusable supplies. By coordinating with other teachers, this could become a school-wide project.

Project 2

Set up recycling bins for glass, paper, and aluminum in the cafeteria and faculty room. Students should create large posters with glued-on samples or pictures of the items that can be discarded in the bins: uneaten food, paper, plastic wrapping, reusable paper bags, and so forth. They can set up a central recycling depot for all the items collected in each classroom. The students should determine through letter-writing (or phone) where these items can be recycled in their community, and whether or not there is a pickup service. If not, they should seek adult volunteers such as faculty or parents to take the recyclable materials regularly to the recycling center.

Project 3

Investigate the costs/benefits of various options to reduce waste. For example, is it cost effective to use disposable plastic eating utensils versus reusable ones and the required hot water and labor to wash them. Then, students can begin by conducting a survey to see what disposable or non-recyclable products used in the school cafeteria (or in their homes) could be replaced with recycled products or glassware—and at what savings or cost. In some situations, it might be more economical and environmentally sound to use disposable products.

Enrichment

If possible, arrange a field trip to a nearby landfill. You should also try to visit an incinerator, waste-to-energy plant, composting facility, or recycling center.

END NOTES...

ASSESSMENT OPPORTUNITY

Have teams from Step 2 present their results and findings to the rest of the class or have the entire class present its results to another class or a group of administrators. Assess how each project was designed, planned, and executed.

RELATED ACTIVITIES

Waste Watchers, Energy Sleuths, Air to Drive, Pollution Search, Talking Trash, Not!, A Peek at Packaging

Overview
Nearly everything we buy comes in some sort of package. Packaging, made from a variety of renewable and nonrenewable resources, is necessary to protect an item, keep it fresh, make it tamper-proof, and make the item easy to transport and store. In this activity, students will examine the pros and cons of different packaging strategies.

LEVELS
Grades 5-8

SUBJECTS
Science, Social Studies, Visual Arts

CONCEPTS
- Our increasing knowledge of the Earth's ecosystems influences strategies used for forest management and environmental stewardship. (14.1)
- Consumers "drive" the marketplace with their demand for goods and services. Such demand shifts with time and may have positive or negative effects on the availability of natural resources and environmental quality. (15.2)
- Industries usually respond to consumer demand for recyclable, recycled, or otherwise environmentally friendly products. (15.3)

SKILLS
Observing, Classifying and Categorizing, Evaluating, Formulating Questions, Analyzing

OBJECTIVES:
Students will ① describe the different purposes for packaging, ② identify the pros and cons of different types of packaging, and ③ explore how packaging affects our decisions as consumers.

MATERIALS
Bring in samples of different kinds of packaging (either unopened containers or those that have been emptied and washed), copies of "Consumer Choices" on student page 324
Students: bring in a variety of common products brought from home, such as household cleaners, cosmetics, foods, toys, or shampoo (can be unopened in their original packaging material, or in empty, washed-out containers)

TIME CONSIDERATIONS
Preparation: 20 minutes

Activity: Part A: 45 minutes
Part B: 45 minutes

Background
At the most basic level, packaging is needed to hold items together in the size or amount desired for purchase. The concept behind product packaging has evolved over time, changing to fit the needs or demands of consumers as much as to fit the economic demands on manufacturers. The earliest forms of packaging employed animal skins, earthenware vessels, and woven baskets. Glass bottles, fired clay amphorae, and finished leather were developed between 2,500 and 3,500 years ago. Packaging as we know it in the late 20th century is relatively new, having had its start with the advent of economically efficient packaging machinery in the latter part of the 19th century.

In addition to its basic role of holding goods together, packaging also protects, preserves, and eases the distribution of many of the products we buy. The very nature of the products we consume dictates the kind of materials used in the packaging process. Canning certain food items and other perishables assures maximum shelf-life and freshness; paper milk cartons or plastic jugs allow for easy pouring and storage; plastic boxes with shrink-wrap packaging for items like compact discs allow for maximum display in a minimum amount of space; large cardboard boxes of laundry detergent help consumers purchase in bulk items that will be used often. In many instances (such as for food and health care products) packaging prevents contamination and provides tamper-proof protection for the consumer. Packaging also provides a convenient surface for displaying important consumer information as well as advertising space for the manufacturer.

Manufacturers and consumers have become more aware of the impact of packaging on the environment, as well as the conservation of natural resources, energy, and waste management.

Some companies are changing the materials used in their packaging; others have reduced, or even eliminated packaging of some products; still others are increasing the amount of recycled material used to make their packaging.

In many instances, the need for packaging, and the kind of materials used in packaging, are self-evident (such as baby food in small, easy-to-use, product-preserving glass jars). Sometimes, however, it may be difficult to understand why a certain package has been used (a tall box of cereal may be only two-thirds full due to the settling that occurs during shipping). Students should be prepared to ask informed questions about packaging and make responsible purchasing decisions based on an analysis of the information. The following activity will help them compare packaging practices and choose wisely the kind of products and their packages that best suit their needs as consumers.

Getting Ready
Bring in examples of different kinds of packaging used for different purposes, such as advertising, freshness, tamper prevention, and convenience (products may still be in their packages).

Make copies of page 324 for each team.

PART A
TAKING A CLOSER LOOK

Doing the Activity
1. Set out the examples of packaging that you brought in. Discuss each package and the product it contains (or contained) with the entire group. Use the questions on "Consumer Choices," page 324 (read them aloud).

2. Ask students why they think each product is packaged the way it is. (cost, ease in shipment, public health, protection from damage) Ask them what the pros and cons are of each package in terms of protection, bulkiness, tamper resistance, recycled materials, and so forth.

PART B
PICK A PRODUCT

Doing the Activity
1. Ask students to bring in two packages that they feel are properly packaged, and two that they feel are improperly or insufficiently packaged.

2. Have students work in teams and select three to five items to evaluate.

3. Give each team a copy of "Consumer Choices" (on page 324) for each item they will evaluate. Have students work together to complete the questions. Point out

how to tell whether a product is made from recycled material. (Look for recycled sign.)

4. Have each team share its analysis of one product with the rest of the group. You might suggest that team members separate their examples into two categories, one for packaging they think could be improved (e.g., by changing the design or material; by adding or eliminating material; etc.) and one for packaging that seems fine the way it is.

Enrichment
Take a trip to a local supermarket for a "Supermarket Safari" in which students try to find at least one item that fits into each category of packaging: ① packaged well; ② packaged poorly; ③ packaged primarily to attract the consumer (packaging that is pretty, colorful, fancy, etc.); ④ packaged in bulk; ⑤ packaged with material that has been recycled; ⑥ packaged with material that is recyclable; and ⑦ packaged in something reusable by the consumer.

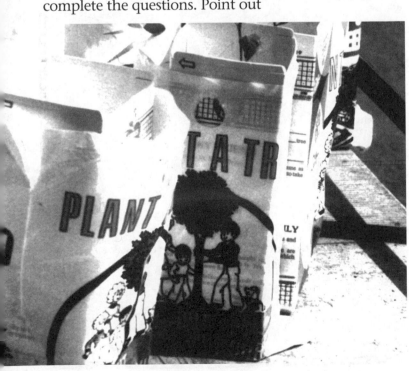

CONSUMER CHOICES

OBSERVE your product closely. DISCUSS the following questions with your team. ANSWER the questions as best you can using your team's knowledge and the information given on your product.

PRODUCT NAME
_____

TYPE OF PRODUCT
_____

LOCATION OF PRODUCER
_____

SHIPPING DISTANCE
_____

NET WEIGHT OF CONTENTS
_____

1. Describe all parts of the packaging.

2. Is the amount or type of packaging influenced by the manufacturer's need (e.g., federal labeling regulations) or desire to include product information and labeling?

3. What materials make up the packaging? (How much of it is paper? Plastic? Glass? Metal? Other?)

4. Is the product made of recycled material? Is the packaging?

5. Is the product biodegradable and/or recyclable? Is the packaging?

6. What purpose does each piece of packaging serve? (portion size, health, safety, freshness, anti-theft, advertising, other reasons) You may give several answers.

7. After the product has been used, what is thrown away?

8. Can you think of a better or different way to package the product?

Overview
In this activity, students will calculate the amount of automobile travel their family does and explore some of the potential environmental consequences of increasing automobile emissions and energy use, as well as ways and benefits of reducing those levels.

Background
One of the reasons that life exists on Earth is that the atmosphere acts like a greenhouse, allowing sunlight to enter while preventing reflected rays from leaving. A portion of the sunlight strikes the surface of the Earth where it is transformed into heat energy and radiated back into the atmosphere. This heat is trapped by atmospheric gases like carbon dioxide, methane, and simple water vapor.

Without this *greenhouse effect*, the temperature on earth would average 4°F (-20°C) instead of 60°F (16°C).

The burning of *fossil fuels* (coal, oil, gasoline, natural gas) produces large amounts of carbon dioxide. The percentage of carbon dioxide in the atmosphere is rising rapidly. As carbon dioxide levels increase, so does the tendency of the atmosphere to trap heat.

The overall effect could be a gradual warming of Earth itself. *Global warming* could lead to global changes such as rising ocean levels, changes in the climate, extremes in weather patterns, and intensity in the violence of storms.

While the threat of global warming is under debate, many scientists agree on three things: ① there is a change in the percentage of gases in the atmosphere; ② because of the change in the percentage of "greenhouse" gases such as carbon dioxide (CO_2), and methane (CH_4), we can expect an overall global change probably related to temperature; and ③ such a change can have environmental consequences.

What scientists cannot agree on is what the consequences will be. To say the whole Earth will warm up is probably not accurate. Some places will warm, others will cool, some will get wetter, others drier. Greenhouse gases trap heat, but certain air pollutants act like clouds, reflecting heat away. Other scientists believe the effects of clouds and air pollution may counterbalance global warming. Scientists also agree that the Earth system is very complex, and that potential global changes are not well understood.

Growing trees and plants offer us a natural way to reduce the amount of carbon dioxide in the atmosphere. Through photosynthesis, each year an average young tree can remove approximately 25 pounds (11.36 kilograms) of carbon dioxide from the atmosphere.

A major source of atmospheric CO_2 is automobiles. Almost 20 pounds (9 kilograms) of CO_2 are produced for each gallon of gasoline burned. An interesting way to look at this fact is to compare the amount of CO_2 given off by an automobile with the number of trees required to take up the same amount of CO_2. This comparison, however, will show that although planting trees is important, the number of trees required for each person to plant to offset the impact of the automobile is high (65 trees per person). However, atmospheric CO_2 can also be lowered by increasing the efficiency of cars or by reducing the number of miles driven by each car owner. By driving 35 miles less each week, families can reduce their consumption of gas by a gallon a week, or 52 gallons (234 l) a year. This would keep 1,040 pounds (471.7 kilograms) of CO_2 out of the atmosphere.

Getting Ready
Students will need to enlist the help of a parent with an automobile. Gather materials for making greenhouses.

LEVELS
Grades 5-8

SUBJECTS
Science, Math, Social Studies

CONCEPTS
■ When the Earth is studied as an interacting ecological system, every action, regardless of its scale, affects the biosphere in some way. (10.3)

■ Our increasing knowledge of the Earth's ecosystems influences strategies used for forest management and environmental stewardship. (14.1)

■ Increased public knowledge of the environment and the need for conservation of natural resources have resulted in lifestyle changes in many cultures. (15.5)

SKILLS
Comprehending, Analyzing, Making Decisions

OBJECTIVES
Students will ① gain knowledge about possible global changes resulting from the emission of greenhouse gases and other pollutants, and ② explain strategies for removing carbon dioxide from the air.

MATERIALS
Part A: a pair of sweat socks (or white cloth rag); dowels or stakes; wire or clothes hangers; wire cutters; plastic sheeting, cellophane, or plastic wrap; tray of potting soil; alfalfa, radish, or bean seeds for sprouting; thermometers
Part B: calculators (optional)

TIME CONSIDERATIONS
Preparation: 20 minutes

Activity: Part A: two class periods plus homework
Part B: one class period plus homework

PART A
DEMONSTRATIONS

Doing the Activity

Students may have a difficult time visualizing what is coming out of the tail pipe of a car, since it is often hard to detect (unless you are in city like Los Angeles on a smoggy day). They may also have trouble understanding what the greenhouse effect is and how it works. The following demonstrations should help students visualize what is happening (see below).

PART B
COUNTING CARBON

Doing the Activity

1. Students will track all family car mileage for one week, using the car's odometer (mileage gauge). They should note the car's beginning and end mileage and should figure the difference.

2. Students will compute the amount of CO_2 produced in pounds using the following sample calculation. (You may choose to allow calculators. If calculations are made in metric equivalents, students should know that 1 mile = 1.609 km, 1 gallon = 3.785 l, and 1 pound = .453 kg.)

DEMONSTRATION 1.

PUT A SOCK IN IT

1. To demonstrate the effect of car exhaust on air quality, have students try this experiment with a parent or other responsible adult.

2. Take a pair of white sweat socks. Pull one sock tightly over the mouth of the car's tail pipe.

3. Have the parent start the engine and let it run for a few minutes.

4. Take the sock off and compare it with the other sock. Chances are, students will see large pollutant particles from the exhaust (ash, smoke, soot, etc.) trapped in the sock fabric, turning it black. Many other pollutants with smaller particles such as ozone and CO_2 pass through the cloth.

NOTE—A white rag torn in half can be used instead of socks. Tie one half of the rag over the exhaust pipe and proceed as above.

DEMONSTRATION 2

A MINI GREENHOUSE

1. Sprout seedlings in a sturdy tray of soil.

2. Build a greenhouse over them using dowels or stakes, wire, and cellophane or plastic wrap. The greenhouse should be at least 10 inches (25.4 cm) high. (See diagram on page 327.)

3. Set up three thermometers; one in the soil, one placed at the highest point inside the greenhouse, and one outside the greenhouse.

4. Place the greenhouse by a window.

5. After several hours, compare the temperatures at the three locations.

6. Which location is hottest and why? Explain similarities to the greenhouse effect caused by gases in our atmosphere. Explain the differences.

NOTE—The plants produce water vapor which is considered a greenhouse gas. The cellophane traps heat and allows for moisture to accumulate, thus causing a greenhouse effect.

Sample calculation—

- miles traveled in a week = 210 miles

- gas consumed in a week = 210 miles/30 mpg = 7 gallons gas

- CO_2 produced in a week = (20 lbs CO_2/gallon) x (7 gallons) = 140 lbs CO_2

- CO_2 produced in a year = (140 lbs/week) (52 weeks/year) = 7,280 lbs/year

To do these calculations, students can assume that

- the average car gets 30 miles per gallon, or they can figure out the gas mileage of the family car using the following:

  When the tank is full, they should start keeping track of the car's mileage. When it is time to refill the tank, they should record how many gallons it takes to fill it up. They should divide the number of miles the car traveled by the number of gallons it used during that time. This figure will give them the car's gas mileage in miles per gallon (mpg).

- approximately 20 pounds (9 kg) of CO_2 are produced per gallon consumed

- the average young tree removes 25 pounds (11.3 kg) of CO_2 per year.

Extra Credit

1. Using the above information, students can make up their own math problems for the class to do.

2. Students can plan a strategy to reduce their family's auto mileage. Challenge students to reduce by 1,000 pounds (453.6 kg) the amount of CO_2 their family car(s) put into the atmosphere each year.

In addition to consuming less gas, students can also plant trees. By planting 10 trees a year, a family could remove 250 pounds (113.4 kg) of CO_2 from the atmosphere. (See "Plant a Tree" on page 95.)

3. Given that an average forest has about 400 trees per acre, students can figure out how many acres of forest must be planted to absorb the amount of CO_2 one car produces in one year.

Enrichment

Set up a friendly competition between classes or groups to see who can keep the most CO_2 out of the atmosphere by walking, biking, or carpooling to school. Everyone must get his or her parents' permission before deciding to walk, bike, or carpool to school; to the grocery store; to the homes of friends; and so forth. Students who take the bus to school can walk, bike, or carpool to another activity to which an adult usually drives them.

END NOTES...

ASSESSMENT OPPORTUNITY

1. Assess the accuracy of the students' calculations.

2. Have students diagram the carbon cycle showing how cars (through combustion) and animals (through respiration) use oxygen and release CO_2 while green plants (through photosynthesis) use CO_2 and release oxygen. Plants also use a small portion of the oxygen they release for their own energy cycle.

RELATED ACTIVITIES

Waste Watchers, Energy Sleuths, Air Plants, Plant a Tree

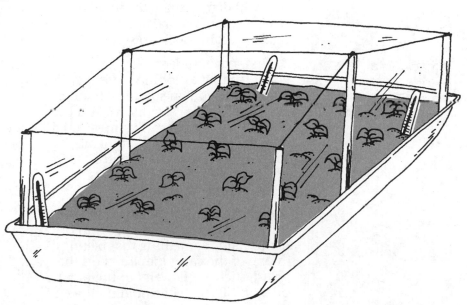

Overview
Patterns of change are evident in the Earth's global systems. By exploring the issues of global change, students will gain an understanding of how we must deal with the possibility of global environmental changes today.

LEVELS
Grades 5-8

SUBJECTS
Science, Social Studies, Language Arts

CONCEPTS:
- Ecosystems change over time through patterns of growth and succession. They are also affected by other phenomena such as disease, insects, fire, weather, and human intervention. (13.4)
- Our increasing knowledge of the Earth's ecosystems influences strategies used for forest management and environmental stewardship. (14.1)
- Altering the environment affects all life forms—including humans—and the interrelationships that link them. (4.2)

SKILLS
Forming Concepts, Defining Problems, Formulating Questions, Analyzing, Evaluating

OBJECTIVES
Students will ① identify some global environmental patterns, ② discuss issues related to global change, and ③ describe actions that people can take to improve the environment and quality of life.

MATERIALS
large ball of yarn, copies of student page 330

TIME CONSIDERATIONS
Preparation: 10 minutes

Activity: 50 minutes

Background
The first pictures the Apollo astronauts took from space showed the Earth surrounded by black space. Exploration of space has only confirmed how very special the Earth is: It's the only planet in our solar system with air to breathe, with liquid water, and with life.

Human activities have set in motion environmental changes that are difficult to assess and measure accurately, but these changes will play a major role in shaping future global conditions. If we are to predict future patterns, it is important to understand past and current patterns of change.

Getting Ready
Make copies of student page 330.

Doing the Activity
1. Have students, working in pairs, read the directions and complete student page 330. The students will diagram some of the interconnected parts of the Earth system.

2. When they are finished, have all the students sit in a circle on the floor. Tell them that they will play a game that will demonstrate the interconnectedness of natural and human-made parts in the Earth system.

3. First, have students suggest categories, so that everything living, non-living, and human-specific would fit into at least one category. Make a list of these on the board. Examples might include: plants, animals, minerals, gases, planets, natural resources, technology, culture, religion, art, recreation, emotions, and so on.

4. Start the game by giving the ball of yarn to a student and asking him or her to name something that belongs in one of the categories listed on the board, such as "flowers" in the plant category. Then, while holding the end of the yarn, that student should roll or toss the yarn to another student. The second student must name something from another category listed on the board, which is somehow connected to the first item named, such as "happy" from the emotions category. He or she should explain the connection (plants such as flowers make people happy) and then should hold the string and pass the ball to a third student. That student should do the same as the second and then pass it to a fourth student. The game continues until all the students are connected.

5. With everyone holding the string, discuss how human actions that directly affect part of the Earth system also indirectly affect many other parts. Use water pollution as one example. Ask which of the students named something that would be negatively affected by water pollution. Choose one of these students (e.g., one that said drinking supply) and have him or her show stress by tugging the string back and forth. Ask the other students if they feel vibrations from the tugging; if they do, it's because they are connected to the drinking supply and are indirectly affected by the water pollution.

6. As you rewind the yarn, ask each person, upon letting go, to name something a person could do to make the Earth a healthier place. When you are done, you will have both your ball of yarn and many ideas of how to help the planet!

Enrichment
Have teams of students pick a "global change" issue to investigate. You may want to assign issues to make sure the major ones are covered; examples include effects of climate change, coastal erosion, ozone depletion,

ocean pollution, deforestation, desertification, population growth, hunger, communicable diseases, air pollution, energy shortages, soil erosion, freshwater pollution, loss of biodiversity, and so on.

Have each team prepare a short presentation to the class with background about the issue, potential effects it could have, and geographic areas likely to be affected. Record the geographic areas of potential change with map pins, shading, or overlays on a map of the world. Discuss each team's map.

- How much of the Earth could be affected by these potential changes?

- Are there any areas that may not be affected?

- Are there areas that are likely to be affected by more than one aspect of global change?

- Are all countries on Earth equally ready to cope with these changes?

- If these predictions come true, how could cities, states, and countries prepare for such changes?

Reports, presentations, maps, and discussions can be evaluated. Ask students to use information from their investigations as they write down some actions that can be taken to make positive changes with regard to these global issues.

END NOTES...

ASSESSMENT OPPORTUNITY

Assess the drawing of the Earth system's web of life (on student page 330) for completeness. See that students included all the italicized items on the work sheet as well as additional items of their own choosing to show the dynamic interrelationship of different parts of the Earth system.

RELATED ACTIVITIES

Web of Life, Environmental Exchange Box, The Forest of S.T. Shrew, People of the Forest, Trees as Habitats

REFERENCES

Allison, Linda. *THE REASONS FOR SEASONS: THE GREAT MEGAGALACTIC TRIP WITHOUT MOVING.* Boston: Little, Brown & Co., 1975.

Amery, Heather. *THE KNOWHOW BOOK OF EXPERIMENTS.* Usborne Publishing, 1977.

Durrell, Lee. *STATE OF THE ARK.* Gaia Books, Doubleday, 1986.

Lauber, Patricia. *SEEING EARTH FROM SPACE.* New York: Orchard Books, 1990.

LOOKING AT THE EARTH activity packet for the Ames Aerospace Encounter. Earth System Science Division, NASA Ames Research Center.

Myers, Norman (ed.). GAIA *AN ATLAS OF PLANET MANAGEMENT.* Gaia Books, Anchor Press, 1984.

PLT FORESTS OF THE WORLD MAP, PLT.

GLOBAL CONNECTIONS

The effects of global change of the Earth's systems are unknown. However, we do know that the Earth's ecosystems are delicately balanced and interconnected. The sun is the driving energy force of the *biosphere*. Within *ecosystems,* the *plants* and *animals* are connected in the flow of *energy* and the cycling of *nutrients* through *water, air,* and *soil. Energy* is transported throughout the biosphere by *winds, ocean currents,* and *climate patterns.* It is also transported from the sun to plants, from plants to the small animals that eat them, and to the larger animals at the top of the food chain. The cycle of life, from birth and growth to *death* and *decay,* links up with the cycles of soil, water, and nutrient elements—this is what is called *biogeochemical cycling.*

Humans have influenced changes in Earth systems by *agriculture, industry,* and *technology,* which have helped to improve the quality of life for many people. Humans throughout history have affected different parts of the Earth system with *pollution.* While we do not know exactly the effect humans will have on the Earth, many people are certain that there will be global changes. As the naturalist John Muir once said: "When we try to pick out anything by itself, we find it hitched to everything else in the Universe."

DIRECTIONS—On a piece of paper (or on the back of this sheet), arrange at least 10 of the concepts *italicized* above to form a schematic diagram in which lines connect to concepts. Write the reason for each connection on the lines. Below is an example.

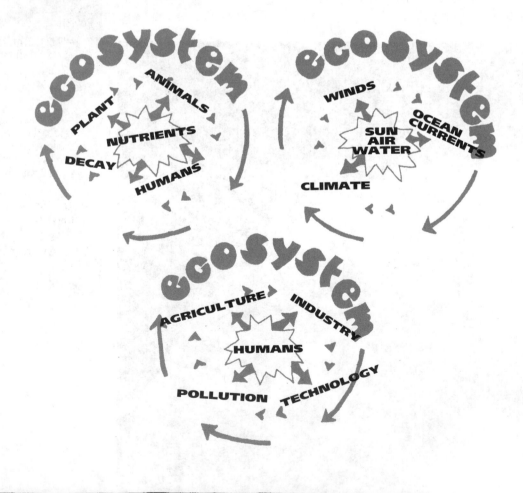

Overview

Children are naturally curious about their environment. They should be encouraged to explore the out–of–doors, while having respect for living things and their habitats. In this activity students will develop a set of guidelines for exploring and enjoying nature.

Background

Read "Teaching Out-of-Doors" and "Bringing Nature Indoors" in the Appendices, pages 379 and 381.

Getting Ready

Try to get a copy of the book *Trapper* (see References). If you cannot find it, use the text on student pages 333-334. If you use these pages, you may want to supply paper and crayons for students to draw pictures.

Doing the Activity

1. Initiate a discussion with your students on the effects humans can have on plants, animals and the environment. Begin by reading the story *Trapper* by Stephen Cosgrove and Robin James. Read it slowly, showing them the pictures in the book. If you use the text on pages 333-334, stop at intervals to summarize the story and to have students draw pictures of what they imagine. For grades PreK-K, it is preferable to learn the story yourself and retell it to students in shorter and simpler form.

2. After reading the story, ask the following questions:

- How did the story make you feel?

- How do you think Trapper felt at different times in the story?

- Why did Muttsok try to collect all the seals?

- Do you think Trapper gave Muttsok good advice?

3. Discuss what natural objects students would like to collect outdoors. Have them generate a list on the board. Go over the list with the students, discussing what might be all right to collect and what should be left in nature. Tell them that even picking flowers is usually not necessary because the flowers can be enjoyed right where they are. Explain how each fallen leaf and rock is a part of the habitat of living things. And while one thing may not be missed, if everyone in the class took one, it could make a big difference.

4. On the chalkboard or poster paper, list short statements that express the students' ideas about environmental manners—you can call them rules or guidelines. Ask students to offer ideas in the form of behaviors they would recommend. They can make positive or negative statements. Here are some examples:

- Stay on marked trails.

- Always think of safety—for yourself and others.

- Be careful not to litter.

- Pick up any litter left by others.

- Don't carve or draw on trees, rocks, or property.

- Show respect and care for all living things.

- Be careful with fire.

- Leave an area in the same condition as or better than when you got there.

5. For 2nd, 3rd and 4th graders, ask students each to choose one of the rules they made in Step 4 and to draw a picture that illustrates it, along with a slogan at the bottom.

The pictures should be line drawings (coloring book style) in pencil. Make photocopies of all the pictures and bind them into coloring books that can be distributed to a group of younger students.

LEVELS
Grades PreK-4

SUBJECTS
Science, Social Studies, Language Arts, Visual Arts

CONCEPTS
- Leisure and recreational pursuits can have an impact on forests and other resource-producing areas. (15.4)
- Increased public knowledge of the environment and the need for conservation of natural resources have resulted in lifestyle changes in many cultures. (15.5)

SKILLS
Discussing, Forming Principles

OBJECTIVE
Students will express appropriate ways to treat living things and to act in forests, parks, and other natural areas.

MATERIALS
black pens or pencils; paper; copy of the story *Trapper* by Stephen Cosgrove and Robin James (if you cannot get the book, use student pages 333-334)

TIME CONSIDERATIONS
Preparation: 10 minutes

Activity: 50 minutes

6. For PreK, K, and 1st graders, lead an exercise in which the students act out the rules they listed in Step 4. After they've practiced each one several times, play a game in which you call out a rule and they act it out until you call out another one.

Enrichment
The Shirt off My Back!

For this demonstration, arrange for a student or adult volunteer to wear many layers of clothing over a bathing suit. Have that person imitate a tree. Each student should walk by and remove one "leaf" (piece of clothing) from the tree. Students quickly see what taking just one leaf can do. Stop the activity before the "tree" gets too embarrassed. Afterward, discuss the lesson that this demonstration teaches us: Do not remove leaves or flowers from plants. One removal might not be damaging, but look what happens when everyone does it.

END NOTES ...

ASSESSMENT OPPORTUNITY

1. Before going on your next field trip, review the rules the students came up with. Assess their behavior on the trip in light of their own rules.

2. Have students create similar "Guidelines" for their environmental behavior at school. Encourage the students to word some of them positively, using "Do's" as well as "Don'ts."

RELATED ACTIVITIES

Values on the Line, A Look at Lifestyles, The Native Way, I'd Like to Visit a Place Where

REFERENCES

Story is reprinted with permission from Cosgrove, Stephen, and Robin James. *TRAPPER*. Los Angeles: Price, Stern, Sloan Publishers, 1978.

TRAPPER

In the crystal reaches of the stormy Atlantic Ocean, off the north coast of Canada, there was a small, frozen island called Samrakan.

The clouds floated freely there, dancing softly in the snow-filled sky as the ocean washed over the icy rocks.

Because of the crisp, brisk weather, furry little creatures called minstrel seals came from all over to play in the cold waters of the island. They were called minstrel seals because they always sang pretty songs to the sea.

The seals spent all of their days eating the delicious fish that lived deep in the bays, and sitting on the rocks and softly humming in the bright sunlight.

Every day, when the sun reached its highest, one of the seals would climb high onto the rocks and begin to sing a gentle melody to the sea. One by one, the other seals would join in harmony, until the most beautiful song was carried by the breeze for miles around.

They would sing like that for hours and hours, until a small minstrel seal called Trapper would join them and quietly begin to hum along. He would get so carried away by the pretty music that he would suddenly bellow out a sour note. It was so sour and so loud that the birds would lose their feathers in fright.

The other seals would cringe at the sound and, one by one, they would slide noisily back into the sea, leaving Trapper all

alone on the island of Samrakan, humming all by himself, way out of tune.

It would have been the very same to this day except that the seals, one by one, started disappearing. Day by day, one or two seals would disappear and the group would be that much smaller.

The other seals didn't really mind because each one enjoyed his own pretty voice anyway, and with fewer seals they could hear themselves better. Besides, it seemed to Trapper that the fewer seals there were, the longer he got to sing along.

Finally, Trapper realized that there were only three seals, including himself, left on the whole island.

"Hmmm," he thought as he munched on his lunch in the bay. "This is getting stranger and stranger. I wonder where everyone has gone. My singing isn't very good but it can't be so bad that everyone would leave."

He decided that right after the singing the next day he would watch carefully to see where everyone went.

The day dawned cold and bright. As he did every day, Trapper played in the surf, and when the sun was at its highest, he went to join the other seals.

He hummed along with the other two for the longest time until, as always, he sang out with a very sour note. The other two seals, with a "tsk" or two, began sliding back into the sea.

Trapper waited for just a moment, then slipped over to the edge of the rocks and

looked below. There was the ugliest creature he had ever seen, and in his arms he had the last two seals on the island of Samrakan.

Trapper quickly hid as the creature ran off with his fellow seals. "That was close!" he thought. "But now I'll be able to sing pretty songs for as long as I like, with no one to say I'm singing wrong." He played in the bay and munched his lunch; everything almost stayed the same.

When the sun got to its highest point, Trapper again climbed the rocks to sing a song to the sea. He sang and sang, but it just wasn't the same. For what good is a pretty song if there's no one around to hear it? Trapper finally realized that he was all alone.

"What will I do?" he cried. "I'm afraid of the ugly creature, but without the other seals I have nothing."

He began swimming around the island, looking in all the bays for his friends, but to no avail. He climbed high onto the rocks and looked and looked. He searched throughout the day and long into the night, but never found a trace of the other seals.

Finally, he became so tired from his search that he climbed out of the water, found a soft patch of frosty grass, and fell fast asleep.

While he slept, he dreamed of all the days he had shared with the other seals and the pretty music they had shared.

Trapper was so tired that he slept the whole night through.

Continued on next page.

TRAPPER

He probably would have slept through the day had he not been shaken awake to find himself hanging upside down.

"What's going on?" he said with a yawn. Then he realized with a start that he was hanging in the arms of the creature.

"Aha! So, you're awake, my little singing minstrel seal. Soon you shall join your friends and you can all sing pretty songs for me."

"Who are you, and what do you want with me?" Trapper cried.

"My name is Muttsok, and I like pretty things. You are going to be part of my collection," he laughed. And with Trapper stuffed neatly under his arm, he headed away from the bay.

Poor Trapper did not know what to do. He thought and thought but was too scared to think of anything.

"I've got to calm down so I can think," he thought. Well, the only thing that would calm him down was to sing, so he began to hum softly to himself, so softly in fact that the creature didn't even hear. Then, as the song built within him, he bellowed his loudest, sourest note ever! The creature was so shocked by the terrible noise that he dropped Trapper so he could hold his hands over his ears.

Trapper hit the ground with a thud and quickly rolled into the safety of the sea.

Trapper hid beneath the waves, but when he realized the creature wasn't following him, he bobbed to the surface and looked around. There on the beach before him was Muttsok, stomping his feet and raging. "Come back here you dumb little seal! You're pretty and I want you."

"Muttsok," shouted Trapper, "why do you have to own everything that is pretty? Can't you enjoy a pretty thing the way it is?"

"No, you stupid seal. What's the fun of seeing something pretty if you can't take it with you?"

"Well," said Trapper carefully, "you can see a pretty sunset and you can't take that with you."

"I tried to take it once," growled Muttsok.

"Yes, but if you had succeeded, then no one else would have been able to see the sunset. Just like all the seals you took, now no one can hear their beautiful song to the sea."

"Well," grumbled the creature as he stirred his foot in the sand, "I still like to collect pretty things."

Trapper thought for a moment. "That's easy, Muttsok. I'll show you all sorts of pretty things to collect."

Trapper swam just a little way up the beach and shouted to Muttsok who had followed. "Look! At your feet there are thousands of beautiful rocks. And look! Above you there are hundreds of pretty winter flowers growing."

Muttsok looked around and saw that there really were pretty things everywhere. He began picking up rocks; then he suddenly stopped. "If I take all the pretty rocks and flowers, then nobody can enjoy them either."

"Ahhh," said Trapper, "you take only the prettiest one and leave the rest for others to share."

So Muttsok took the prettiest rock. Then he climbed way up and picked the prettiest flower, and with them safely clutched in his hand, he rushed back to set the seals free.

After a while, things returned to normal on the island of Samrakan, and the minstrel seals once again sang their beautiful songs to the sea.

Some of the time Muttsok sat with a flower in his hand and a gentle smile upon his face, with small, silent Trapper by his side. If you listened very carefully, you could hear the two of them singing softly out of tune.

If you see those pretty things that nature likes to show remember all those seals that sing and leave them there to grow

Overview
Patterns of change can be observed in the diversity of species on Earth. In this activity, students will become advocates for endangered species of plants or animals, and create "public relations campaigns" on behalf of these species.

Background

There is evidence in the fossil record showing that changes in the number and type of *species* that live on the Earth have occurred regularly and continuously through time. There have been several periods of mass extinction in the Earth's history. In these events, individuals of a species were not able to adapt to large-scale changes such as climate change. The geological record shows that species extinction has been nearly as common as species origination, but it is difficult to determine if the extinction rate we are observing today is normal or a sign of a global problem. While we know that change is normal, some people fear that many of the changes brought about by humans today are causing larger numbers of animals to become extinct, and at a faster rate than is healthy for the planet.

In most places, where animals are threatened with extinction, it is because of habitat destruction. A habitat is made up of both the living and nonliving factors on which an animal depends. Habitat loss is the single greatest obstacle to helping many endangered plants and animals recover. Scientists are also working to find out more about how much habitat each species needs to survive, how we can restore habitats that have already been lost, and how we can balance human needs with the needs of other life on the planet.

Besides direct destruction of habitats by humans, other threats to plants and animals and their habitats include air pollution, destroyed *watersheds*, herbicides, and pesticides, as well as exotic species that are introduced and that out-compete the native species. (Definitions for Rare, Threatened, and Endangered Species are provided on student page 338.) A lot of attention is focused on endangered animals, but

we should not overlook endangered plants. Plants form the basis of ecosystems, and people directly depend on plants for food, clothing, building materials, medicine, and much more. Most of the world's plant species have not yet been identified, let alone studied to determine their usefulness to humans.

The welfare of one species of plant or animal is likely to have a direct effect on other species, as well as on the functioning of the entire ecosystem.

Many times, just removing the problem that threatens an endangered species will allow it to recover on its own. But sometimes the survival of an endangered species requires more extensive human intervention. Today these efforts are in the form of habitat protection in parks and preserves, habitat restoration, and zoos and botanical gardens that breed animals and plants, thereby preserving genetic diversity.

Getting Ready

PART A
Have students prepare four or five large paper mats, each a different color. Variation: Cut two 3" x 3" (7.6 cm x 7.6 cm) squares out of brown, blue, and white construction paper for each person in the group.

PART B
Obtain a list of locally rare, threatened, and endangered plant and animal species from your state natural resource agencies, the U.S. Fish and Wildlife Service, the U.S. Department of Agriculture, the Nature Conservancy, or the National Wildlife Federation. (See addresses on page 382.) Outside the United States, contact the comparable agencies in your country. Have students write letters to obtain some of this information. Ask your local librarian to set aside books on some

LEVELS
Grades 4-8

SUBJECTS
Science, Social Studies

CONCEPTS
- Organisms change throughout their lifetimes. Species of organisms change over long periods of time. (13.1)
- Although species become extinct naturally, the increasing number of extinctions in recent history may be linked to the rapid increase in human population. (13.2)
- Increased public knowledge of the environment and the need for conservation of natural resources have resulted in lifestyle changes in many cultures. (15.5)
- International cooperation directed toward conserving resources and protecting environmental quality is beneficial to human health and the well-being of other life forms. (5.3)

SKILLS
Researching, Analyzing, Synthesizing and Creating

OBJECTIVES
Students will ① identify environmental factors that can cause species to become endangered, ② research the current status of several endangered plants or animals, and ③ present persuasive arguments for the protection of a particular plant or animal species.

MATERIALS
Activity: large sheets of colored construction paper, copies of student pages 338 and 339
Variation: pieces of brown, white, and blue paper

TIME CONSIDERATIONS
Preparation: Several days to gather information

Activity: Part A: 45 minutes
Part B: 50 minutes

of these endangered species. Make copies of student page 339.

PART A
HABITAT SCRAMBLE

Doing the Activity

1. What happens to wildlife when a habitat is altered, either naturally or by humans? Have each student assume the identity of an animal (bird, fish, mammal, reptile, etc.) Place large (colored) pieces of paper or mats on the ground and label them to represent different habitats—rainforest, *deciduous*, forest, field, pond, *tundra*, ocean, and so on.

2. According to their animal identities, have students choose an appropriate habitat. (They must stand with at least one foot on the mat. More than one animal can occupy a habitat mat.)

3. When everyone is in place, tell a brief story describing the destruction or alteration of a particular habitat (i.e., a wetland is drained to build a housing development or dries up in a severe drought). After the story, pull away the colored mat representing that habitat. The animals that were standing there must scramble to find a new habitat that is suitable and stand with one foot on it. If they cannot adapt to another habitat, they do not survive and are out of the game.

4. Continue telling stories of habitat destruction and removing habitat mats after each one. As habitats disappear, students must scramble to find another suitable habitat mat to stand on or they die. Crowding, tension, and aggressive behavior will result, mimicking what often occurs in nature. Class management is essential, and the game should be stopped when most animals have lost their habitat.

5. Afterward, discuss the principles that the game demonstrated. Point out how habitat study and planning for development is important for wildlife and people. Also point out that many plants and animals can often adapt to changes in their habitat.

Every Species for Itself

Students will simulate how animals and often entire species compete for their essential needs (food, water, and space).

1. Tell students to pick an endangered animal species they would like to portray. They can choose from the sample profiles of endangered animals on page 339. Ask the students why they chose the species they did.

2. Give each student a colored piece of paper. Have students stand on their paper about 4 feet (1.2 m) apart. Students must keep one foot on this spot at all times, since it represents their habitat.

3. Randomly scatter the colored squares (prepared earlier) on the floor around the students so that they're about 1-2 feet (1.2-6.1 m) apart.

4. Tell the students that they'll be playing a game called "Every Species for Itself!" The object of the game is for each animal to gather as many of the squares as it can. Explain that each colored square represents a necessity for species survival. Brown squares represent food, white signify space, and blue symbolize water.

5. Give the signal to start the first round. Have the "animals" reach with their arms to gather their requirements. Tell them they cannot step off the mat (habitat) at any time.

6. Let students gather requirements for 10 seconds. Afterward, have the students record how many squares of each color they gathered. Use the following questions to discuss the results of the first round:

■ How many requirements did each animal get?

■ Are any animals lacking a particular requirement?

■ What might happen to an animal species that is lacking a requirement? (It might eventually become extinct.)

7. Have students stand in groups of two or three per habitat square. Gather the requirements and spread them around the room again. Play another round and have students record their results.

8. Compare the results of this round with those of the first. In most cases, more students will be lacking essential requirements. Ask if they can come to any conclusions about what might happen when a species is crowded together. (They are often in competition for essential requirements.) Ask if any of the "animals" "died" because they couldn't get a particular requirement. (You can allow animals to fall down if they haven't received their basic needs.)

9. Ask students how scientists might use their knowledge of competition to help endangered species survive.

10. Try several more rounds, comparing the results each time. Here are suggestions for how to set up additional rounds: (As before, students should record their results for each round. Older students can later graph or chart the results of each round and draw conclusions.)

- Have only half the class participate.

- Use fewer water squares (representing drought or water contamination).

- Use fewer space squares (signifying a smaller habitat caused by human encroachment or the introduction of a species not native to the region).

- Use fewer food squares (illustrating decreased availability of food, whether attributable to disease or natural disaster).

11. Ask students to consider the endangered species they learned about. Which ones do they think are more vulnerable to extinction and why? (Ones that are naturally rare within limited habitat range; ones that require very specialized diets and several habitats that they migrate to; ones that adapt very poorly to habitat or environmental changes.)

PART B
SPECIES SPECIFICATION

Doing the Activity

1. Discuss the definitions of rare, threatened, and endangered species on page 338 with your students. Provide students with a short list of rare, threatened, or endangered species. (If possible, try to get a list of local endangered or threatened species from the state department of natural resources.) Ask students to select a species to research from the list. Instruct them to gather as much information as they can from encyclopedias and other resources, and put together a profile for that species. As students investigate, they should consider the questions on page 338. Sample species profiles are provided on page 339.

2. Students should then take the role of an advocate for the species they selected. They should imagine that they work for a public relations or advertising firm that has been hired to communicate to the public that the species is endangered and that the public needs to take action. Teams of students should create a campaign that might include slogans, posters, TV commercials, and so forth.

3. Teams should present their campaign to the rest of the group.

Enrichment

Have students create "clue cards" about the species they researched. Each card should have about five descriptive statements of the species, from general to specific. The answer should be on the back of the card. Hold an endangered species "bee" (like a spelling bee) to see who can identify the most species with the fewest clues. The following is an example:

- I live in the tropical rainforest.
- My fur looks green from algae that grows on it.
- My kind gives birth to live young.
- I move very, very slowly.
- My kind has three long toenails.

ANSWER *Three-toed sloth*

LIFE ON THE EDGE

Endangered Species—
a native species or subspecies that is in serious danger of becoming extinct throughout all, or a significant portion, of its range as a result of one or more causes, including loss of habitat, overexploitation, competition, or disease.

Threatened Species—
a native species that, while not presently threatened with extinction, is likely to become endangered in the foreseeable future if not given special protection and management efforts.

Rare Species—a native species that, although not presently threatened with extinction, exists in such small numbers throughout its range that it may become threatened if its present environmental conditions worsen.

Species name

1. What is its status? (see above)

2. Where does it live?

3. What does it look like?

4. What is its habitat?

5. What is the current range of its population? Has its range changed over the course of history?

6. Why is it rare, threatened, or endangered?

7. Are any current actions being taken to improve its chances of survival? If so, describe them. If not, or if you do not know of any, can you suggest some?

8. What are some ways in which people can reduce or eliminate the threats to the survival of the species?

9. What other species depend on it?

10. Give some reasons why it is important that this species survive.

REPRODUCTION SAMPLES

Giant Panda

Pandas live in the Himalayan range of central Asia, generally at altitudes between 5,000 and 10,000 feet (1,524 and 3,048 meters). It is believed that this territory is only a fraction of their former range. A few thousand years ago, giant pandas roamed throughout much of eastern China. Their range was diminished largely by the destruction of their natural habitat, the bamboo forest on steep mountain slopes.

The primary danger to the giant panda is the destruction of their bamboo habitat caused by development. According to some maps, roads now penetrate the deep bamboo forests.

Bald Eagle

Bald eagles once inhabited most of North America. They frequent conifer forests located near water with abundant supplies of fish. They feed on carrion, rodents, and other small mammals. Bald eagles migrate south in the fall and roost in huge, communal nests they use year after year. Both parents incubate their usual two eggs. The parents share the responsibilities in feeding and caring for the young until they are about four years old.

The debilitating results of DDT poisoning (banned in the United States since 1972), poaching, and habitat loss have left a dwindling population. Bald eagles are endangered in most of the continental United States, except for the stable bald eagle population of 30,000 in Alaska and the threatened population in Washington, Oregon, Minnesota, Wisconsin, and Michigan. However, with gradual preservation and recovery efforts along

with the banning of certain pesticides, the bald eagle has been making a slow comeback.

Key Deer

A subspecies of white-tailed deer, the Key deer of the Florida Keys prefer the hardwood, pine, and mangrove forests by day, but venture into meadows at night to feed. This deer has lived in isolation from the continental United States for thousands of years and exhibits solitary behavior that contrasts sharply with other white-tailed deer, which are communal in nature. About the size of a large dog, the Key deer breeds from September to November when it is three to five years old and usually has one offspring.

Motor traffic and loss of habitat caused by resort development have devastated the Key deer population, reducing it to fewer than 300 members. Strategies for strengthening the deer population include extending the boundaries of the Key Deer Refuge, enforcing lower speed limits at night, and filling the deep ditches in which fawns often drown.

Bengal Tiger

Lurking in the forests and mangrove swamps of India, Myanmar, Bangladesh, Bhutan, and Nepal, the 500-pound (226.5-kg) Bengal tiger subsists on a daily diet of about 60-80 pounds (27.2-36.2 kg) of meat. Of the 40,000 tigers found in India in 1900, fewer than 2,000 of these carnivores remained in 1973. Habitat loss-of both tigers and their prey-and direct killing of tigers are principal factors in reducing the population. So extensive is the loss of habitat that the Bengal tiger often

resorts to killing livestock. Three of the eight subspecies of tigers are already considered extinct. With conservation efforts that involve both preservation of habitat space and natural prey, the number of Bengal tigers has recently increased to about 4,000.

Jaguarundi

Weighing 10-15 pounds (4.5-6.8 kg), this wild cat is indigenous to the Americas, living in regions that vary from the tropical Central and South American forests to the deserts of Texas, Arizona, and Mexico. Unlike most wild cats, the jaguarundi actively hunts for its meals (usually rodents) during morning hours, instead of at night. The jaguarundi abandons its solitary existence only to mate. This agile cat is endangered by habitat destruction and poaching.

Red Ruffed Lemur

Although resembling monkeys, the lemur stands distinct from other primates because of its smaller brain, pointed snout, comb-like teeth, and scent glands. Inhabiting the tropical rain forests of eastern Madagascar, this endangered animal feeds on fruit and flowers during the day.

Separated from mainland Africa by nearly 200 miles and for approximately 65 million years, Madagascar is home to plants and animals that are found no place else on Earth. The prosimians, a primitive group of primates to which red ruffed lemurs belong, is an example. Deforestation and hunting of these animals contribute to dwindling populations. Fourteen species of prosimians are extinct.

Overview
By reading fables such as *The Lorax* by Dr. Seuss or *The Man Who Planted Trees* by Jean Giono, students can examine the importance of conserving natural resources.

LEVELS:
Part A: Grades 2-8
Part B: Grades 6-8

SUBJECTS:
Science, Social Studies, Language Arts

CONCEPTS
- Our increasing knowledge of the Earth's ecosystems influences strategies used for forest management and environmental stewardship. (14.1)
- Increased public knowledge of the environment and the need for conservation of natural resources have resulted in lifestyle changes in many cultures. (15.5)

SKILLS
Discussing, Forming Concepts, Evaluating, Comparing and Contrasting, Identifying Main Ideas

OBJECTIVE
Students will discuss and analyze a fictional story relating to the proper and improper use of natural resources.

MATERIALS
one copy of *The Lorax* by Dr. Seuss and *The Man Who Planted Trees* by Jean Giono; paper, crayons, markers, and posterboard for the Enrichment activity

TIME CONSIDERATIONS
Preparation: 15 minutes

Activity: 50-minute period for each book

Background
A quick look around the home or school reveals how many items are made from wood and other forest resources. Trees are important to us whether they are used for products or left in their natural environment where they provide oxygen, soil protection, beauty, and a habitat for plants and animals.

Humans have always depended on trees for firewood, shelters, tools, paper, and many other needs. In many parts of the world, trees are removed from forested areas without being adequately replanted. This process of **deforestation** can have severe environmental consequences on a regional and a global scale.

Getting Ready
Obtain a copy of *The Lorax* or *The Man Who Planted Trees* to read aloud to your students. Motion pictures or videos of both stories are also available. For the Variation in Part A, write each question on an index card. Do the same for the questions in Part B.

PART A
THE LORAX

Doing the Activity
1. Read *The Lorax* aloud or watch the video.

2. Ask students to list what they think the major ideas of the story are.

3. Have them think about and answer the following questions:

- Why do you think the Once-ler did what he did?

- What patterns of change in the environment did we observe?

- What were environmental conditions like before the company started making Thneeds? What were they like afterward?

- What was the author's message concerning what one person can do to save or destroy the environment?

VARIATION FOR GRADES 5–8

1. Read *The Lorax* aloud or watch the movie.

2. Divide the class into six groups. Give each group a card with one of the questions written on it.

Each group should discuss one of the following sets of questions, write down the answers, and be prepared to read them to the entire group.

- How could the Once-ler have managed his company to protect natural resources and not run out of trees to manufacture "Thneeds"? Is it necessary to protect all trees "from axes that hack"?

- What did the Once-ler mean by "UNLESS"? What responsibility does he seem to think "someone like you" needs to take? What kinds of things can we do today to ensure that trees will be available for all different purposes in the future?

- Compare the Once-ler's attitude toward the environment at the beginning of the story with his attitude at the end.

- The Once-ler explains his actions by saying, "If I didn't do it, someone else would." Is this a good excuse for doing what he did?

- The Lorax says he speaks for the trees. What does this mean to you? What is the Lorax's attitude at the end of the story?

- What seems to be Dr. Seuss's purpose in writing this fable? (A fable is a fictional story that teaches a lesson.)

4. After groups have had time for discussion, have each group read their questions and answers to the class. Students can agree, disagree, or add to the answers given by their classmates.

PART B
THE MAN WHO PLANTED TREES

Doing the Activity

1. Make copies of the story for students to read, or show the video. Ask students to list what they think the major ideas are. After listing their ideas on the chalkboard, discuss the following questions with the entire group:

- Why do you think Elzeard did what he did?

- What changes did the narrator notice between his visits?

- What were the environmental conditions like before Elzeard planted the trees? What were they like afterward?

- What was the author's message about the difference one person can make?

2. Divide the class into six groups. Give each group an index card with one of the following six statements on it. Each group should decide if students agree or disagree with the statement.

If they agree, they should give three reasons why, and then give an example from real life of how this statement is true. If they disagree, they should state why and modify it into a statement they agree with.

- The balance of nature is important to all life on Earth and can easily be destroyed.

- Humans cannot place themselves apart from nature in making decisions about natural resources.

- Actions taken without thought or planning can have disastrous consequences.

- Natural resources are not limitless and can be used up if they are not managed carefully for the long run.

- Each person has a responsibility to help conserve resources and protect the environment.

- Consumers should demand that manufacturers produce products in an environmentally sound manner.

3. After students have had time for discussion, have each group read its statement and then present the results of its discussion. The group leading the discussion should encourage classmates to say whether they agree, disagree, or have ideas to add.

Enrichment

1. Either alone or in small groups, students can write and illustrate a sequel to *The Lorax*. The sequel might explain how the Truffula tree made a comeback through replanting and proper care. The sequel could say what the new managers of the Truffula Tree Company are going to do to maintain environmental quality and at the same time make Thneeds.

After the sequels are finished, ask older students to consider the following questions:

- Does either the original Lorax story or your sequel accurately portray industry?

- Which version, the original or your sequel, appears to best describe people's attitudes in the region you live?

- What social and economic implications will the actions suggested in your sequel have for ensuring a quality environment? For example, who will pay for the environmental protection?

- Who will pay for the damage to the environment if these actions prove unsuccessful?

- What does the Truffula Tree Company provide to the local economy?

- Who will provide Thneeds if the Truffula Tree Company doesn't?

2. Have students prepare a sequence to the key events in *The Lorax*. Then, have them draw a diagram or flow chart showing the connections between characters in the story (Swomee-Swans, Bar-ba-loots, Lorax) and the natural resources (Truffula trees, clean air, clean water).

END NOTES...

ASSESSMENT OPPORTUNITY
Students' answers to the questions at the end of each story can be used to assess students' understanding of the environmental messages contained in the stories.

RELATED ACTIVITIES
Tree Treasures, Tale of the Sun, Life on the Edge, We All Need Trees, Three Cheers for Trees

REFERENCES
Books for Activities:

Dr. Seuss. THE LORAX. New York: Random House, 1971. (also available on video tape)

Giono, Jean. THE MAN WHO PLANTED TREES. Chelsea Green Publishing Co., 1985. (also available on video tape)

Other Children's Stories on Caring for Trees and Forests:

Donahue, Mike. THE GRANDPA TREE. Boulder, CO: Robert Rinehart, 1988.

Kellog, Steven. JOHNNY APPLESEED. New York: William Morrow and Co., 1988.

Kerven, Rosalind. THE TREE IN THE MOON (AND OTHER LEGENDS OF TREES AND PLANTS). Cambridge: University of Cambridge Press Syndicate, 1989.

Morimoto, Jukno. KENJU'S FOREST. Australia: Collins Publishers, 1989.

Taylor, Mildred D. SONG OF THE TREES. Bantam-Skylark.

Van Allsburg, Chris. JUST A DREAM. Boston: Houghton Mifflin Co., 1990.

Overview

Patterns of change can be observed in human uses of natural resources. In this activity, students will explore some traditional Native American attitudes and lifestyles with respect to the land and its resources and will compare those attitudes with their own.

Background

The ancestors of most Native Americans probably first came to North America about 25,000 years ago. As we study those peoples, one of the first things we discover is that they belong to many different groups. What we see portrayed as American Indian or Native American on television or in movies—tepees, moccasins, beaded clothing, feather headdresses, braids, tomahawks—is actually a mixture of elements from several different and diverse cultures. An explorer traveling across the United States during the 1600s would have observed ever-changing styles of clothing, housing, land practices, rituals, tools, and language.

However, many of the diverse Native American cultures share a common ancestry, and so they also share many similarities.

Before the arrival of Europeans, Native American communities rarely contained more than 100 members. Several communities might live together in a village or camp, but each community was free to leave at any time and start its own village. When one of those communities increased to more than 150 individuals, part of the group would split and form a new village. A likely explanation is that when a community was too big, it became difficult to keep social order and to feed everyone.

It is believed that this is how so many tribal bands and cultures developed across North America. Yet as far back as 12,000 to 8,500 years ago, small nomadic groups of Paleo-Indian peoples dwelled in North America and were followed by the hunters and gatherers of the Archaic Culture who lived about 8,500 to 3,000 years ago. It is even estimated that there were between one and two million

Native Americans living at the time Columbus arrived.

At that time, the densest Native American populations were along the western and eastern coasts of what is now the United States, but Indians were well represented across the land. According to the U.S. Bureau of the Census, 552,228 Native Americans lived on the North American continent (in 1960).

Today, Native Americans live in diverse communities throughout North America. Many also live in communities on Native American Reservations.

Basic modes of Native American lifestyles fall generally into seven categories, listed below with a few tribal examples:

- Eastern Woodland Area (Iroquois, Ojibway, Delaware, Naskapi)

- Southeastern Area (Creek, Yuchi, Natchez, Seminole)

- Plains Area (Dakota, Pawnee, Crow, Blackfoot)

- Southwest Area (Zuni, Navajo, Apache, Pima)

- California (Pomo, Yokuts, Maidu, Wintun, Miwok)

- Plateau Area (Nez Perce, Spokan, Kutenai)

- North Pacific Coast Area (Tlingit, Makah)

Native American cultures ranged from hunter/gatherer, to nomadic, to agrarian, and they had extensive trade networks. Food, shelters, tools, and clothing were all made by hand from natural materials. Plants were used for food as well as for other purposes, such as baskets and dyes for clothing. In some parts of the United States, wild rice was gathered and then stored

LEVELS
Grades 4–8

SUBJECTS
Science, Social Studies, Language Arts

CONCEPTS
■ Increased public knowledge of the environment and the need for conservation of natural resources have resulted in lifestyle changes in many cultures. (15.5)

■ Humans throughout the world create differing social, cultural, and economic systems and organizations to help them meet their physical and spiritual needs. (3.2)

■ Natural beauty, as experienced in forests and other habitats, enhances the quality of human life by providing artistic and spiritual inspiration, as well as recreational and intellectual opportunities. (3.4)

SKILLS
Identifying Relationships and Patterns, Identifying Attributes and Components, Interpreting, Evaluating

OBJECTIVE
Students will describe traditional Native American lifestyles and Native Americans' use of natural resources and the land.

MATERIALS
Copy of "Chief Seattle's Statement" on student page 347; copy of "Message from Lakota Chief Luther Standing Bear" on student page 348; candle

TIME CONSIDERATIONS
Preparation: 15 minutes

Activity: 50-minutes

in birch bark bags for the winter. All parts of animals were used. Besides meat for food, bones were used for tools, sinews for thread, and bladders for jugs. The skins were tanned and the hides used for clothes, shoes, ropes, and shelters. Shelters were fashioned from young sapling trees and bark. Tools were artfully crafted from rocks and wood. In some larger villages, certain foods were cultivated. In some cultures, fires were deliberately started to flush game or to encourage growth of favored plants.

Native Americans generally had strong spiritual beliefs and looked on the land as a place where spirits dwelled. Most Native Americans engaged regularly in prayers, ceremonies, and rituals.

There were prayers to begin the hunt and prayers for the animals killed. There were prayers during both the planting and harvesting of crops. Women digging clay for pottery would ask Mother Earth for permission to remove it.

When studying the attitude of Native American culture, people often read a speech attributed to Chief Seattle. The speech was made in 1854 in response to President Franklin Pierce's offer to create a Reservation for the Indian people in exchange for Native American land.

In the fall 1989 issue of Environmental Ethics, the editor, Eugene Hargrove wrote, "It has been informally known for years that Chief Seattle's famous speech—sometimes known as the fifth gospel and considered by many to be the best statement ever made on behalf of nature—is actually a work of fiction."

The facts as we know them today are that Chief Seattle did make a speech in 1854, in connection with negotiations that led to the Port Elliot Treaty of 1855. The chief spoke in Duwamish, and his words were translated into English. Dr. Henry Smith, a white American, took down as much of the speech as he could. Smith seems to have made an honest effort to record the speech accurately, although somewhat of a sentimental attitude did show through. Smith's transcription was reprinted in various obscure anthologies.

In 1970, Ted Perry, from the University of Texas, contracted with the Southern Baptist Convention to write a filmscript for a TV program on pollution. For one of his sources in creating a "generic Indian chief" for TV, he used a William Arrowsmith adaptation of Seattle's speech. Perry had heard the adaptation at an Earth Day rally. The actual words of Seattle make up only about 25 percent of the "generic" or synthesized speech. The program was very popular, and after-ward the speech was reprinted and attributed to Seattle or referred to as a "letter" from Seattle to President Franklin Pierce.

Getting Ready

Make copies of student pages 346-348.

Doing the Activity

1. Have students read the fictionalized version of Chief Seattle's speech and the version that is believed to be closer to his actual words.

2. After they've read both speeches, have students break into small groups to discuss how the two speeches differ. What might account for these differences? Can the roots of the environmental message in the synthesized speech be found in the authentic one?

3. Darken the room as if you are preparing for a movie. Explain that you are about to share a Native American message. (If possible, invite a guest, perhaps a Native American or someone with Native American ancestry to come and read this passage.) Clear a space so the entire class can sit in a circle. Light a single candle in the center of the circle. Read aloud the "Message from Chief Luther Standing Bear" on student page 348. Have the students answer the questions on page 348.

Enrichment

1. Have students research the historical existence of native peoples in your region. Determine what influence these peoples have had in your region. Find out if any traditions have been maintained and what the major influences are that affect the way these people live today. Have students consider the following questions. (Local libraries and museums are good sources of information.)

- What influences have forests had on the history of Native American tribes? What have been the influences of grasslands? Of wildlife?

- Is there a consistent philosophy about humans and their relationship to nature that you can identify in Native American cultures you studied?

- How have Native American affected, and been affected by, population growth and development in the United States?

2. Investigate the lifestyles of indigenous people today in other parts of the world—such as Africa, Asia, or South America. Many native cultures have systems of land management that have been sustained over thousands of years. One of the consequences of population growth and development is that some of these native peoples no longer have access to the amount or kinds of land they need to sustain their traditional systems. In many cases the cultural systems have been lost forever.

END NOTES...

ASSESSMENT OPPORTUNITY

Have each student write a message from "Mother Earth" that tells us how to care for the Earth and its systems. The message should reflect some of the beliefs of the Native American cultures that the students studied.

RELATED ACTIVITIES

A Look at Lifestyles, In the Good Old Days, Tale of the Sun, People of the Forest, Tepee Talk

REFERENCES

Hargrove, Eugene. ENVIRONMENTAL ETHICS. Fall 1989.

Jaimes, M. Annette (ed.). THE STATE OF NATIVE AMERICA: GENOCIDE, COLONIZATION, AND RESISTANCE. South End Press.

Maybury-Lewis, David. MILLENNIUM: TRIBAL WISDOM IN THE MODERN WORLD. New York: Viking Penguin, 1992.

Wissler, Clark. INDIANS OF THE UNITED STATES. New York: Doubleday, 1966.

NEWS FROM NATIVE CALIFORNIA. Berkeley, CA: Heyday Books.

SYNTHESIZED VERSION OF CHIEF SEATTLE'S STATEMENT

How can you buy or sell the sky, the warmth of the land? The idea is strange to us.

If we do not own the freshness of the air and the sparkle of the water, how can you buy them?

Every part of this earth is sacred to my people. Every shining pine needle, every sandy shore, every mist in the dark woods, every clearing and humming insect is holy in the memory and experience of my people. The sap that courses through the trees carries the memories of the red man....

The white man's dead forget the country of their birth when they go walk among the stars. Our dead never forget this beautiful earth, for it is the mother of the red man. We are part of the earth and it is part of us. The perfumed flowers are our sisters; the deer, the horse, the great eagle, these are our brothers. The rocky crests, the juices in the meadows, the body heat of the pony, and man—all belong to the same family. So, when the Great Chief in Washington sends word that he wishes to buy our land, he asks much of us. The Great Chief sends word he will reserve us a place so that we can live comfortably to ourselves. He will be our father and we will be his children. So we will consider your offer to buy our land. But it will not be easy. For this land is sacred to us....

We know that the white man does not understand our ways. One portion of land is the same to him as the next, for he is a stranger who comes in the night and takes from the land whatever he needs. The earth is not his brother, but his enemy, and when he has conquered it, he moves on. He leaves his fathers' graves behind and he does not care. His fathers' graves and his children's birthright are forgotten. He treats his mother, the earth, and his brother, the sky, as things to be bought, plundered, sold like sheep or bright beads. His appetite will devour the earth and leave behind only desert....

You must teach your children that the ground beneath their feet is the ashes of our grandfathers. So that they will respect the land, tell your children that the earth is rich with the lives of our kin. Teach your children what we have taught our children—that the earth is our mother. Whatever befalls the earth befalls the sons of the earth. If men spit upon the ground, they spit upon themselves.... Man did not weave the web of life; he is merely a strand of it. Whatever he does to the web, he does to himself....

But in your perishing you will shine brightly, fired by the strength of God who brought you to this land and for some special purpose gave you dominion over this land and over the red man. That destiny is a mystery to us, for we do not understand when the buffalo are all slaughtered, the wild horses are tamed, the sacred corners of the forest heavy with the scent of many men, and the view of the ripe hills blotted by talking wires. Where is the thicket? Gone. Where is the eagle? Gone. The end of living and the beginning of survival.

WHAT CHIEF SEATTLE REALLY SAID

"Yonder sky has wept tears of compassion on our fathers for centuries untold, and which, to us, looks eternal, may change. Today it is fair, tomorrow it may be overcast with clouds. My words are like the stars that never set. What Seattle says the great chief, Washington, can rely upon, with as much certainty as our pale-face brothers can rely upon the return of the seasons. The son of the white chief says his father sends us greetings of friendship and good-will. This is kind, for we know he has little need of our friendship in return, because his people are many. They are like the grass that covers the vast prairies, while my people are few, and resemble the scattering trees of a wind-swept plain.

"The great, and I presume also good, white chief sends us word that he wants to buy our lands but is willing to allow us to reserve enough to live on comfortably. This indeed appears generous, for the red man no longer has rights that he need respect, and the offer may be wise, also, for we are no longer in need of a great country. There was a time when our people covered the whole land as the waves of a wind-ruffled sea cover its shell-paved floor. But that time has long since passed away with the greatness of tribes almost forgotten. I will not mourn over our untimely decay, nor reproach my pale-face brothers with hastening it, for we, too, may have been somewhat to blame.

"When our young men grow angry at some real or imaginary wrong and disfigure their faces with black paint, their hearts, also, are disfigured and turn black, and then their cruelty is relentless and knows no bounds, and our old men are not able to restrain them. But let us hope that no hostilities between the red man and his pale-faced brothers may ever return. We would have everything to lose and nothing to gain.

"True it is that revenge, with our young braves, is considered gain, even at the cost of their own lives, but old men who stay at home in times of war, and old women who have sons to lose, know better.

"Our great father, Washington, for I presume he is now our father as well as yours, since George has moved his boundaries to the north. Our great and good father, I say, sends us word by his son, who, no doubt, is a great chief among his people, that if we do as he desires, he will protect us. His brave armies will be to us a bristling wall of strength, and his great ships of war will fill our harbors so that our ancient enemies far to the northward, the Simsiams and Haidas, will no longer frighten our women and old men. Then he will be our father and we will be his children.

"But can this ever be? Your God loves your people and hates mine; he folds his strong arms lovingly around the white man and leads him as a father leads his infant son, but he has forsaken his red children; he makes your people wax strong every day, and soon they will fill the land; while our people are ebbing away like a fast-receding tide, never to flow again. The white man's God cannot love his red children or he would protect them. They seem to be orphans and can look nowhere for help. How then can we become brothers? How can your father become our father and bring us prosperity and awaken in us dreams of returning greatness?

"Your God seems to be partial. He came to the white man. We never saw Him, never even heard His voice. He gave the white man laws but He had no word for His red children whose teeming millions filled this vast continent as the stars fill the firmament. No, we are two distinct races and must ever remain so. There is little in common between us.

"The ashes of our ancestors are sacred and their final resting place is hallowed ground, while you wander away from the tombs of your fathers seemingly without regret. Your religion was written on tables of stone by the iron finger of an angry God, lest you might forget it. The red man could never remember or comprehend it. Our religion is the traditions of our ancestors, the dreams of our old men, given them by the great Spirit, and the visions of our sachems, and is written in the hearts of our people.

"Your dead cease to love you and the homes of their nativity as soon as they pass the portals of the tomb. They wander off beyond the stars, are soon forgotten and never return. Our dead never forget the beautiful world that gave them being. They still love its winding rivers, its great mountains and its sequestered vales, and they ever yearn in tenderest affection over the lonely-hearted living, and often return to visit and comfort them.

"Day and night cannot dwell together. The red man has ever fled the approach of the white man, as the changing mists on the mountain side flee before the blazing morning sun.

"However, your proposition seems a just one, and I think my folks will accept it and will retire to the reservation you offer them, and we will dwell apart and in peace, for the words of the great white chief seem to be the voice of nature speaking to my people out of the thick darkness that is fast gathering around them like a dense fog floating inward from a midnight sea.

"It matters but little where we pass the remainder of our days. They are not many. The Indian's night promises to be dark. No bright star hovers about the horizon. Sad-voiced winds moan in the distance. Some grim Nemesis of our race is on the red man's trail, and wherever he goes he will still hear the sure approaching footsteps of the fell destroyer and prepare to meet his doom, as does the wounded doe that hears the approaching footsteps of the hunter. A few more moons, a few more winters and not one of all the mighty hosts that once tilled this broad land or that now roam in fragmentary bands through these vast solitudes will remain to weep over the tombs of a people once as powerful and as hopeful as your own.

"But why should we repine? Why should I murmur at the fate of my people? Tribes are made up of individuals and are no better than they. Men come and go like the waves of the sea. A tear, a tamahnous [a religious ritual], a dirge, and they are gone from our longing eyes forever. Even the white man, whose God walked and talked with him, as friend to friend, is not exempt from the common destiny. We may be brothers after all. We shall see.

"We will ponder your proposition, and when we have decided, we will tell you. But should we accept it, I here and now make this the first condition. That we will not be denied the privilege, without molestation, of visiting at will the graves of our ancestors and friends. Every part of this country is sacred to my people. Every hillside, every valley, every plain and grove has been hallowed by some fond memory or some sad experience of my tribe. Even the rocks that seem to lie dumb as they swelter in the sun along the silent seashore in solemn grandeur thrill with the fate of my people, and the very dust under your feet responds more lovingly to our footsteps than to yours, because it is the ashes of our ancestors, and our bare feet are conscious of the sympathetic touch, for the soil is rich with the life of our kindred.

"The sable braves, and fond mothers, and glad-hearted maidens, and the little children who lived and rejoiced here, and whose very names are now forgotten, still love these solitudes, and their deep fastnesses at eventide grow shadowy with the presence of dusky spirits. And when the last red man shall have perished from the earth and his memory among white men shall have become a myth, these shores shall swarm with the invisible dead of my tribe, and when your children's children shall think themselves alone in the field, the shop, upon the highway or in the silence of the woods they will not be alone. In all the earth there is no place dedicated to solitude. At night when the streets of your cities and villages shall be silent, and you think them deserted, they will throng with the returning hosts that once filled and still love this beautiful land. The white man will never be alone. Let him be just and deal kindly with my people, for the dead are not altogether powerless."

A MESSAGE FROM CHIEF LUTHER STANDING BEAR

The following is said to be a quote from Chief Luther Standing Bear, speaking of the (Sioux) Lakota tribe of the Western plains, now known as the Sioux:

The Lakota was a true naturalist—a lover of nature. He loved the Earth and all things of the Earth, the attachment growing with age. The old people came literally to love the soil and they sat or reclined on the ground with a feeling of being close to a mothering power. It was good for the skin to touch the Earth [and the old people] liked to remove their moccasins and walk with bare feet on the sacred Earth. Their tepees were built upon the Earth and their altars were made of Earth. The birds that flew in the air came to rest upon the Earth and it was the final abiding place of all things that lived and grew. The soil was soothing, strengthening, cleansing and healing.

That is why the Indian still sits upon the Earth instead of propping himself up and away from its life-giving forces. For him, to sit or lie upon the ground is to be able to think more deeply and to feel more keenly; he can see more clearly into the mysteries of life and come closer in kinship to other lives about him…. Kinship with all creatures of the Earth, sky and water was a real and active principle. For the animal and bird world there existed a brotherly feeling that kept the Lakota safe among them and so close did some of the Lakotas come to their feathered and furred friends that in true brotherhood they spoke a common tongue.

The old Lakota was wise. He knows that man's heart away from nature becomes hard; he knew that lack of respect for growing, living things soon led to lack of respect for humans too. So he kept his youth close to its softening influence.

Questions

1. What is the message of this speech?

2. What happens to people's feelings for the Earth as they grow older?

3. What kind of relationship does he say we should have with animals?

4. What kinds of feelings and thoughts did being in touch with the Earth provide the Lakota people?

5. What did the Lakota think happened to a person's heart if he or she was out of touch with nature?

6. How did the Lakota teach their young to respect other people?

Overview
Human attitudes and values, and therefore behavior, with regard to the environment can change over the course of generations. In this activity, students will study the writings of men and women who have shaped the way people think about the environment.

Background
In the mid-1800s, most Americans were either farmers or members of small rural communities.

They had first-hand, everyday experience with nature. Under the Homestead Act of 1862, people were given free tracts of land if they would clear the trees and build a farm or ranch. Besides the Homestead Act, there was other legislation (such as mining laws) that allowed, and even encouraged, people to clear the land. But even early on, people with vision, such as George Washington, Thomas Jefferson, and Patrick Henry, voiced concern over resource depletion and despoliation.

President Theodore Roosevelt was concerned with preserving wilderness and conserving natural resources such as timber, soil, wildlife, and minerals. He felt that resource mismanagement might have tragic future consequences as America's population continued to grow rapidly. In 1908 he held a White House Conference, out of which developed the National Conservation Commission, under the leadership of Gifford Pinchot. This commission conducted the nation's first comprehensive natural resource inventory.

Inspired by the writers of his day, such as Henry David Thoreau and John Muir, Theodore Roosevelt created the Antiquities Act (under which National Monuments and Parks were established) and the Forest Service. During this period, the National Park Service, the National Resources Board, the Soil Conservation Service, and the Wildlife Restoration Act were created.

In the 1960s, under President John F. Kennedy, a natural resource program was created that included preservation of wilderness areas, development of marine resources, preservation of shorelines for public use, and the expansion of outdoor recreation opportunities.

Rachel Carson, Aldo Leopold, and other great conservation and environmental writers inspired much of the nation.

In 1970, the first Earth Day took place, inspiring the nation and the world to a new awareness and consciousness of environmental issues.

Getting Ready
Part A: Prepare a list of important environmental or conservation figures (which can include scientists, political leaders, writers, artists, and photographers) about whom students can find information in your school or nearby library. (See References on page 351 for suggestions.)

Part B: Make copies of student page 352.

PART A
PAST PERSPECTIVES

Doing the Activity
1. Use the information in the Background to give students a brief sketch of the history of conservation in the United States.

2. Divide the students into teams and have each team select a historical figure from the list you prepared (see Getting Ready). In addition to finding out about the person, they should find out what life was like in the person's time, how people of the day felt about environmental quality, and how environmental concerns were communicated. The report should include these:

■ A brief biography of the person

■ A hand-copied piece of that person's writing, which addresses his or her thinking on the environment

LEVELS:
Part A: Grades 4-8
Part B: Grades 6-8

SUBJECTS
Science, Social Studies, Visual Arts, Language Arts, Performing Arts

CONCEPTS
■ Governments change and evolve over the years. Such changes affect the lives of the citizens, as well as resource management and environmental policies. (15.1)

■ Increased public knowledge of the environment and the need for conservation of natural resources have resulted in lifestyle changes in many cultures. (15.5)

SKILLS
Researching, Interpreting, Identifying Main Ideas, Composing

OBJECTIVES
Students will ① describe important events in the history of conservation, ② explain how environmental problems and perceptions of environmental quality have changed through history, and ③ express the point of view of a famous figure in the history of conservation.

MATERIALS
copies of student page 352, access to library or media center, art supplies, paper and writing materials, camera, tape recorder, optional video equipment

TIME CONSIDERATIONS
Preparation: 45 minutes

Activity: Part A: Two to three 50-minute periods
Part B: 50 minutes

- An assessment of how events in that person's lifetime might have influenced his or her attitudes toward the environment

- An assessment of general public attitudes toward the environment in that time (i.e., was the person considered a visionary, was he or she respected, or was he or she dismissed)

- A description of how the person communicated his or her message about the environment

3. Using their research, have team members prepare creative presentations that show the impact their historical figure had on the conservation or environmental movement. They can use role-playing to portray how the person felt about the environment. They can use the communications media of their historical figure's time (posters, essays, radio, lectures, photographs, etc.) to show how the person communicated his or her point of view and raised public awareness on environmental issues.

4. Each team should also briefly share the results of its report to the rest of the group, and comment on what was "good" and what was "not so good" in the good old days when that person lived. The inspirational quote or passage that each team selected can be read aloud to the group. The class can arrange the quotes according to various topics or themes and then make copies of a booklet to keep and to distribute to other groups.

PART B
FOREST OF WORDS

Doing the Activity

1. Discuss with students how the writings of authors from different periods may reflect the views of their time period, as well as the authors' personal feelings.

2. Have students think about how they feel about forests. Each student can write an essay or poem, sketch a drawing, or find another way to express his or her personal feelings toward forests.

3. Discuss what students came up with, and have volunteers share their feelings. Can they identify any specific events in their lives that have influenced their attitude?

4. Pass out a copy of "Tales of the Forest" on page 352 to each student. Explain that each of the passages expresses its author's views about forests or a viewpoint from his or her time. Give everyone enough time to read the passages.

5. Divide the group into small teams. Explain that team members should work together to find when each author lived, and to gather information about events in the author's life that might have shaped his or her view about forests. They can consult encyclopedias, periodicals, anthologies, *Who's Who*, or other literary references, or can look for a biographical sketch in the author's works.

6. As a group, discuss how attitudes toward forests differed among the authors. You might want to use the following questions in your discussion:

- Can you trace any general differences in attitudes toward forests over the course of history?

- How could events during each author's life have affected his or her feelings toward forests?

- Compare certain passages to see how writing styles have changed over the course of time. For example, how is Annie Dillard's use of language different from Nathaniel Hawthorne's?

- How do these authors' views compare with values people have today about forests?

Enrichment

Aldo Leopold said, "We abuse land because we regard it as a commodity belonging to us. When we see land as a community to which we belong, we may begin to use it with love and respect." Gifford Pinchot said, "Conservation is the foresighted utilization, preservation, and renewal of forests, waters, lands, and minerals, for the greatest good of the greatest number [of people] for the longest time." Present both quotes to students, and ask them to consider how both men may be saying something similar or how they may be construed as saying very different things.

END NOTES...

ASSESSMENT OPPORTUNITY

After doing Part A or B, conduct a class discussion asking the following questions:

1. Has the quality of the environment in the United States changed in the past 200 years? How?

2. Has our understanding of environmental problems changed in the past 200 years? How?

3. What historical (or modern) individuals have been important in communicating information about the quality of the environment and environmental problems to the general public?

4. Have there been individuals, other than those already mentioned, who were especially important to you?

5. In what ways did these figures communicate their views to the general public?

RELATED ACTIVITIES

Values on the Line, Tale of the Sun, People of the Forest, Forest Consequences, The Native Way, A Look at Lifestyles

REFERENCES

Abbey, Edward. *Appalachia, Appalachian Wilderness.*

Berry, Wendell. *An Entrance to the Woods, Recollected Essays 1965-1980.*

Bode, Carl (ed.). *The Portable Thoreau.* Viking Portable Library. 1947, 1977.

Browning, Peter. *John Muir: In His Own Words.*

Carson, Rachel. *A Sense of Wonder.* HarperCollins Publishers, 1987

Carson, Rachel. *Silent Spring,* 25th anniversary ed. Boston: Houghton Mifflin, 1987.

Davis, Richard C. (ed.) *Encyclopedia of American Forest and Conservation History, Vols I and II.* NY: Macmillan Publishing Co., 1983.

Dillard, Annie. *Pilgrim at Tinker Creek.* Harper Perennial, 1974.

Emerson, Ralph Waldo. *Nature, Essays: Second Series.*

Finch, Robert, and John Elder, eds. *The Norton Book of Nature Writing.* New York: W.W. Norton Company, 1990.

Fox, Stephen. *John Muir and His Legacy: The American Conservation Movement.* Boston: Little, Brown & Co., 1981.

Hawthorne, Nathaniel. *Young Goodman Brown and Other Short Stories.* Thrift Editions, 1972.

Leopold, Aldo. *A Sand County Almanac.* New York: Ballantine Books, 1966.

Muir, John. *The Mountains of California.* Fulcum Publishers, 1988.

Muir, John. *Wilderness Essays.* Perequine Smith Literary Naturalist Series, 1989.

Olson, Sigurd, *The Singing Wilderness.* Alfred A. Knopf, 1956.

Petulla, Joseph M. *American Environmental History,* 2nd ed. Columbus, OH: Merrill Publishing Co., 1988.

Strong, Douglas H. *Dreamers and Defenders: American Conservationists.* Lincoln, NE: University of Nebraska Press, 1988.

Thoreau, Henry David. *Walden.* Rutland, VT: Charles E. Tutle & Co., 1992.

Watkins, T.J. *Father of the Forests, Journal of Forestry.*

TALES OF THE FOREST

Today, as always when I am afoot in the woods, I feel the possibility, the reasonableness, the practicability of living in the world in a way that would enlarge rather than diminish the hope of life. I feel the possibility, of a frugal and protective love for the creation that would be unimaginably more meaningful and joyful than our present destructive and wasteful economy. The absence of human society, that made me so uneasy last night, now begins to be a comfort to me. I am afoot in the woods. I am alive in the world, this moment, without the help or the interference of any machine.

—Wendell Berry,
An Entrance to the Woods,
Recollected Essays 1965-1980.
Born in 1934, Wendell Berry writes most often about farming, wilderness, and the need for different attitudes toward the land.

In the woods is perpetual youth. Within these plantations of God, a decorum and sanctity reign, a perennial festival is dressed, and the guest sees not how he should tire of them in a thousand years. In the woods we return to reason and faith. There I feel that nothing can befall me in life—no disgrace, no calamity… which nature cannot repair…. I become a transparent eyeball; I am nothing; I see all; the currents of the Universal Being circulate through me; I am part or parcel of God.

—Ralph Waldo Emerson,
Nature, Essays: Second Series.
Born in Boston in 1803, Ralph Waldo Emerson was educated at Harvard Divinity School. He taught and preached, and later became a renowned philosopher, writer, and poet.

There was a town set in the cup of the great hills. In the Alleghenies. A town of trees, two-story houses, red-brick hardware stores, church steeples, the clock tower, the courthouse, and over all the blue haze—partly dust, partly smoke, but mostly moisture—that veils the Appalachian world most of the time—that diaphanous veil that conceals nothing. And the field beyond the town, the zigzag of rail fences, the old gray barns and gaunt gothic farm houses, the webwork of winding roads, and the sulfurous creeks, and black coal mines—and scattered everywhere—the woods. The trees. The vegetation cradle of North America. All those trees transpiring patiently through the wet and exhilarating winds of spring, through the heavy, sultry, sullen summers and into the smokey autumns. Through seasons, years, millennia. Sensitive and sensible plants, with who knows what aspirations of their own.

—Edward Abbey,
Appalachia, Appalachian Wilderness.
Edward Abbey was born in 1927. Much of his writing is based on his experiences as a fire lookout and park ranger in the Southeast.

It's amazing that trees can turn gravel and bitter salts into these soft-lipped lobes, as if I were to bite down on a granite slab and start to swell, bud, and flower. Trees seem to do their feats effortlessly. Every year a given tree creates from scratch 99 percent of its living parts. Water lifting in tree trunks can climb 150 feet per hour in full summer and a tree can heave a ton of water every day. A big elm in a single season might make as many as six million leaves, each wholly intricate; without budging one inch, a tree stands there, accumulating dead wood, mutely rigid as an obelisk, but secretly it seethes, splits, sucks, and stretches.

—Annie Dillard,
Pilgrim at Tinker Creek.
Born in Pittsburgh in 1945, Annie Dillard has written most about the Roanoke Valley of the Blue Ridge Mountains.

And, maddened with despair, so that he laughed loud and long, did Goodman Brown grasp his staff and set forth again, at such a rate that he seemed to fly along the forest path rather than to walk or run. The road grew wilder and drearier and more faintly traced, and vanished at length, leaving him in the heart of the dark wilderness, still rushing onward with the instinct that guides mortal man to evil. The whole forest was peopled with frightful sounds—the creaking of the trees, the howling of wild beasts and the yell of Indians; while sometimes the wind tolled like a distant church bell, and sometimes gave a broad run around the traveller, as if all Nature were laughing him to scorn.

—Nathaniel Hawthorne,
Young Goodman Brown.
Nathaniel Hawthorne was born in 1804, in Salem, Massachusetts. Hawthorne was descended from Puritan settlers, and his writings often focused on and rebel against Puritanical teachings regarding good and evil.

Overview
By examining the historical attitudes of Native Americans and American pioneers toward the environment and natural resources, students can reflect on their own lifestyles, and identify trade-offs between simple subsistence and the modern technology-based living.

Background
The natural resources of America seemed limitless to settlers arriving 200 or more years ago. The farming and hunting of the one to two million Native Americans living in what is now the contiguous 48 states had done little to disrupt the land's rich natural heritage of water, forest, range, and wildlife.

Early settlers used these natural resources for food and shelter. Initially, their influence on the resources was small and posed little threat to the sustainability of the resources. But, gradually, the small, largely self-sufficient settlements were replaced by bustling cities that depended on the agriculture and forest products. Wildlife provided furs, hides, and meat; timber provided the 18th century's most common building material and fuel source.

As the population and economy grew, pioneers pushed the frontier westward. Settlers harvested forests and wildlife for the products they provided, and sometimes they cut and burned forests because trees were perceived as obstacles to settlement and agriculture. Large areas of forest were gradually converted to cropland and pasture for domestic livestock grazing. By 1850, 76 million acres, of what had once been a vast forest covering the eastern United States, were converted into crops.

Getting Ready
Make copies of student pages 356-358.

PART A
DEFINING OUR NEEDS

Doing the Activity
1. Ask students to name what living things need to live, and write the answers on the chalkboard (e.g., food, water, sun, home, apartment, stores, parents, telephones, transportation, gas).

2. Ask each student to copy this list on a piece of paper and put one of the following letters next to each item on the list:

S It is essential for basic survival by all living things.
M I need it to maintain my current lifestyle.
L I don't need this item, but I like having it. It is a luxury that makes my life easier or nicer.

3. On the chalkboard or on poster paper, make three columns: S–Survival, M–Maintain current Lifestyle, L–Luxury. Ask students each to contribute at least one item for each column from their lists to make a class list.

4. Have students look over all three columns on the board carefully. Discuss the following questions:

- Are there any items listed as essential for survival that really are not?

- What are the criteria for evaluating an item's necessity?

- Which items, if any, listed under "Maintain current Lifestyle" are really luxuries?

- On what basis do you judge an item a luxury?

- Which items on the luxury list could you give up without a major change in your lifestyle? With a major change?

5. Finally, ask students to identify where the items come from. (Guide the discussion continually back to the source of each item until they begin to realize they all come from natural resources.) Explain that there are two types of resources: renewable and nonrenewable. (For a discussion of renewable and nonrenewable resources, see "Renewable or Not" on page 43.) After, discuss the differences; put an **R** next to items made from renewable resources on all three lists, **N** next to those made from nonrenewable resources, or **B** for those items made from both.

LEVELS
Grades 5-8

SUBJECTS
Science, Social Studies, Language Arts, Performing Arts

CONCEPTS
- Increased public knowledge of the environment and the need for conservation of natural resources have resulted in lifestyle changes in many cultures. (15.5)
- Humans throughout the world create differing social, cultural, and economic systems and organizations to help them meet their physical and spiritual needs. (3.2)
- The standard of living of various peoples throughout the world depends on environmental quality; the availability, use, and distribution of resources; and the societies' political structure and culture. (3.3)

SKILLS
Researching, Organizing Information, Reasoning, Analyzing, Comparing and Contrasting, Evaluating

OBJECTIVES
Students will ① analyze a Native American legend and traditional Native American attitudes toward using the land, ② identify some of the values of the early American pioneers, and ③ create a chart comparing our own environmental beliefs and behaviors with those of traditional Native Americans and early pioneers.

MATERIALS
chalkboard, chart paper and pens, access to Native American resource books and materials, copies of student pages 356-358

TIME CONSIDERATIONS
Preparation: 15 minutes

Activity: Part A: 30 minutes
Part B: 30 minutes
Part C: 30 minutes

6. Explain that over the next couple of class periods, they will explore how traditional Native Americans and early pioneers viewed and used resources in their lives.

PART B
WITH RESPECT FOR THE EARTH

Doing the Activity

1. The Lakota [Sioux] give us the legend of the sacred pipe and the circle. The legend describes the unity of all things, and the balance of the cycles of life and death, the seasons and stars, of all living and nonliving things. It reminds us that the cycles of the Earth system were established long before humans first appeared and that humans are both a part of the cycles and an influence of change. Read to the students the version of this legend titled "The White Buffalo Calf Woman and the Sacred Pipe" on student page 356, or distribute copies for the students to read themselves. (As a reference you might explain that this legend is from the Lakota, the same tribe depicted in the movie *Dances With Wolves*.) After reading the legend aloud, give students their own copies to refer to.

2. Discuss the following questions:

- What are the parts of the White Buffalo Calf Woman's sacred pipe? What do these parts stand for? (the unity of all things and the cycle of life)

- What does she mean when she tells the people to take the right direction of the Good Red Road? (to live in harmony with nature)

- She shows the people how to offer the pipe to six places: the Sky, Earth, and the Four Sacred Directions. What do you think these places represent? (forces of nature) Why do you think these places are important? (all the forces of nature are linked together)

- What does it mean when the story says the people lived happily and well when they remembered that all things around them are connected like the parts of a pipe?

- How can we affect plants, animals, people, and the rest of the Earth by the things we do? What can we do to take care of the Earth and keep the Earth strong and healthy in the future?

3. Assign students to research (at school, the local library, local museum, university) the traditional lifestyle customs of a local or regional Indian tribe.

- How did they get their food? (Did they hunt? farm? fish?)

- How did they prepare their food?

- Where did they live? (open plains, woodlands, riverbanks, shore)

- What kinds of homes did they have?

- What kinds of transportation did they use? (horses, boats?)

- What was their clothing like? What was it made from?

- What artifacts did they leave? (jewelry, baskets, pottery, weapons)

PART C
THE PIONEER SPIRIT

Doing the Activity

1. In a class discussion, ask your students to describe a pioneer. What role did pioneers have in building America? Discuss the following questions:

- Did pioneers settle in the forest? If so, what were the first things they probably did when they got there? (cleared land for cabin, planted crops)

- Did they use the same forest resources as traditional Native Americans?

- What do you think pioneers learned from Native Americans? Did Native Americans learn anything from pioneers?

- Do you think pioneers harvested forest products for their own use? Did they sell or trade them? If so, which ones?

2. Explain that students are going to divide into groups to explore some of the attitudes toward natural resources that the pioneer settlers had. Each group will assume the role of a pioneer family.

3. Pass out a copy of "Pioneers in the Wilderness," student page 357, to each group. Ask each group to assign one person to each role listed on the sheet.

4. Each group should discuss and answer the following questions. Afterward, bring the groups together to sit in a circle and share their answers.

- In your role as a pioneer, how would you describe your attitude toward the forest when you began establishing your homestead?

- What impact do you think you would have made on the environment?

- How does your real-life attitude toward the forest compare with the attitude you held when you imagined yourself an early settler?

- What factors do you think have contributed to changes in Americans' attitudes toward the environment since the 1840s?

- Can we criticize early American pioneers or industrialists for exploiting the environment? Why or why not?

- Do you believe the practices and traditions of the past are representative in present behavior of society and industry? Why or why not?

- How can we more effectively judge how our actions affect the environment today? (One way to judge an action could be to ask, "What if every person in America did that?")

Enrichment

Watch one of the movies listed in the References and identify the messages given about the environment. Based on the discussion questions used in the activity, have students make up four questions to answer, that explore values and lifestyles in the film. Discuss their insights afterward.

Students could then write a review about the movie's environmental message, as if they were writing for a newspaper. For structure and ideas, have students read movie reviews from local or national newspapers.

END NOTES...

ASSESSMENT OPPORTUNITY

1. Have students refer to their research and class discussion as they fill out the work sheet titled "Beliefs and Behaviors" on page 358.

2. Divide the class into three groups: Traditional Native American, Early Pioneer, and Modern Industrial. Have the groups discuss and combine their "Belief and Behavior" statements down to the three to five most important that they can agree on. Each group should record its three to five statements on a large class wall chart.

3. Hold a class debate among the three groups, with each group defending their lifestyle. As moderator, ask each group to answer the following questions:

- In your lifestyle, how did you use the forest and other natural resources?

- In what ways did your lifestyle exploit natural resources?

- In what ways did your lifestyle show concern for resource conservation?

- In what ways did the time period in which you lived and your circumstances affect the way you used your forests and other natural resources?

- Did events happening outside your region influence the decisions you made about using natural resources?

- How did tools and technology developed during your time in history help you to conserve or to exploit natural resources?

RELATED ACTIVITIES

People of the Forest, Tale of the Sun, Native Way, In the Good Old Days, Earth Manners, Where Are the Cedars of Lebanon?

REFERENCES

Caduto, Michael J., and Joseph Bruchac. *KEEPERS OF THE EARTH.* Fulcrum Publishing, 1989.

Beliefs and Behaviors student page adapted, with permission, from California EE Guide, 1981.

Background information adapted, with permission, from Frederick, D. Kenneth, and Roger A. Sedjo. *AMERICA'S RENEWABLE RESOURCES: HISTORICAL TRENDS AND CURRENT CHALLENGES.* Washington, DC: Resources for the Future, 1991.

Mitchell, John Hanson. *CEREMONIAL TIME—FIFTEEN THOUSAND YEARS ON ONE SQUARE MILE.* Boston: Houghton Mifflin, 1991.

Schlissel, Lillian. *WOMEN'S DIARIES OF THE WESTWARD JOURNEY.* Shocken, 1987.

Related Films: Check each film's rating to make sure it's appropriate for your group.

Dances With Wolves*
Pale Rider*
Medicine Man
The Gods Must Be Crazy
Black Robe
Last of the Mohicans

(*Teachers guide is available from studio.)

THE WHITE BUFFALO CALF WOMAN AND THE SACRED PIPE

It was a time when there was little food left in the camp, and the people were hungry. Two young men were sent out to scout for game. They went on foot, for this was a time long before the horses, the great Spirit Dogs, were given to the people. The two young men hunted a long time but had no luck. Finally, they climbed to the top of a hill and looked to the west.

"What is that?" said one of the young men.

"I cannot tell, but it is coming toward us," said the other.

And so it was. At first they thought that it was an animal, but as the shape drew closer they saw it was a woman. She was dressed in white buffalo skin and carried something in her hands. She walked so lightly that it seemed as if she were not walking at all, but floating with her feet barely touching the Earth.

Then the first young man realized that she must be a Holy Person, and his mind filled with good thoughts. But the second young man did not see her that way. He saw her only as a beautiful young woman and his mind filled with bad thoughts. She was now very close, and he reached out to grab her. As soon as he did so, though, there was a sound of lightning and the young man was covered by a cloud. When it cleared away, there was nothing left of the second young man but a skeleton.

Then the White Buffalo Calf Woman spoke. "Go to your people," she said, holding up the bundle in her hands so that the first young man could see it. "Tell your people that it is a good thing I am bringing. I am bringing a holy thing to your nation, a message from the Buffalo People. Put up a medicine lodge for me and make it ready. I will come there after four days have passed."

The first young man did as he was told. He went back to his people and gave them the message. Then the crier went through camp and told all the people that something sacred was coming and that all things should be made ready. They built the medicine lodge and made an earth altar that faced the west.

Four days passed and then the people saw something coming toward them. When it came closer, they saw it was the White Buffalo Calf Woman. In her hands she carried the bundle and a bunch of sacred sage. The people welcomed her into the medicine lodge and gave her the seat of honor. Then she unwrapped the bundle to show them what was inside. It was the Sacred Pipe. As she held it out to them, she told them what it meant.

"The bowl of the Sacred Pipe," she said, "is made of the red stone. It represents the flesh and blood of the Buffalo People and all other Peoples. The wooden stem of the Pipe represents all the trees and plants, all the things green and growing on this Earth. The smoke that passes through the Pipe represents the sacred wind, the breath that carries prayers up to Wakan Tanka, the Creator."

When she finished showing them the pipe, she told the people how to hold it and how to offer it to Earth and Sky and the Four Sacred Directions. She told them many things to remember.

"The Sacred Pipe," said the White Buffalo Calf Woman, "will show you the Good Red Road. Follow it and it will take you in the right direction. Now," she said, "I am going to leave, but you will see me again."

Then she began to walk toward the setting sun. The people watched her as she went, and they saw her stop and roll once on the Earth. When she stood up she was a black buffalo. Then she went farther and rolled again on the Earth. This time when she stood up she was a brown buffalo. She went farther and rolled a third time and stood up. Now the people saw that she was a red buffalo. Again she walked farther and for a fourth and final time she rolled upon the Earth. This time she became a white calf and continued to walk until she disappeared over the horizon.

As soon as the White Buffalo Calf Woman was gone, herds of buffalo were seen all around the camp. The people were able to hunt them and they gave thanks with the Sacred Pipe for the blessings they had been given. As long as they followed the Good Red Road of the Sacred Pipe and remembered, as the White Buffalo Calf Woman had taught them, that all things were as connected as parts of the Sacred Pipe, they lived happily and well.

(Story adapted from Michael J. Caduto and Joseph Bruchac's KEEPERS OF THE EARTH with permission from Fulcrum Publishing, Inc., 1989.)

PIONEERS IN THE WILDERNESS

Assign each group member to a role, and read this page aloud in your groups.

Pioneer family in Conestoga covered wagon-

Father:

Mother:

Teenage daughter:

Young son:

Grandfather:

Grandmother:

You are a family from Philadelphia. The year is 1840 and you have decided to emigrate to the Oregon Territory. In Philadelphia there is little opportunity for a person to acquire land. But in the Oregon Territory, land is yours for the settling. The government is encouraging you to go. For the price of the move and a few years hard work, each family member can claim 160 acres of land. However, the journey is several months of travel by wagon, half of which will be done in the winter. You will arrive in mid-September of 1842. Winters in that part of Oregon have significant rainfall and occasional snow. Temperatures are generally mild and livestock can survive without shelter.

The frontier land is covered with dense deciduous and coniferous forests. Wildlife abounds, including bear, deer, bobcat, quail, grouse, passenger pigeon, wolf, cougar and salmon. There is a resident population of Indians, but the settlers have had little contact with them.

You have brought with you vegetable and grain seeds, a few hand tools, and a plow. Your livestock consists of only a milk cow, two pigs, two sheep, a horse, two oxen (to pull the wagon), and 10 chickens. In whatever room is left, you bring a few prize possessions.

As a family, you must now have a discussion about the things you have to do to establish a home in the Oregon wilderness:

1. Make a list of things that must be done in your first year.

2. Arrange the items in your list in the order in which they must be accomplished.

3. Who will do what?

4. Evaluate your list to make sure it's realistic in terms of season and weather.

5. Discuss and make a second list describing the environmental impact each activity will have.

BELIEFS AND BEHAVIORS

Write down several statements that reflect the beliefs and behaviors of each of the following lifestyles:

TRADITIONAL NATIVE AMERICANS	EARLY AMERICAN PIONEER	MODERN INDUSTRIAL

Overview
Humans have always had a strong need to record the events of their lives. From cave painting to writing paper, humans have preserved their history in many ways. In this activity, students will discover how the development of paper revolutionized the way people communicate and record information.

Background
Communicating and recording information has always been a basic part of human society. In earliest times, humans used stone paintings and carvings to record their ideas. Humans have used stone and clay tablets, leaves and bark, animal skins, bronze, and cloth to find the ideal surface to record and transport the written word.

In China in A.D. 105, a Chinese court official invented paper as we know it today. This first paper was made from fibers of hemp, cloth, and mulberry bark that were mixed with water and mashed, then pressed into a sheet and allowed to dry in the sun. Early papermaking technology traveled from China, across the Near East to North Africa and Europe. But it was not until a French scientist in 1719 observed wasps building their nests from bits of wood that wood fiber entered papermaking.

Since that time, the basic principle of papermaking has remained the same, but the process has become much more efficient. Wood fiber is still the principal ingredient, but recovered waste paper is playing an increasingly large role.

Getting Ready
You may want to try the activity "Make Your Own Paper" on page 176 to develop students' interest before doing this activity.

Make sure you have examples of different types of paper by asking students to bring samples from home. Make copies of student page 361.

Doing the Activity
1. Divide students into ten teams. Assign each team a numbered period in the history of papermaking (see "History of Papermaking" on page 361).

2. After group members have read page 361 and reviewed and discussed their time period, have groups create a mural that depicts their time period's paper making technology. They can use actual paper samples to make their murals (e.g., coarse, brown paper towels for early paper; homemade paper for the Chinese era, computer paper for the recent era).

3. Have each group describe its mural to the other groups. Teams should mount their murals on the wall in chronological order. Groups also should create a paper chain out of their symbolic paper stock to link each era to the next.

LEVELS
Grades 4-8

SUBJECTS
Social Studies, Language Arts, Visual Arts

CONCEPTS
■ Technologies that are developed to meet the needs of an increasing world population should also be environmentally sound. (14.2)

■ Evolving technologies require well-educated and skilled workers who are dedicated to the conservation ethic. (14.3)

■ Consumers "drive" the marketplace with their demands for goods and services. Such demands shift with time and may have positive or negative effects on the availability of natural resources and environmental quality. (15.2)

SKILLS
Ordering and Arranging, Identifying Attributes and Components, Identifying Main Ideas, Making Decisions, Evaluating

OBJECTIVES
Students will ① chronicle the major events in the history of papermaking and ② create a pictorial representation of the history of paper.

MATERIALS
a wide variety of different types and colors of paper such as paper towels, tissues, napkins, paper plates, newsprint, white xerox paper, stationery, tracing paper, manila envelopes, or cardboard; glue or gluesticks; drawing materials; copies of student page 361

TIME CONSIDERATIONS
Preparation: 15 minutes

Activity: 50 minutes

Enrichment

1. Using different kinds of paper (paper towels, typing paper, cloth paper, homemade paper, colored paper, newspaper, etc.), representing different historical periods, have students in their groups create a collage or mosaic of paper representing those different periods in paper-making history.

2. Students can investigate current trends in the way humans record information (e.g., using magnetic tape, microfilm, silicon chips, and compact disks in place of paper). By interviewing parents and other adult users of computers and other electronic equipment, students will discover what kinds of information are stored in new electronic ways and what kinds still must be stored on paper. Do these systems really cut down on our paper use? What are the pros and cons for the storage of information on paper versus electronic storage?

END NOTES...

ASSESSMENT OPPORTUNITY

Using the "around-the-room" mural they created, students should each sketch an informational timeline of papermaking. The timeline should include at least six major periods in papermaking technology.

RELATED ACTIVITIES

Make Your Own Paper, A Few of My Favorite Things, Tree Treasures, A Look at Aluminum, We All Need Trees

REFERENCES

American Paper Institute. *Paper and Paper Manufacture.* New York, 1981 and 1987.

Hunter, Dard. *Papermaking.* New York: Dover, 1978.

Most Wonderful Machine: Mechanization and Social Change in Berkshire Papermaking, 1801-1885. Princeton, NJ: Princeton University Press, 1987.

Smith, David C. *History of Papermaking in the United States.* New York: Lockwood Publishing Co., 1970.

Wright, Helena. *300 Years of American Papermaking.* Washington, DC: Smithsonian Institution, 1991.

HISTORY OF PAPERMAKING

1. Humans have always had the need to communicate their experiences and ideas. In ancient times, people worked hard carving pictures and symbols into the walls of caves, and on rock and bone. As human civilizations developed, surfaces were found that were easier to write on, such as beeswaxed boards, palm leaves, bronze, silk, parchment made from animal skins, and clay tablets.

2. Long before humans thought of making paper, wasps were doing it. Paper wasps build their nests by chewing tiny slivers of wood to make a paste that dries as paper.

3. About 4,000 years ago, the Egyptians discovered how to make a writing surface out of papyrus, a type of reed that grows along waterways in southern Europe and North Africa. The reed was cross-woven into a mat and then pounded into a hard thin sheet. The word "papyrus" is the origin of the word "paper."

4. The Chinese invented papermaking in A.D. 105 (about 2,000 years ago). A court official named Ts'ai Lun under the Chinese Emperor Ho Ti made paper from hemp, old cloth, and mulberry bark mixed with water. This mixture was formed into a sheet, the water was squeezed out, and the sheet was allowed to dry in the sun. Paper remained a secret of the Chinese until A.D. 751, when Muslim invaders captured a Chinese paper mill and took the secret across the Near East and North Africa to Europe. In 1151, the first paper mill was built in Spain.

5. Paper was still very scarce and expensive because it was made by hand from rags of cloth—which were limited in supply. Somehow as the craft of papermaking spread across Eurasia, the technique of using wood as the source was lost. Worn-out clothing, which was mostly linen (made from flax), and cotton fiber provided the raw material for paper. Each sheet was made by dipping a screen into a mixture of 99 percent water and 1 percent pulp fibers, and then filtering the water away from the fibers. Only about 750 sheets could be made in a day. But after Johann

Gutenberg invented the moveable-type printing press (in about 1450), the demand for paper grew. Mechanical pulpers and beaters were invented, and rags as raw materials became scarce.

6. In 1690, a group of Americans from Philadelphia formed a partnership to build America's first paper mill. William Penn and Benjamin Franklin were among early Americans to support the development of papermaking in America, and the industry thrived as the 18th century progressed. During the Revolutionary War, the demand for paper was so great that soldiers had to tear up old books to make wadding for their muzzle-loading guns. Messages to General George Washington were sent on small scraps of paper. By the end of the Revolutionary War, the new nation had nearly 100 paper mills and by 1810, nearly 200. In this period people used the ancient process of spreading and drying pulp in a sheet on a screen with a wooden frame called a "paper mould." The mould was dipped into a vat, and the water drained away. The wet sheets of paper were turned off the mould and layered with blankets of felt. Then they were pressed and separated for drying.

7. About the middle of the 18th century, a French scientist, Rene de Reaumur, observed wasps using tiny fibers of wood to make their nests. Some years later, a German named Friedrich Gottlob Keller invented a machine designed to turn wood into pulp by grinding away its structure with a revolving grindstone. Englishman Hugh Burgess improved this process with chemical pulping—digesting wood with solutions of various chemicals. Wood chips were boiled in a caustic chemical soda (sodium hydroxide); this was called the "soda process." Later another chemical (sodium sulfate) was used, and this was called the "sulfate process."

8. In 1798, paper went from being handmade to machine-made. Nicholas Louis Robert, a clerk at a papermaking mill in France, invented a large hand-cranked machine with an endless wire screen that filtered the pulp—the mixture of fibers were ground up and suspended in water. Robert sold his design

to the Fourdrinier brothers, two English papermakers, who improved his design and produced the machines for sale. Paper could now be made by rollers that squeezed out the excess water from the pulp on the screens, and the damp paper was rolled up at one end of the machine. However, the raw material for pulp, cloth rags, was still in short supply.

9. America's early papermaking mills were located mostly in New York and the New England states. The spruce trees in those areas made excellent ground wood and sulfate pulp. The industry expanded to Wisconsin, Michigan, and Minnesota where there were spruce and balsam trees; to Washington, Oregon, and California where there were hemlock, fir, and pine; and to the southeast, which had mostly pine. By the turn of the 20th century, the age of mass-produced paper had been launched in the United States. Newspapers and magazines appeared on stands. School slates disappeared in favor of notebooks and lined paper. Five-and-ten-cent novels rolled off the presses. Plentiful, low-cost paper and paperboard were important to the Industrial Revolution and the development of the United States and the world.

10. Today, raw logs, industrial wood and paper waste, and recovered paper are the primary sources of paper pulp. However, fibers from cotton, flax, sugar cane, and other fibrous plants are used for special papers. The pulp can be produced by either mechanical or chemical processes. In the mechanical processes, wood logs or chips are reduced to fiber by holding them against huge grindstones. In chemical processes, wood chips are cooked in a giant pressure cooker or digester where the wood is dissolved into fibers. The chemical pulps are often bleached to produce bright paper required for books, writing, and business. Unbleached pulps are used in the manufacture of cardboard, grocery bags, and other products. Today, recycled waste paper is also being used—it is repulped and used in the production of many paper and paperboard products.

Overview
Throughout history, people have depended on natural resources for survival. The availability of food, water, and resources to build shelters has generally determined where humans have settled and how cultures evolved over time. In this activity, students will explore how ancient civilizations developed systems for using their natural resources.

LEVELS
Grades 6-8

SUBJECT
Social Studies, Science

CONCEPTS
■ Ecosystems change over time through patterns of growth and succession. They are also affected by other phenomena such as disease, insects, fire, weather, and human intervention. (13.4)

■ Governments change and evolve over the years. Such changes affect the lives of the citizens, as well as resource management and environmental policies. (15.1)

■ Human societies and cultures throughout the world interact with each other and affect natural systems upon which they depend. (6.1)

■ Demographics influence environmental quality, government policy, and resource use. Structure and systems change over various periods of time. (12.3)

SKILLS
Researching, Analyzing, Concluding

OBJECTIVES
Students will ① investigate how ancient civilizations used natural resources and affected the environment and ② apply environmental lessons learned in the past toward solving current environmental problems.

MATERIALS
copies of student pages 364-365

TIME CONSIDERATIONS
Preparation: 15 minutes
Activity: 50 minutes

Background

One definition of ecology is "the science of interrelationships between living organisms and their environment." The term "human ecology" generally refers to the relationship between humans and their environment—the way humans use the environment within the context of their society and culture.

Many civilizations throughout history have lived in balance with their resources for hundreds, even thousands of years. These societies may have been the ones whose use of resources was balanced with the Earth's ability to renew itself and who had the ability to adapt to changing environmental conditions.

Other civilizations may have overexploited their resources. This could have been the result of new technologies or population growth that put more stress on natural resources. Changing climate conditions or other environmental factors (such as prolonged drought) also may have affected resource availability and caused societies to disperse and eventually disappear. For example, the disappearance of the Anasazi Indians in the United States may be linked to changing environmental conditions. Needless to say, factors such as politics, war, and disease also have enormous influence on the history of civilizations.

Getting Ready

Make copies of student pages 364-365.

Doing the Activity

1. Divide your group into two teams, and prepare for a debate on the land-use practices of the ancient Babylonian culture. Choose a particular debate statement, for example, "the downfall of the Babylonian society was primarily caused by its use and abuse of natural resources, particularly the soil."

2. Have students read the article on student page 364, "By the Rivers of Babylon," and fill in the "Role of Land Use" section for the Babylonian Culture. This exercise will help your students determine the costs and benefits of each land use practice.

3. In the debate, one team is to argue that land use or abuse had a major influence on the downfall of Babylonian society, while the other should take the position that land use or abuse played a minor role in its collapse. In preparing their arguments, both teams should consider the costs and benefits of the land use practices they identified on the student pages. Students may use additional resources to support their arguments.

VARIATION—BEFORE & AFTER

Instead of a debate, you can try the following activity:

1. Have students read page 364, "By the Rivers of Babylon."

2. Divide your group into teams of three to five students. Have each team draw two murals (using both sides of the same paper). One side should depict a scene of Babylon before its decline; the other should depict a scene after its decline.

3. Each team should present its view of Babylonia's decline by first showing the "before" and then the "after" pictures. They should explain what caused each change.

4. As a wrap-up, each team can fill–out "The Role of Land Use" on page 365 for the Babylonian culture.

Enrichment

1. Have students research the land-use practices of other ancient cultures, such as ancient China, Greece, Rome, or Egypt (see References). Make extra copies of student page 365, and have students fill out "The Role of Land Use" for each culture or civilization they research.

2. Have students research and discuss present-day problems related to land use, such as soil conservation, deforestation, over-grazing, famine, and so on. Students can use periodicals to research modern environmental catastrophes, such as the 1983-85 famine in Ethiopia in which an estimated one million people died of starvation.

They should consider the political, economic, social, and security factors involved in each situation. You might also have them write an "update" on the land areas involved in the ancient cultures that they studied. For example, the land once called "Babylonia" is now Iraq.

END NOTES...

ASSESSMENT OPPORTUNITY

Examine the students' work on the student page to see whether they identified both sides of an issue, not just the side they were assigned to debate. Look for evidence that they understand that there are different approaches to analyzing and interpreting historical events.

RELATED ACTIVITIES

Then and Now, In the Good Old Days, A Look at Lifestyles

REFERENCES

Gore, Al. *EARTH IN THE BALANCE. ECOLOGY AND THE HUMAN SPIRIT.* Boston: Houghton Mifflin, 1992.

Helfman, Elizabeth S. *LAND, PEOPLE, AND HISTORY.* New York: David McKay Co., 1962.

Lamb, H.H. *CLIMATE HISTORY OF THE MODERN WORLD.* 1982.

BY THE RIVERS OF BABYLON

In the fertile valley where the Tigris and Euphrates rivers meet (in present-day Iraq), great ancient civilizations once flourished. One of the first peoples to settle in the valley were the Sumerians in about 4500 B.C. The Sumerians cleared the land for growing food and irrigated it by digging canals and draining swamps along the rivers. Because of irrigation and the fertility of the soil, the Sumerians had time to develop other aspects of their civilization.

During the time of Babylonian culture, which followed the Sumerian in about 1800 B.C., people kept digging canals. The water of the rivers became muddy, not just during the spring floods as in the past, but all the time. Deposits of silt settled in the canals and over time clogged them up. To keep the canals open to water the fields, people carried the silt out of the canals in baskets. Settlements grew around each system of canals, and each town had to be responsible for its own land and water, because to neglect either would mean starvation. Land and water were so important that the first Babylonian king, Hammurabi, decreed death to any person who wasted water or spoiled the land.

However, as the people of Babylon became prosperous and accustomed to luxury, they did not take as good care of the land. King Nebuchadnezzar, ruling more than a thousand years after Hammurabi, was recorded as saying: "That which no king before me had done, I did…. Great canals I dug and lined them with burnt brick laid in bitumen and brought abundant waters to all the people…. I paved the streets of Babylon with stone from the mountain…. Magnificent palaces and temples I have built…. Huge cedars from Mount Lebanon I cut down…."

Because of erosion from canal digging, logging, and grazing, more and more silt kept washing down the rivers from the hills to the north. As the soil washed off the unprotected hills and settled in the irrigation canals of Babylonia, more and more people had to spend all their time maintaining the canals. War captives and slaves were even brought in to do the work.

Invasions by Alexander the Great and others in the fourth century B.C. meant that the soil and canals were neglected. As time went on and silt filled the valley, the land could support fewer and fewer people. About 700 years ago, the Babylonian canals were finally destroyed by the invasion of the Mongols who destroyed the irrigation system and allowed the land to return to desert.

ROLE OF LAND USE

Role of Land Use in the _____ Culture

Position in Debate:

....

....

....

....

....

....

....

....

....

....

....

....

....

Overview
In this activity, students will study changes in their local environment over short and long periods and will identify patterns of change.

LEVELS
Part A: Grades K-4
Part B: Grades 3-8

SUBJECTS
Social Studies, Language Arts, Visual Arts

CONCEPTS
- Ecosystems change over time through patterns of growth and succession. They are also affected by other phenomena such as disease, insects, fire, weather, and human intervention. (13.4)
- Governments change and evolve over the years. Such changes affect the lives of the citizens, as well as resource management and environmental policies. (15.1)
- Increased public knowledge of the environment and the need for conservation of natural resources have resulted in lifestyle changes in many cultures. (15.5)

SKILLS
Researching, Comparing and Contrasting, Identifying Relationships and Patterns, Concluding

OBJECTIVES
Students will ① identify changes in their local environment over the course of time, and ② create a timeline to illustrate patterns of change over time.

MATERIALS
roll of paper such as butcher paper or newsprint for timeline, colored markers, copies of "Timeline Plan" on student page 368

TIME CONSIDERATIONS
Preparation: 30 minutes

Activity: One to five 50-minute periods

Background
It has been said that change is really the only constant in the universe. Change is all around us—sometimes we notice it, and sometimes we do not. One pattern of change is the 24-hour day. The Earth rotates on its axis, causing the cycle we know as day and night. Small changes in the rotation and the tilt of the Earth cause changes in the length of day and night throughout the seasons, but these, too, are predictable.

Some changes happen fast, such as a tree falling in a storm. Others happen so slowly, like the slow washing of mountains into the sea, that we are hardly aware of them. Some changes are noticeable through patient observation, like the movement of the tide. Some systems are so complex, like a forest, that we hardly notice when changes take place.

History is a record of changes, be it the history of a tree, forest, society, or nation. Humans have been recording the history of people, places, and things for thousands of years; much of this information can be found in libraries and museums. Historians, people who study and record history, can be a great help in tracing the changes over time.

Historical information may be stored in books, photographs, movies, computer records, government documents, or a person's memory.

One example of change in your community could be transportation systems. Today you move around in cars, trains, buses, on bicycles, and on foot. Just 50 or 60 years ago, you probably would have observed a lot more people riding bikes and walking, and not as many cars. A hundred years ago, people probably walked, rode on horses, or drove in horse-drawn carriages—things we seldom see today!

The challenge is to be aware and notice changes as they happen, and then to look back to identify patterns.

Getting Ready
Contact your local library or historical society for historic photos, books, and information about your community. Cut butcher paper into five 4-6-foot (1.2-1.8-m) sections, or prepare similar-sized pieces of paper.

(Optional) Try the activity "Then and Now" on page 131. Schedule a visit to the local museum. Invite a local historian or elderly person to talk about changes that have taken place in the local community.

PART A
CHANGES IN YOU

Doing the Activity
1. Ask students what major changes happened in their lives between their birth and age four. Encourage them to brainstorm ideas, and record their answers on the chalkboard under the heading "Changes From Birth to Four." (grew taller, learned to eat real food, toilet trained, learned to walk, learned to talk) Then ask them how they know these things—can they remember? Did someone tell them? Did they see pictures?

2. Now ask students to brainstorm about how they have changed since they started school. Record answers under the heading "Changes Since Starting School." (go to school every day, play with friends, learned to read, etc.)

3. Now ask students to think about how they have changed just since they woke up this morning. Record answers under the heading "Changes Since This Morning." (hair changed from messy to neat after brushing, stomach changed from hungry to full after eating breakfast, etc.)

4. Discuss how some of these changes are obvious (such as learning to walk). Other changes are harder to see—such as gaining knowledge. Point out how changes can sometimes be linked to a time or date. Demonstrate how students can make a timeline of their life changes from birth to the present.

PART B
MAKING A TIMELINE

Doing the Activity

1. Ask students to gather information about the history of their community by visiting a museum, listening to a historian invited to talk to the group, or visiting a library.

Share with students any information you've already gathered.

2. Tell students that they are going to create a timeline of the history of the local community. Divide the class into five groups, and make each responsible for chronicling a particular time period, either one decade of the past 50 years or one of the periods listed below.

- Ancient Times (native peoples)

- Early Years (early settlers or community development)

- Olden Days (grandparents' lifetimes and earlier)

- Recent History (parents' lifetimes)

- Modern Times (today)

Students should compile information about their time period from interviews, museums, and libraries.

3. Give each group ample time to collect information. Before beginning their timeline, each group should complete a "Timeline Plan" on student page 368, describing at least five events students plan to include. Tell them to consider changes in landscape, wildlife, and human lifestyle over their time period. Ask what might have been the causes of some of these changes, and then have them incorporate changes into their timeline period.

4. They should then draw or paint the events of their decade or time period on the timeline mural. Students can use poster paints or markers on butcher paper to make their section of the mural. Five separate mural pieces—one for each team—are easiest to manage; these can later be joined by masking tape when all are finished and dry.

Enrichment

1. If you're working with older students, you might consider getting permission to paint your timeline mural on a blank outdoor or indoor wall—making a permanent artistic expression of the local history.

2. Have students become cultural archaeologists and go searching with a parent through the attic, basement, closets, shelves, and drawers for "really old stuff." Have students ask the parent if he or she knows the history of the items found. Who was the original owner? Where did it come from? What was it used for? Have students write a real or imaginary story about one of the items that interests them.

END NOTES...

ASSESSMENT OPPORTUNITY

Ask each team to explain the history of the changes they recorded in their section of the mural. After reviewing the entire mural, discuss the following:

- What are changes in the environment, wildlife, and human lifestyle?

- What caused some of these changes?

- Do you think these changes have made your community a better or worse place to live, or have they made no difference?

- Did any changes that were considered good at some time turn out to be bad?

- Can you identify any trends and what implications they might have for the future?

RELATED ACTIVITIES

Then and Now; In the Good Old Days; People, Places, and Things; Planning the Ideal Community

TIMELINE PLAN FOR YOUR LOCAL AREA

Team members:

_____

_____

_____

_____

Option 1

A decade of the past 50 years

___ 1950s

___ 1960s

___ 1970s

___ 1980s

___ 1990s

Option 2

A time period:

___ Ancient Times (native peoples)

___ Early Years (pioneers and settlers)

___ Olden Days (grandparents' or great-grand parents' lifetimes)

___ Recent Times (parents' lifetimes)

___ Modern Times (today)

Describe at least five events from your time period and the dates when they happened. Include this information in your part of the timeline:

In your community, what changes have taken place in:

■ vegetation: _____

■ wildlife: _____

■ human environment and lifestyle: (homes, transportation, work, schools)

_____

What are some of the causes of these changes?

Explain whether you think these changes have made your community a better or worse place in which to live, or have made no difference.

Overview
Each living thing has a habitat—a place to live that suits its needs. For human beings, the community they live in is their habitat. In this activity, students are encouraged to take action to improve their community by making some positive environmental changes.

Background
Students should consider various improvement projects at school or at nearby places. Simple projects might include picking up litter from an area; planting flowers, grass, shrubs, or trees; painting benches; putting up fencing; scrubbing graffiti off walls; or designing a mural for a nearby wall. A more elaborate project might be designing an environmental study area. Students can plan their project to coincide with Earth Day (April 22), Arbor Day (date varies by state, so you should contact your state forester), or the birthday of an environmental or community leader.

Getting Ready
Before tackling an improvement project, consider the scope of the project and the limitations of what you can do. Your group can simply survey the existing school or community grounds and make recommendations for improvement to the appropriate authorities. Or they can seek funding from the PTA, school board, or a garden club to actually carry out an improvement project.

Doing the Activity
1. Take your students outside to survey the local area for signs of damage or neglect such as soil *erosion*, soil *compaction*, or excess litter; dead grass; lack of trees and other plants; broken play equipment, drinking fountains, or benches. Students might also want to interview and survey people who use the area to get those people's opinions on how the area could be improved.

2. Students should sketch a simple map of the area.

3. After this initial survey, you should help students create a single, large map of the site as it currently exists.

You may need to make a large grid on which to lay out the map. The map can have simple symbols such as circles for trees, squares or triangles for play equipment, and so on.

4. Have teams of students brainstorm ideas on how they might improve the area. Each team should propose its ideas to the rest of the group. Write these ideas on the chalkboard, and then have students vote for the one they'd like to try.

5. Your group should develop an "Action Plan" to achieve these improvements. In creating their plan, students should realize that they will have to persuade the PTA, school board, or another decision-making body to approve their plan. Your group can divide into five teams, each with responsibility to prepare one of the following pieces of the plan:

- Background information (Describing the area they want to improve. Who uses it? What is the need for this project?)

- Method of study (Describing the survey they conducted to identify problems.)

- What students found out (Describing the problems and their location on the map.)

- Recommendations (Describing the priority projects and future projects.)

- Details of the priority projects (Identifying who will be involved, how much it will cost, who will do the work, and how the project will benefit the community.)

6. When students have finished a draft of their plan, they should evaluate it using the following questions:

LEVELS
Grades 5-8

SUBJECTS
Science, Social Studies, Visual Arts

CONCEPTS
- Governments change and evolve over the years. Such changes affect the lives of the citizens, as well as resource management and environmental policies. (15.1)

- Increased public knowledge of the environment and the need for conservation of natural resources have resulted in lifestyle changes in many cultures. (15.5)

SKILLS
Defining Problems, Solving Problems, Evaluating

OBJECTIVES
Students will ① identify ways they can improve their local area, and ② carry out plans to improve the area.

MATERIALS
paper, rulers, stencils, drawing pencils, markers, tracing paper, or transparent overlays

TIME CONSIDERATIONS
Preparation: none

Activity: multiple class periods to plan and complete an improvement project

(You can select the questions you want to use.)

- Is there sufficient evidence to warrant action on this issue?

- Are there alternative actions available for use? What are they?

- Is the action chosen the most effective one available?

- What are the ecological consequences of this action?

- Are there legal consequences of this action? If so, what are they? (If some parents are lawyers, ask them.)

- Will there be social consequences of this action? If so, what are they?

- Will there be economic consequences of this action? If so, what are they?

- Do our personal values support this action?

- Do we understand the procedures necessary to take this action? If not, who can help?

- Do we have the skills needed to take this action? If not, who can help?

- Do we have the time needed to take this action? If not, who can help?

- Do we have all the other resources needed to make this action effective?

Using this evaluation, students can make adjustments to their plans. They should also be prepared to answer questions like these when they propose their plan to the decision-making group.

Enrichment

1. Even if an actual project is impossible to undertake, hold a simulated PTA or council meeting (another class or group of faculty can represent this council), and have students present their plan.

2. Create a group picture of a "dream site,"—their chosen area with all their improvements included.

3. Have students contact their state or local forestry office for information on school improvement projects using trees and shrubs.

END NOTES...

ASSESSMENT OPPORTUNITY
Have students present their maps, overlays, and action plans to a decisionmaking individual or group. Have that person or group provide feedback on the thoroughness and clarity of their plan and presentation.

RELATED ACTIVITIES
Planning the Ideal Community, I'd Like to Visit a Place Where, Then and Now

REFERENCES
IT'S YOUR ENVIRONMENT: THINGS TO THINK ABOUT THINGS TO DO. Environmental Action Coalition, New York: Charles Scribners Sons, 1976.

Questions in Step 6 are adapted, with permission, from Hungerford and Peyton's A PARADIGM FOR CITIZEN RESPONSIBILITY.

ABIOTIC (adj)—a nonliving factor or element in an environment; e.g., light, water, heat, rock, and gases.

ACID RAIN—precipitation with a pH less than 5.6 (the pH of normal tap water) that forms in the atmosphere when certain pollutants mix with water vapor. The major sources of acid rain pollutants are sulfur dioxide and nitrogen oxide emissions from fossil fuel-burning power plants and motor vehicles.

ACTIVE SOLAR POWER—a solar energy collection system in which water, air, or another heat-absorbing fluid is actively pumped through a solar collector. After absorbing the heat from the sun, the fluid is stored in insulated tanks until the heat energy is needed.

ADAPTATION—the process of making adjustments to the environment over time. For example, a plant with unusually long roots, enabling it to absorb water over a wide area, may be more likely to survive during periods of drought.

AIR QUALITY—a gauge of the concentration of one or more chemicals in the atmosphere that could potentially be harmful to humans, other animals, vegetation, or materials.

ANGIOSPERM—a vascular plant (one containing xylem and phloem) that protects its seeds in a fruit.

ANNUAL—a plant that completes its life cycle from seedling to mature seed-bearing plant during a single growing season.

ASBESTOS—a natural fibrous material that was once commonly used for fireproofing and sound or heat insulation. In 1974 and 1989, the U.S. Environmental Protection Agency passed resolutions restricting its use. Asbestosis is a lung disease resulting from the prolonged inhalation of very fine asbestos particles.

ATMOSPHERE—consists of the troposphere and the stratosphere which comprise the whole mass of air surrounding the Earth. The troposphere is the innermost layer of the atmosphere, containing about 95% of the mass of the Earth's air and extending 11 miles (17 km) above sea level. The stratosphere is the second layer of the atmosphere and extends from about 11 to 30 miles (17 to 48 km) above the Earth's surface.

BACTERIA—single-celled microorganisms that lack chlorophyll. Many bacteria break down organic matter in the air, the water, and the soil. Some bacteria are capable of causing diseases in humans, other animals, and plants.

BARK—the tough exterior covering of a woody root or stem.

BAUXITE—a mineral which is composed of 45 to 60% aluminum, making it the primary source of this versatile metal. Australia is the world's largest supplier of bauxite ore, and the United States is the largest processor of aluminum from bauxite.

BIENNIAL—a plant that lives for two growing seasons, producing foliage during the first season and flowers, fruit, and seeds during the second.

BIODEGRADABLE—the property of a substance that permits it to be broken down by micro organisms into simple, stable compounds such as carbon dioxide, water, and minerals..

BIOGEOCHEMICAL CYCLES—movement of matter within or between ecosystems caused by the interaction of living organisms, geologic forces, or chemical reactions. Examples of biogeochemical cycles include the water, nitrogen, and phosphorous cycles.

BIOLOGICAL DIVERSITY or BIODIVERSITY—the variety and complexity of species present and interacting in an ecosystem and the relative abundance of each.

BIOMASS—the total weight (mass) of all living matter in a particular habitat or area at a given moment in time.

BIOME—a complex of communities characterized by a distinctive type of vegetation and maintained under the climatic conditions of the region. The biomes of North America include the tundra, the desert, the eastern deciduous forest, the prairie, the northern boreal forest, and the western coniferous forests.

BIOSPHERE—the part of the Earth's crust, water, and atmosphere where living organisms can exist.

BIOTA—the animal and plant life of a region or period.

BIOTIC (adj)—an environmental factor related to or produced by living organisms.

BOARD FOOT (fbm or bf)—a unit of wood equivalent to a piece of wood 12 inches (30 cm) square and 1 inch (2.5 cm) thick.

BOG—a wetland formed in a former glacial depression by the accumulation of organic matter, known as peat, and which supports mosses tolerant of acidic conditions.

BOREAL FOREST—the northernmost broad band of mixed coniferous and deciduous trees that stretches across northern North America, Europe, and Asia.

BOTANIST—a specialist in the study of plants.

BOTTOMLANDS—an open grassland or forest area usually near a stream, river, or other moving body of water. Bottomlands are subject to periodic flooding.

BROADLEAFED (adj)—describes a plant with wide-bladed leaves, such as an oak or maple. This term is generally used to describe flowering trees (angiosperms) rather than conifers (gymnosperms).

BROMELIAD—a member of a family of tropical American and epiphytic herbaceous plants that includes the pineapple and various ornamentals.

CAMBIUM—a thin layer of living, dividing cells just under the bark of trees. This layer give rise to the tree's secondary growth.

CAMOUFLAGE—color, tones, patterns, shapes or behavior that enable an organism to blend in with its surroundings. Some organisms, for example, have a skin or coat color that enables them to hide from predators.

CANOPY—the forest layer formed by the leaves and branches of trees or shrubs. There may be several canopy layers.

CARBOHYDRATES—sugars, starches, and celluloses that are produced by green plants and are important nutritional sources of energy for many animals.

CARBON CYCLE—the circulation and recycling of carbon atoms, especially through the processes of photosynthesis, respiration and decomposition.

CARNIVORE—an animal that consumes other animals.

CARRYING CAPACITY—the maximum number of organisms of a given species that can survive in a particular ecosystem on a long-term basis.

CELL—the smallest living unit of an organism.

CELLULOSE—a complex carbohydrate that constitutes the chief part of the cell walls of higher plants and yields fiber for many products.

CHAPARRAL—dense scrub vegetation of broadleaf, evergreen, or wintergreen shrubs.

CHLOROFLUOROCARBONS (CFCs)—chemical compounds commonly used as spray propellants or refrigerants. When released into the air, CFCs tend to accumulate in the upper atmosphere, where they break down and trigger chemical reactions that can destroy ozone. The ozone of the upper atmosphere is important for filtering out harmful ultraviolet radiation.

CHLOROPHYLL—a group of pigments that produce the green hue of plants, essential to photosynthesis.

CHLOROPLASTS—the structures within plants that contain chlorophyll and enable photosynthesis to occur.

CLEARCUT—a method of harvest in which all trees in a given area are removed, and the area is then replanted or allowed to regenerate. This method is usually used with shade-intolerant species.

CLIMATE—the kind of weather a place has over a period of years, based on conditions of heat and cold, moisture and dryness, clearness and cloudiness, wind and calm.

CLIMAX COMMUNITY—the relatively stable association under existing conditions of soil and climate that represents the final stage of succession. Unlike earlier stages of succession, climax communities usually contain a large variety of different species and complex interactions.

COMBUSTION—an oxidative chemical process that results in the creation of heat and light.

COMMENSALISM—a relationship between two organisms of different species in which one organism benefits, while the other is generally neither helped nor harmed.

COMMERCIAL FOREST LAND—a forest land capable of bearing merchantable timber currently or prospectively accessible and not withdrawn from such use. See **TIMBERLAND.**

COMMUNITY—all organisms in a particular habitat that are bound together by food chains and other interrelationships.

COMPOUND LEAF—a leaf that is subdivided into many leaflets. A leaf that is comprised of a single leaf blade is a **SIMPLE LEAF.**

CONDENSATION—the physical change of state in which a gas or vapor is transformed into a liquid, as in the formation of water droplets when water vapor cools.

CONE—a structure composed of many spirally-arranged scales in which pollen ovules are produced.

CONIFER (n), CONIFEROUS (adj)—a plant that bears its seeds in cones. Usually refers to **NEEDLELEAF** trees, although some needleleaf trees, such as the yew, do not bear cones.

CONSERVATION—the use of natural resources in a way that assures their continuing availability to future generations; the intelligent use of natural resources for long-term benefits.

CONSUMER—1) an organism that obtains energy by feeding on other organisms and their remains. Usually, consumers are classified as primary consumers (herbivores), secondary consumers (carnivores), and microconsumers (decomposers). 2) any person or other entity when using goods for its own needs, and neither for resale nor for the manufacture of other goods.

CONVENTIONAL CRUDE OIL—the viscous liquid drilled and pumped from underground oil deposits, or reserves. After the crude oil has been extracted, it is sent to a refinery for processing into gasoline, heating oil, and other petroleum products.

CONVENTIONAL NATURAL GAS—underground deposits of gases that are associated with crude oil deposits. Natural gas consists primarily of the gas methane.

CONVENTIONAL NUCLEAR FISSION—the process by which the nucleus of a heavy element (such as uranium-235 or plutonium-239) is split into lighter nuclei, resulting in the release of a large amount of heat. This heat is then used to power a turbine that generates electrical energy.

CROWN—the top branches of a tree.

DBH—the diameter of a tree as measured at breast height. Standard DBH is measured at 4.5 foot (135 cm) above the ground.

DECIBEL—a unit of intensity of sound. A measurement of 50 decibels is considered moderate sound; 80, loud; and 100, the level beyond which the sound becomes intolerable.

DECIDUOUS (adj)—describes a plant that periodically (typically in autumn) loses all its leaves. Most North American broadleaf trees are deciduous. A few conifers, such as the larch and cypress, are also deciduous. See **EVERGREEN.**

DECOMPOSER—a plant or organism that feeds on dead material and causes its mechanical or chemical breakdown.

DEFOLIATION—the loss of leaves from plants.

DEFORESTATION—the permanent replacement of forests by non-forest uses.

DENDROLOGY—a branch of botany devoted to the study of trees.

DENDROCHRONOLOGY—the science of dating events and variations in the environment in former periods by comparative study of growth rings in trees and aged wood.

DESERT—an arid habitat with limited amounts of vegetation.

DIVERSITY—variety or complexity. See **BIOLOGICAL DIVERSITY.**

EARLY SUCCESSIONAL—describes a species adapted to the beginning stages of biotic succession, i.e., a species that does best in open areas and full sun.

ECOLOGICAL DIVERSITY—the variety of forests, deserts, grasslands, oceans, streams, lakes, and other biological communities interacting with one another and with their nonliving environment.

ECOLOGICAL SUCCESSION—the changes, over time, in the structure and function of an ecosystem. When no previous vegetation exists on a site, the process is called primary succession. When a site supported vegetation previously, the process is called secondary succession.

ECOLOGY—the scientific study of the relations of living things to one another and to their environment. A scientist who studies these relationships is called an ecologist.

ECOSYSTEM—the interacting system of a biological community and its nonliving environment; also, the place where these interactions occur.

ECOSYSTEM MANAGEMENT—use of ecosystem concepts to predict effects of management actions on the ecosystem and to guide management planning and actions.

EDGE HABITAT—the transition zone between two different habitat types.

EFFLUENT—the outflows from sewage or industrial plants, and the like.

EMERGENT—a tree that grows above the general level of the forest canopy.

ENDANGERED SPECIES—a species that is in imminent danger of extinction. The California condor is an example of an endangered species.

ENERGY FLOW—the one-way passage or transfer of energy through an ecosystem according to the laws of thermodynamics.

ENVIRONMENT—the sum of all external conditions and influences that affect the development and, ultimately, the survival of an organism or group of organisms.

EPIPHYTE—a plant that grows on the surface of another plant.

EROSION—the wearing away of the land surface by wind or water. Erosion occurs naturally from weather or runoff, but it is often intensified by some human practices.

ESTUARY—a partly enclosed body of water where sea water and fresh water meet and mix.

ETHANOL—a grain alcohol produced by fermentation or the anaerobic (occurring in the absence of oxygen) digestion of plant materials with a high sugar content. Ethanol is also an unconventional or alternative fuel source for automobile engines.

ETHNOBOTANY—the study of the relationship between societies and the plants of their environment.

EVAPORATION—a physical change of state in which a liquid is transformed into a vapor or gas.

EVEN-AGED STAND—a forest area in which all the trees are the same age due to simultaneous germination, planting or harvesting. Even-aged stands are desirable for species whose young trees do not thrive in the shade of taller trees.

EVERGREEN—a plant that retains its leaves year-round, generally a conifer.

EXTINCTION—the complete elimination of a species from the Earth.

FIBER—a thread–like body or filament many times longer than its diameter. Paper pulps are composed of fibers, usually of vegetable origin, but sometimes animal, mineral, or synthetic, for special types of papers.

FIELD—an area devoid of trees, and generally characterized by having grasses.

FOOD CHAIN—the transfer of food energy from organisms in one nutritional level to those in another. For example, in a simple food chain, a green plant may be consumed by a leaf-eating insect; and the insect, in turn, may be consumed by an insect-eating bird.

FOOD WEB—the complex and interlocking series of **FOOD CHAINS.**

FOREST—a large area of land primarily covered with trees as well as the other organisms, soil, water, and air associated with them.

FOREST ASSOCIATION—a grouping of plants and animals that repeatedly occur together in a forest region. Associations may be identified in terms of their predominant tree association, such as the oak-hickory forest.

FOREST FLOOR—the layer of decomposing material that covers the soil in a forest.

FOREST MANAGEMENT—the practical application of scientific, economic, and social principles to the administration of a forest.

FOREST REGION—an extensive area of a continent in which the mature-forest associations are closely similar.

FORESTER—a person trained in and practicing **FORESTRY**.

FORESTLAND—to be classified as forestland, an area must be at least one acre in size and contain 10% or more tree cover.

FORESTRY—the principles and practices utilized in the management, use, and enjoyment of forests. Forestry includes a broad range of activities such as managing timber, fish, wildlife, range, watersheds and recreation.

FOSSIL FUEL—coal, oil, and other energy sources that formed over millions of years from the remains of ancient plants and animals. Fossil-fuel use is a major factor in pollution issues.

FUNGI—small, often microscopic, plant-like organisms that lack chlorophyll and cellulose in their cell walls. Some fungi can infect and cause disease in plants or animals. Fungi are important decomposers of organic wastes.

GAS—the physical state of a compound that characteristically has no fixed shape or size. Gases will fill and take the shape of any container in which they are placed.

GENETIC DIVERSITY—variability in the genetic or hereditary makeup among individuals within a single species.

GEOTHERMAL ENERGY—heat transferred from the earth's interior to underground concentrations of steam or hot water trapped in fractured or porous rock.

GLACIER—a flowing body of ice, formed in a region where snowfall exceeds melting.

GLOBAL CLIMATE CHANGE—the long term changes in temperature, moisture, and air mass movements occurring globally as a result of changes in the earth's atmosphere.

GLOBAL WARMING—the observed increase in the average temperature of the Earth's innermost atmosphere, which is believed to be a result of the **GREENHOUSE EFFECT.**

GRASSLAND—a vegetation community in which grasses are the dominant plants.

GREENHOUSE EFFECT—the trapping of heat by gases, such as **CHLOROFLUOROCARBONS** and carbon dioxide, in the Earth's atmosphere.

GREENHOUSE GASES—gases in Earth's lower atmosphere (troposphere) that trap heat. Examples are carbon dioxide, **CHLORLOFLUOROCARBONS, OZONE,** methane, water vapor, and nitrous oxide.

GROSS NATIONAL PRODUCT (GNP)—total market value in current dollars of all goods and services produced by a country's economy for final use during a year.

GROUNDWATER—water that infiltrates into the soil and is stored in slowly flowing and slowly renewed underground reservoirs called aquifers.

GROUP SELECTION—the harvest of clusters of two or more trees in a forest stand. The creation of gaps in the canopy promotes the regeneration of seedlings that grow well in direct or partial sunlight.

GYMNOSPERM—a plant that produces "naked" seeds that are not enclosed in a fruit.

HABITAT—an area that provides an animal or plant with adequate food, water, shelter, and living space in a suitable arrangement.

HARDWOOD—a deciduous or broadleaf tree; also applies to the wood from such trees. See **SOFTWOOD**.

HEARTWOOD—the older, harder, nonliving central portion of wood of some trees that is usually darker, denser, less permeable, and more durable than the surrounding sapwood. Many trees do not form a true heartwood.

HERB—any flowering plant or fern that has a soft, rather than woody, stem.

HERBICIDE—a substance or preparation used for killing undesirable plants. See also **PESTICIDE.**

HERBIVORE—an organism that feeds on vegetation.

HORTICULTURE—the science of growing plants.

HUMUS—decomposed material in the soil that is a highly complex mixture of organic and inorganic substances.

HYDROELECTRICITY/ HYDROPOWER—electric energy produced by falling or flowing water.

ICEBERG—a large floating mass of ice detached from a glacier.

IGNEOUS ROCK—rock formed by the cooling of magma, or molten rock, from within the Earth; e.g., basalt, lava, granite.

INCREMENT BORER—an instrument used to take core samples allowing one to determine the rate of a tree's radial growth and its age.

INNER BARK—see **PHLOEM.**

LANDFILL (n)—a specially engineered site for disposing of solid waste on land, designed to confine the refuse to the smallest practical area and reduce it to the smallest practical volume.

LATE SUCCESSIONAL—describes a species adapted to the later stages (those approaching the climax community) of biotic succession.

LEACHING—the removal of soluble substances from soil by percolating water.

LIANA—a climbing vine common in tropical rain forests. Unlike **BROMELIADS** and **EPIPHYTES,** lianas are rooted in the ground.

LIFE CYCLE—the phases, changes, or stages through which an organism passes during its lifetime.

LOAM—soil containing a mixture of clay, sand, silt, and humus.

MARSH—a wetland without trees, and which often has standing water.

METAMORPHIC ROCK—rock formed when a pre-existing rock is exposed to high heat or pressure or undergoes a chemical reaction.

METHANOL—alcohol made from wood.

MICROCLIMATE—a "small climate." The environmental conditions within a restricted area.

MICROHABITAT—a "small habitat" within a larger one in which environmental conditions differ from those in the surrounding area.

MINERAL—a naturally occurring inorganic crystalline material found in the Earth's crust.

MIXED FOREST—a forest that includes both coniferous and deciduous trees.

MONOCULTURE—a crop of a single species, generally even-aged. Corn fields and pine plantations are two examples

MONTANE ZONE—the band of vegetation that occurs at intermediate elevations in mountainous regions between foothill and subalpine zones. See **VERTICAL VEGETATION ZONES.**

MULTIPLE-USE FORESTRY—any practice of forestry fulfilling two or more objectives of management.

MULTIPLE-USE MANAGEMENT—the practice of managing forest resources for a variety of benefits including water quality and yield, forage, wildlife habitat, wood, recreation, wilderness, and minerals.

MUTUALISM—a symbiotic relationship between organisms of two different species in which both benefit from the association.

MYCELIUM—the mass of interwoven filaments that forms the vegetative portion of a fungus.

NATURALIST—a specialist who studies and/or teaches about nature.

NATURAL RESOURCES—those raw materials supplied by the Earth and its processes. Natural resources include nutrients, minerals, water, plants, animals, etc.

NEEDLELEAF—describes a tree or shrub with narrow, needle-like leaves. See **CONIFER.**

NICHE—the ecological role played by organisms. Also refers to specific places where an individual organism can live (spatial niche).

NONRENEWABLE RESOURCES—substances such as oil, gas, coal, copper, and gold, which, once used, cannot be replaced in this geological age.

NUCLEAR FUSION—nuclear change in which two nuclei of isotopes of elements with a low mass number (such as hydrogen–2 and hydrogen–3) are forced together at extremely high temperatures until they fuse to form a heavier nucleus (such as helium–4). This process releases a large amount of energy.

NUTRIENT—a substance required for growth and development. Plants, for example, need water and minerals in order to grow and reproduce.

OLD GROWTH FORESTS—forests containing trees that are often hundreds, sometimes thousands, of years old. Examples include forests of Douglas fir, western hemlock, giant sequoia, and coast redwoods in the western United States.

OMNIVORES—organisms that eat both animals and plants.

ORGANIC—referring to or derived from living organisms. In chemistry, any compound containing carbon.

ORGANIC MATTER—those compounds containing carbon, many of which can be synthesized by living things.

ORGANISM—any living form of life.

OZONE—a form of oxygen (O_3). Low-level ozone, the main ingredient in smog, is found near ground level and is produced when sunlight stimulates a reaction between pollutants. The ozone layer is a protective layer of ozone high in the earth's atmosphere that filters out much of the sun's harmful ultraviolet radiation.

PARASITISM—any relationship in which a consumer organism lives on or in and feeds on a living plant or animal, known as the host. The parasite draws nourishment from and may gradually weaken its host and kill it.

PARTIAL CUTTING—tree removal other than by **CLEARCUTTING.**

PARTICULATES—small particles of liquid or solid in matter.

PASSIVE SOLAR POWER—a solar energy collection system in which natural materials or large stationary absorptive surfaces absorb and temporarily store the heat of the sun. Heat collected during the day is usually released from the absorptive surfaces at night.

PEAT—moist, semi-decayed organic matter.

PERENNIAL—a plant that lives for several years and when mature usually produces seeds each year.

PERPETUAL RESOURCE—a resource, such as solar energy, that is virtually inexhaustible on a human time scale.

PEST—an undesirable, harmful, or noxious organism.

PESTICIDE—an agent used to control undesirable organisms. This can be an insecticide for insect control, an herbicide for weed control, a fungicide for control of fungal plant diseases, or a rodenticide for killing rats and mice. Some pesticides can contaminate water, air, or soil, or accumulate in the tissues of living organisms, and should therefore be used carefully.

pH—a measure of the acidity or alkalinity of a material, liquid, or solid. pH is represented on a scale of 0 to 14; 7 represents a neutral state; 0, the most acidic; and 14, the most alkaline.

PHLOEM—the plant tissue that transports dissolved nutrients from the leaves to the other parts of the plant. Also called the **INNER BARK.**

PHOTOSYNTHESIS—the process by which green plants manufacture simple sugars in the presence of sunlight, carbon dioxide, and water. Chlorophyll is essential to the series of complex chemical reactions involved.

PIGMENT—a chemical substance that reflects or transmits only certain light rays and thus imparts color to an object. For example, a substance that absorbs all but red rays, which it reflects, will appear red. See **CHLOROPHYLL.**

PIONEER SPECIES—an organism capable of growing on bare sites such as a newly exposed soil or rock surface, and persisting there until supplanted by successor species.

PLANTATION—a forest established by planting seeds or seedlings.

POLLINATION—the transfer of pollen from the male part of the plant (anther) to the female portion of the plant (stigma).

POLLUTANT—any introduced gas, liquid, or solid that makes a resource less useful or unfit for a specific purpose.

POLLUTION—harmful substances deposited in the air, water, or land, leading to a state of dirtiness, impurity, or unhealthiness.

PRECIPITATION—water from the atmosphere that falls to the ground as rain, snow, sleet, or hail.

PREDATOR—an animal that hunts or captures other animals for food.

PRESCRIBED BURNING—the planned application of fire to a forest, stand, prairie, or slash pile with the intent to confine the burning to a predetermined area.

PRIMARY SUCCESSION—the establishment of vegetation and animal species on a site previously unoccupied by living organisms (e.g., on a cooled lava flow, on a sand dune).

PRODUCER—an organism that synthesizes organic compounds from inorganic substances via photosynthesis (by green plants) or chemosynthesis (by anaerobic bacteria).

PROPANE—a heavy, flammable, gaseous, paraffin hydrocarbon found in crude petroleum and natural gas and used especially as fuel and in chemical synthesis.

PROTOPLASM—the complex of protein, other organic and inorganic substances, and water that constitutes the living nucleus, cytoplasm, plastids, and mitochondria of the cell.

PUBLIC LAND—land owned by the citizens and administered and managed by the local, state, or federal government agencies.

PULP—fiberous material prepared from wood, recovered paper, cotton, grasses, etc., by chemical or mechanical processes for use in making paper or cellulose products.

PULPWOOD—timber that is cut and made into pulp for paper and other products.

RADON—an odorless, colorless gas produced naturally from the radioactive decay of radium-226. Radon breaks down into several radioactive parts which can attach to large particles in the air. When inhaled, these particles settle in the lungs and increase the risk of lung cancer.

RANGELAND—an open region of land that produces grasses and other forms of vegetation on which organisms can feed. Two common types of rangeland are pasture (enclosed, managed grazing lands) and open range (unmanaged, open grazing lands).

RARE SPECIES—a species that populates a site or region infrequently or in very low numbers. However, rare species are not necessarily endangered.

RECYCLE (v)—a multi-phased process which includes removal, separation, and/or diversion of materials from the waste stream; use of such materials as raw materials for the manufacture of new products; and the use of the new product.

RECYCLABLE (n, adj)—a resource or product that can be collected and reprocessed and made into new products. For example, an aluminum container can be melted down and used to make a new can or other aluminum product.

REFERENDUM—a measure passed upon or proposed by a legislative body or by citizen initiative and then submitted to a popular vote.

REFORESTATION—the renewal of forest cover by natural regeneration or the planting of seeds or seedlings.

REGENERATION—the renewal of vegetation by natural or artificial means. A regeneration period can be the period required or allowed in the plan for regenerating following timber harvest.

RENEWABLE RESOURCE—a naturally occurring raw material or form of energy which has the capacity to replenish itself through ecological cycles and sound management practices. The sun, wind, falling water, and trees are examples of renewable resources.

RESPIRATION—a complex process that occurs in the cells of most living organisms in which nutrient organic molecules such as glucose combine with oxygen and produce carbon dioxide, water, and energy.

REUSABLE RESOURCE—a product or material which can be used more than once in its present form for similar or dissimilar purposes. For example, an empty jar can be reused.

ROOT HAIRS—a filamentous outgrowth near the tip of a **ROOTLET** that functions in absorption of water and minerals.

ROOTLET—a small root.

ROTATION—the planned number of years between the formation of a crop and its final cutting at a specified stage of maturity.

RUNOFF WATER—fresh water from precipitation and melting ice that flows on the ground surface into nearby streams, lakes, wetlands, and reservoirs.

SAMARA—a dry, one-seeded, winged fruit, i.e., the seed of a maple tree.

SANITARY FILL—the dumping process whereby garbage or other refuse is covered with soil.

SAP—the fluid part of a vascular plant or, more specifically, the material transported via the xylem and the phloem of a tree.

SAPLING—a young tree normally more than 4 1/2 feet (1.5 m) high and less than 4 inches (10 cm) in diameter.

SAPROPHYTE—an organism that obtains food by absorbing the products of decomposition; a saprophyte lives off dead organisms, i.e, a fungus.

SAPWOOD—the younger, softer, living or physiologically active outer portion of a tree's wood that lies between the cambium and the heartwood and is more permeable, less durable, and usually lighter in color than the heartwood. The tree's water and nutrient needs are transported within the sapwood.

SAVANNA—a grassland with scattered trees or clumps of trees. Savannas are common to tropical and subtropical regions.

SCAVENGER—an animal that eats the dead remains and wastes of other animals and plants.

SCRUB—a low, woody vegetation composed principally of shrubs.

SECONDARY SUCCESSION— the sequential development of communities in an area in which natural vegetation has been removed or destroyed but the soil is not destroyed.

SEDIMENT—the solid precipitate or matter that settles to the bottom of a liquid. The material deposited by water, wind, or glaciers.

SEDIMENTARY ROCK—rock that is formed by the accumulation of materials (soil from erosion, skeletons, shells, etc.) that are compacted and solidified with heat, pressure, or chemical reactions.

SEDIMENTATION—the action or process of depositing sediment.

SEEDLING—a young tree grown from a seed up to a small sapling.

SEED–TREE—a tree left behind when a stand is harvested or partially cleared to provide a source of seed for the species desired to be renewed.

SELECTIVE CUTTING—the cutting of intermediate-aged, mature, or diseased trees in an uneven-aged forest stand, either singly or in small groups. This encourages the growth of younger trees and maintains an uneven-aged stand.

SELECTIVE HARVESTING—removal of individual or small clusters of trees to manage a forest stand for a mixture of age classes and products.

SERE—the series of communities that follow one another in a natural succession, as in the change from a bare field to a mature forest. A seral stage refers to one such community.

SHELTERBELT (or WINDBREAK)— a row of trees and shrubs planted along the edge of a cultivated field to limit soil erosion caused by wind.

SHELTERWOOD CUTTING—the removal of the understory of a forest so that younger saplings can grow in the shade of older and larger trees.

SHRUB—a woody plant less than 12 feet (4 m) tall, usually with more than one stem rising from the ground.

SILT—very fine particles of earth, sand, clay, etc., often transported by water and deposited as sediment.

SILVICULTURE—the science and art of cultivating forest crops based on the study of the life history and general characteristics of forest trees. A silviculturalist is a person who practices silviculture.

SINGLE-TREE SELECTION—harvesting single trees in a forest stand.

SMOG—originally, a combination of smoke and fog; now applied also to photochemical haze produced by the action of the sun and the atmosphere on automobile and industrial exhausts.

SNAG—a standing dead tree from which most of the branches have fallen. Snags frequently provide homes for wildlife.

SOFTWOOD—a coniferous tree. The term softwood is commonly used but not strictly accurate; the wood of many conifers is harder than that of some so-called hardwood trees.

SOIL COMPACTION—the compression of soil to a smaller volume.

SOLAR ENERGY—heat from the sun that can be used to perform work.

SOLID WASTE—discarded solid materials excluding recovered materials.

SPECIES—a population of organisms composed of related individuals that resemble one another and are able to breed among themselves, but are not able to breed with members of another species.

SPECIES DIVERSITY—the number of different species and their relative abundances in a given area.

STAND—a contiguous group of trees sufficiently uniform in species composition, arrangement of age classes, and condition to be considered a distinguishable unit.

STOMA—a microscopic opening in the surface of a leaf that allows gases to pass in and out.

SUCCESSION—the gradual replacement of one community by another. See **SERE.**

SUCCESSIONAL STAGE—a distinguishable stage in the process of succession. See **SERE.**

SUSTAINED YIELD—the rate at which a resource may be used without reducing its long-term availability or limiting its ability to renew itself.

SWAMP—a wetland dominated by trees.

SYMBIOSIS—see **SYMBIOTIC RELATIONSHIP.**

SYMBIOTIC RELATIONSHIP— species interaction in which two kinds of organisms live together in an intimate association, with members of one or both species benefiting from the association. For example, lichen is a symbiotic relationship between fungus and algae.

TAPROOT—a primary root that grows vertically downward and gives off small lateral roots; one that has a deep

central position in a line of growth or development.

TEMPERATE FOREST—a forest with moderate year-round temperatures and distinct seasons that is characterized by both broadleaf evergreens and conifers. Some characteristic trees of a temperate forest include oaks, magnolias, and royal palms.

TERRITORY—an area used for breeding, feeding, or both, which is defended by an animal against others of the same species.

THIN (v)—to reduce the number of trees in a stand.

THREATENED SPECIES—a species that is abundant in nature but, because of a decline in its numbers, may become endangered. See **ENDANGERED SPECIES.**

TIMBER—a forest stand containing trees of commercial size and quality suitable for sawing into lumber.

TIMBER CRUISE—a survey of a forest or forest stand to mark trees to be harvested.

TIMBERLAND—forests that are capable of growing 20 cubic feet (.6 m^3) per acre per year of commercial wood.

TIMBERLINE—the upper limit of tree growth on mountains. See **VERTICAL VEGETATION ZONES.**

TISSUE—a group of cells, usually a particular kind, that function together and form a structural material in an organism.

TRANSPIRATION—the process by which water evaporates from plant tissues.

TREE—a woody plant usually 12 or more feet (4 or more m) tall with a single main stem (trunk) and a more or less distinct crown of leaves.

TROPICAL RAINFOREST—wet, evergreen forests circling the equator in South and Central America, Africa, Asia, and many of the Pacific Islands. Their environment is distinguished by a warm, humid climate, capable of supporting an immense variety of life.

TUNDRA—treeless, low-lying vegetation in regions with long winters and low annual temperatures.

UNEVEN–AGED STAND—a forest area composed of intermingling trees that differ markedly in age.

UNDERSTORY—the layer formed by the crowns of smaller trees in a forest.

VEGETATION—the mass of plants that covers a given area. Flora, a term often wrongly used interchangeably with vegetation, is a list of the species of plants that compose the vegetation.

VEGETATIVE REPRODUCTION—asexual means of propagating new plants through root shoots, bulbs, leaf cuttings, underground stems, etc.

VERTICAL VEGETATION ZONES— the belts of distinctive plant cover in mountainous regions, resulting from climatic changes related to elevation changes.

VOC (Volatile Organic Compound)—a "naturally"-derived compound which can cause serious environmental and health threats when found in high concentrations or used in poorly-ventilated areas. VOCs can be found in several products, including household cleaners, paints, woodfinishes, and pesticides.

WASTE STREAM, SOLID (n)— discarded solid materials excluding recovered materials.

WATERSHED—the land area that delivers run-off water and sediment to a major river or stream and its tributaries.

WETLAND—an area that is regularly wet or flooded, and where the water table stands at or above the land surface for at least part of the year, and which has a plant community comprised of species which require wet soil.

WILDERNESS AREA—an area established by the federal government to be managed and preserved in an essentially untouched condition. Wilderness areas are open to some recreational activities. Use of machinery, mining, logging, and many other commercial pursuits are generally not allowed in wilderness areas.

WILDFIRE—any fire other than a controlled or prescribed burn occurring on wild land.

WILDLIFE—a loose term that includes nondomesticated animals, especially mammals, birds, and fish.

WIND ENERGY—power harnessed from the wind by the use of windmills or turbines.

WOODLANDS (or OPEN FOREST)—a wooded area in which the crowns of the trees do not form a closed canopy.

XYLEM—the complex woody tissue of higher plants that includes systems for transporting water, storing nutrients, and structural support.

ZOOLOGIST—a specialist who studies the animal kingdom with respect to the behavior of individual animals, species, or both.

THEME
DIVERSITY

Throughout the world, there is a great diversity of habitats, organisms, societies, technologies, and cultures.

Diversity in Environments

1.1 Biological diversity results from the interaction of living and nonliving environmental components such as air, water, climate, and geologic features.

1.2 Forests, as well as other ecosystems, contain numerous habitats that support diverse populations of organisms.

1.3 The Earth's atmosphere, water, soil, climate, and geology vary from region to region, thus creating a wide diversity of biological communities.

Diversity of Resources and Technologies

2.1 Humans use tools and technologies to adapt and alter environments and resources to meet their physical, social, and cultural needs.

2.2 Technologies vary from simple hand tools to large-scale and complex machinery, mechanisms, and systems.

2.3 Successful technologies are those that are appropriate to the efficient and sustainable use of resources, and to the preservation and enhancement of environmental quality.

Diversity Among and Within Societies and Cultures

3.1 Human societies vary greatly and inhabit many land forms and climates throughout the world.

3.2 Humans throughout the world create differing social, cultural, and economic systems and organizations to help them meet their physical and spiritual needs.

3.3 The standard of living of various peoples throughout the world is dependent on environmental quality; the availability, utilization, and distribution of resources; the government; and culture of its inhabitants.

3.4 Natural beauty, as experienced in forests and other habitats, enhances the quality of human life by providing artistic and spiritual inspiration, as well as recreational and intellectual opportunities.

THEME
INTERRELATIONSHIPS

The ecological, technological, and socio-cultural systems are interactive and interdependent.

Environmental Interrelationships

4.1 Organisms are interdependent, and depend on nonliving components of the Earth.

4.2 Altering the environment affects all life forms-including humans-and the interrelationships that link them.

4.3 Organisms adapt to changes in the environment according to the genetic and behavioral capacity of their species.

Resource and Technological Interrelationships

5.1 Resource management technologies interact and influence environmental quality; the acquisition, extraction and transportation of natural resources; all life forms; and each other.

5.2 While technological advances decrease the incidence of disease and death, the ever-increasing world population is placing heavy demands on the finite resources of the Earth.

5.3 International cooperation directed toward conserving resources and protecting environmental quality is beneficial to human health and the well-being of other life forms.

5.4 By reducing waste and recycling materials, individuals and societies can extend the value and utility of resources and also promote environmental quality.

Societal and Cultural Interrelationships

6.1 Human societies and cultures throughout the world interact with each other and affect natural systems upon which they depend.

6.2 The quantity and quality of resources and their use—or misuse—by humans affect the standard of living of societies.

6.3 Cultural and societal perspectives influence the attitudes, beliefs, and biases of people toward the use of resources and environmental protection.

6.4 All humans consume products and thereby affect the availability of renewable and nonrenewable natural resources.

6.5 The extracting, processing, transporting, and marketing of natural resources provide employment opportunities for many people.

THEME
SYSTEMS

Environmental, technological, and social systems are interconnected and interacting.

Environmental Systems

7.1 In biological systems, energy flows and materials continually cycle in predictable and measurable patterns.

7.2 Plant and animal populations exhibit interrelated cycles of growth and decline.

7.3 Pollutants are harmful by-products of human and natural systems which can enter ecosystems in various ways.

7.4 Ecosystems possess measurable indicators of environmental health.

Resource Management and Technological Systems

8.1 The application of scientific knowledge and technological systems can have positive or negative effects on the environment.

8.2 Resource management and technological systems can help societies meet, within limits, the needs of a growing human population.

8.3 Conservation technology enables humans to maintain and extend the productivity of vital resources.

Systems in Society and Culture

9.1 Most cultures have beliefs, values, and traditions that shape human interactions with the environment and its resources.

9.2 In democratic societies, citizens have a voice in shaping resource and environmental management policies. They also share in the responsibility of conserving resources and behaving in an environmentally responsible manner.

9.3 In democratic societies, individuals and groups, working through governmental channels, can influence the way public and private lands and resources are managed.

9.4 Effective citizen involvement in the environmental decision-making process involves a careful study of all sides of the issues, along with the ability to differentiate between honest, factually accurate information and propaganda.

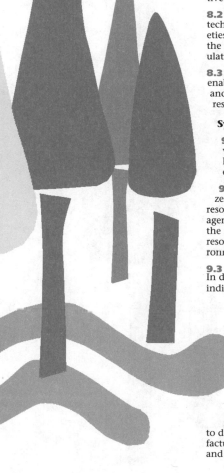

THEME
STRUCTURE AND SCALE

Technologies, societal institutions, and components of natural and human-built environments vary in structure and scale.

Structures and Scale in Environments

10.1 Populations of organisms exhibit variations in size and structure as a result of their adaptation to their habitats.

10.2 The structure and scale of an ecosystem are influenced by factors such as soil type, climate, availability of water, and human activities.

10.3 When the Earth is studied as an interacting ecological system, every action, regardless of its scale, affects the biosphere in some way.

Structure and Scale in Resources and Technology

11.1 Technologies vary in size, structure, and complexity and in their positive and negative effects on the environment.

11.2 Conservation and management technologies, when appropriately applied to the use or preservation of natural resources, can enhance and extend the usefulness of the resource as well as the quality of the environment.

11.3 Human-built environments, if planned, constructed, and landscaped to be compatible with the environment in which they will be located, can conserve resources, enhance environmental quality, and promote the comfort and well-being of those who will live within them.

11.4 International cooperation on resource management and environmental improvement programs can be beneficial to people in many parts of the world.

Structure and Scale in Societies and Cultures

12.1 The structure and scale of the natural resources in a given area shape the economy upon which the society and its culture is based.

12.2 Governmental, social, and cultural structures and actions affect the management of resources and environmental quality.

12.3 Demographics influence environmental quality, government policy, and resource use.

THEME
PATTERNS OF CHANGE

Structure and systems change over various periods of time.

Patterns of Change in the Environment

13.1 Organisms change throughout their lifetimes. Species of organisms change over long periods of time.

13.2 Although species become extinct naturally, the increasing number of extinctions in recent history may be linked to the rapid increase in human population.

13.3 As organisms go through their life cycle of growth, maturity, decline, and death, their role in the ecosystem also changes.

13.4 Ecosystems change over time through patterns of growth and succession. They are also affected by other phenomena such as disease, insects, fire, weather, and human intervention.

Patterns of Change in Resource and Technologies

14.1 Our increasing knowledge of the Earth's ecosystems influences strategies used for resource management and environmental stewardship.

14.2 Technologies that are developed to meet the needs of an increasing world population should also be environmentally sound.

14.3 To be most effective, new technologies require well-informed and highly skilled workers.

Patterns of Change in Society and Culture

15.1 Governments change and evolve over the years. Such changes affect the lives of its citizens, as well as resource management and environmental policies.

15.2 Consumers "drive" the marketplace with their demands for goods and services. Such demands shift with time and may have positive or negative effects on the resource base and environmental quality.

15.3 Industries usually respond to consumer demand for recyclable, recycled, or otherwise environmentally friendly products.

15.4 Leisure and recreational pursuits can have an impact on forests and other resource-producing areas.

15.5 Increased public knowledge of the environment and the need for conservation of natural resources have resulted in lifestyle changes in many cultures.

APPENDIX 1

TEACHING SUGGESTIONS

TEACHING AND ASSESSING FOR CONCEPTUAL UNDERSTANDING

It has long been known that students are not empty vessels waiting to be filled; instead, students must actively participate in the teaching-learning process. Teaching for conceptual understanding often means covering less breadth and more depth. One way to make "less" go farther is to use themes to connect concepts and transcend traditional subject areas. Themes help students organize bits of previously disconnected knowledge and easily store and recall new information. For example, if we study our environment using the theme of "diversity," we may discover that a diversity of biological characteristics among organisms improves the stability of an ecosystem. If we apply this same theme to studying human society, we may also find that a diversity of values and lifestyles is inherent in social systems. More and more educators are using authentic assessment in their programs. Authentic assessment means designing evaluation to match the instructional goals. If the instructional goal is teaching about a plant's requirements, then the assessment should be caring for a plant rather than taking a multiple choice test. However, you cannot change assessment without changing instruction.

What type of instruction supports authentic assessment? Since the purpose of authentic assessment is to assess conceptual understanding, instruction must emphasize the application of knowledge. Recent studies have shown that students develop new knowledge through active construction. This means they combine new information with pre-existing knowledge in an effort to construct meaning. The instructor should realize that students often have deep rooted preconceptions, and must be guided through discussion and new experiences toward achieving new conceptual understanding.

TEACHING STRATEGIES

PLT activities combine diverse, yet compatible, teaching strategies. Activities allow for large group, small group, and individual experiences. The following highlights teaching strategies:

- Direct Instruction (Whole Group) may include—
  –key concept introduction and vocabulary
  –demonstration/reading
  –discussions
  –building charts or lists

- Indirect Instruction (Cooperative Groups) may include—
  –hands-on activities (indoors/outdoors)
  –brainstorming
  –planning
  –student-directed projects

SUCCESSFUL COOPERATIVE LEARNING

Cooperative learning is an instructional method in which students work together in small groups to achieve common goals. Cooperative learning can encourage skills of cooperation and communication and can be a valuable addition to your repertoire.

Used appropriately, cooperative learning can help motivate students, promote active learning, foster respect, improve language skills, and increase teacher effectiveness. The essential feature of cooperative learning is that the success of one student helps other students to be successful. It helps promote equality of all students by encouraging them to cooperate with each other to complete projects.

STEPS

1. Form cooperative groups.
Carefully select members for each group. Mix academic and social abilities, gender, cultural backgrounds, handicaps, and interests.

2. Assign roles.
Students are more likely to work together if each one has a job which contributes to the task. Roles need to be taught and modeled to students, and practiced. Depending on the activity, assign students any of the following roles—
Recorder—writes the group's answers.
Reporter—reports the group's answer to the entire class.
Manager—gathers and returns materials used by the group.
Facilitator—organizes the group's work, makes sure the group understands its job, takes the group's questions to the teacher after trying to get the answers from the group.
Reader—reads the directions of other materials to the group out loud in such a way that team members can understand it.
Artist—draws illustrations or diagrams for the group.
Researcher—looks up unknown words in the dictionary and/or encyclopedia.

3. Develop and post classroom rules.
Review the rules and explain with examples of effective behavior, i.e., what does good listening look like? Set
expectations for effective group behavior. Examples of rules—
  –Everyone participates and helps others.
  –Everyone listens to others.
  –Each student uses a quiet voice.
  –Each student does the task assigned.

4. Arrange groups in small clusters.
Arrange desks and chairs to allow students within the group to see and hear each other as they work together.

5. Encourage students to practice positive social skills.
Students must be taught to practice the social skills necessary for effective cooperative work. These skills include sharing, compromising, listening, taking turns, helping each other, praising, providing positive feedback, accepting individual differences, and disagreeing respectfully. Students must develop the feeling that they are responsible for and accountable to the group for doing their best. They need the opportunity to help each other. This can be encouraged by establishing mutual goals and joint rewards, and sharing materials and information.

6. State directions clearly and model appropriate procedures.
Clearly state the task and the time allotted. Check for understanding. Describe the criteria which would signify that the group was successful. Remind students of the specific behaviors expected, such as everyone participating.

7. Monitor groups.
Teach students the skills you see them lacking. Turn problems back to the group to solve as you act as a facilitator or consultant. Practice is the key to the successful use of cooperative learning. When necessary, encourage students to solve problems or to teach skills to one another.

8. Evaluate outcomes and debrief after each lesson.
During debriefing evaluate how effectively students are using their social skills when working together and how they could use them more effectively next time. This is the key to improving groups that are not working effectively together, as well as rewarding those who are. Use the following questions to focus students on their experiences:

- Did everyone in your group participate? How could you encourage someone to participate?

- How did you help your group during the activity?

- What would you do to make your group work better together?

Adapted from "Tips for Successful Cooperative Learning." A Child's Place in the Environment—Unit 2—Protecting Soil. Sacramento, CA: California Department of Education (in press).

APPENDIX 2

Many years ago John Hug, Environmental Education supervisor for the Ohio Department of Education and the Ohio PLT coordinator, wrote the following article. Hug's advice is still valid and bears repeating. It also follows the Project Learning Tree philosophy of teaching students how to think, not what to think, about complex environmental issues.

TWO HATS

It would appear that environmental educators have a bad case of the "two hat" problem. We have come by the problem naturally and therefore, we have paid little attention to it.

The problem is simply that industry, utilities, labor, business, media, and other segments of the population and the general public have consistently recognized only one hat when talking about environmentalists and environmental educators. It is not uncommon for dedicated environmental educators to be summarily dismissed as troublemakers—environmentalists. Perhaps definitions will help clarify the problem.

Any world citizen who advocates with greater or lesser action that wrongs against our environment must be stopped is an environmentalist. Perhaps the negative reputation environmentalists have stems from the dramatic and radical actions of a few.

An environmental educator, on the other hand, is any world citizen who uses information and educational processes to help people analyze the merits of the many and varied points of view usually present on a given environmental issue. The environmental educator is not the "mediator," "trade-off specialist," or "negotiator," but a developer of skills and an information analyst who prepares the people (from any segment of the population) who will participate in environmental decision making.

Environmental educators, therefore, need to be as "value fair" or "value free" as they can when working in this role. They must scrupulously strive to get all the facts, examine and illuminate all the viewpoints, and keep from letting their own particular position (as an environmentalist) from mixing with their educator role.

My suggestion is simply that environmental educators make an effort to clarify the two distinct roles. At every opportunity, we should emphasize the neutral nature of environmental education activity. Strong advocacies are all around us, each using the techniques of persuasion and propaganda to build their constituencies. We must ourselves be familiar with all sides, stand firm for each advocate's right to be heard, and provide a rational stage for informed debate.

Environmental educators have the right to be environmentalists, but the dual roles must adhere to the original premise—to keep each hat on its proper head, while utilizing to the fullest the professional skills of the environmental educators.

Reprinted with permission from John Hug.

■ As you teach the lessons, keep parents and administrators informed. Describe for them the students' activities and your observations as students learn about an environmental issue.

■ After you have taught the lessons, provide administrators with a concise assessment of student learning. Describe ways that you would modify the lessons in the future.

This article was adapted, with permission, from Toxics: Taking Charge *which is available for $6.50, plus 8% sales tax, from the Alameda County Office of Education, Media Sales, 313 West Winston Ave., Hayward, CA 94544-1198.*

APPENDIX 3

TEACHING CONTROVERSIAL ISSUES

Many teachers steer clear of controversy in the classroom and do not discuss environmental issues, which sometimes are controversial, with their students. Yet controversy can provide opportunities for increasing the quality of students' thinking and students' ability to solve problems.

Although controversy is often uncomfortable, it also tends to be intellectually stimulating. As long as students clearly understand that controversial issues are controversial precisely because they are too complex to have clear-cut "right" and "wrong" solutions, they can focus on the process of clarifying their own viewpoints through debate and reflection.

Jean Piaget, Lawrence Kohlberg, and other learning theorists address the importance of cognitive disequilibration in intellectual and moral development. Students benefit from opportunities to consider other viewpoints and defend their own. Productive conflict appears to promote the development of cognitive and moral reasoning; it thus has a valid place in a learning environment.

THE ROLE OF THE TEACHER

Teaching about an environmental issue in the classroom may require a shift in your role as teacher. The teacher operates more like a conductor orchestrating opportunities for students to think about complex issues in a safe, supportive atmosphere, rather than focusing primarily on teaching information to be learned. Teachers need to allow ideas to develop, understanding to deepen, and judgements to be made and tested.

Teachers can support student learning by encouraging and facilitating discussion, by providing accurate factual information, and by providing sufficient time to study a multifaceted environmental issue.

INSTRUCTIONAL STRATEGIES

Activities should emphasize strategies that minimize polarization of viewpoints and maximize quantity and quality of ideas. Through frequent class discussions and cooperative learning experiences, students should examine their thoughts and opinions without pressure to come to the "right" conclusion. Emphasis is on the process of sharing opinions, acquiring and judging new information, and making and reflecting on those decisions. The following suggestions support a classroom climate that allows for this kind of thinking and learning:

■ Establish clear rules for behavior during class discussions. These rules should first and foremost preserve the integrity of the individual. Personal attacks and name calling should be forbidden, and students should be reminded that any conflicts that arise must be conflicts of ideas, not people. Conflicts of ideas can be positive ways of advancing one's thinking.

■ Pay attention and respond to feelings underlying expressed ideas. Sometimes students are afraid to voice personal beliefs and convictions; they need to be reassured that this is okay.

■ When a conflict arises, observe the group, describe what you observe, and provide time for students to describe what they observe and feel. Engage students in conflict resolution techniques such as reversing roles in arguments or negotiating a win-win resolution (so that everyone wins in some way). Provide support for students who are anxious throughout the conflict; many people are uncomfortable with disagreement.

■ Use questioning strategies to clarify and advance students' thinking. Ask students to restate an idea in another way, to elaborate, or to reiterate what they hear in order to confirm or clarify. Questions can also be used to advance thinking. Ask students to apply an idea to a real or hypothetical situation, to consider discrepancies in their thinking, or to reassess their idea in light of new information.

■ Take time after each class discussion to analyze your students' and your own thinking so that you value the evolution of thinking rather than only the views expressed. By identifying individual biases, defense strategies, and styles of argumentation, a group can operate more consciously as it tries to fully understand a controversial issue.

WORKING WITH PARENTS AND ADMINISTRATORS

A primary reason that many teachers avoid teaching about controversial issues is fear of resistance from parents and administrators. The following suggestions will help you avoid resistance and gain administrative and parental support.

■ Examine community attitudes about environmental issues in local newspapers and listen to public discourse on these problems. This will help you anticipate potential concerns and choose how and when to teach a particular environmental issue.

■ Consider the occupations of parents in the community. Will any of them be particularly sensitive to certain environmental issues? If so, think through how to best work with these parents so they do not feel threatened by your lesson unit.

■ Determine if any lesson or part of a lesson will raise concern among parents or administrators and modify the lesson accordingly.

■ Choose a method to inform administrators, then parents, of your plan and to gather their input. Include examples of lessons. Emphasize that the teacher's role is to facilitate discussion and to help students find out how to think about an issue—not what to think.

■ Provide plenty of time for feedback from administrators and parents. Incorporate their ideas in ways that make the lessons more instructionally sound.

APPENDIX 4

MULTICULTURAL EDUCATION

CONNECTING WITH ENVIRONMENTAL EDUCATION

Environmental and multicultural education are compatible efforts united by mutual interests and shared perspectives. Both are primarily interested in human interactions; environmental education examines the human-nature relationship, whereas multicultural education probes the human-human relationship. Each discipline views a student's actions as being embedded within a cultural context, a context which mediates his or her attitudes and behaviors.

Increasingly, both environmental and multicultural educators are advocating a problem–posing and problem-solving approach to take students beyond the fear of diversity and difference. Through the use of such an approach, each hopes (1) to enable students to critique our society's habits regarding diversity and (2) to examine how our life choices can be changed so as to achieve a more caring, connected, and respectful way of living.

Another approach is to acknowledge that environmental education can be both multicultural and cultural specific. For example, almost all cultures recognize that water is an important resource and study it to better understand its properties and functions. These cultures are presently concerned about how to protect and/or restore the quality of their water resources and how to use what they have more wisely. However, all cultures do not arrive at the same solutions to water issues. The solutions themselves are culturally embedded and unique. Interestingly, as world scientists have come to accept and value this diversity among possible solutions, the potential for solving global environmental problems has increased.

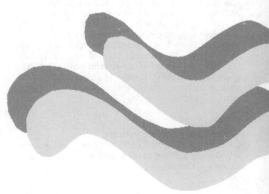

SUGGESTED PRACTICES

Provide opportunities for students to develop:

- Self-awareness.

- A means of pursuing their own interests regarding the topic of study, in a manner consistent with their own learning style.

- Ways of coming to know the topic of study through learning styles that are less familiar to them.

- Interpersonal and group communication skills around the topic of study.

- An understanding of the meaning of 'culture.'

- An understanding that everyone embodies a culture.

- An appreciation for different perspectives and how that diversity provides a richer, more complex pool of ideas concerning the topic of study.

- A sense of community within the classroom; that is, creating a place where students feel comfortable, yet engaged, and different points of view can be expressed.

- Familiarity with a variety of ethnic and cultural communities' experiences with, and contributions to, the topic being studied.

Students can try:

- Interviewing family members about, or relating the family's country or countries of origin, to the topic of study.

- Finding and reading books and magazines authored by individuals from the various cultures that relate to the topic of study.

- Analyzing the assumptions and biases inherent in the lessons, support materials, and other media resources.

- Examining the roots of prejudice, racism, and stereotyping as they relate to the topic of study.

- Asking how a certain course of action will affect people, i.e., will all people be affected in the same way? Are the perspectives of all people given the same authority and status by society?

- Inviting people of different ethnic communities into the classroom, especially people who are not representative of the classroom population.

- Going into the community and talking with members of different ethnic groups, especially people who are not representative of the classroom population.

Adapted from Frederickson, Jean. A Multicultural Overview. A Child's Place in the Environment. Sacramento, CA: California Department of Education, 1993 (in press).

APPENDIX 5

WORKING WITH EXCEPTIONAL STUDENTS

The activities included in the Project Learning Tree curriculum can be implemented successfully with the broad spectrum of students found in public and private schools. All activities have been tested in actual classrooms and were found to meet a variety of student needs.

Federal and state legislation mandates that children with special needs be taught in the least restrictive environment. The concepts of mainstreaming and integration help to bring students with handicapping conditions, from mild learning disabilities to profound physical and mental involvement, into the regular classroom to be among their peers. The activities in the PLT curriculum can be easily adapted to meet individual needs without having to alter the basic program format. The pairing of a student in the regular classroom with a mainstreamed or integrated student to help him or her complete the activities proved to be a successful and beneficial teaching method in the field-testing classrooms. Self-contained special education classroom teachers will be able to modify the activities as needed based upon their students' skills and abilities. These activities can be used across the basic curriculum to cover many skill areas.

The activities can also be modified and adapted to reach the needs of the gifted and talented population in the school system. Higher-level skills and critical thinking can be used to take the concepts presented to a more involved and detailed level for students needing a greater challenge.

Written by Karen Blodgett, Multi–disabled Teacher, Catoctin Elementary School, Leesburg, VA

APPENDIX 6

TEACHING OUT–OF–DOORS

Every opportunity a child has to learn in the outdoors has the potential to become an experience that will be remembered for many years. Treat every occasion as a special event. Taking students outdoors can be made easier with the help of parents or older students. Set up a meeting signal to get everyone together once you are outside, such as raising your hand, clapping several times, or using a bird call.

Discuss appropriate outdoor behavior. Examples of some rules are listed below:

- All living things, including plants, are to be respected and not injured in any way. Follow the rule: look, learn, leave alone.

- Stay within the boundaries.

- Stay with a partner.

- Be safe.

- Bring all equipment necessary. (You may not be able to return to class until the end of the activity.)

- Follow all directions. (Make sure your directions are clear and that all students understand.)

Before beginning the outdoor experience, briefly explain the activity to your students. Next, let students complete the activity. As necessary, remind students of appropriate outdoor behavior. If many students are acting inappropriately, you may have to delay the activity. Go back to the classroom and try again the next day. Discuss appropriate behaviors that you or your students noticed.

Before (and maybe after) returning to the classroom, let students share their experiences. Then share your own experience in the outdoors.

OTHER TIPS:

- For the first several times that students study the outdoors, provide short, focused investigations. You might also gather students in a circle and read some literature books outside.

- If students are not following rules, consider having an adult take one or two groups out at a time to complete the task while the rest of the class works indoors.

- Being outside means "playtime" to some students. Be patient and allow students to practice appropriate behavior. Eventually your students will get used to investigating the out-of-doors in an appropriate fashion.

- If you go on a field trip, let students choose a partner, then have students "count off" (they can record their number on their journal). Whenever you need to make sure all are present, get the class together, and have the first pair begin counting.

COLLECTING PLANTS AND ANIMALS

There are several reasons to limit your collection of organisms:

- To model respect for all living things.

- To model that all organisms are best studied in their natural environment without interference from observers.

- To keep from impacting the organisms in an area, especially if many classes visit the same site.

- To avoid making the main focus of the activity collecting animals instead of understanding ecological concepts.

If you determine that you want your students to collect some organisms for closer observation, several recommendations are listed below:

■ Never collect material from an area unless you have permission from the person or organization who owns the land. You may not collect any material from national or state parks.

■ Never collect rare or endangered species. Someone at your state Department of Natural Resources or local cooperative extension service should be able to tell you if there are any such species in your area. See your phone book for the telephone numbers of these agencies.

■ Never collect a plant if it's the only one growing in a particular area. Instead, collect plants that are growing in groups or stands.

■ Instruct students to minimize the number of organisms they collect.

■ Take care when keeping living organisms in a container. Make the animal as comfortable as possible and provide for its basic needs.

■ Place all containers away from direct sunlight.

■ Provide items in the container under which the organisms can hide.

■ If it is necessary to handle organisms, be gentle. Be aware that some animals might bite to protect themselves.

■ If aquatic animals are collected, use water for the containers from the area where the organisms were found. If the water in the containers with aquatic animals becomes warm, replenish with cool fresh water.

■ Return all organisms to the spot they were found as soon as the observations are complete.

Adapted from Angell, Kathy. Helpful Hints for Leading Outdoor Activities. A Child's Place in the Environment. Sacramento, CA: California Department of Education (in press).

APPENDIX 7

ENVIRONMENTAL CLUBS AND OUTDOOR CLASSROOMS

STARTING AN ENVIRONMENTAL CLUB

Talk to students about the idea of forming an environmental club. You may want to ask another teacher to co-sponsor the club with you, especially if more than 10-15 students are interested.

1. Announce the formation of the club to the student body, and set up an informational meeting. You will need to make scheduling arrangements appropriate for your school, depending upon whether you have activity time available or you will need to meet after school.

2. At the first meeting, sign up students and discuss the meeting time. You can brainstorm, as a group, some goals for the club's first activities. Some ideas:

■ Energy Awareness Week

■ establishment of a school recycling program

■ a school or community clean-up effort

■ other projects suggested in PLT activities

You will have the most success if you start small and "grow" with experience. Encourage club members to plan and execute fun and constructive activities that will generate enthusiasm—[and perhaps financial resources]—and do something good for the environment.

3. You may want to elect or decide upon club officers. Alternately, students can work as a group, sharing decision making and responsibilities. The most important thing is to keep everyone involved, focused, and having fun.

IDEAS FOR AN OUTDOOR CLASSROOM

Nature Trail

An established foot trail is a good way to prevent students from trampling over tree seedlings, ground–nesting animals, and vegetation with low tolerance for foot traffic. Much planning is required before you can establish a trail. Topography, soil types, drain-age, vegetation, and obstacles are some of the considerations to be made, as well as routing the trail to points of interest. If possible, seek professional assistance from your local resource conservation district.

Trails could be surfaced with woodchips or gravel to reduce soil compaction and for ease of walking. Access over or through wet areas should be provided by constructing foot bridges and boardwalks. Slopes along the trail should be protected from erosion by using water bars, dips, or retaining structures, and by designing switchbacks.

You may want to have a nature trail guide, and corresponding numbered markers along the trail. To place markers, set posts in the ground anchored in concrete at least two feet (60 cm) in the ground. All wood should be chemically treated to prevent decay, and the tops of all posts should be cut off at a slant so they will shed water. Number the posts according to the trail guide.

Outdoor Seating Area

A seating area may range from a nice amphitheater or shelter house to a simple circle of telephone poles or railroad ties. One of the simplest and least expensive benches is made by erecting 4" x 4" (10 cm x 10 cm) treated posts and securing a treated (not with creosote) 2" x 10" (5 cm x 2 cm) board across the top.

Bird Station

Install a number of various–sized bird houses in this area. Also install a bird feeder, a suet feeder for woodpeckers, and a hummingbird feeder. Develop a bird list for this station.

Nesting Boxes

Artificial nesting boxes can be built by students and placed in various locations on your school grounds. This will attract wildlife, and allow students to observe and study nesting characteristics of small animals.

A wildlife biologist can provide specifications and information on what kinds of nesting boxes to build for your area. Wooded fence rows, grassy meadows, forested areas, and the banks of ponds and creeks are good locations for nesting boxes. Hollow trees, old fence posts, and burrows in the ground can be existing natural nesting sites. Old, dead trees (called snags) not in danger of falling on a structure are good to leave for wildlife nesting. Always use a ladder to place artificial nesting boxes out of easy reach of vandals.

Forage Plot

This should be a small planted plot of native plants that produce berries or other fruits that attract or are eaten by wildlife. Depending on your climate, you might include such plants as mulberry, crabapple, wild plum, persimmon, pawpaw, hawthorne, and blueberries. For quick growth, beautiful color, wildlife food and cover, erosion control, and general outdoor studies, it's hard to beat berry–

producing shrubs. Autumn olive, purple willow, honeysuckle, highbush blueberry, and huckleberry are examples of shrubs suitable for some outdoor classroom planting. Small trees such as flowering crabapple, flowering dogwood, hawthorne, and redbud may be appropriate. Before planting be sure to know what kind of soil to use and any other limitations the shrub species may have. Plant in clumps or rows, preferably near your food plots and herbaceous plantings of grasses and legumes.

Weather Station

Even schools with very little space can probably find room to establish a small weather station. Students can keep records of temperature, rainfall, barometric pressure, wind speed, direction, etc. Weather instruments are available through school science supply catalogs. Instrument costs will vary, and some simple instruments can be made by students. Weather stations with more sophisticated equipment should probably be fenced for protection. All weather equipment should be returned to the school building each night for security.

Animal Tracking Plot

Even an urban area is frequented by many species of wildlife. Birds, mice, squirrels, rabbits, opossums, raccoons, and even deer can find themselves at home in the city. Whether your school is located in a rural or urban area, an animal tracking plot can yield some

interesting tracks to study. An area about 3' x 3' (1m x 1m) or larger is all that is needed to create this feature. The area should be cleared of all grass or other vegetation and filled with sand. Food scraps, grain or other "bait" should then be placed in the middle of the plot regularly to attract wildlife to the area. Students may be surprised at the variety of "critters" right in their own back yard! Plaster casts can be made of tracks.

Wildflower Plot
Wildflowers not only add an attractive atmosphere and aroma to an area, but can be used to produce dyes for fabric or paints. Areas of full sunlight or total shade can both be used to establish plantings of wildflowers. Wildflowers also attract many species of insects and birds for study.

Agriculture and Herb Garden
Measure a grid of 10' x 10' (3 m x 3 m) plots. These plots can be used for various agricultural crop demonstrations. The plots can also be used for chemical testing, water testing, erosion studies, etc.

A small area of the school grounds can be designated as an herb garden. This area should be located in a sunny area. Herbs used for cooking or with alleged medicinal qualities can be grown for study.

Wildlife Brushpiles
Fallen or pruned limbs and even discarded Christmas trees can be useful building material for wildlife brush piles. Brushpiles are like natural magnets when it comes to attracting wildlife. Piles should be at least 12 feet (3.6 m) in diameter and 5 feet (1.5 m) high to be effective.

Rotting Stump/Log Station
Leave stumps and parts of log whenever possible to demonstrate the effects that living and nonliving things have on them. Discuss or diagram one of the cycles taking place in the rotten log or stump and their interrelationships of living and nonliving things.

Plant Succession Areas
By not mowing selected areas of your school site, a greater diversity of plants and plant maturity will occur. This process of gradual (and predictable) replacement of one community of plants and animals by another is referred to as *succession*. Students can observe and record the various successional stages that occur.

Soil Studies
"Dirt" is what you sweep off the floor or wash from your hands. "Soil" is a precious natural resource. This difference should be recognized by your students before any other form of soil study is undertaken.

Students should become familiar with your county soil survey. Using the information in the survey, determine the location and various characteristics of the soils found on your school grounds. A soil testing area for each of the soil types should be established. Students should carefully examine the soil, layer by layer, starting at the surface and observing the types of vegetation growing there.

There are many good soil testing kits available for purchase from school supply catalogs. Try to obtain some of these. A very useful Soil Conserva-tion Service booklet titled "Teaching Soil and Water Conservation. A Classroom and Field Guide," PA 341, is available from your county soil and water conservation office.

Information supplied by The Columbus Academy, Gahanna, Ohio, and Twin Oaks Elementary School, Baton Rouge, LA.

APPENDIX 8

BRINGING NATURE INDOORS

Here's some basic information that will help you and your students set up terrariums. Also included are some reference materials you can use to set up salt or freshwater aquariums.

THE BASICS

Container
The first thing you will need for your terrarium is a container. Aquariums, goldfish bowls, wide-mouthed jars, old glass coffeepots, and clear plastic storage boxes can all work well. Just look for containers with the following characteristics:

- Made of transparent, uncolored glass or plastic;

- Big enough so that you can get your hand through the top to set it up; and

- Large enough to provide enough room for plants to grow. The plants' roots will need soil that's about an inch (2.5 cm) deep and, once planted, should have 2-3 inches (5-7.5 cm) of room to grow above the soil.

You'll also need a cover for your terrarium if you're setting up a woodland or tropical terrarium (see below). A panel of plastic, glass (use caution), screening, wire mesh, or even plastic wrap will work as long as it covers the top of the terrarium completely.

Getting Your Hands Dirty
We suggest three kinds of terrariums to make: desert, woodland, and tropical. Woodland and tropical terrariums are essentially the same except for the types of plants that grow in them and the amounts of light and heat they need. For any terrarium, you will need three basic things: gravel or pebbles, soil, and plants. You can get all these supplies at a garden supply store. You can also collect plants and soil for the terrarium from the wild. However, please see "Tips for Takers" below, before you do any collecting. Here are the basic directions for setting up each of the three main types of terrariums.

Desert
1. Cover the bottom of your container with about 3/4 inch (1.88 cm) of gravel or pebbles. Spread a piece of cheesecloth or an old nylon stocking across the top of the gravel.

2. Mix up a batch of "desert soil" by mixing equal parts of potting soil, perlite, and sand. Layer 2-3 inches (5-7.5 cm) of this mixture on top of the gravel.

3. Plant your desert plants and then spray the terrarium with water until the soil is moist.

4. Wipe the terrarium clean and place it in a spot that gets about 3-4 hours of direct sun a day.

Woodland
1. Cover the bottom of your container with about 3/4 inch (1.88 cm) of gravel or pebbles. Spread a piece of cheesecloth or an old nylon stocking across the top of the gravel.

2. Layer 2-3 inches (5-7.5 cm) of garden or potting soil on top of the gravel.

3. Plant the woodland plants and then spread a small amount of garden soil around all the plants and smooth it out.

4. Water the terrarium until the soil is moist.

5. Wipe the finished terrarium clean, cover it with a piece of plastic (or glass—use caution), and put it in a cool location with indirect light.

Tropical
1. Cover the bottom of your container with about 3/4 inch (1.88 cm) of gravel or pebbles. Spread a piece of cheesecloth or an old nylon stocking across the top of the gravel.

2. Layer 2-3 inches (5-7.5 cm) of garden or potting soil on top of the gravel.

3. Plant the tropical plants and then spread a small amount of garden soil around all the plants and smooth it out.

4. Water the terrarium until the soil is moist.

5. Wipe the finished terrarium clean, cover it with a piece of glass or plastic, and put it in a warm location with bright but not too hot (preferably fluorescent) light.

SPECIAL TOUCHES
You can customize your terrarium in several ways. For one thing, you might want to create "hills" and "valleys" in your terrarium by piling up soil in some parts before you plant your plants. You might also want to add rocks, twigs, seeds, or other objects to the terrarium after you've planted your plants to make the scene more "natural" and interesting.

WATER, WATER EVERYWHERE
You'll probably need to water woodland and tropical terrariums at least once a week. To check whether the plants need watering, push your finger about 1/2 inch (1.25 cm) into the soil. If the soil is dry, the plants need watering. If large amounts of moisture collect on the

sides of the terrarium, lift off the cover for a day or so and let the moisture evaporate. If large amounts of moisture continually collect on the sides, you may need to create an air space between the cover and the top of the container. For example, you can glue a small piece of cork to each corner of an aquarium so that the glass top rests about 1/8 inch (3 mm) above the frame.

Desert terrariums will need watering less frequently than tropical and woodland terrariums. When you do water, though, be sure to spray the soil until it's moist.

ANIMALS

You might want to put an animal in your terrarium. If so, contact an expert to find out what type of animal would do well in your terrarium, where to get it, and how to care for it. Your local zoo, nature center, science or children's museum, or pet store can provide this information.

DISCUSSION

Ask students what the differences are between their terrarium and the real ecosystem it represents (lacks animals; plastic or glass container is an artificial barrier disconnecting it from other ecosystems, weather and other patterns of change are missing). What can we learn about natural ecosystems from a terrarium?

TIPS FOR TAKERS

1. Never collect material from an area unless you have permission from the person or organization who owns the land. You may not collect any material from national or state parks.

2. Never collect rare or endangered species. Someone at your state Department of Natural Resources or local cooperative extension service should be able to tell you if there are any such species in your area. See your phone book for the telephone numbers of these agencies.

3. Never collect a plant if it's the only one growing in a particular area. Instead, collect plants that are growing in groups, or stands.

4. Collect only healthy plants. Don't dig up plants that are infested with insects or look sick. Also be sure to wash the leaves, stems, and roots of all the plants you collect before you plant them in your terrarium.

5. Be sure to collect plants that are growing under the same light, temperature, and moisture conditions. It will be difficult (if not impossible!) to set up a terrarium in which sun-loving plants and those that need lots of shade coexist.

6. As you dig up each plant, be sure to get as many of the plant's roots as you can.

7. Use plastic bags to protect the plants you collect. Loosely wrap the plant's roots in a wet paper towel, place it in a small plastic bag, and then trap some air in the bag and seal it.

8. If you collect your own soil, be sure to sterilize it before you use it in your terrarium. Just place the soil in a shallow baking dish, bake it at 250°F for two hours, and then let it cool.

RESOURCES

Broekel, Ray. *AQUARIUMS AND TERRARIUMS*. Children's Press, 1982.
Burgess, Warren E. *THE ABCS OF MARINE AQUARIUMS*. TFH Publications, 1986.
Coborn, John. *BEGINNER'S GUIDE TO AQUARIUMS*. Howell Book House, 1986.
Fitch, Charles Marden. *THE COMPLETE BOOK OF TERRARIUMS*. Hawthorn Books, Inc., 1974.
Haas, Richard. *A BEGINNER'S GUIDE TO TERRARIUMS*. TFH Publications, 1986. (Juvenile)
Herda, D.J. *MAKING A NATIVE PLANT TERRARIUM*. Messner, 1977. (Juvenile)
Kelly, Jim. *A COMPLETE INTRODUCTION TO SETTING UP AN AQUARIUM*. TFH Publications, 1987.
Parker, Alice. *Terrariums*. Franklin Watts, 1977. (Juvenile)

GUIDELINES FOR REQUESTING INFORMATION AND ASSISTANCE

BE SPECIFIC

Your chances of obtaining useful information will be greatly increased if you state exactly which materials you need, which issues interest you, or what questions you want answered. The "send everything you have" approach is uneconomical and unecological.

AVOID CLASS-WIDE REQUESTS

Limit requests for information from any single source to one or two students and pool the collected data. If you cannot avoid a situation where many students ask for similar information, send all the requests in one envelope and ask that materials returned be mailed in one package to one address.

REQUEST ONLY WHAT YOU NEED

...and use what you get.

TRY LOCAL SOURCES FIRST

Many community and regional agencies, organizations, and industrial associations can provide valuable information and assistance, particularly on local issues and conditions. Your school librarian or your public library can also help you locate information .

SEND A SELF-ADDRESSED, STAMPED ENVELOPE

If you request material or information from volunteer organizations, include a self–addressed, stamped envelope. This will bring a quicker response because these organizations have very limited budgets and secretarial staff.

PLAN ON TWO TO THREE WEEKS OF LEAD TIME

If you plan to use the material in conjunction with an activity, send your request at least two or three weeks ahead of time.

MAKE SPEAKER REQUESTS WELL IN ADVANCE

Most state agencies and volunteer organizations cannot afford to send their staff or members great distances to speak to one class. However, many resource agencies will assign personnel to meet with students on field trips near their field stations or offices. Most often, the educational experience provided by the presentation in the field is superior to a formal speech in the classroom.

ADDRESSES FOR ADDITIONAL INFORMATION AND MATERIAL

ORGANIZATIONS

AIR AND WASTE MANAGEMENT ASSOCIATION
1 Gateway Center, 3rd Floor, Pittsburgh, PA 15222

ALUMINUM ASSOCIATION
900 19th Street, Suite 300, Washington, DC 20006; www.aluminum.org

AMERICAN FOREST AND PAPER ASSOCIATION
1111 19th Street, NW, Washington, DC 20036
www.afandpa.org

AMERICAN FOREST FOUNDATION
1111 19th Street, NW, Washington, DC 20036, publishes *PROJECT LEARNING TREE* , *TREE FARMER*, *THE BRANCH*
www.affoundation.org

AMERICAN FORESTS
910 17th Street, NW, Washington, DC 20006, publishes *AMERICAN FORESTS;* www.amfor.org

AMERICAN NATURE STUDY SOCIETY
RR2 Box 1010, Dingmans Ferry, PA 18328 publishes *ANSS NEWSLETTER, NATURE STUDY: A JOURNAL OF ENVIRONMENTAL EDUCATION AND INTERPRETATION*

AMERICAN PLASTICS COUNCIL
1801 K Street, NW, Suite 500, Washington, DC 20005 publishes a variety of educational pamphlets; www.plasticsresource.com

AMERICAN PULPWOOD ASSOCIATION
600 Jefferson Plaza, #350, Rockville, MD, 20852

THE CONSERVATION FOUNDATION
1250 24th Street, NW, Suite 500, Washington, DC, 20037, publishes *CF LETTER, RESOLVE* (affiliated with World Wildlife Fund—U.S.)

CONSERVATION INTERNATIONAL FOUNDATION
2501 M Street, NW, Washington, DC 20037; www.conservation.org

COUNCIL FOR SOLID WASTE SOLUTIONS
1275 K Street, NW, Suite 400, Washington, DC 20005

CULTURAL SURVIVAL
11 Divinity Avenue, Cambridge, MA 02138, publishes *CULTURAL SURVIVAL QUARTERLY*

DEFENDERS OF WILDLIFE
1101 14th Street, NW, Suite 1400, Washington, DC 20005, publishes *DEFENDERS;* www.defenders.org

DUCKS UNLIMITED
One Waterfowl Way, Memphis, TN 38120

ENVIRONMENTAL ACTION
6930 Carroll Avenue, Suite 600, Takoma Park, MD 20912, publishes *ENVIRONMENTAL ACTION*

ENVIRONMENTAL DEFENSE FUND
257 Park Avenue South, 16th Floor, New York, NY 10010; www.@edf.org

FOREST HISTORY SOCIETY
701 Vickers Avenue, Durham, NC 27701, publishes *JOURNAL OF FOREST HISTORY, CRUISER*

FORESTRY CANADA
Ministry of Natural Resources, Corporate and Public Affairs Directorate, 351 St. Joseph Blvd., Hull, Quebec, K1A 1G5 CANADA

FRIENDS OF THE EARTH
1025 Vermont Ave., NW, Suite 300, Washington, DC 20005, publishes *NOT MAN APART, ATMOSPHERE;* www.foe.org.

GIRL SCOUTS OF THE USA
420 Fifth Avenue, New York, NY 10018; www.gsusa.org

GLOBAL NETWORK OF ENVIRONMENTAL EDUCATION CENTERS
7010 Little River Turnpike, Suite 290, Annandale, VA 22003, publishes *GLOBE NEEC News*

HARDWOOD MANUFACTURERS' ASSOCIATION
400 Penn Blvd., Suite 530, Pittsburgh, PA 15235

IZAAK WALTON LEAGUE OF AMERICA, INC
1401 Wilson Boulevard, Level B, Arlington, VA 22209, publishes *OUTDOOR AMERICA, SAVE OUR STREAMS*

KEEP AMERICA BEAUTIFUL
Mill River Plaza, 9 West Broad Street, Stamford, CT 06092

LEAGUE OF CONSERVATION VOTERS
1707 L Street, NW, Suite 550, Washington, DC 20036; www.lcv.org

LEAGUE OF WOMEN VOTERS OF THE US
1730 M Street, NW, Washington, DC 20036, publishes *THE NATIONAL VOTER*; www.lwv.org

NATIONAL ARBOR DAY FOUNDATION
100 Arbor Avenue, Nebraska City, NE 68410, publishes *ARBOR DAY*; www.arborday.org

NATIONAL AUDUBON SOCIETY
700 Broadway, New York, NY 10003-9501, publishes *AUDUBON, AUDUBON ACTIVIST*; www.audubon.org

NATIONAL GEOGRAPHIC SOCIETY
17th & M Streets, NW, Washington, DC 20036, publishes *NATIONAL GEOGRAPHIC AND WORLD*; www.nationalgeographic.com

NATIONAL PARK SERVICE
1849 C Street, NW, Washington, DC 20024; www.nps.gov

NATIONAL RESOURCES CONSERVATION SERVICE(formerly USDA Soil Conservation Service)
PO Box 2890, Washington, DC 20013; www.nrcs.usda.gov

NATIONAL SOLID WASTE MANAGEMENT ASSOCIATION
4301 Connecticut Ave., NW, Suite 300, Washington, DC 20008; www.envasns.org

THE NATIONAL TREE TRUST
1120 G Street, NW, Suite 770, Washington, DC 20005

THE NATIONAL WILDLIFE FEDERATION
8925 Leesburg Pike, Vienna, VA 22184, publishes *NATIONAL WILDLIFE, RANGER RICK, YOUR BIG BACK YARD, NATURESCOPE, INTERNATIONAL WILDLIFE, CONSERVATION DIRECTORY*; www.nwf.org/nwf

NATURAL SCIENCE FOR YOUTH FOUNDATION
130 Azalea Dr., Roswell, GA, publishes *DIRECTORY OF NATURAL SCIENCE CENTERS*

THE NATURE CONSERVANCY
1815 North Lynn Street, Arlington, VA 22209, publishes *THE CONSERVANCY NEWS*; www.tnc.org

NORTH AMERICAN ASSOCIATION FOR ENVIRONMENTAL EDUCATION
1255 23rd Street, NW, Suite 400, Washington, DC 20037, publishes *THE ENVIRONMENTAL COMMUNICATOR* AND OFFERS *THE JOURNAL OF ENVIRONMENTAL EDUCATION*; http://eelink.umich.edu/naaee.html

POPULATION-ENVIRONMENT BALANCE, INC
2000 P Street, NW, Suite 210, Washington, DC 20036-5915, publishes *BALANCE REPORT*

POPULATION REFERENCE BUREAU
1875 Connecticut Avenue, NW, Suite 520, Washington, DC 20009; www.prb.org/prb

RAINFOREST ALLIANCE
270 Lafayette Street, Suite 512, New York, NY 10012, publishes *THE CANOPY*

RESOURCES FOR THE FUTURE
1616 P Street, NW, Washington, DC 20036; www.rff.org

SCIENTISTS' INSTITUTE FOR PUBLIC INFORMATION
355 Lexington Avenue, 16th Floor, New York, NY 10017, publishes *ENVIRONMENT, SIPISCOPE, CURRENT CONTROVERSY*

SIERRA CLUB
85 2nd St., 2nd Floor, San Francisco, CA 94105, publishes *SIERRA, NATIONAL NEWS REPORT*; www.sierraclub.org

SOCIETY OF AMERICAN FORESTERS
5400 Grosvenor Lane, Bethesda, MD 20814-2198, publishes *JOURNAL OF FORESTRY*; www.safnet.org

SOIL AND WATER CONSERVATION SOCIETY OF AMERICA
7515 NE Ankeny Road, Ankeny, IA 50021, publishes *JOURNAL OF SOIL, AND WATER CONSERVATION*; www.swcs.org

TECHNOLOGICAL ASSOCIATION FOR THE PULP & PAPER INDUSTRY
PO Box 102556, Atlanta, GA 30368-0556

U.S. ARMY CORPS OF ENGINEERS
20 Massachusetts Avenue, NW, Washington, DC 20314-1000; www.usace.mil

U.S. BUREAU OF LAND MANAGEMENT
Department of the Interior, 1620 L Street, NW, Washington, DC 20240; www.blm.gov

U.S. DEPARTMENT OF AGRICULTURE
14th Street and Independence Avenue, SW, Washington, DC 20250; www.usda.gov

USDA FOREST SERVICE
Natural Resources and Conservation Education Program, PO Box 96090, Washington, DC 20090-6090; www.usda.gov

U.S. ENVIRONMENTAL PROTECTION AGENCY
Waterside Mall, 401 M Street, SW, Washington, DC 20250; www.epa.gov

U.S. FISH AND WILDLIFE SERVICE
Department of the Interior, 1849 C Street, NW, Rm 3445, Washington, DC 20240 or 4401 North Fairfax Drive, Room 452, Arlington, VA 22203

THE WILDERNESS SOCIETY
900 17th Street, NW, Washington, DC 20006, publishes *WILDERNESS*; www.wilderness.org

WILDLIFE CONSERVATION SOCIETY
185th Street and Southern Boulevard, Bronx, NY 10460, publishes *WILDLIFE CONSERVATION MAGAZINE, WCI BULLETIN*; www.wcs.org

WILDLIFE MANAGEMENT INSTITUTE
1101 14th Street, NW, Suite 801, Washington, DC 20005, publishes *OUTDOOR NEWS BULLETIN*

THE WILDLIFE SOCIETY
5410 Grosvenor Lane, Bethesda, MD 20814-2197, publishes *JOURNAL OF WILDLIFE MANAGEMENT*; www.wildlife.org/wildlife

WORLD FORESTRY CENTER
4033 SW Canyon Road, Portland, OR 97221; www.worldforest.org/~wfc/

WORLD RESOURCES INSTITUTE
1709 New York Avenue, NW, Washington, DC 20006, publishes *WORLD RESOURCES REPORT, ENVIRONMENTAL ALMANAC*; www.wri.org

WORLD WILDLIFE FUND
1250 24th Street, NW, Suite 500, Washington, DC 20037, publishes *FOCUS, WWF LETTER*; www.wwf.org

WORLDWATCH INSTITUTE
1776 Massachusetts Avenue, NW, Washington, DC 20036, publishes *WORLDWATCH PAPERS, STATE OF THE WORLD SERIES, WORLDWATCH*; www.worldwatch.org

ZERO POPULATION GROWTH
1400 16th Street, NW, Suite 320, Washington, DC 20036, publishes *ZPG REPORTER*; www.zpg.org

For a more extensive listing of organizations, see the Conservation Directory published by the National Wildlife Federation.

JOURNALS AND PERIODICALS (WITH ADDRESSES)

BIOCYCLE JOURNAL OF WASTE RECYCLING
The J.G. Press, 419 State Avenue, Emmaus, PA 18049

BOTTLE/CAN RECYCLING UPDATE
PO Box 10540, Portland, OR 97210

CATALYST FOR ENVIRONMENT/ENERGY
274 Madison Avenue, New York, NY 10016

E: THE ENVIRONMENTAL MAGAZINE
The-E, 28 Knight Street, Norwalk, CT 06851

EARTH ISLAND JOURNAL
Earth Island Institute, 300 Broadway, San Francisco, CA 94133

EARTHWATCH
680 Mount Auburn Street, PO Box 403, Watertown, MA 02272

EARTHWORD
580 Broadway, Suite 200, Laguna Beach, CA 92651

ECOLOGY USA
CJE Associates, 237 Gretna Green Court, Alexandria, VA 22304-5602

ENVIRONMENT
1319 18th Street, NW, Washington, DC 20036-1802

ENVIRONMENT ABSTRACTS
Bowker A&I Publishing, 121 Chanlon Road, New Providence, NJ 07974

ENVIRONMENT REPORT
Trends Publishing, 1079 National Press Building, Washington, DC 20045

ENVIRONMENT REPORTER
Bureau of National Affairs, 1231 25th Street, NW, Washington, DC 20037

ENVIRONMENTAL ETHICS
Department of Philosophy and Religion Studies, University of North Texas, PO Box 13496, Denton, TX 76203-3496

ENVIRONMENTAL OUTLOOK
Institute for Environmental Studies, University of Washington, FM-12, Seattle, WA 98195.

GARBAGE: THE PRACTICAL JOURNAL FOR THE ENVIRONMENT
Dovetail Publishers, The Blackburn Tavern, 2 Main Street, Gloucester, MA 01930

NATURAL HISTORY
American Museum of Natural History, Central Park West at 79th Street, New York, NY 10024

NATURAL RESOURCES JOURNAL
University of New Mexico School of Law, 1117 Stanford, NE, Albuquerque, NM 87131

QUEST
Bureau 924, Montreal, Quebec, H2Y 1N3 Canada

RESOURCE RECYCLING, NORTH AMERICA'S RECYCLING JOURNAL
PO Box 10540, Portland, OR 97210

SMITHSONIAN MAGAZINE
900 Jefferson Drive, Washington DC, 20560

AUDIO VISUAL SERVICES

BULLFROG FILMS
Oley, PA 19547

DIRECT CINEMA LIMITED, INC.
PO Box 69799, Los Angeles, CA 90069

MEDIA NETWORK
121 Fulton Street, 5th Floor, New York, NY 10038

MODERN TALKING PICTURE SERVICE
500 Park Street, North, St. Petersburg, FL 33709

NATIONAL AUDIOVISUAL CENTER
National Archives and Records Service, General Services Administration, Washington, DC 20409

U.S. DEPARTMENT OF THE INTERIOR FILMS
U.S. Department of the Interior, 18th & C Street, NW, Washington, DC 20240

U.S. FOREST SERVICE FILMS
Available through regional offices or private contractors. Free catalogs.

Alaska Region, Federal Office Bldg., PO Box 1628, Juneau, AK 99802

California Region, 630 Sansome Street, San Francisco, CA 94111

Eastern Region, 633 W. Wisconsin Avenue, Milwaukee, WI 53203

Intermountain Region, 324 25th Street, Ogden, UT 84401

Northern Region, Federal Bldg., Missoula, MT 59801

Pacific Northwest Region, 319 S.W. Pine Street, PO Box 3623, Portland, OR 97208

Rocky Mountain Region, Cromars, 1200 Stout Street, Denver, CO 80204

Southern Region, 1720 Peachtree Road, N.W., Atlanta, GA 30309

Southwestern Region, Federal Bldg, 517 Gold Avenue, SW, Albuquerque, NM 87102.

BIBLIOGRAPHY

BIBLIOGRAPHY AND OTHER RESOURCES

BOOKS

Allison, Linda. *The Reasons for Seasons—The Great Cosmic Megagalactic Trip Without Moving From Your Chair.* Boston, MA: Little, Brown, and Company, 1975.

Amery, Heather. *The KnowHow Book of Experiments.* Tulsa, OK: Usborne Publishing, 1977.

Anderson, David A. and I. I. Holland. *Forests and Forestry.* Danville, IL: Interstate Printers and Publishers, 1982.

Angelou, Maya. *On the Pulse of Morning.* New York, NY: Random House, 1993.

Applehof, Mary. *Worms Eat My Garbage.* Kalamazoo, MI: Flower Press, 1982.

Baumbardt, John Philip. *How to Care for Shade and Ornamental Trees.* Kansas City, MO: Intertec Publishing Corporation, 1974.

Berry, Wendell. *An Entrance to the Woods.* Recollected Essays: 1965-1980. San Francisco, CA: North Point Press, 1981.

Browning, Peter. *John Muir In His Own Words: A Book of Quotations.* Lafayette, CA: Great West Books, 1988.

Burdette, Janet. *The Manufacture of Pulp and Paper: Science and Engineering* Concepts. Atlanta, GA: TAPPI Press, 1988.

Burger, Julian. *The Gaia Atlas of First Peoples: A Future for the Indigenous World.* New York, NY: Doubleday, 1990.

Camp, William G. and Thomas B. Daugherty. *Managing Our National Resources.* Albany, NY: Delmar Publishers, Inc., 1991.

Campbell, Stu. *Let It Rot!: The Gardener's Guide to Composting.* Pownal, VT: Garden Way Publishers, 1990.

Carson, Rachel. *A Sense of Wonder.* New York, NY: HarperCollins Publishers, Inc., 1987.

Carson, Rachel. *Silent Spring: 25th Anniversary Edition.* Boston, MA: Houghton Mifflin, 1987.

Clay, Jason W. *Indigenous Peoples and Tropical Forests.* Cambridge, MA: Cultural Survival, 1988.

Clepper, Henry and Arthur B. Meyer, eds. *American Forestry: Six Decades of Growth.* Washington, DC: Society of American Foresters, 1960.

Cornell, Joseph. *Sharing Nature With Children.* Nevada City, CA: Dawn Publications, 1979.

Cornell, Joseph. *Sharing the Joy of Nature: Nature Activities for All Ages.* Nevada City, CA: Dawn Publications, 1989.

Cox, George W. *Conservation Ecology: Biosphere and Biosurvival.* Dubuque, IA: Wm. C. Brown Publishers, 1993.

Dahl, Thomas E. *Wetlands: Losses in the United States, 1780s to 1980s.* Washington, DC: U.S. Department of the Interior, U.S. Fish and Wildlife Service, 1990.

Dahl, Thomas E. *Wetlands: Status and Trends in the Conterminous United States, mid-1970s to mid-1980s.* Washington, DC: U.S. Department of the Interior, U.S. Fish and Wildlife Service, 1991.

Davis, Richard C., ed. *Encyclopedia of American Forest and Conservation History, Vols. I & II.* New York, NY: Macmillan Publishing Company, 1983.

de Golia, Jack. *Fire: The Story behind a Force of Nature.* Las Vegas, NV: KC Publications, 1989.

Despain, Don, et al. *Wildlife in Transition: Man and Nature on Yellowstone's Northern Range.* Boulder, CO: Roberts Rinehart Publishers, 1986.

Dillard, Annie. *Pilgrim at Tinker Creek.* New York, NY: HarperCollins Publishers, Inc., 1988.

DiSilvestro, Roger L. *The Endangered Kingdom: The Struggle to Save America's Wildlife.* New York, NY: Wiley Science Editions, 1989.

Durrell, Lee. *State of the Ark.* New York, NY: Gaia Books, Doubleday, 1986.

Emerson, Ralph Waldo. *Nature in Complete Works* (Notable American Authors Series). Irvine, CA: Reprint Services Corporation, 1992.

Ervin, Keith. *Fragile Majesty: The Battle for North America's Last Great Forest.* Seattle, WA: The Mountaineers, 1989.

Eyre, F.H. *Forest Cover Types of the United States and Canada.* Washington, DC: Society of American Foresters, 1980.

Finch, Robert and John Elder, eds. *The Norton Book of Nature Writing.* New York, NY: W.W. Norton Company, 1990.

Forestry Canada. *Forestry Facts.* Hull, Quebec: Forestry Canada, 1990.

Fox, Stephen. *John Muir and His Legacy: The American Conservation Movement.* Boston, MA: Little, Brown and Company, 1981.

Frederick, D. Kenneth and A. Roger Sedjo. *America's Renewable Resources: Historical Trends and Current Challenges.* Washington, DC: Resources for the Future, 1991.

Gore, Al. *Earth in the Balance: Ecology and the Human Spirit.* Boston, MA: Houghton Mifflin, 1992.

Hammond, Allen L., ed. *The 1992 Information Please Environmental Almanac.* Boston, MA: Houghton Mifflin, 1992.

Hammond, Allen L., ed. *World Resources 1992-1993: A Report by the World Resources Institute in Collaboration with the UNDP.* New York, NY: Oxford University Press, 1992.

Helfman, Elizabeth S. *Land, People, and History.* New York, NY: David McKay Co., 1962.

Hunter, Dard. *Papermaking.* New York, NY: Dover, 1978.

Jaimes, M. Annette, ed. *The State of Native America: Genocide, Colonization, and Resistance.* Boston, MA: South End Press, 1992.

Josephsy, Alvin M., Jr. *The Indian Heritage of America.* New York, NY: Bantam Books, 1968.

Ketchum, Richard M. *The Secret Life of the Forest.* New York, NY: American Heritage Press, 1970.

Lamb, H.H. *Climate, History, and the Modern World.* New York, NY: Routledge Chapman and Hall, Inc., 1982.

Lauber, Patricia. *Seeing Earth From Space.* New York, NY: Orchard Books, 1990.

Leopold, Aldo. *A Sand County Almanac.* New York, NY: Ballantine Books, 1966.

Levey, Jane Freundel. *If You Want Air Time: A Publicity Handbook.* Washington, DC: National Association of Broadcasters, 1987.

Lipkis, Andy and Katie Lipkis. *The Simple Act of Planting a Tree: A Citizen Forester's Guide to Healing Your Neighborhood, Your City, and Your World.* Los Angeles, CA: Jeremy P. Tarcher, 1990.

Maybury-Lewis, David. *Millennium: Tribal Wisdom and the Modern World.* New York, NY: Viking Penguin, 1992.

McCormick, Jack. *The Life of the Forest.* New York, NY: McGraw-Hill, Inc., 1966.

McGaw, Judith A. *Most Wonderful Machine: Mechanization and Social Change in Berkshire Papermaking, 1801-1885.* Princeton, NJ: Princeton University Press, 1992.

McPhee, John. *Encounters with the Archdruid.* New York, NY: Farrar, Straus and Giroux, 1971.

Miller, G. Tyler. *Living in the Environment, 7th Edition.* Belmont, CA: Wadsworth Publishing Co., 1992.

Miller, Kenton and Laura Tangley. *Trees of Life: Saving Tropical Forests and Their Biological Wealth.* Boston, MA: Beacon Press, 1991.

Mitchell, John Hanson. *Ceremonial Time: Fifteen Thousand Years on One Square Mile.* Boston, MA: Houghton Mifflin and Co., 1991.

Moll, Gary and Sara Ebenreck. *Shading Our Cities.* Washington, DC: Island Press, 1989.

Morris, Ramona and Desmond Morris. *The Giant Panda.* New York, NY: Papermac, 1981.

Muir, John. *The Mountains of California.* Golden, CO: Fulcrum Publishers, 1988.

Muir, John. *Wilderness Essays* (Peregrine Smith Literary Naturalist Series). Layton, UT: Gibbs Smith Publishing, 1989.

Murphy, Richard C. and William E. Meyer. *The Care and Feeding of Trees.* New York, NY: Crown Publishers, 1969.

Myers, Norman. *Gaia: An Atlas of Planet Management.* Garden City, NJ: Gaia Books, Anchor Press, 1984.

Olson, Sigurd. *The Singing Wilderness.* New York, NY: Alfred A. Knopf, 1956.

Owen, Oliver S. and Daniel D. Chiras. *Natural Resource Conservation: An Ecological Approach.* New York, NY: Macmillan Publishing, 1990.

Perlin, John. *A Forest Journey: The Role of Wood in the Development of Civilization.* Cambridge, MA: Harvard University Press, 1991.

Petulla, Joseph M. *American Environmental History, 2nd ed.* Columbus, OH: Merrill Publishing Company, 1988.

Pirone, Pascal Pompey. *Tree Maintenance.* New York, NY: Oxford University Press, 1988.

Pyne, Stephen J. *Fire in America: A Cultural History of Wildland and Rural Fire.* Princeton, NJ: Princeton University Press, 1982.

Raphael, Ray. *Tree Talk: The People and Politics of Timber.* Covelo, CA: Island Press, 1981.

Repetto, Robert. *The Forest for the Trees? Government Policies and the Misuse of Forest Resources.* Washington, DC: World Resources Institute, 1988.

Ritchie, Donald D. and Robert Carola. *Biology.* Reading, MA: Addison-Wesley Publishing Co., 1979.

Rockey, Sherry and Alice L. Hughey. *A Citizen's Guide to Community Education on Global Issues.* Washington, DC: League of Women Voters Education Fund, 1988.

Rolston, Holmes. *Environmental Ethics.* Philadelphia, PA: Temple University Press, 1988.

Schaller, George B. *The Last Panda.* Chicago, IL: University of Chicago Press, 1993.

Schissel, Lillian. *Women's Diaries of the Westward Journey.* New York, NY: Schocken Books, Inc., 1987.

Singer, Max. *Passage to a Human World.* New Brunswick, NJ: Transaction Publishers, 1989.

Smith, David C. *History of Papermaking in the United States.* New York, NY: Lockwood Publishing Co., 1970.

Smith, David M. *THE PRACTICE OF SILVICULTURE, 8TH EDITION.* New York, NY: John Wiley & Sons, 1986.

Smith, Robert Leo. *ECOLOGY AND FIELD BIOLOGY, 4TH EDITION.* New York, NY: HarperCollins Publishers, 1990.

Society of American Foresters with cooperation of The Wildlife Society. *CHOICES IN SILVICULTURE FOR AMERICAN FORESTS.* Washington, DC: Society of American Foresters, 1981.

Stephanides Brothers. *THE MYTH OF PERSEPHONE: DEMETER—ARTEMIS, 3RD ED.* Athens, Greece: Sigma Publications, 1984.

Stewart, George R. *FIRE.* Lincoln, NE: University of Nebraska Press, 1984.

Stotsky, Sandra. *CIVIC WRITING IN THE CLASSROOM.* Bloomington, IN: ERIC Clearinghouse for Social Studies/Social Science Education, 1987.

Strong, Douglas H. *DREAMERS AND DEFENDERS: AMERICAN CONSERVATIONISTS.* Lincoln, NE: University of Nebraska Press, 1988.

Suzuki, David T. and Peter Knudtson. *WISDOM OF THE ELDERS: HONORING SACRED NATIVE VISIONS OF NATURE.* New York, NY: Bantam, 1992.

Swift, Ernest. *A CONSERVATION SAGA.* Washington, DC: National Wildlife Federation, 1967.

Swiss, Martha B. *AIR POLLUTION.* Pittsburgh, PA: Air and Waste Management Association, Public Education Division, 1991.

Thoreau, Henry David. *PORTABLE THOREAU.* Edited by Carl Bode. New York, NY: Viking Penguin, 1977.

Thoreau, Henry David. *WALDEN.* Rutland, VT: Charles E. Tuttle and Co., 1992.

Tilden, Freeman. *THE NATIONAL PARKS.* New York, NY: Alfred A. Knopf, 1986.

Turnbull, Colin. *THE FOREST PEOPLE.* New York, NY: Simon and Schuster, 1968.

Turner, Frederick. *REDISCOVERING AMERICA: JOHN MUIR IN HIS TIME AND OURS.* San Francisco, CA: Sierra Club Books, 1985.

U.S. Forest Service. *TREES OF OUR NATIONAL FORESTS.* Washington, DC: USDA Forest Service, 1980.

Walker, Laurence C. *FORESTS: A NATURALIST'S GUIDE TO TREES AND FOREST ECOLOGY.* New York, NY: John Wiley and Sons, 1990.

Weatherford, Jack. *INDIAN GIVERS: HOW THE INDIANS OF THE AMERICAS TRANSFORMED THE NEW WORLD.* New York, NY: Crown Publishers, 1988.

Weiss, Harvey. *SHELTERS: FROM TEPEE TO IGLOO.* New York, NY: HarperCollins Children's Books, 1988.

Wissler, Clark. *INDIANS OF THE UNITED STATES.* New York, NY: Doubleday, 1966.

WorldWatch Institute, *STATE OF THE WORLD 1992: A WORLDWATCH INSTITUTE REPORT ON PROGRESS TOWARD A SUSTAINABLE SOCIETY.* New York, NY: W.W. Norton, 1992.

Wright, Henry A. and Arthur W. Bailey. *FIRE ECOLOGY: THE UNITED STATES AND SOUTHERN CANADA.* New York, NY: John Wiley and Sons, 1982.

Wuerthner, George. *YELLOWSTONE AND THE FIRES OF CHANGE.* Salt Lake City, UT: Haggis House Publications, 1988.

Yepsen, Roger B., Jr. *TREES FOR THE YARD, ORCHARD, AND WOODLOT: PROPAGATION, PRUNING, LANDSCAPING, ORCHARDING, SUGARING, WOODLOT MANAGEMENT, TRADITIONAL USES.* Emmaus, PA: Rodale Press, 1976.

Young, Raymond A. *INTRODUCTION TO FOREST SCIENCE (2ND EDITION).* New York, NY: John Wiley and Sons, 1990.

CHILDREN'S AND YOUNG ADULT BOOKS; FOLKLORE

Folklore Arkhurst, Joyce C. *THE ADVENTURES OF SPIDER.* Boston, MA: Little, Brown, and Co., 1964.

Arnosky, Jim. *IN THE FOREST.* New York, NY: Lothrop, Lee and Shepard Books, 1989.

Baker, Jeannie. *WHERE THE FOREST MEETS THE SEA.* New York, NY: Greenwillow Books, 1987.

Baker, Jeannie. *WINDOW.* New York, NY: Greenwillow Books, 1991.

Brockett, Eleanor. *BURMESE AND THAI FAIRY TALES.* Chicago, IL: Follet, 1967.

Burne, David. *TREE.* New York, NY: Alfred A. Knopf, 1988.

Buscaglia, Leo. *THE FALL OF FREDDIE THE LEAF.* New York, NY: H. Holt and Company, 1982.

Caduto, Michael J. and Joseph Bruchac. *KEEPERS OF THE ANIMALS.* Golden, CO: Fulcrum Publishing, 1991.

Caduto, Michael J. and Joseph Bruchac. *KEEPERS OF THE EARTH: NATIVE AMERICAN STORIES AND ENVIRONMENTAL ACTIVITIES FOR CHILDREN.* Golden, CO: Fulcrum Publishing, 1988.

Cherry, Lynne. *GREAT KAPOK TREE: A TALE OF THE AMAZON RAIN FOREST.* Orlando, FL: Harcourt Brace Jovanovich, 1990.

Cosgrove, Stephen and Robin James. *TRAPPER.* Los Angeles, CA: Price, Stern, Sloan Publishers, 1978.

Donahue, Mike. *THE GRANDPA TREE.* Boulder, CO: Robert Rinehart, 1988.

Esbensen, Barbara Juster. *THE STAR MAIDEN: AN OJIBWAY TALE.* Boston, MA: Little, Brown & Co., 1988.

Field, Edward. *ESKIMO SONGS AND STORIES.* New York, NY: Dell Publishing Company, 1973.

George, Jean Craighead. *THE HOLE IN THE TREE.* New York, NY: E.P. Dutton, 1957.

Gile, John. *THE FIRST FOREST.* Rockford, IL: J. Gile Communications, 1989.

Giono, Jean. *THE MAN WHO PLANTED TREES.* Chelsea, VT: Chelsea Green Publishing Company, 1985.

Grummer, Arnold E. *PAPER BY KIDS.* Minneapolis, MN: Dillon Press, 1980.

Helfman, Elizabeth S. *THE BUSHMEN AND THEIR STORIES.* San Francisco, CA: Seabury, 1971.

Hiscock, Bruce. *THE BIG TREE.* New York, NY: Macmillan Children's Book Group, 1991.

Jaspersohn, William. *HOW THE FOREST GREW.* New York, NY: Greenwillow Books, 1989.

Johnston, Tony. *YONDER* (Dial Books for Young Readers). New York, NY: Henry Holt and Company, 1988.

Kellogg, Steven. *JOHNNY APPLESEED.* New York, NY: William Morrow and Co., 1988.

Kerven, Rosalind. *EARTH MAGIC, SKY MAGIC: NORTH AMERICAN INDIAN TALES.* New York, NY: Cambridge University Press, 1991.

Kerven, Rosalind. *THE TREE IN THE MOON AND OTHER LEGENDS OF PLANTS AND TREES.* New York, NY: Cambridge University Press, 1989.

Kuhn, Dwight. *THE HIDDEN LIFE OF THE FOREST.* New York, NY: Crown Publishers, 1988.

Lavies, Bianca. *COMPOST CRITTERS.* New York, NY: Duttons Children's Books, 1993.

Lewis, Barbara A. *THE KID'S GUIDE TO SOCIAL ACTION.* Minneapolis, MN: Free Spirit Publishing, 1991.

Mayo, Gretchen Will. *EARTHMAKER'S TALES: NORTH AMERICAN INDIAN STORIES ABOUT EARTH HAPPENINGS.* New York, NY: Walker and Co., 1989.

Monroe, Jean Guard and Ray Williamson. *THEY DANCE IN THE SKY.* Boston, MA: Houghton Mifflin, 1987.

Morimoto, Junko. *KENJU'S FOREST.* New York, NY: HarperCollins Publishers, 1991.

Parnell, Peter. *APPLE TREE.* New York, NY: MacMillan, 1987.

Romanova, Natalia. *ONCE THERE WAS A TREE.* New York, NY: Henry Holt and Company, 1985.

Rose, Deborah L. *THE PEOPLE WHO HUGGED THE TREES: AN ENVIRONMENTAL FOLK TALE.* Niwot, CO: Roberts Rinehart, 1990.

Ryder, Joanne. *HELLO TREE!* New York, NY: Dutton Children's Books, 1991.

Seuss, Dr. *THE CAT IN THE HAT COMES BACK.* New York, NY: Beginner Books/Random House, 1958.

Seuss, Dr. *THE LORAX.* New York, NY: Random House, 1971.

Silverstein, Shel. *THE GIVING TREE.* New York, NY: HarperCollins Children's Books, 1964.

Taylor, Mildred D. *SONG OF THE TREES.* New York, NY: Bantam Books, Inc., 1984.

Thompson, Vivian L. *HAWAIIAN MYTHS OF EARTH, SEA, AND SKY.* Honolulu, HI: University of Hawaii Press, 1988.

Tresselt, Alvin. *THE GIFT OF THE TREE.* New York, NY: Lothrop, Lee, and Shepard Books, 1992.

Van Allsburg, Chris. *JUST A DREAM.* Boston, MA: Houghton Mifflin Co., 1990.

FIELD GUIDES AND SERIES

Audubon Society. *THE AUDUBON SOCIETY FIELD GUIDE SERIES.* New York, NY: Alfred A. Knopf.

GOLDEN GUIDE NATURE SERIES. New York, NY: Golden Press.

Little, Elbert L. *THE AUDUBON SOCIETY FIELD GUIDE TO NORTH AMERICAN TREES.* New York, NY: Alfred A. Knopf, 1980.

Mohlenbrock, Robert H. *THE FIELD GUIDE TO NATIONAL FORESTS.* New York, NY: Congdon and Weed, 1984.

Newcomb, Lawrence. *NEWCOMB'S WILDFLOWER GUIDE: AN INGENIOUS NEW KEY SYSTEM FOR QUICK POSITIVE FIELD IDENTIFICATION OF WILDFLOWERS, FLOWERING SHRUBS AND VINES.* Boston, MA: Little, 1989.

THE PETERSON FIELD GUIDE SERIES. Boston, MA: Houghton Mifflin Co.

Petrides, George. *PETERSON FIELD GUIDE TO TREES AND SHRUBS.* Boston, MA: Houghton Mifflin, 1972.

Randall, W.R., R.F. Keniston, and D.N. Bever. *MANUAL OF OREGON TREES AND SHRUBS.* Corvallis, OR: Oregon State University Bookstores, 1978.

SIERRA CLUB NATURALIST GUIDES. San Francisco, CA: Sierra Club Press.

Symonds, George W.D., *THE SHRUB IDENTIFICATION BOOK.* New York, NY: William Morrow & Company, 1963.

Symonds, George W.D. *THE SHRUB IDENTIFICATION BOOK.* New York, NY: William Morrow & Company, 1963.

U.S. Forest Service. *INSECTS OF EASTERN FORESTS.* Washington, DC: USDA Forest Service, 1985.

Whitney, Stephen. Audubon Society Nature Guides: *WESTERN FORESTS.* New York, NY: Alfred A. Knopf, 1985.

DIRECTORIES

DIRECTORY OF ENVIRONMENTAL GROUPS IN NEW ENGLAND. Boston, MA: Environmental Protection Agency, Region 1.

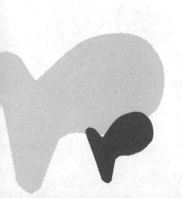

Erickson, Judith B. *DIRECTORY OF AMERICAN YOUTH ORGANIZATIONS: A GUIDE TO OVER 400 CLUBS, GROUPS, TROOPS, TEAMS, SOCIETIES, LODGES, AND MORE FOR YOUNG PEOPLE, 1990-91 EDITION.* Minneapolis, MN: Free Spirit Publishing, 1990.

Gordon, Rue E., ed. *1996 CONSERVATION DIRECTORY, 41ST EDITION.* Washington DC: National Wildlife Federation, 1996.

Sierra Club. *WORLD DIRECTORY OF ENVIRONMENTAL ORGANIZATIONS.* Claremont, CA: Sierra Club and Center for California Public Affairs, 1976.

ARTICLES AND SPECIAL ISSUES OF PERIODICALS

ART TO ZOO (a publication of the Smithsonian Institution's Office of Elementary and Secondary Education.) Spring 1987.

Brooks, David J. and Gordon E. Grant. *NEW APPROACHES TO FOREST MANAGEMENT.* Journal of Forestry 90(1): 25-28. (January 1992)

CELEBRATING A TREASURE: 100 YEARS OF NATIONAL FORESTS. American Forests 97(5/6): 21-27+. (May/June 1991)

DEADLY DANGER IN U.S. HOMES. Weekly Reader 4-6 (6). (October 12, 1990)

Findley, Rowe. *OUR NATIONAL FORESTS: PROBLEMS IN PARADISE.* National Geographic 162 (3): 306-339. (September 1982.)

Monastersky, Richard. *THE DEFORESTATION DEBATE.* Science News 144: 26. (July 10, 1993)

PACKAGING IN THE 90S. Garbage. December/January 1993.

Watkins, T.H. *FATHER OF THE FORESTS.* Journal of Forestry 90 (1): 12-15. (January 1992)

Wiley, J.W. and G.P. Bauer. *CARIBBEAN NATIONAL FOREST, PUERTO RICO.* American Birds 39(1): 12-18. (Spring 1985)

Young, John E. *ALUMINUM'S REAL TAB.* WorldWatch, March/April 1992, pp. 26-33.

PAMPHLETS, BROCHURES, FACT SHEETS

Aluminum Association. *ALUMINUM RECYCLING: AMERICA'S ENVIRONMENTAL SUCCESS STORY.* Washington, DC: Aluminum Association, 1990.

American Forestry Association (currently known as American Forests). *FORESTS AND FORESTRY IN THE U.S.A.* Washington, DC: American Forestry Association, 1989.

American Forest and Paper Association. *How to Make Paper.* Washington, DC: American Forest and Paper Association, 1993.

American Paper Institute, Inc. (currently known as the American Forest and Paper Association). *How to Recycle Waste Paper.* New York, NY: American Paper Institute, Inc., 1991.

American Paper Institute, Inc. (currently known as the American Forest and Paper Association). *Paper and Paper Manufacture.* New York, NY: American Paper Institute, Inc., 1987.

American Paper Institute, Inc. (currently known as the American Forest and Paper Association). *Paper: Linking People and Nature.* New York, NY: American Paper Institute, Inc. Kentucky's Trees: Putting on Airs. Frankfort, KY: Kentucky Division of Forestry, Natural Resources, and Environmental Protection.

Lee, Helen. *Bibliography of Papermaking for Children and Young Adults.* Atlanta, GA: Technical Association for the Pulp and Paper Industry, 1990.

National Wildlife Federation. *Rainforests: Help Save Their Layers of Life.* Washington, DC: National Wildlife Federation, 1993.

Ogden Projects, Inc. *Recycling and Waste-to-Energy: Teaming up for a Cleaner World.* Fairfield, NJ: Ogden Projects, Inc.

Paper Information Center, American Paper Institute, Inc. (currently known as the American Forest and Paper Association). *Paper Recycling.* New York, NY: American Paper Institute, Inc., 1992.

Rowntree, Rowan. *HOW MANY TREES DOES IT TAKE TO STORE THE CARBON YOU PRODUCE?: A GUIDE TO HELP YOU CONTRIBUTE TO THE PREVENTION OF GLOBAL CLIMATE CHANGE.* Washington, DC: U.S. Department of Agriculture, Forest Service.

Shigo, Alex L. *TREE DECAY: AN EXPANDED CONCEPT.* Washington, DC: U.S. Department of Agriculture, Forest Service, 1979. (Document # A 1.75: 419)

U.S. Congress, Senate, Committee on Environment and Public Works. *AUTHORIZATION OF APPROPRIATIONS FOR THE OFFICE OF ENVIRONMENTAL QUALITY.* Washington, DC: U.S. Government Printing Office, 1990. (Document # Y 1.1/5: 101-352)

U.S. Department of Agriculture, Forest Service. *WHAT THE FOREST SERVICE DOES.* Washington, DC: U.S. Department of Agriculture, Forest Service, 1986. (Document # A 13.2: F 76/77/ 986)

U.S. Environmental Protection Agency. *A CITIZEN'S GUIDE TO RADON: WHAT IT IS AND WHAT TO DO ABOUT IT.* Washington, DC: U.S. Environmental Protection Agency, Office of Air and Radiation, 1986. (Document # EP 1.8: C 49/2)

U.S. Environmental Protection Agency. *EPA ACTIVITIES UPDATE.* Washington, D.C.: U.S. Environmental Protection Agency, Office of Communications and Public Affairs, October 15, 1991.

Willett, Edward F. *HOW OUR LAWS ARE MADE.* Washington, DC: U.S. Government Printing Office, 1986. (Document # Y 1.1/7: 99-158)

Wright, Helena. *300 YEARS OF AMERICAN PAPERMAKING.* Washington, D.C.: Smithsonian Institution, 1991. (Catalogue No. 50)

REPORTS

American Paper Institute, Inc. (currently known as the American Forest and Paper Association). *U.S. PAPER INDUSTRY COMMITS TO MAJOR EXPANSION IN PAPER RECYCLING.* New York, NY: American Paper Institute, Inc., 1990.

Franklin, E. William. *PAPER RECYCLING: THE VIEW TO 1995, SUMMARY REPORT.* Franklin Associates, Ltd., 1990.

Minnesota Waste Management Board. *WASTE EDUCATION ROUNDTABLE, FINAL REPORT.* Minnesota, MN: Minnesota Waste Management Board, 1986.

U.S. Department of Agriculture, Forest Service. *A DESCRIPTION OF FOREST SERVICE PROGRAMS AND RESPONSIBILITIES.* Washington, DC: U.S. Department of Agriculture, Forest Service, General Technical Report RM-176.

U.S. Department of the Interior, National Park Service. *STATE OF THE PARKS.* Washington, DC: U.S. Department of the Interior, National Park Service.

Yamaski, G, D. Itano, and R. Davis. *A STUDY OF AND RECOMMENDATIONS FOR THE MANAGEMENT OF THE MANGROVE AND LAGOON AREAS OF NU'UULI AND TAFUNA, AMERICAN SAMOA.* Silver Spring, MD: NOAA, 1985.

CURRICULA AND TEACHER'S GUIDES

Air and Waste Management Association. *ENVIRONMENTAL RESOURCE GUIDE: AIR QUALITY.* Pittsburgh, PA: Air and Waste Management Association, 1991.

Applehof, M., M. F. Fenton, and B. Harris. *WORMS EAT OUR GARBAGE: CLASSROOM ACTIVITIES FOR A BETTER PLANET.* Kalamazoo, MI: Flower Press, 1993.

Braus, Judy, ed. *RANGER RICK'S NATURE SCOPE SERIES: AMAZING MAMMALS PARTS I AND II, BIRDS! BIRDS! BIRDS!, RAINFORESTS—TROPICAL TREASURES, TREES ARE TERRIFIC!* Washington, DC: National Wildlife Federation, 1985-89.

California Department of Education. *SCIENCE FRAMEWORK FOR CALIFORNIA PUBLIC SCHOOLS.* Sacramento, CA: California Department of Education, 1990.

Clymire, Olga, ed. *A CHILD'S PLACE IN THE ENVIRONMENT.* Sacramento, CA: California Department of Education, 1993.

Finkelstein, Robert J. *CENTRAL PARK WORKBOOK: ACTIVITIES FOR AN URBAN PARK.* New York, NY: 1980. ForesTree Explorations. British Columbia Forestry Association, Surrey, British Columbia, Canada.

The Institute for Environmental Education. *CLOSING THE LOOP: INTEGRATED WASTE MANAGEMENT ACTIVITIES FOR SCHOOL AND HOME—A SCHOOL-BASED WASTE MINIMIZATION AND EDUCATION PROGRAM.* Cleveland, OH: The Institute for Environmental Education, 1992.

Kennedy, Caroline. *EXPLORING WILD-LIFE COMMUNITIES WITH CHILDREN.* New York, NY: Girl Scouts of the U.S.A., 1981.

Minnesota Office of Waste Management. *TO DEVELOP CURRICULA FOR SOLID AND HAZARDOUS WASTE MANAGEMENT EDUCATION FOR GRADES 7-12.* Minnesota, MN: Minnesota Office of Waste Management, 1991.

O'Conner, Maura and McGlauflin, Kathy. *LIVING LIGHTLY IN THE CITY.* Milwaukee, WI: Schlitz Audubon Center, 1983, 1993.

Paden, Mary, ed. *TEACHER'S GUIDE TO WORLD RESOURCES 1992-93* Washington, DC: World Resources Institute, 1992.

PROJECT WILD. Bethesda, MD: Council for Environmental Education, 1992.

Slattery, Britt Eckhardt. *WOW! THE WONDERS OF WETLANDS: AN EDUCATOR'S GUIDE.* St. Michaels, MD: Environmental Concern, 1991.

TEACHER'S GUIDE TO THE NORTH GROVE. Arnold, CA: Calaveras Big Trees Association, 1990.

U.S. Department of Agriculture, Soil Conservation Service. *TEACHING SOIL AND WATER CONSERVATION.* A Classroom and Field Guide. (Program Aid #341). Washington, DC: U.S. Department of Agriculture, Soil Conservation Service, 1986. (Document # A 1.68: 341)

U.S. Environmental Protection Agency. Let's Reduce and Recycle: Curriculum for Solid Waste Awareness. Lesson plans for Grades K-6 and 7-12. Washington, DC: U.S. Environmental Protection Agency, 1990. (Document # EP 1.17: 530-SW-90-005)

Wasserman, Pamela, and Andrea Doyle. *EARTH MATTERS.* Washington, DC: Zero Population Growth, Inc., 1991.

VIDEOS

Aluminum Association. *CALL ME CAN.* (VHS videocassette, 18 minutes.) Aluminum Association, 900 19th Street, NW, Washington, DC 20006.

Back, Frederic, director. *THE MAN WHO PLANTED TREES.* (VHS videocassette, 30 minutes, color.) Direct Cinema Limited, Inc., P.O. Box 69799, Los Angeles, CA 90069.

Dow Plastics. *TRACES OF TODAY* (1/2 inch VHS videocassette). Order by calling 1-800-258-2436.

Forest History Society. *UP IN FLAMES: A HISTORY OF FIRE FIGHTING IN THE FOREST* (29 minutes). Forest History Society, Inc. 701 Vickers Avenue, Durham, NC 27701. Phone 919-682-9319.

Forest History Society. *TIMBER ON THE MOVE: A HISTORY OF LOG MOVING TECHNOLOGY* (34 minutes). Forest History Society, Inc. 701 Vickers Avenue, Durham, NC 27701. Phone 919-682-9319.

Public Broadcast System. *BATTLE FOR WILDERNESS: THE AMERICAN EXPERIENCE.* PBS special on the conflicting perspectives of Gifford Pinchot and John Muir.

Travel Montana and Wyoming Travel Commission. *YELLOWSTONE IN THE SUMMER '88.* (17 minutes.) Sage Advertising, P.O. Box 1142, Helena, MT 59624. Phone 406-442-9500.

Video Visions. *YELLOWSTONE FOREST 1988.* (1 hour.) Video Visions, P.O. Box 6721, Bozeman, MT 59715.

AUDIOCASSETTES

Brennan, Bill. *BILLY B. SINGS ABOUT TREES.* (record/cassette, 14 songs.) Do Dreams Music, P.O. Box 5623, Takoma Park, MD 20913. Or call 1-800/424-5592

MAPS

Project Learning Tree. *FEDERAL LANDS & FORESTS OF THE WORLD.* For more information, contact Project Learning Tree, American Forest Foundation, 1111 19th Street, NW, Washington, DC 20036. Phone 202/463-2462.

POSTERS

National Wildlife Federation. *RAIN-FORESTS: HELP SAVE THE LAYERS OF LIFE: NATIONAL WILDLIFE WEEK, APRIL 18-24.* Washington, DC: National Wildlife Federation, 1993.

Project Learning Tree. *WE ALL NEED TREES.* For more information, contact Project Learning Tree, American Forest Foundation, 1111 19th Street, NW, Washington, DC 20036. Phone 202/463-2462.

U.S. Department of Agriculture, Forest Service. *HOW A TREE GROWS.* Washington, DC: U.S. Department of Agriculture, Forest Service, 1987. (Document # A 13.2: T 71/41)

U.S. Department of Agriculture, Forest Service. *LIFE, DEATH, AND REBIRTH OF A TREE.* Washington, DC: U.S. Department of Agriculture, Forest Service, 1980. (Document # FS-356).

U.S. Department of Agriculture, Forest Service. *WHY LEAVES CHANGE COLOR.* Washington, DC: U.S. Department of Agriculture, Forest Service, 1992. (Document # A 13.2: L 48/5)

U.S. Department of Agriculture, Forest Service. *LIFE, DEATH, AND REBIRTH OF A TREE.* Washington, DC: U.S. Department of Agriculture, Forest Service, 1980. (Document # FS-356).

U.S. Department of Agriculture, Forest Service. *WHY LEAVES CHANGE COLOR.* Washington, DC: U.S. Department of Agriculture, Forest Service, 1992. (Document # A 13.2: L 48/5)

TOPIC INDEX

SUBJECT INDEX

		VISUAL ARTS	LANGUAGE ARTS	MATH	PHYS ED	SCIENCE	SOCIAL STUDIES	PERFORMING ARTS
DIVERSITY								
1	The Shape of Things	✽	✽	✽		✽		
2	Get in Touch with Trees	✽	✽			✽		
3	Peppermint Beetle					✽	✽	
4	Sounds Around		✽	✽		✽	✽	
5	Poet-Tree		✽			✽	✽	
6	Picture This!	✽		✽		✽		
7	Habitat Pen Pals		✽			✽		
8	The Forest Of S.T. Shrew	✽	✽			✽		
9	Planet Of Plenty	✽	✽			✽		
10	Charting Diversity					✽		
11	Can It Be Real?		✽			✽		
12	Tree Treasures	✽				✽	✽	
13	We All Need Trees		✽			✽	✽	
14	Renewable or Not?					✽	✽	
15	A Few Of My Favorite Things	✽				✽	✽	
16	Pass The Plants, Please		✽	✽		✽	✽	
17	People Of The Forest		✽			✽	✽	
18	Tale of the Sun		✽			✽	✽	
19	Values On The Line					✽	✽	
20	Environmental Exchange Box					✽	✽	
INTERRELATIONSHIPS								
21	Adopt a Tree	✽	✽	✽		✽	✽	
22	Trees as Habitats	✽		✽		✽	✽	
23	The Fallen Log	✽				✽		
24	Nature's Recyclers		✽			✽		
25	Birds and Worms			✽	✽	✽		
26	Dynamic Duos		✽			✽		
27	Every Tree for Itself			✽		✽		
28	Air Plants			✽		✽		
29	Rain Reasons			✽		✽	✽	
30	Three Cheers for Trees	✽				✽	✽	
31	Plant a Tree					✽	✽	
32	A Forest of Many Uses					✽	✽	
33	Forest Consequences		✽			✽	✽	
34	Who Works in this Forest?					✽	✽	
35	Loving It Too Much		✽			✽	✽	
36	Pollution Search			✽		✽	✽	

#	Title	VISUAL ARTS	LANGUAGE ARTS	MATH	PHYS ED	SCIENCE	SOCIAL STUDIES	PERFORMING ARTS
37	Talking Trash, Not!			●		●	●	
38	Every Drop Counts			●		●	●	
39	Energy Sleuths					●	●	
40	Then and Now		●			●	●	

SYSTEMS

#	Title	VISUAL ARTS	LANGUAGE ARTS	MATH	PHYS ED	SCIENCE	SOCIAL STUDIES	PERFORMING ARTS
41	How Plants Grow			●		●		
42	Sunlight and Shades of Green		●			●		
43	Have Seeds, Will Travel	●				●		
44	Water Wonders		●		●	●		
45	Web of Life	●	●			●		
46	School Yard Safari		●			●		
47	Are Vacant Lots Vacant?	●		●		●		
48	Field, Forest, and Stream			●		●		
49	Tropical Treehouse	●	●			●	●	●
50	400-Acre Wood			●		●	●	
51	Make Your Own Paper	●	●			●	●	
52	A Look at Aluminum					●	●	
53	On the Move	●		●		●	●	
54	I'd Like to Visit a Place Where...	●	●	●	●	●	●	
55	Planning the Ideal Community	●	●	●			●	
56	We Can Work it Out	●	●				●	
57	Democracy in Action	●					●	
58	There Ought to be a Law	●	●	●			●	
59	Power of Print	●	●				●	
60	Publicize It!	●	●			●	●	●

STRUCTURE AND SCALE

#	Title	VISUAL ARTS	LANGUAGE ARTS	MATH	PHYS ED	SCIENCE	SOCIAL STUDIES	PERFORMING ARTS
61	The Closer You Look	●	●			●		
62	To Be a Tree	●				●		●
63	Tree Factory				●	●		●
64	Looking at Leaves	●				●		
65	Bursting Buds	●				●		
66	Germinating Giants			●		●		
67	How Big is Your Tree?			●		●	●	
68	Name that Tree				●	●		
69	Forest for the Trees			●		●	●	
70	Soil Stories			●		●	●	
71	Watch On Wetlands		●			●	●	●

	VISUAL ARTS	LANGUAGE ARTS	MATH	PHYS ED	SCIENCE	SOCIAL STUDIES	PERFORMING ARTS
72 Air We Breathe		✓			✓		
73 Waste Watchers			✓		✓	✓	
74 People, Places, Things						✓	
75 Tepee Talk	✓				✓	✓	

PATTERNS OF CHANGE

	VISUAL ARTS	LANGUAGE ARTS	MATH	PHYS ED	SCIENCE	SOCIAL STUDIES	PERFORMING ARTS
76 Tree Cookies	✓	✓			✓	✓	
77 Trees in Trouble		✓	✓		✓	✓	✓
78 Signs of Fall	✓	✓			✓		
79 Tree Lifecycle	✓	✓			✓		✓
80 Nothing Succeeds Like Succession	✓	✓	✓		✓		
81 Living with Fire					✓	✓	
82 Resource-Go-Round					✓	✓	
83 Reduce, Reuse, Recycle		✓	✓		✓	✓	
84 A Peek at Packaging	✓				✓	✓	
85 Air to Drive			✓		✓	✓	
86 Our Changing World		✓			✓	✓	
87 Earth Manners	✓	✓			✓	✓	
88 Life on the Edge					✓	✓	
89 Trees for Many Reasons		✓			✓	✓	
90 The Native Way		✓			✓	✓	
91 In the Good Old Days	✓	✓			✓	✓	✓
92 A Look at Lifestyles		✓			✓		✓
93 Paper Civilizations	✓	✓				✓	
94 Where are the Cedars Of Lebanon?					✓	✓	
95 Did You Notice?	✓	✓				✓	
96 Improve Your Place	✓				✓	✓	

GRADE INDEX

	Pre-K	K	1	2	3	4	5	6	7	8
DIVERSITY										
1 The Shape of Things	✓	✓	✓	✓	✓					
2 Get in Touch with Trees	✓	✓	✓	✓	✓	✓	✓	✓		
3 Peppermint Beetle		✓	✓	✓	✓					
4 Sounds Around	✓	✓	✓	✓	✓	✓	✓		✓	✓
5 Poet-Tree					✓	✓	✓	✓	✓	✓
6 Picture This!	✓	✓		✓						
7 Habitat Pen Pals					✓	✓	✓	✓		
8 The Forest Of S.T. Shrew			✓	✓	✓	✓	✓	✓		
9 Planet Of Plenty						✓	✓	✓		
10 Charting Diversity						✓	✓	✓	✓	✓
11 Can It Be Real?						✓	✓	✓	✓	✓
12 Tree Treasures	✓	✓	✓	✓	✓	✓	✓	✓		
13 We All Need Trees						✓	✓	✓		
14 Renewable or Not?						✓	✓	✓	✓	✓
15 A Few Of My Favorite Things						✓	✓	✓	✓	✓
16 Pass The Plants, Please	✓	✓	✓	✓	✓	✓	✓	✓	✓	✓
17 People Of The Forest						✓	✓	✓	✓	✓
18 Tale of the Sun		✓	✓	✓	✓	✓	✓			
19 Values On The Line								✓	✓	✓
20 Environmental Exchange Box		✓	✓	✓	✓	✓	✓	✓	✓	✓
INTERRELATIONSHIPS										
21 Adopt a Tree	✓	✓	✓	✓	✓	✓	✓	✓	✓	✓
22 Trees as Habitats	✓	✓	✓	✓	✓	✓	✓	✓	✓	✓
23 The Fallen Log						✓	✓	✓	✓	✓
24 Nature's Recyclers			✓	✓	✓	✓	✓	✓		
25 Birds and Worms		✓	✓	✓						
26 Dynamic Duos							✓	✓	✓	✓
27 Every Tree for Itself		✓	✓	✓						
28 Air Plants					✓	✓	✓			
29 Rain Reasons								✓	✓	✓
30 Three Cheers for Trees			✓	✓	✓	✓	✓	✓		
31 Plant a Tree			✓	✓	✓	✓	✓	✓	✓	
32 A Forest of Many Uses			✓	✓	✓	✓	✓	✓		
33 Forest Consequences								✓	✓	✓
34 Who Works in this Forest?					✓	✓	✓	✓		
35 Loving It Too Much								✓	✓	✓
36 Pollution Search	✓	✓	✓	✓	✓	✓	✓	✓		
37 Talking Trash, Not!			✓	✓	✓	✓	✓			
38 Every Drop Counts						✓	✓	✓	✓	✓

#	Activity	PRE-K	K	1	2	3	4	5	6	7	8
39	Energy Sleuths								X	X	X
40	Then and Now					X	X	X	X	X	X

SYSTEMS

#	Activity	PRE-K	K	1	2	3	4	5	6	7	8
41	How Plants Grow		X	X	X		X	X	X	X	X
42	Sunlight and Shades of Green				X	X	X	X	X	X	X
43	Have Seeds, Will Travel		X	X	X	X	X	X	X	X	X
44	Water Wonders						X	X	X	X	X
45	Web of Life						X	X	X	X	X
46	School Yard Safari	X	X	X	X	X	X	X	X		
47	Are Vacant Lots Vacant?		X	X	X	X	X	X			X
48	Field, Forest, and Stream			X	X	X	X	X	X	X	X
49	Tropical Treehouse	X	X	X	X	X	X	X	X	X	X
50	400-Acre Wood								X	X	X
51	Make Your Own Paper			X	X	X		X	X	X	X
52	A Look at Aluminum						X	X	X	X	X
53	On the Move						X	X	X	X	X
54	I'd Like to Visit a Place Where…	X	X	X	X	X	X	X	X	X	X
55	Planning the Ideal Community								X	X	X
56	We Can Work it Out							X	X	X	X
57	Democracy in Action								X	X	X
58	There Ought to be a Law					X	X	X	X	X	X
59	Power of Print					X	X	X	X	X	X
60	Publicize It!								X	X	X

STRUCTURE AND SCALE

#	Activity	PRE-K	K	1	2	3	4	5	6	7	8
61	The Closer You Look	X	X	X	X	X	X	X	X		
62	To Be a Tree	X	X	X	X	X	X	X	X		
63	Tree Factory	X	X	X	X	X	X	X	X		
64	Looking at Leaves	X	X	X	X	X	X			X	X
65	Bursting Buds		X	X	X	X	X	X	X		
66	Germinating Giants						X	X	X		
67	How Big is Your Tree?	X	X	X	X	X	X	X	X	X	X
68	Name that Tree				X	X	X	X	X	X	X
69	Forest for the Trees						X	X	X	X	X
70	Soil Stories							X	X	X	X
71	Watch On Wetlands								X	X	X
72	Air We Breathe							X	X	X	X
73	Waste Watchers								X	X	X
74	People, Places, Things		X	X	X	X					
75	Tepee Talk						X	X	X	X	X

PATTERNS OF CHANGE

	PRE-K	K	1	2	3	4	5	6	7	8
76 Tree Cookies			✓	✓	✓	✓	✓	✓	✓	✓
77 Trees in Trouble			✓	✓	✓	✓	✓	✓	✓	✓
78 Signs of Fall		✓	✓	✓	✓	✓	✓	✓		
79 Tree Lifecycle	✓	✓	✓	✓	✓	✓				
80 Nothing Succeeds Like Succession					✓	✓	✓	✓	✓	✓
81 Living with Fire	✓	✓	✓	✓		✓	✓	✓	✓	✓
82 Resource-Go-Round						✓	✓	✓	✓	✓
83 Reduce, Reuse, Recycle						✓	✓	✓	✓	✓
84 A Peek at Packaging							✓	✓	✓	✓
85 Air to Drive							✓	✓	✓	✓
86 Our Changing World								✓	✓	✓
87 Earth Manners	✓	✓	✓	✓	✓	✓				
88 Life on the Edge							✓	✓	✓	✓
89 Trees for Many Reasons				✓	✓	✓	✓	✓	✓	
90 The Native Way							✓	✓	✓	✓
91 In the Good Old Days							✓	✓	✓	✓
92 A Look at Lifestyles							✓	✓	✓	✓
93 Paper Civilizations						✓	✓	✓	✓	✓
94 Where are the Cedars Of Lebanon?								✓	✓	✓
95 Did You Notice?		✓	✓	✓	✓	✓	✓	✓	✓	✓
96 Improve Your Place							✓	✓	✓	✓

TIME CONSIDERATION

DIVERSITY

#	Activity	1 PERIOD	2-4 PERIODS	SEMESTER/YEAR	INDOOR	OUTDOOR	INDOOR & OUTDOOR
1	The Shape of Things	✓					✓
2	Get in Touch with Trees	✓					✓
3	Peppermint Beetle	✓				✓	
4	Sounds Around		✓				✓
5	Poet-Tree	✓					✓
6	Picture This!		✓		✓		
7	Habitat Pen Pals	✓			✓		
8	The Forest Of S.T. Shrew	✓			✓		
9	Planet Of Plenty		✓				✓
10	Charting Diversity	✓			✓		
11	Can It Be Real?		✓		✓		
12	Tree Treasures	✓			✓		
13	We All Need Trees		✓		✓		
14	Renewable or Not?		✓		✓		
15	A Few Of My Favorite Things		✓		✓		
16	Pass The Plants, Please		✓		✓		
17	People Of The Forest		✓		✓		
18	Tale of the Sun	✓			✓		
19	Values On The Line	✓			✓		
20	Environmental Exchange Box			✓	✓		

INTERRELATIONSHIPS

#	Activity	1 PERIOD	2-4 PERIODS	SEMESTER/YEAR	INDOOR	OUTDOOR	INDOOR & OUTDOOR
21	Adopt a Tree	✓		✓			✓
22	Trees as Habitats	✓					✓
23	The Fallen Log	✓				✓	
24	Nature's Recyclers		✓				✓
25	Birds and Worms	✓					✓
26	Dynamic Duos	✓			✓		
27	Every Tree for Itself	✓					✓
28	Air Plants		✓				✓
29	Rain Reasons		✓		✓		
30	Three Cheers for Trees	✓			✓		
31	Plant a Tree		✓	✓			✓
32	A Forest of Many Uses	✓			✓		
33	Forest Consequences	✓			✓		
34	Who Works in this Forest?	✓			✓		
35	Loving It Too Much		✓		✓		
36	Pollution Search	✓					✓
37	Talking Trash, Not!		✓	✓	✓		
38	Every Drop Counts		✓		✓		

		1 PERIOD	2-4 PERIODS	SEMESTER/YEAR	INDOOR	OUTDOOR	INDOOR & OUTDOOR
39	Energy Sleuths		X		X		
40	Then and Now	X			X		

SYSTEMS

		1 PERIOD	2-4 PERIODS	SEMESTER/YEAR	INDOOR	OUTDOOR	INDOOR & OUTDOOR
41	How Plants Grow		X	X	X		
42	Sunlight and Shades of Green		X				X
43	Have Seeds, Will Travel	X					X
44	Water Wonders		X		X		
45	Web of Life		X		X		
46	School Yard Safari	X				X	
47	Are Vacant Lots Vacant?	X				X	
48	Field, Forest, and Stream	X				X	
49	Tropical Treehouse	X			X		
50	400-Acre Wood		X		X		
51	Make Your Own Paper		X		X		
52	A Look at Aluminum		X		X		
53	On the Move		X		X		
54	I'd Like to Visit a Place Where		X				X
55	Planning the Ideal Community			X		X	
56	We Can Work it Out	X			X		
57	Democracy in Action		X	X	X		
58	There Ought to be a Law		X		X		
59	Power of Print		X		X		
60	Publicize It!			X	X		

STRUCTURE AND SCALE

		1 PERIOD	2-4 PERIODS	SEMESTER/YEAR	INDOOR	OUTDOOR	INDOOR & OUTDOOR
61	The Closer You Look	X					X
62	To Be a Tree		X				X
63	Tree Factory	X					X
64	Looking at Leaves	X					X
65	Bursting Buds		X				X
66	Germinating Giants	X					X
67	How Big is Your Tree?	X					X
68	Name that Tree	X					X
69	Forest for the Trees	X			X		
70	Soil Stories		X				X
71	Watch On Wetlands		X				X
72	Air We Breathe		X	X	X		
73	Waste Watchers		X		X		
74	People, Places, Things		X				X
75	Tepee Talk	X			X		

PATTERNS OF CHANGE

#	Activity	1 PERIOD	2-4 PERIODS	SEMESTER/YEAR	INDOOR	OUTDOOR	INDOOR & OUTDOOR
76	Tree Cookies	✓			✓		
77	Trees in Trouble		✓	✓			✓
78	Signs of Fall	✓					✓
79	Tree Lifecycle	✓			✓		
80	Nothing Succeeds Like Succession	✓	✓	✓			✓
81	Living with Fire	✓					✓
82	Resource-Go-Round	✓			✓		
83	Reduce, Reuse, Recycle		✓	✓	✓		
84	A Peek at Packaging	✓			✓		
85	Air to Drive		✓				✓
86	Our Changing World	✓			✓		
87	Earth Manners	✓			✓		
88	Life on the Edge	✓	✓		✓		
89	Trees for Many Reasons	✓			✓		
90	The Native Way	✓			✓		
91	In the Good Old Days		✓		✓		
92	A Look at Lifestyles	✓	✓		✓		
93	Paper Civilizations	✓			✓		
94	Where are the Cedars Of Lebanon?	✓			✓		
95	Did You Notice?		✓		✓		
96	Improve Your Place		✓	✓			✓

NOTE—The following list of thinking processes and skills is a combination of lists put forth by the Association for Supervision and Curriculum Development and the American Association for the Advancement of Science. The activities under each heading are those which are geared specifically to that process or skill and have listed it in the activity side-bar.

Thinking processes are mental strategies that include specific thinking skills; they are used in dealing with complex issues. Some examples of thinking processes are problem solving and decision making. Thinking skills are specific cognitive operations that can be used either independently or as part of a complex thinking process. Examples of thinking skills include comparing and classifying.

COMPREHENDING
Air to Drive; The Forest of S.T. Shrew; Loving it Too Much; Tale of the Sun; Tree Factory

CONCEPT FORMING
The Forest of S.T. Shrew; Our Changing World; Sunlight and Shades of Green; Trees for Many Reasons

PRINCIPLE FORMING
Earth Manners; Values on the Line

REASONING
Adopt a Tree; Dynamic Duos; A Look at Lifestyles; Peppermint Beetle; Reduce, Reuse, Recycle; Tropical Treehouse

DISCUSSING
A Few of My Favorite Things; Forest Consequences; A Forest of Many Uses; The Forest of S.T. Shrew; A Look at Aluminum; Pass the Plants, Please; People, Places, Things; Poet-Tree; Renewable or Not; Tale of the Sun; There Ought to Be a Law; Three Cheers for Trees; Trees for Many Reasons; Tropical Treehouse; Values on the Line; We Can Work It Out; Web of Life; Who Works in this Forest?

COMPOSING
Adopt a Tree; Habitat Pen Pals; In the Good Old Days; Poet-Tree; Power of Print; Renewable or Not?

RESEARCHING
Charting Diversity; Democracy in Action; Did You Notice?; Earth Manners; Energy Sleuths; Habitat Pen Pals; In the Good Old Days; Life on the Edge; A Look at Lifestyles; Pass the Plants, Please; People of the Forest; Plant a Tree; Resource-Go-Round; Talking Trash, Not!; Then and Now; There Ought to Be a Law; Tree Cookies; Tree Treasures; Trees in Trouble; Tropical Treehouse; Web of Life; Where Are the Cedars of Lebanon?

PROBLEM SOLVING
400-Acre Wood; Air We Breathe; Democracy in Action; Every Drop Counts; Forest Consequences; Forest for the Trees; Germinating Giants; I'd Like to Visit a Place Where...; Improve Your Place; Pollution Search; Power of Print; Rain Reasons; Sounds Around; Talking Trash, Not!; Then and Now; Trees in Trouble; Waste Watchers; We Can Work It Out

DECISION MAKING
Air to Drive; Forest Consequences; Plant a Tree; Publicize It!; Reduce, Reuse, Recycle; Watch on Wetlands; We Can Work It Out

EVALUATING
Charting Diversity; Energy Sleuths; A Forest of Many Uses; Improve Your Place; A Look at Lifestyles; The Native Way; Nothing Succeeds Like Succession; Our Changing World; A Peek at Packaging; Plant a Tree; Pollution Search; Publicize It!; Reduce, Reuse, Recycle; Three Cheers for Trees; Tree Treasures; Trees for Many Reasons; Values on the Line; Waste Watchers

DEFINING PROBLEMS
Air We Breathe; Energy Sleuths; Forest Consequences; I'd Like to Visit a Place Where...; Improve Your Place; Our Changing World; Plant a Tree

OBSERVING
Adopt a Tree; Air We Breathe; Are Vacant Lots Vacant?; Bursting Buds; The Closer You Look; Environmental Exchange Box; The Fallen Log; Field, Forest, and Stream; Get in Touch With Trees; Have Seeds—Will Travel; How Plants Grow; How Big is Your Tree?; I'd Like to Visit a Place Where...; Living with Fire; Make Your Own Paper; Nature's Recyclers; Nothing Succeeds Like Succession; A Peek at Packaging; People, Places, Things; Picture This!; Planet of Plenty; Poet-Tree; Pollution Search; Rain Reasons; School Yard Safari; The Shape of Things; Signs of Fall; Soil Stories; Sunlight and Shades of Green; Tale of the Sun; Talking Trash, Not!; Tepee Talk; Tree Cookies; Trees as Habitats; Trees in Trouble; Waste Watchers

FORMULATING QUESTIONS
Environmental Exchange Box; Our Changing World; A Peek at Packaging; Plant a Tree; Then and Now; Who Works in This Forest?

COMPARING AND CONTRASTING
Air We Breathe; The Closer You Look; Environmental Exchange Box; Field, Forest, and Stream; The Forest of S.T. Shrew; Germinating Giants; Get in Touch with Trees; How Big is Your Tree?; I'd Like to Visit a Place Where...; Living with Fire; Looking at Leaves; Make Your Own Paper; Name That Tree; Nothing Succeeds Like Succession; On the Move; A Peek at Packaging; People of the Forest; Pollution Search; Power of Print; Reduce, Reuse, Recycle; The Shape of Things; Then and Now; Three Cheers for Trees; Water Wonders; We Can Work It Out

CLASSIFYING AND CATEGORIZING
A Forest of Many Uses; Get in Touch with Trees; Habitat Pen Pals; Have Seeds, Will Travel; Looking at Leaves; Name That Tree; People, Places, Things; Picture This!; Planet of Plenty; Sounds Around; Talking Trash, Not!; Tree Treasures; We All Need Trees

ORDERING AND ARRANGING
Bursting Buds; A Look at Aluminum; To Be a Tree; Tree Factory; Tree Lifecycle

REPRESENTING
Air Plants; Environmental Exchange Box; The Fallen Log; A Few of My Favorite Things; Loving it Too Much; People of the Forest; People, Places, Things; Planning the Ideal Community; Renewable or Not?; To Be a Tree; Tree Factory; Tree Lifecycle; Who Works in this Forest?

TRANSLATING
How Big is Your Tree?

ORGANIZING INFORMATION
Adopt a Tree; Are Vacant Lots Vacant?; Energy Sleuths; Every Drop Counts; The Fallen Log; Field, Forest and Stream; Habitat Pen Pals; Have Seeds, Will Travel; How Plants Grow; A Look at Lifestyles; Make Your Own Paper; Nature's Recyclers; Pass the Plants, Please; People of the Forest; Planet of Plenty; Pollution Search; Resource-Go-Round; The Shape of Things; Sounds Around; Trees as Habitats; Water Wonders

RESTRUCTURING
A Look at Aluminum; Planning the Ideal Community

DETERMINING CAUSES AND EFFECTS
Air We Breathe; Birds and Worms; Every Tree for Itself; Rain Reasons

IDENTIFYING ATTRIBUTES AND COMPONENTS
Bursting Buds; Charting Diversity; The Closer You Look; Energy Sleuths; Germinating Giants; Looking at Leaves; Name that Tree; The Native Way; Nothing Succeeds Like Succession; Pass the Plants, Please; Planning the Ideal Community; The Shape of Things; Soil Stories; Tepee Talk; Three Cheers for Trees; To Be a Tree; Tree Treasures; Tree Factory; Watch on Wetlands; Who Works in This Forest?

IDENTIFYING RELATIONSHIPS AND PATTERNS
Are Vacant Lots Vacant?; Birds and Worms; Can It Be Real?; Did You Notice?; Every Tree for Itself; Field, Forest, and Stream; The Native Way; Nature's Recyclers; Nothing Succeeds Like Succession; Peppermint Beetle; Signs of Fall; Sounds Around; Tree Cookies; Tree Lifecycle; Trees as Habitats; Web of Life

IDENTIFYING MAIN IDEAS
400-Acre Wood; Forest for the Trees; In the Good Old Days; Publicize It!; Trees for Many Reasons

MAKING ANALOGIES AND METAPHORS
Get in Touch with Trees; A Look at Aluminum

ANALYZING
400-Acre Wood; Air to Drive; Air Plants; Air We Breathe; Are Vacant Lots Vacant?; Birds and Worms; Can It Be Real?; Democracy in Action; Dynamic Duos; The Fallen Log; A Few of My Favorite Things; Forest for the Trees; How Plants Grow; How Big is Your Tree?; Life on the Edge; Living with Fire; A Look at Lifestyles; A Look at Aluminum; Loving It Too Much; Nature's Recyclers; Nothing Succeeds Like Succession; On the Move; Our Changing World; Pass the Plants, Please; A Peek at Packaging; Power of Print; Resource-Go-Round; Talking Trash, Not!; There Ought to Be a Law; Trees as Habitats; Trees in Trouble; Watch on Wetlands; We All Need Trees; Where are the Cedars of Lebanon?

INFERRING
Air We Breathe; Can It Be Real?; Have Seeds, Will Travel; Nature's Recyclers; Power of Print; Signs of Fall; Sunlight and Shades of Green; Trees as Habitats; Watch on Wetlands

INTERPRETING
Air We Breathe; The Closer You Look; In the Good Old Days; Loving It Too Much; The Native Way; Picture This!; Renewable or Not?; School Yard Safari; Tale of the Sun; Tree Cookies; Tropical Treehouse; Watch on Wetlands; We All Need Trees

SYNTHESIZING AND CREATING
Forest for the Trees; Life on the Edge; On the Move; Planning the Ideal Community; Power of Print

ELABORATING
A Few of My Favorite Things

PREDICTING
Air Plants; Birds and Worms; Can It Be Real?; Every Tree for Itself; Every Drop Counts; How Plants Grow; Loving It Too Much; Rain Reasons; Renewable or Not?; Talking Trash, Not!; Trees as Habitats; Water Wonders; Web of Life

SUMMARIZING
Energy Sleuths; Living with Fire; People, Places, Things

GENERALIZING
Pollution Search; Then and Now

ESTIMATING
Every Drop Counts!

CONCLUDING
Bursting Buds; Did You Notice?; The Forest of S.T. Shrew; Germinating Giants; How Plants Grow; Peppermint Beetle; School Yard Safari; Soil Stories; Sunlight and Shades of Green; Where Are the Cedars of Lebanon?

ESTABLISHING CRITERIA
Energy Sleuths; Values on the Line

VERIFYING
Air Plants; Rain Reasons

ALPHABETICAL INDEX

Listed by activity number